# NATURAL FEATURES OF INDIANA

# INDIANA ACADEMY OF SCIENCE

*Incorporated* 1887

## OFFICERS FOR 1966

CARROLLE A. MARKLE, Earlham College, *President*
RICHARD A. LAUBENGAYER, Wabash College,
   *Honorary President*
ALTON A. LINDSEY, Purdue University, *President-Elect*
CLARENCE F. DINEEN, Saint Mary's College, *Secretary*
FRANK A. GUTHRIE, Rose Polytechnic Institute, *Treasurer*
WILLIAM A. EBERLY, Manchester College, *Editor*
JAMES A. CLARK, Department of Natural Resources,
   *Director of Public Relations*
WARREN E. HOFFMAN, Indiana Institute of Technology,
   *Chairman Program Committee*

## SPECIAL SESQUICENTENNIAL PROGRAM
Spring Meeting, April 22-23, 1966
Wabash College, Crawfordsville

## INDIANA SESQUICENTENNIAL COMMITTEE OF THE ACADEMY

LOIS BURTON, State Library
RALPH E. CLELAND, Indiana University
NELLE M. COATS, State Library
CLARENCE F. DINEEN, Saint Mary's College
WILLIAM R. EBERLY, Manchester College
NED GUTHRIE, Hanover College
EDWARD L. HAENISCH, Wabash College
WARREN E. HOFFMAN, Indiana Institute of Technology
WILLIS H. JOHNSON, Wabash College
CARROLLE A. MARKLE, Earlham College
WILLIAM J. WAYNE, Indiana Geological Survey
ALTON A. LINDSEY, Purdue University, *Chairman*

## LOCAL ARRANGEMENTS FOR THE MEETING

EDWARD L. HAENISCH, ELIOT C. WILLIAMS, JR., and
WILLIS H. JOHNSON, *Chairman*

Indiana Department of Natural Resources photo

### JOHN SHEPARD WRIGHT

#### October 17, 1870 — July 11, 1951

Medical botanist, businessman, conservationist and historian, John S. Wright served the Indiana Academy of Science as Secretary during 1895-1905, and was President in 1905. The John Shepard Wright Memorial Library of the Indiana Academy of Science is housed at the State Library at Indianapolis and is the permanent headquarters of the Academy. The Academy is pleased to acknowledge its gratitude for his many years of dedicated service and an endowment fund which makes possible the publication of this volume and support of research grants for Indiana scientists.

*Frontispiece.* Changes with time are shown by the flow and ebb of sand in Nature's long-term hourglass at Indiana Dunes State Park. Several hundred years ago the rising dune buried large white pines growing on this spot. In recent years, winds re-exposed their remnants in extensive dune "blowouts."

1816-1966

# Indiana Sesquicentennial Volume

*Indiana Academy of Science*

*Founded December* 29, 1885

# Natural Features

# of

# Indiana

ALTON A. LINDSEY, Editor

Purdue University
Lafayette, Indiana

A Symposium held April 22-23, 1966, at

Wabash College, Crawfordsville, Indiana

Published July 1966
INDIANA ACADEMY OF SCIENCE
INDIANA STATE LIBRARY
Indianapolis, Indiana

# Dedication

The Indiana Academy of Science respectfully dedicates this book to the memory of ten pioneer scientific men who explored the natural features of Indiana in or about 1816.

**John James Audubon,** Bird Artist

**Timothy Flint,** Geographer

**Charles Alexandre Lesueur,** Ichthyologist

**William Maclure,** Geologist

**Francois Andre Michaux,** Botanist

**Thomas Nuttall,** Botanist

**David Dale Owen,** Geologist

**Constantine Samuel Rafinesque,** Naturalist

**Thomas Say,** Entomologist

**David B. Thomas,** Botanist

# *Preface*

It is with great pleasure and considerable pride that the Indiana Academy of Science presents to the public this book on the **Natural Features of Indiana** as a commemorative volume in recognition of Indiana's Sesquicentennial. Individuals who are considered leading authorities in the state were invited by the Academy's Sesquicentennial Committee to present a concise and somewhat popularized, contemporary picture of their particular field of natural history, and hence the volume represents the collaboration of forty-four scientists from fifteen of our colleges, universities, governmental and other agencies or institutions. An effort has been made to present material about all the natural resources of the state and their use, from bedrock to birds, and from cultural history of Indians to present patterns of agriculture, population and outdoor recreation. It is, we believe, a unique volume.

On behalf of the Indiana Academy of Science I gratefully acknowledge the contributions of the individuals who have assisted in the preparation of this volume, and express appreciation first to the committee who initiated the plans for the series of papers, and particularly to Dr. Alton A. Lindsey who has been largely responsible for the idea and its execution as well as the onerous task of editorship; and second, to the many persons who took time out from already busy schedules to make possible this fine resume of the natural features of our state.

What we see of the natural resources of Indiana in this volume is very different from that observed and recorded by the group of deputy-surveyors who were in the field in 1816, and this review of the present status logically points to the final chapters on the achievements as well as the shortcomings and needs in the field of conservation. May this volume not only prove enlightening and interesting to the reader, but may it also stir the imagination, interest and desires of the people of Indiana to look ahead and plan so that Indiana can continue to enjoy its natural resources and speak with pride at the time of its other centennials in the tomorrows.

Earlham College  
Richmond, Indiana  
April 1966

CARROLLE A. MARKLE, PRESIDENT  
Indiana Academy of Science

# Contents

INTRODUCTION

# THE INDIANA OF 1816

*When Daniel Boone goes by at night*
*The phantom deer arise,*
*And all lost, wild America*
*Is burning in their eyes.*

—Stephen Vincent Benét

The important features of Indiana to the self-sufficient pioneers were the God-given, not man-made, ones. Occupation by Indians had modified natural conditions somewhat, but negligibly in comparison with the state as we see it in 1966. Since the white population[15] in 1816 was only 63,900, the impress of European civilization was still inconsequential. Indiana was not yet important as a social, political, or economic unit. It was overwhelmingly natural — a freshly minted land.

The natural aspects of our state as they exist today remain vitally important to its citizens in many ways. For our culture and science to advance, knowledge of what Nature provides is essential. Economic life, too, is solidly based on natural resources such as soils, climate, surface and ground waters, minerals, scenery, timber and wildlife. And in the coming age of increased leisure and recreation, the health of our environment will crucially affect the quality of life, as well as the material standard of living.

The scientific exploration of Indiana, which made this book possible, was forecast by one observer who traveled extensively here about 1825.

> The spirit of enquiry, resulting from our free institutions, is pervading the country, and a thirst for all kinds of information is universal. This state will soon take a high place among her sister states, in point of population. It is hoped that her advance in intellectual improvement, and social and religious institutions, will be in corresponding proportion. [12]

In the chapters to follow, others will survey the high spots of modern knowledge of the natural stage-setting and resource base. Let us first glance over our shoulder at Indiana as it was a century and a half ago.

**A Naturalist's Travels in the Summer of 1816**

The two most thorough contemporary reports are the records made by the early land surveyors and the book by David Thomas. The botanist Thomas[27] was a competent observer in many outdoor sciences. While especially interested in plant life, geology and Indian earthworks, he wrote about the subjects of nearly all the chapters of the present book.

On June 29, 1816, he crossed the Ohio River into the southeast corner of Indiana at Rising Sun. While visiting Madison, Thomas met some delegates returning homeward from the state constitutional convention in Corydon. Thomas wrote concerning log cabins at Madison, "Though these buildings neither shine much in description, nor add to the beauty of these villages, yet posterity from such specimens will learn with interest the simplicity of new founded empires; for in a few years they will be only *remembered*."

At Lexington, Thomas saw a salt mine with a shaft that had been dug more than 700 feet by machinery powered by a horse. He passed by Pigeon Roost settlement where the worst Indian attack on civilians, a massacre of 21 women and children, had occurred during the war four years before. (Far greater hazards were communicable diseases, especially malaria and cholera[7]. The number of infant graves seen in old cemeteries is appalling). Traveling westward to Salem, Thomas was fascinated by the geology of the Knobs region, as it was already termed. Later he described the Lost River area and such traits of the limestone plain as natural bridges and sinkholes. He called the karst country "cellared", with "nearly all the brooks more or less subterranean".

At "French Licks", where his horse found salt that formed a whitish coat, like frost, on the stones, Thomas reported the colorful Carolina parakeet continually flying about in flocks and screaming. (This little native parrot has been everywhere exterminated).

On one homestead a non-conformist farmer from New York state had used "the eastern method of clearing land", i. e. removing the trees completely, instead of girdling to kill and leaving them standing until seasoned, then burning. Thomas estimated the resulting crop as half again every other he had seen in the country.

He forded the east fork of the White above its falls where the river plunged four feet over a sandstone ledge. "The thick woods on the opposite shore, the clear sky, the smooth expanse of water, the foam of the cascade, and the unbroken quiet, formed one of the sweetest scenes of solitude."

Washington, Indiana, was then called Liverpool and consisted of three houses.

At times when Thomas interrupted his narrative for geological speculations, his mind seemed groping toward the idea of continental glaciation that Agassiz introduced years later. He wondered whether out-of-place rocks had been "brought by the great northern deluge from the ridge that divides the waters of the Ohio and St. Lawrence."

> As some rocks of granite are also scattered here, doubtless this land has been overwhelmed by the same deluge. I allude not to the inundations produced by extraordinary rains, but to a preternatural flood which swept over the highest hills, and which, to my view, was occasioned by exterior attraction.

His quaint, vaguely stated ideas on this matter contrast very interestingly with our present detailed knowledge of the behavior and effects of glaciers in Indiana, summarized in the chapter "Ice and Land" of the present book. But we have not yet reached firm conclusions about the underlying *causes* of the continental ice sheets, which played extremely important roles in producing the Indiana of today.

Bees were reported as very plentiful in the woods along the Wabash; one man found 12 bee trees in less than half a day. Thomas correctly decided, partly because Indians called them "white people's flies", that honey bees were not native, thus supporting Thomas Jefferson's opinion.

Our representative to the 1816 scene was much impressed by three conspicuous "Indian mounds" a few miles south of Vincennes. "These remains of antiquity show that this plain has been the seat of wealth and power . . . though it is now only a frontier town of a new race." These mounds may be natural formations, not man-made.

For at least two weeks of this unusually cool summer, after July 5, Thomas explored the Indiana side of the Wabash between Vincennes and Raccoon Creek, including "Terre Haute Prairie". Fort Harrison was built 3 miles north of the site of Terre Haute settlement, by Governor Harrison on his expedition to Tippecanoe battleground in 1811. Terre Haute was founded in 1816, and appears on Thomas' map but not in his narrative. This fold-out map of "Vincennes District" shows that only Indian lands lay north of a northwest-southeast line passing through the mouth of Raccoon Creek. He could not have legally crossed the Indian boundary nor could the federal land surveyors until after the purchase treaty of 1818. The diary narrative ends with a note on abandoned wigwams on Spring Creek, made by Indians with "much skill and neatness" for winter use. Other observations he made during his journey will be mentioned under specific headings following the next section.

### The Original Land Surveys

The earliest systematic examination of Indiana by trained observers was made between 1799 and 1834 in the original survey by the General Land Office[14] of the federal government. These teams of disciplined nomads "lived off the country" during their rectilinear travels. Eight massive volumes of GLO records are in the Archives Division of the State Library in Indianapolis. This is by far the most explicit and voluminous early record we have on the natural features of the state as a whole. The chairman of the committee which first instituted this town-range method of survey was that versatile Virginian, Thomas Jefferson.

Each township was described on 3 official forms. One was a plat of the 36 square miles (sections) depicting streams, lakes, ponds, prairies, swamps, marshes, land grants, settlements, Indian villages, areas of windthrown timber, salt licks, etc. Another form was for the running descriptions, along each survey line, of the physiography, drainage, soil quality, timber species and other vegetational notes, and a variety of other natural and man-made features. Emotional responses sometimes broke through official reserve, in such entries as "This mile mostly a terrible swamp; holes and sloughs and most outrageous places!" The adjective "terrible" often occurs in characterizing mires, or the simple but eloquent "Water! Water!"

The most detailed form was to enable future local surveyors to relocate section and quarter-section corners. Such intersection points were placed every half mile on the north-south and east-west section lines; these "corners" were marked on the site and described in permanent records. Marking was done in treeless country by setting posts, often over buried charcoal which resists decay, and raising a mound around the base of the post. But in most of Indiana it was possible to blaze and scribe two (compass) "bearing" trees at each point. Data recorded, for finding the point later, were: common name of tree species, diameter of the tree, and its distance and compass bearing from the point. A thorough knowledge of tree identification was part of the stock in trade of the experienced outdoorsmen who worked under contract as deputy surveyors. (Survey records made by the young George Washington in Virginia show that he had a good knowledge of tree species.[26]) They listed a respectable 73 species of trees throughout Indiana, using substantially the same common names we use today.

In geographic studies of the Calumet and Kankakee regions,[23] the landscape has been reconstructed from early survey records. So far, Indiana is the only state that has had the vegetation of the entire state described[20][24] by use of early surveyors records. By analyzing[20] the surveyors tree data with the aid of modern computers, ecologists have described the Indiana forests of circa 1816 in essentially the same ways they describe a forest stand of today.

Chapter 16 has a map of original vegetation of Indiana based on the GLO records and other evidence. For anyone able to distinguish the several different forest and prairie vegetation types as they are now, that map will convey a vivid idea of how the landscape of Indiana looked about 1816.

Surveyors data have also been used[9] along with modern soil maps to determine just what soil and site properties favored or hindered particular tree species under the natural conditions of forest competition still found in presettlement days.

Early Indiana survey records were introduced (to establish contemporary environmental conditions) by the U. S. Department of Justice in legal battles with Indians from 1961 on. In a consolidation of 14 cases involving Indiana north of the Wabash River, the tribes claim $50 million damages. Although the Indians allege that the purchase treaties had undervalued the land, and that the United States let the installment payments lapse, they have not repossessed their alleged property. The Indian Claims Commission has not yet resolved the complex of conflicting claims of the various tribes to aboriginal title. If the Commission should decide that any of the Indian petitioners had aboriginal title to any of these lands, land valuation hearings would next be held, at which the fairness of the treaty prices (averaging perhaps twenty-five cents per acre) would become an issue. Indian lands cases throughout the country have usually been won by the Indians, as was a smaller suit in 1964 involving land in central Indiana.

### Original Prevalence of Wet Terrain

The replacement of extensive forests by cultivation was a change obvious in retrospect. But in the northern third of Indiana generally, and especially in the northwestern part, another very striking landscape change is little appreciated. This was the elimination of extensive natural ponding through organized drainage projects since 1885. In 1816, approximately half[20] of the surface area of the northwestern eighth of the state was ponded during about 6 months of a year of normal rainfall, and quite worthless for agriculture during the long period before artificial drainage.

The early settlers of Benton County (which was 69 per cent wetlands) called the tall-grass wet prairie "the lost lands" in the belief they would never be used for farming.[6] Today these are the richest agricultural soils in the state, as generally productive as any in the world.

The 1834 survey plat[14] of 4 townships in northern Newton County showed Beaver Lake occupying 28,500 acres. By 1917, it had shrunk to 10,000, and has since disappeared through drainage; therefore, the motorist on U. S. 41 traversing its flat bottom may wonder at the origin of the name of nearby Lake Village. Northeast of the present village of English Lake in Starke County was a 12-mile long lake of the same name which was a wide, permanent spread[14] of the Kankakee River. This lake, and the extensive Kankakee marshes,[23] famous for teeming waterfowl, were destroyed by dredging and straightening the river and tiling and ditching the emergent lands. This public project was inaugurated[22] by attorney H. R. Robbins of Knox, in 1884.

So high was the average level of the water table that, when floods raised it still more, even the portages across the watershed divides were submerged and navigable.[13] Speaking before the U. S. Congress, General P. B. Porter "whose geographical knowledge of the country bordering the lakes is exceeded by that of no gentlemen in the western country"[13] reported in 1810 that more than 20 portages of this nature existed between Lakes Michigan and Erie on the one hand, and the Wabash, Illinois and Miami Rivers on the other. He stated that these rivers had their branches interwoven with those of streams running into the Great Lakes, issuing in opposite directions from the same marsh, prairie pond or lake. When floods covered the intermediate marsh or prairie, boats could cross the "divides" without being unloaded. Porter's remarkable claim was corroborated by David Thomas, the Hon. N. Pope, Flint, Volney, and the *Western Gazeteer*. An instructive project for Explorer Scouts would be to locate, first on airphotos and contour maps and later on the ground, the specific sites of portages mentioned in early accounts, comparing the modern situation there following heavy rains. Their exploration would be by hiking, not canoe.

The location of towns and cemeteries in northwest Indiana reflected the settlers' avoidance of low ground. In southern Newton County,[25] Kentland, Goodland, Morocco, Mt. Ayr and other towns were established on dry prairie sites. In northern Newton County, near the Kankakee, scarcely any dry prairie occurred. Various low ground soil types predominated but none of the towns (Thayer, Roselawn, Conrad, Lake Village) were founded on these lands.

Both the number of springs and their flow was much greater prior to clearing of forests and installation of draintiles, drainage ditches, and the straightening and dredging of rivers like the Kankakee that converted them into ditches. "A true pioneer never drives his stakes where there is not a spring."[28] The cool plashy spring house was a charm of pioneer life that was unsuited for preservation in historical museums.

### Streams and their Flooding

The Sugar Creeks in Indiana were named for a dominant tree, the sugar maple, which the surveyors and pioneers called

simply "sugar". The Eel River which flows into the Wabash
at Logansport was named for the fish, but it has been claimed
that the Eel River flowing southward into the White River
was originally called "Oeil", the French word for "eye". If a
very early reference to the "Eel" River can be shown to mean
the southern one, this might extend a certain aboriginal title
southward to include much more land, and bring the tribal
descendents many millions of dollars more in a settlement
of a pending Indian claims case against the federal government.

The passenger pigeon was incredibly abundant in Indiana
and Ohio where beech mast from the predominant (beech-
maple) forest type was its chief food in autumn. This bird
was later exterminated by market hunters and clearing of
forests; the last individual died in the Cincinnati zoo in 1914.
The names of three Indiana streams recall the days when its
"inexhaustible" flocks darkened midwestern skies — Pigeon
River near the Indiana-Michigan line, and Pigeon Creek and
Little Pigeon River which join the Ohio River.

The Blue River (Salem) contained considerable common
salt.[8] It seems a safe assumption that it, and the Big Blue
River (Shelbyville) and Salt Creek (Bedford) attracted buffalo, although the herds were smaller in Indiana than about
Blue Lick, Kentucky, where the country was more open. By
1816, buffalo had practically disappeared from the Wabash
country, and had all gone from Indiana by 1825 except the
one on the official state seal; elk were gone by 1830.

In 1816 Congress passed the Enabling Act for Indiana statehood. Along with setting aside one section of each township
for public schools, this legislation provided ". . . that all salt
springs . . . shall be granted to the said state [Indiana] for
the use of the people of said state . . ." and that "the state
legislature shall never sell or lease the same for a longer
period than 10 years at any one time."

There were great floods in pioneer times,[2] as there had
been before white settlement began. The "march" on Vincennes led by George Rogers Clark in February, 1779,
traversed many miles of flooded bottomlands of the Embarrass and Wabash.[11] In 1816, on the Ohio at Rising Sun,
Thomas reported a 60 foot difference between low and high

water. Along the Wabash between Merom and Terre Haute the flood marks on the trees were higher than he could reach on horseback. "Neither the Ohio nor the Wabash can be ascended in time of flood by common boats"[27].

The *great* floods, which typically occur in winter or spring, are meteorological events for which man is not responsible and which continue to occur regardless of anything he has done.[29] The fact that flood plains, built by floods, have always bordered streams shows that flooding has been a normal occurrence from time immemorial. Floods have been aggravated, but not caused, by clearing and cultivation; nor can *great* floods be prevented by engineering works on rivers, even though smaller ones, which do less damage, are more controllable. The sure way of preventing damage or destruction to structures by the infrequent great floods is to zone construction out of the natural paths of floodwaters, as some states do by law.

Sometimes caused by floods was a strange, now obsolete, phenomenon which gave the name "Embarrass" to not a few midwestern streams. An embarrass was a long raft of uprooted trees obstructing the stream, perhaps for many miles. A riverman described it as follows.

> An accumulation of trunks, roots, branches and entire trees swept away by great rises of waters, which are caught up first near the banks and are in a short time covered with mud and sand, which finally stops them altogether. The first ones serve as a stay for others, which serve in turn for those which follow, and all by being entwined and gathered together become a solid mass and form an immovable bridge, all bristling with branches and stumps. . . . The water, incapable of breaking this dyke, escapes from it with extreme rapidity. [3]

### Trees and Forests

The largest trees of early Indiana were bald cypress, sycamore and tulip tree. The latter was called "poplar" by early settlers and surveyors, and is often termed "yellow poplar" today.

The upper terraces or high-bottoms of the lower Wabash supported the most spectacular forests[19,21] of North America east of the Rockies. By careful measurements the Smithsonian naturalist Robert Ridgway determined the average tree-top level as 130 feet, but "the by no means infrequent monarchs" attained between 180 and 200 feet. Ridgway, who lived in Wheatland, wrote that this forest type was quite comparable in grandeur with the tropical rain forest of Central America. He backed up his claim with many photographs, height triangulations of standing trees and taping of felled ones. Several stumps of felled cypress above the mouth of the White River measured nine and ten feet in diameter *above* the butt swell. One photograph[21] shows four tulip trees near Vincennes with trunk diameters from 5 to 7 feet. The maximum diameter he found for a live tulip tree was 11 feet, but a stump measured 12. The average of 25 tulip trees measured was 6.2 feet. A Shumard's red oak was 6 feet in diameter at 12 feet up; within 100 yards of it were two black walnuts, each 6 feet in diameter above the swell. (In 1965 a single 3 foot walnut tree sold for veneer at Franklin for $12,600.).

This superlative forest type occupied the lower Wabash Valley until about 1860-1870. The only original remnant of it existing anywhere today is in Beall Woods[19] or Forest of the Wabash, eight miles south of Mt. Carmel, Illinois. In 1965 this stand was the subject of a court case[5] and saved from becoming whisky barrels in the nick of time by the state government. It is now an Illinois state park, with trails for public use. Cutting this museum-piece forest would be comparable with a case we may imagine, in which a "practical" Greek farmer excavates a marble statue by ancient Praxiteles, then pounds it into powder for liming his field to increase crop yield. Wood, like lime, is obtainable from sources which are not priceless.

The tulip tree, large, easily felled and straight-grained, was a favorite for cabins; the logs were split into 6-inch-thick planks and dressed with a broadax. It is said that tulip tree wood contains a substance that repels termites, and the pioneers may have found this out by experience. An old cabin of two-foot-wide tulip tree timbers houses the nature museum at Turkey Run State Park.

Logs from centuries-old trees were rolled into piles by community effort and burned.[8] Hindsight indicates that far too much land was cleared, and that eroded abandoned farms of today might better have stayed in wood production from the first. Dr. Paul Sears, land use authority and past-President of the American Association for the Advancement of Science, judges that about 40 per cent of rural land in a humid region might well remain forested. This would be too high a figure for level land and too low for rough country. While land in agricultural crops is more productive, it is also much more unstable and subject to harmful changes (erosion by water and wind, plant diseases, insect devastation, and noxious weeds). But forest cover is protective as well as productive; it is stable, near a steady-state, and capable of buffering the environment against catastrophic changes. A mosaic of productive cropland and protective timberland, which also provides for outdoor recreation and natural beauty, is ideal. President Theodore Roosevelt believed, "Nothing is more practical in the long run than the preservation of beauty."

## Prairies

On his way to the first session of circuit court held in LaPorte in 1833, young Judge Hugh McCulloch rode through a nearby tall grass prairie.

> Its surface was undulating like the waves of the sea after a storm, and covered with luxuriant grass interspersed with wild flowers of every hue. . . . I have seen since then many parks of great natural and artistic beauty, but none so charming as was the rolling prairie on that bright morning in June.
> LaPorte prairie received its name from the fact that on its western border there was an opening like a door in the forest which everywhere else inclosed it. Near the center of the prairie, upon a charming little lake, was the county seat, LaPorte. 28

The chief grass of tall grass prairie, big blue stem, grew so tall in Benton County wet prairie that a man on horseback could tie the ends together over the top of his head.⁴ In Jasper and Newton counties, it frequently reached a height to hide a

Plate I. (*Above*) Pine Hills Natural Area, annex to The Shades State Park, is one of the few places in Indiana scarcely changed since 1816. Clifty Creek and Indian Creek (tributaries of Sugar Creek, *background*) during the early Pleistocene cut a "cloverleaf" of curving gorges 100 feet deep into the Borden Sandstone, of Mississippian age. Mill Cut Backbone (*foreground*) was notched through in 1869 for the mill race of a woolen mill at this site. (*Below*) Male Wild Turkey. This species was extirpated in Indiana before 1900. A few attempts were recently made to reintroduce the birds. In his autobiography, Abraham Lincoln wrote of an experience he had as a turkey hunter when a young boy in southern Indiana: "A few days before the completion of his eighth year, in the absence of his father, a flock of wild turkeys approached the new log cabin, and Abraham with a rifle-gun, standing inside, shot through a crack and killed one of them. He has never since pulled a trigger on any larger game."

Purdue Laboratory of Plant Ecology photo

Durward L. Allen photo

Purdue Laboratory of Plant Ecology photo

Plate II. (*Above*). Small Yellow Lady's-slipper (*Cypripedium Calceolus* var. *parviflorum*), a wild plant that is very rarely seen in Indiana today. (*Below*) Young thirteen-lined ground squirrels (*Citellus tridecemlineatus*) watch for danger from their burrow entrance.

Russell E. Mumford photo

man on horseback. A fire whipped by high wind at night was a sight to see — from a distance.

David Thomas[27] anticipated modern ecologists in his perceptive explanation of Indiana prairies as *not* being due to climate too dry for forest growth. "Though the woodlands decrease as we advance westward, the cause ought not to be attributed to climate. Our search must therefore be confined to soil . . . and to fire and inundation". Prairies were "called *"barrens"* but improperly, for the soil is very fertile". The term "barrens" reflected the initial bias of some pioneers, brought up in the forested east, against land they considered too infertile to grow trees. This error prejudiced them against the very best agricultural soils of the Midwest. Of course, uninterrupted prairie would not provide material for log cabins. Oak brushlands were also termed "barrens" by the survey crews.

Grass cover is more tolerant than forest to fire and both wet and dry extremes of drainage. Indians for centuries had set fires deliberately to promote edge effect for improvement of hunting. "The timber on the drier parts of this strip" wrote Thomas, "is chiefly black oak. The ravages of fire amongst it has been very considerable; and in this part, the prairie was visibly gaining on the woods." The numerous beautiful prairies [14,27] found in 1816 along the Wabash were probably due largely to Indians.

Survey crews in the oak-openings, oak-brushlands, and barrens frequently reported "stool grubs". These were underground stems of oak trees; the aboveground shoots repeatedly "stooled out" and were as often killed back by fire. Such sprouts were usually one to six feet high. The buried "grubs" grew to many feet in diameter and interfered with plowing; grubbing them out was often extremely laborious.

The prairies at this time were covered with a luxuriant growth of wild grass, the roots of which formed a tenacious sod. The teams by which this sod could be successfully broken must necessarily be very strong. Every settler could not have a team of his own of sufficient strength to do this work, nor would it have paid if he could, perhaps. This gave rise to the formation of "breaking teams", which went over the prairies from place to place and "broke" this prairie sod for the settlers for the first time . . . The team consisted of six or eight yoke of oxen . . . to which was trained a huge unwieldy plow which would make a little ditch at every furrow. The "deck" of hands consisted of a plowman and a driver . . . . [1]

Crops, in the first season that the prairies are plowed, exhibit but little of that luxuriance . . . which in succeeding years is so remarkable. This is imputed to the hardness of the wild grass roots, which . . . yield very slowly to decay. [27]

## The Lincoln Family, Snakeroot and Destiny

Thomas Lincoln brought his family into southwestern Indiana within a few days of the December 11, 1816, beginning of this state. For two dollars an acre he bought from the government a quarter-section in the valley of Little Pigeon River (or Creek). His son Abraham was nearly eight.

No history book we have seen gives a wholly correct interpretation of the 1805 survey record and plat relative to the Lincoln quarter-section. The plat is reproduced here (Fig. 1)

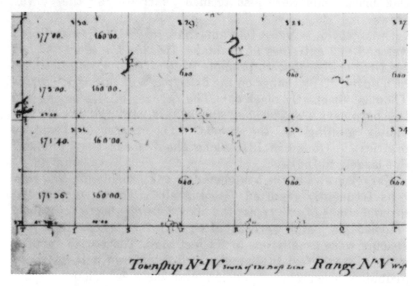

Fig. 1. Photocopy of original 1805 land survey plat including Abraham Lincoln's boyhood home (1816-1830) in what is now Spencer County, Indiana. The Lincoln quarter-section is the third small square from the left in the lowest row, directly above the word "Township". See text for surveyor's descriptions of land and timber.

to clarify the facts regarding their southwest quarter of Section 32 in T4S, R5W. The boundary lines of the square mile sections, not the sections themselves, were described; the course of the stream between the short stretches visible from where it crossed the survey lines was only estimated and drawn in lightly on the plat to indicate this. The cabin was on a knoll; not "on the banks of Little Pigeon Creek" as some writers place it, since only a small (8 ft. wide) tributary of that stream was within their land (Fig. 1). The clerk who transcribed the deputy surveyor's field notes happened to write the description of the south boundary into the wrong place on the official form, so we must go back to the original fieldbook in the State Library archives. The line from "r" to "S" (Fig. 1) formed the Lincolns' southern boundary, and the description applying to the whole mile "R" to "S" in general was "Level and rich, Jack Ok (sic), Black Oak, Hickory, etc." The west boundary of their farm was the southern half of the section line running north from "S" which was termed "Flat brushy briery wet Oak-timbered soil." The north and east boundaries were quarter-section lines, for which running descriptions were not given because the original surveyors did not traverse lines within sections.

There in Carter Township the land in general was too well drained to be first rate for farming; this is indicated by the predominance of black oak over any other tree in the survey records. In this township, Abraham Lincoln from age 7 to 21 became intimately acquainted with trees, their species properties and uses. The 1805 survey there recorded "bearing" trees in these species percentages, by the common names we still use: black oak 29 per cent, white oak 18, hickory 18, dogwood 14, gum 8, elm 4, cherry 3, maple 2, and black walnut 1 per cent. Minor trees were "plumb", red oak, persimmon, sassafras, [yellow] poplar and crab apple.

After nearly two years residence there, Nancy Hanks Lincoln died[16,17,30,31] from milk sickness, as did several near neighbors. We now know this "disease" was due to the poison "trematol" from the wild herb white snakeroot (*Eupatorium rugosum*) eaten by cattle. This ailment brought about abandonment of many farms in the county.[30] The normal habitat of the plant prior to timber clearing was low wet woods and flood plains of streams; the stream that traversed the Lincoln acreage provided such a habitat. A modern botanist[17] wrote, "During the year or two following removal of timber from an area where it [snakeroot] is established, it often forms dense stands to the exclusion of almost all other herbaceous plants." Hence the milk sickness was a serious scourge while forests were being cleared wholesale in southern Indiana and the plant was a likely item of cattle food.

Dennis Hanks lost both his foster parents from milk poisoning and, on account of its ravages in Spencer County, he proposed and accompanied the Lincoln family trek to Illinois.[30] Hanks explained in a letter, "Reson is this we war perplext By a Disease cald Milk Sick . . . I was determed to leve and hunt a country whare the milk was not . . ." If this was really his chief motive in deciding to leave for Illinois and persuading the Lincolns to do so, a poisonous herb not only killed Abraham Lincoln's mother but also later unsettled Abe's life at the crucial age of manhood. He might have made the break from his parents and found his way into politics had the family stayed on the farm in sparsely settled Spencer County, Indiana, or he might not.

Yet, we can be certain that the natural and human environment of pioneer Indiana molded young Abe into a man with strength to save the Union. The effect of the natural surroundings on Lincoln's character was never better expressed than in these lines from Edwin Markham's poem.

> *. . . Sprung from the West,*
> *He drank the valorous youth of a new world . . .*
> *The color of the ground was in him, the red earth;*
> *The smack and tang of elemental things:*
> *The strength of virgin forests braced his mind,*
> *The hush of spacious prairies stilled his soul.*
> *His words were oaks in acorns; and his thoughts*
> *Were roots that firmly gript the granite truth . . .*
> *Here was a man to hold against the world,*
> *A man to match the mountains and the sea.*

### Pioneers and Posterity

What manner of men were the first white settlers of the new state? They were the sort who could encounter the harshly beautiful wildness of early Indiana, and, by opposing, end it. From our technological vantage of 1966, all honor to those who cleared the fields, broke the sod, survived or perished from the fevers, and laid the footings of our society. We admire and envy their tough fibre, and thank them for a good start.

Yet did not their descendants perpetuate too long an aggressive hostility toward the natural environment? Longer than changing circumstances warranted, we have followed rather singlemindedly their example of prodigal waste and careless exploitation of resources. But there were some farsighted men like Charles Deam, the great Indiana botanist who served as the first State Forester, and Richard Lieber, the father of our state park system.

Was it necessary to beat Nature into submission so completely that scarcely any museum-piece forests and no single remnant of Indiana virgin prairie, however small, were protected? No longer can children learning history, geography and biology visit a great Indiana prairie and imagine how it was to ride the Conestoga wagons.

The first settlers toiled incessantly, and not always with success, to keep Nature from conquering them. Colossal human effort eventually brought man to the arrogant belief that he had truly conquered Nature. It would be unwise to press our present advantage too far. Outdoor sciences, dealing with the network of inter-relationships on this planet, reveal that thoughtful trusteeship, not all-out technological bludgeoning of Nature, is needed from now on. Merely because we now easily *can* do something irrevocable to the earth and its life, does not mean we *should*. We serve our continuing interests better by respecting, understanding and working along with natural processes than by ignoring or opposing them. A square deal for environment is essential for future prosperity and viability, and to sustain and renew the diversity of natural life that makes this world a more fascinating place for us.

Many Hoosiers might regard the villagers of Oaxaca, Mexico, as ignorant and superstitious because they zealously protect their famous giant cypress as a sacred trust, to bequeath to their posterity. Haven't those back-numbers heard of Progress? What has posterity ever done for them? In the enlightened, progressive Indiana of 1966, you and I *are* posterity! Where are our wild parakeets, passenger pigeons, prairie chickens, wild turkeys and 12-foot diameter tulip trees? Will our own posterity at the two hundredth observance of statehood ask pointed questions concerning their Lake Michigan dunes or free-flowing streams? Will they have a venous network of highways with nothing left outdoors worth traveling on them to see, or state parks with the wild beauty smothered under runaway commercial "development"? Money is wonderful, but it is possible to pay too high a price for it. May their atmosphere not be heavy with carbon dioxide, nor all their waters strait-jacketed and befouled, nor their lands clogged with radioactive impurities, pesticide residues, concrete and people themselves.

What happened to the 13-foot sycamore shown as the frontispiece of *Trees of Indiana*,[10] once the largest tree east of the Rockies? Who knows or cares?

It is to encourage knowing and caring that this book is written.

ALTON A. LINDSEY, *Editor*
Department of Biological Sciences
Purdue University

April 20, 1966

## LITERATURE

1. Anonymous. 1880. History of La Porte County, Indiana. C. C. Chapman Co., Chicago.
2. AUDUBON, J. J. 1926 (posthumous). Delineations of American scenery and character. Baker Co., New York.
3. BAKELESS, JOHN. 1961. The eyes of discovery. America as seen by the first explorers. Dover, New York.
4. BARCE, ELMORE. 1925. Annals of Benton County. Fowler, Indiana.
5. BEECHER, W. J. 1965. The trial of the forest primeval. Chicago Tribune Magazine, May 23, 1965: 46-53.
6. BIRCH, J. S. 1928. Benton County and historic Oxford, Indiana. Vol. I. Ms. in Indiana State Library.
7. BLOODGOOD. D. E. 1952. Early health conditions in Indiana. Proc. Indiana Acad. Sci. 61:253-260.
8. BULEY, R. CARLYLE. 1950. The old Northwest, pioneer period 1815-1840. Vols. 1 and 2. Indiana University Press, Bloomington.
9. CRANKSHAW, W. B., S. A. QADIR AND A. A. LINDSEY. 1965. Edaphic controls of tree species in presettlement Indiana. Ecology 46:688-698.
10. DEAM, C. C. AND T. E. SHAW. 1953. Trees of Indiana. Third Ed. Indiana Dept. of Conservation. Indianapolis.
11. DeVOTO, BERNARD. 1952. The course of empire. Houghton, Mifflin. Boston.
12. FLINT, TIMOTHY. 1828. A condensed geography and history of the Western States. Vol. II. Cincinnati.
13. _____. 1832. The history and geography of the Mississippi Valley. Vol. I, 2nd Ed. Cincinnati.
14. General Land Office survey records for Indiana. 1799-1834 Vols. 1-8. Archives, State Library, Indianapolis.
15. Indiana Department of Statistics and Geology. 1879. First Annual Report. Douglas and Carlson. Indianapolis.
16. JORDAN, P. D. 1944. The death of Nancy Hanks Lincoln. Indiana Mag. of Hist. 40:103-110.

17. KINGSBURY, J. M. 1964. Poisonous plants of the United States and Canada. Prentice-Hall. Englewood Cliffs, N. J.
18. LINDLEY, HARLOW. 1916. Indiana as seen by early travelers, a collection of reprints from books of travel, letters and diaries prior to 1830. Indiana Hist. Commission. Indianapolis.
19. LINDSEY, A. A. 1963. Analysis of an original forest of the lower Wabash floodplain and upland. Proc. Ind. Acad. Sci. **73**:282-287.
20. ————————, W. B. CRANKSHAW AND S. A. QADIR. 1965. Soil relations and distribution map of the vegetation of presettlement Indiana. Botanical Gaz. **126**:155-163.
21. ————————, R. O. PETTY, D. K. STERLING, AND W. VAN ASDALL. 1961. Vegetation and environment along the Wabash and Tippecanoe Rivers. Ecological Monog. **31**:105-156.
22. McCORMICK, J. N. 1915. A standard history of Starke County, Indiana. Chicago and New York.
23. MEYER, A. H. 1936. The Kankakee "Marsh" of northern Indiana and Illinois. Papers Michigan Acad. Sci., Arts and Letters **21**:359-396.
24. POTZGER, J. E., MARGARET E. POTZGER AND JACK McCORMICK. 1956. The forest primeval of Indiana as recorded on the original U. S. land surveys and an evaluation of previous interpretations of Indiana vegetation. Butler Univ. Bot. Studies **13**:95-111.
25. ROGERS, O. C., T. M. BUSHNELL, T. E. BARNES, S. MYERS, G. H. ROBINSON, P. T. VEALE, AND A. P. BELL. 1955. Soil Survey of Newton County, Indiana. U. S. Soil Conservation Service and Purdue Univ. Agr. Expt. Sta. Ser. 1941, No. 14.
26. SPURR, S. H. 1951. George Washington, surveyor and ecological observer. Ecology **32**:544-549.
27. THOMAS, DAVID. 1819. Travels through the western country in the summer of 1816, including notices of the natural history, topography, commerce, antiquities, agriculture and manufactures; with a map of the Wabash country, now settling. Auburn, N. Y.
28. THORNBROUGH, G., AND DOROTHY RIKER. 1956. Readings in Indiana History. Indiana Historical Bureau.
29. VISHER, S. S. 1944. Climate of Indiana. Indiana University Publ. Sci. Ser. No. 13. Bloomington.
30. WARREN, L. A. 1959. Lincoln's Youth, Indiana Years; Seven to Twenty One; 1816-1830. Ind. Hist. Soc. Indianapolis.
31. ZERFAS, L. G. 1936. Milksickness and the Lincoln family. Jour. Indiana State Medical Assn. **29**:88-89.

# 1
# Bedrock Geology

RAYMOND C. GUTSCHICK
Department of Geology, University of Notre Dame

The geologist studies the spatial and chronologic relations of earth materials—minerals, rocks (and formations), fossils, and fluids (water, oil, and gas) of an area to understand their collective geological history. This scientific approach is fundamental if it is to serve the greatest benefit to mankind through knowledge gained and the resultant discovery of our economic resources. Much has been learned through the works and publications of the state and federal geological surveys and innumerable geologists who have contributed to our present understanding of this history during the 150 years of statehood.[6,7,12] This human endeavor and wealth of information is gratefully acknowledged for this essay.

The purpose of this paper is to present what we know of the bedrock surface geology of Indiana and that portion of the earth's crust down to the "basement". It deals essentially with the history of our state before the great Pleistocene ice age and particularly with Paleozoic rocks which make up the bedrock. It also dwells on geological principles and data necessary to interpret and understand these relations. Insight is sought through graphic presentation using maps, cross-sections, and block diagrams. This article is not written for the professional geologist but is directed toward the students who are interested in understanding the significance of Indiana geology.

## Bedrock Surface Geology of Indiana

What is bedrock? What is a bedrock geology map? What is the source of data? How is the map constructed? What are the principles which form the basis of interpretation of such map? How can four-dimensional thinking be derived from the map to project the data in depth and time (chronologic sequence) in addition to a real (length and breadth) distribution of the rocks? Of what value is a bedrock geology map? What are some of its future developments?

To answer these questions one must start with the stratigraphic key, that is, the geologic timescale (Fig. 2) and succession of rock strata in the order in which they were deposited from the older beds at the base to the youngest layers at the top. Next, *bedrock* (Fig. 3) is any solid rock underlying soil, sand, clay, etc. (A. G. I. Glossary[6]). The latter materials constitute *mantle rock* or regolith defined as loose, incoherent rock materials, of whatever origin, that nearly everywhere forms the surface of the land and rests on bedrock[6]. Note that mantle is also used to refer to that portion of the earth's interior between the core and the crust.

Surface mantle obscures the bedrock surface formations (Figs. 4A, 5B). It may be transported by glaciers and deposited directly by the ice or by meltwaters from the ice. It can develop in the form of beaches (waves and water currents), dunes or loess (wind energy), or as alluvial deposits (streams). It may range in thickness from almost nothing, bedrock exposure or outcrop, to more than 400 feet where it fills depressions or valleys on the bedrock surface. In sharp contrast, an area in southern Indiana outside the glacier terminus is thinly covered by residual soils. These are produced from weathering of the bedrock and become transitional with it.

The bedrock geology map of Indiana (Figs. 3, 4C) may be difficult to visualize and understand since it is a projection of surfaces into the plane of the paper. Three-dimensional imagination is helpful and is achieved in part by construction of strategic cross-sections. Basically the bedrock map represents a pattern of intersection of an irregular topographic surface on top of the bedrock with the bedding surface boundaries between layered rock units. Configuration of this bedrock surface is shown contoured in Fig. 4B and the corresponding physiographic diagram in Fig. 4D. The bedrock geology map (Fig. 3) portrays the distribution of rock systems or formations which project upwards to the bedrock surface.

Bedrock geological data come from observations of rocks in natural exposures or outcrops where there is no regolith or from man-made excavations and subsurface exploration such as quarries, open pits, wells, and mine shafts (Fig. 5A). In a particular situation, the geologist notes the location, determines the type of rock and its age, and the formation is

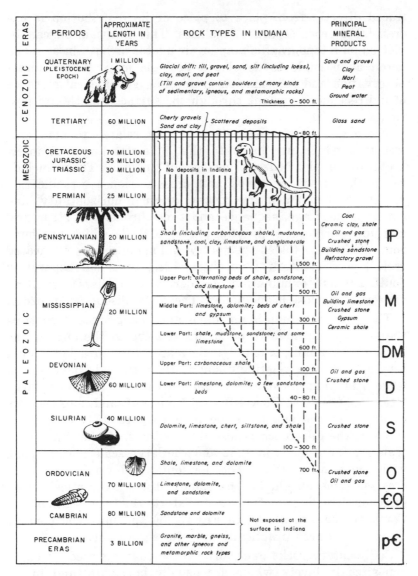

| ERAS | PERIODS | APPROXIMATE LENGTH IN YEARS | ROCK TYPES IN INDIANA | PRINCIPAL MINERAL PRODUCTS | |
|---|---|---|---|---|---|
| CENOZOIC | QUATERNARY (PLEISTOCENE EPOCH) | 1 MILLION | Glacial drift: till, gravel, sand, silt (including loess), clay, marl, and peat (Till and gravel contain boulders of many kinds of sedimentary, igneous, and metamorphic rocks) Thickness 0 - 500 ft. | Sand and gravel Clay Marl Peat Ground water | |
| CENOZOIC | TERTIARY | 60 MILLION | Cherty gravels Sand and clay } Scattered deposits 0 - 80 ft. | Glass sand | |
| MESOZOIC | CRETACEOUS JURASSIC TRIASSIC | 70 MILLION 35 MILLION 30 MILLION | No deposits in Indiana | | |
| MESOZOIC | PERMIAN | 25 MILLION | | | |
| PALEOZOIC | PENNSYLVANIAN | 20 MILLION | Shale (including carbonaceous shale), mudstone, sandstone, coal, clay, limestone, and conglomerate 1,500 ft. | Coal Ceramic clay, shale Oil and gas Crushed stone Building sandstone Refractory gravel | ℙ |
| PALEOZOIC | MISSISSIPPIAN | 20 MILLION | Upper Part: alternating beds of shale, sandstone, and limestone 500 ft. | Oil and gas Building limestone Crushed stone Gypsum Ceramic shale | M |
| PALEOZOIC | MISSISSIPPIAN | 20 MILLION | Middle Part: limestone, dolomite; beds of chert and gypsum 300 ft. | Oil and gas Building limestone Crushed stone Gypsum Ceramic shale | M |
| PALEOZOIC | MISSISSIPPIAN | 20 MILLION | Lower Part: shale, mudstone, sandstone; and some limestone 600 ft. | Oil and gas Building limestone Crushed stone Gypsum Ceramic shale | DM |
| PALEOZOIC | DEVONIAN | 60 MILLION | Upper Part: carbonaceous shale 100 ft. | Oil and gas Crushed stone | DM |
| PALEOZOIC | DEVONIAN | 60 MILLION | Lower Part: limestone, dolomite; a few sandstone beds 40 - 80 ft. | Oil and gas Crushed stone | D |
| PALEOZOIC | SILURIAN | 40 MILLION | Dolomite, limestone, chert, siltstone, and shale 100 - 300 ft. | Crushed stone | S |
| PALEOZOIC | ORDOVICIAN | 70 MILLION | Shale, limestone, and dolomite 700 ft. | Crushed stone Oil and gas | O |
| PALEOZOIC | ORDOVICIAN | 70 MILLION | Limestone, dolomite, and sandstone | Crushed stone Oil and gas | ЄO |
| PALEOZOIC | CAMBRIAN | 80 MILLION | Sandstone and dolomite Not exposed at the surface in Indiana | | ЄO |
| PALEOZOIC | PRECAMBRIAN ERAS | 3 BILLION | Granite, marble, gneiss, and other igneous and metamorphic rock types | | pЄ |

GEOLOGIC TIMESCALE AND INDIANA ROCK CHART
(From Indiana Department of Conservation, Geological Survey, Circular No. 5)

Fig. 2—Geologic Timescale and Indiana Rock Chart (after Wayne, 1958). Rocks from Permian to Early Tertiary have not been found in Indiana (closely-spaced vertical lines). Rocks from Ordovician to Pennsylvanian make up bedrock surface (widely-spaced vertical dashed lines indicate erosional truncation). Letter symbols in right-hand column are referred to in subsequent text-figures.

traced directly from place to place or its distribution is extrapolated from separate localities. This information can be plotted on a topographic map or air photos or both in as much detail as possible to develop a geologic map. Where direct observation and information is missing, geophysical methods of indirect measurement through the surface mantle are possible.

There are certain geologic principles related to map construction which are basic to the understanding and interpretation of the bedrock geology of Indiana. These include the scales used for maps and cross-sections; stratification (layering of sedimentary rocks), original horizontality, and superposition; age, sequence and time-chronology; structural attitude (strike and dip of a plane) of beds which are horizontal, tilted, or folded; geometry and symmetry of truncated rock layers (pattern); unconformities, erosional separation (outliers) and exhumation of older rocks (inliers); faulting and cryptoexplosion anomalies. These are discussed in order.

The scale of a map is an important factor since it controls the detail of an area to be shown relative to the size of the map. For example, a small scale map refers to a large area represented on a relatively small size map and conversely a large scale map illustrates a small area on a relatively large size map. Compare Figure 3 with Figure 4C and note the loss of detail in the smaller scale map (Figure 4C). Of course, some of the difference is also due to the fact that the small scale map was made in 1952 and the large scale map in 1955 with more information. The horizontal and vertical scale of cross-sections should be the same; otherwise vertical exaggeration, which is so often used, distorts the true relationship. Compare the two blocks in Figure 6E and note the concept of basin and arch practically loses its significance.

Sedimentary rocks generally can be characterized as being deposited in layers which are usually horizontal and in sequence from the earliest or initial deposits at the bottom to the most recent or youngest sediments at the top. In time the rocks are compacted and cemented to form hard layers. The left-hand side of Figure 6A shows a normal sequence 1, 2, and 3 in order with the bottom and top of each succeeding layer in the proper relation. The right-hand side shows the

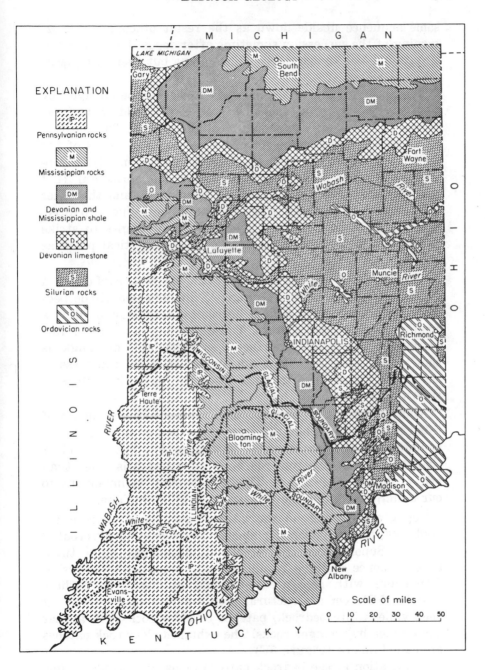

Fig. 3—Generalized bedrock geology map of Indiana (after Patton, 1955, p. 12).

same sequence upside down as the result of complete overturning of the succession sometime after deposition. The latter situation is not known to occur in Indiana but there are places where it exists.

The horizontality of sedimentary rocks can be changed by tilting of the layers as shown in Figure 6B. Bedding surfaces between rock layers are shown ideally as planes. The position of a bedding plane in space can be expressed in terms of the strike and dip of the beds. In the example given, strike represents the intersection of two planes, one horizontal (flat rock surface, or water surface, or imaginary) and the other the bedding surface, resulting in a North-South line. Dip direction (West in this case) is always at right angles to strike and the true angle of dip is measured in a vertical plane as shown.

The width of the formation at the bedrock surface is a function of its thickness, or angle of dip, or slope of the bedrock surface which is seldom horizontal or planar, or it is a combination of these factors. The difference in width of formation on the bedrock surface due to variable dip angle is shown in Figure 5C. That due to variation in thickness is shown in Figure 5D. In both cases the bedrock surface is shown as a flat plane.

Another important fact becomes apparent in a sequence of tilted rocks in that they dip from the oldest beds towards the youngest rocks. For example, in Figure 6B, bed 3 is older than bed 5 and dips towards 5. In turn bed 5 is older than bed 7 and dips toward 7. This relationship is important to our understanding of the bedrock geology of Indiana.

Topographic relief on the bedrock surface in Indiana exceeds 500 feet (Figure 4B) and is the product of differential erosion. Superimpose this erosional topography on a tilted rock sequence and the result will be eroded wedge-edges of formations with separated erosional remnants or outliers (Figure 5E). On a structural arch where streams have cut deep valleys into bedrock, patches of older rocks will appear surrounded by younger rocks. The exhumed older rock patches are called inliers (Figure 5F).

A variation in the bedrock pattern of parallel bands of formations occurs where there is lateral thinning of one or more of the formations. After deposition of the Paleozoic sedimentary sequence through strata of Mississippian age, pre-Pennsylvanian erosional truncation has beveled the rocks laterally. Pennsylvanian rocks were then deposited on this erosional surface. This case which is one type of unconformity is illustrated in Figure 6D part A and represents the situation in southwestern Indiana. Note that a similar effect can be produced by conformable depositional thinning of one of the units (Fig. 6D part B).

## Indiana's Structural Framework

We can apply the above principles to specific examples of bedrock relations in Indiana; however, a knowledge of Indiana's position in the regional structural framework is necessary. Two maps present the structural foundation which surrounds Indiana and on which rests the thin Paleozoic sedimentary veneer of the earth's crust (Figures 7A and 7B). Since Figure 7B is a contoured construction of the top of the basement complex, an explanation of what is meant by "basement" is in order.

Although rocks of Precambrian age do not crop out nor do they form the bedrock surface in Indiana, they exist throughout the state beneath the Paleozoic sequence cover (Figure 6E). It is this Precambrian foundation of igneous and metamorphic rocks, which includes meta-sedimentary rocks also, that constitutes the "Basement". Top of the basement complex surface therefore is marked by the boundary between Paleozoic sedimentary rocks and Precambrian crystalline rocks. Direct knowledge of the "basement" is based on some 10 wells which penetrated the Paleozoic sequence into the upper part of the "basement". The limit of most deep drilling is this basement and once it is recognized in the rock cuttings or cores, drilling ceases and the well is completed. This is because the object of past deep drilling has been to seek oil and gas reservoirs in Paleozoic sediments and the Precambrian crystalline rocks offer little economic incentive for finding such fluid resources. More recently geophysics has been used to indirectly determine the depth and configuration of the top of the basement surface.

Getting back to Figure 7B, the map represents the depth

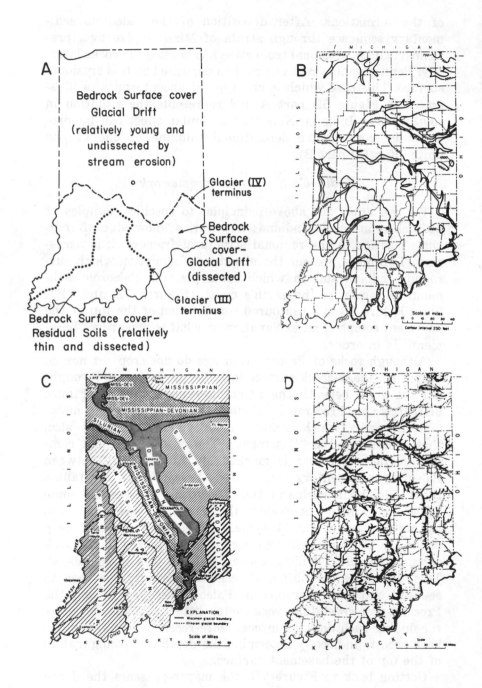

of the basement relative to mean sealevel datum. Each contour line represents points of equal depth along it. Interpolation of depths can be made between contour lines for any location in Indiana. A generalized interpretation of the patterns outlined in Figure 7B is given in Figure 7A. In the regional picture Indiana occupies portions of two basins, the Illinois and Michigan Basins, separated by the Cincinnati Arch and its branches, the Findlay and Wisconsin Arches.

A detailed picture is given in Figure 6C where the map data are based on approximately 300 wells for control points. In each well the elevation of the top surface of the Ordovician Trenton Limestone Formation is determined relative to the position of sealevel and the value for each location is plotted and contoured. This structure contour map gives the configuration of this continuous surface throughout Indiana. Assuming that the limestone layers were deposited horizontal as an extensive sheet in an Ordovician marine basin, the beds have subsequently been deformed into a "saddle-like" structure. The cross-section (Fig. 6E) drawn along a line from the NE to the SW corners of the state (Fig. 6C) shows the flanks of this saddle with the downwarped Illinois Basin to the southwest and the Michigan Basin to the northeast. The top of the Trenton Limestone (datum surface) is shown in relation to sealevel. From this map can be predicted the depth of the top of the Trenton Limestone for any location in Indiana.

## Geologic Map Pattern

With the geologic principles and structural framework as background, we can take another look at the bedrock geology of Indiana (Fig. 3). The distributional pattern of mappable bedrock systems designated by symbols O, S, D, DM, M, and P which veneer the bedrock surface is the result of uninterrupt-

Fig. 4—A—Transported (glacial) and residual mantle versus bedrock relations in Indiana.
B—Generalized map of bedrock topography. Contours indicate elevations above sealevel (after Wayne, 1956, p. 22).
C—Generalized bedrock geology map of Indiana (after Patton, in Deiss, 1952, pl. 5). Compare with figure 3 for differences in scale and detail.
D—Physiographic diagram based on figure 4B to depict pre-glacial topography (after Wayne, 1956, p. 26). Note three escarpments on resistant tilted rock layers in southern half of state, Teays Valley in central portion of the state flowing from east to west, and resistant hills in northeastern Indiana.

ed post-Paleozoic to pre-Pleistocene erosion. As a consequence, formations which have been arched upward have been truncated and their very slightly tilted edges beveled along the flanks of the arch. Three general areas of geology are conspicuous and these are related to the gross structural features of the state, e.g., Illinois and Michigan Basins, and the Cincinnati and Wisconsin Arches.

The area of greatest uplift in Indiana is along the Cincinnati Arch in the southeast portion of the state. In this area on the upwarp, Paleozoic strata have been stripped away exposing classic Ordovician rocks (Richmond Group) south of Richmond where they crop out along stream valleys draining into the Ohio River system. Several inliers of Ordovician rocks are present along the Arch in east-central Indiana where erosion has cut down through the Silurian system to expose the underlying Ordovician rocks. The axis of uplift extends northwestward to join the Wisconsin Arch; however the amount of uplift has been variable along the axis. Middle Paleozoic rocks have been removed over the crest of the Arch. Except for a narrow band of Devonian limestone preserved in the trough of the structural saddle in northwestern Indiana, Silurian rocks cover the crest of the Arch along its axis. A number of Devonian limestone outliers lie outside the beveled feather edge as remnants of the former sheet of Devonian beds.

On either side of the Cincinnati-Wisconsin Arch axis the rocks dip into structural basins which flank the Arch. Strata in ordered succession from Ordovician to Pennsylvanian dip westward and southwestward from the axis of the Arch into the Illinois Basin. The dip of the rocks into the basin is slight indeed ranging from 10 to 30 feet per mile. A one degree (1°) dip is equivalent to approximately 92 feet per mile so that the dip of the Paleozoic rocks into the Illinois Basin is only a fraction of a single degree! In a similar manner rocks dip northeast and northward on the north side of the Arch axis into the Michigan Basin. The

Fig. 5—A—Sources of direct bedrock observations on which surface and subsurface geological interpretations are based.
B—Block diagram to show general mantle-bedrock relations in Indiana.
C—Bedrock width of formation as a function of dip angle.
D—Bedrock width of formation as a function of thickness.
E—Outliers - isolated erosional remnants separated from the main body.
F—Inliers - isolated exposures of older layers beneath younger rocks.

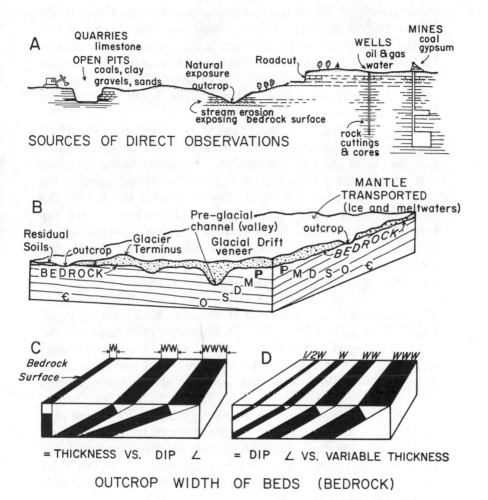

A

QUARRIES
limestone
OPEN PITS
coals, clay
gravels, sands

Natural
exposure
outcrop

Roadcut

WELLS
oil & gas
water

MINES
coal
gypsum

stream erosion
exposing bedrock surface

rock
cuttings
& cores

SOURCES OF DIRECT OBSERVATIONS

B

MANTLE
TRANSPORTED
(Ice and meltwaters)

Pre-glacial
channel (valley)     outcrop

Residual
Soils    outcrop   Glacier
Terminus

Glacial Drift
veneer

BEDROCK

BEDROCK            P

ₚ   P M D S O ∈

M
∈             O   S‾D

C

Bedrock
Surface

M    WW    WWW

D

1/2W   W   WW   WWW

= THICKNESS VS. DIP ∠          = DIP ∠ VS. VARIABLE THICKNESS

OUTCROP WIDTH OF BEDS (BEDROCK)

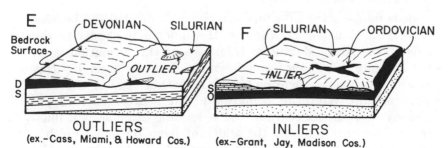

E

DEVONIAN    SILURIAN

Bedrock
Surface

OUTLIER

D
S

OUTLIERS
(ex.-Cass, Miami, & Howard Cos.)

F

SILURIAN    ORDOVICIAN

INLIER

S
O

INLIERS
(ex.-Grant, Jay, Madison Cos.)

average rate of dip of Indiana rocks into the Michigan Basin is only 20 feet per mile which is less than one-quarter of one degree ($\frac{1}{4}°$). Only rocks ranging in age from Ordovician and Silurian to Mississippian are present at the bedrock surface in Indiana on the Michigan Basin side of the Arch. Pennsylvanian rocks which are extensive in the Illinois Basin occur to the north in Michigan.

For practical purpose, the trend of the formational band on the map is also the direction of formational strike, e.g., the formational band marked DM strikes NNW-SSE in the southern half of the state; whereas, in the northernmost part of the state it strikes essentially E-W. The reason for this is that the map represents the horizontal plane which intersects the top and bottom bedding of the formation to define the strike of the beds. Dip is at right angles to the direction of strike in the direction in which the beds are inclined which in this case is into the basin, with amounts of dip less than one degree.

The pattern of formations diagonally across Indiana, SW to NE, normal to the Cincinnati-Wisconsin Arch axis is P, M, DM, D, S, O, S, D, DM, and M. This general pattern shows the oldest rocks on the crest of the Arch and progressively younger rocks into the basin. This follows the rule that rocks dip in the direction from old toward the younger strata for a normal tilted truncated sequence as in the case in Indiana for the Illinois and Michigan Basins. In the above example, the symmetry of formational pattern about 0 is also important. This symmetrical arrangement of formations reflects the structural-erosional history of the rocks. One can interpret this as the older rocks along the axis of the arch or dome and the younger beds in the center of the basin.

Beds flanking the Cincinnati Arch are truncated and beveled with their thin feather edge on the inner side closest to the axis of the Arch. Maximum thickness of the formation is on the opposite side of the band down dip. Directly overlying this maximum thickness will be the thin feather edge of the next younger unit. Width of formation at the bedrock surface has already been discussed; however a specific example will illustrate the point. Compare the width of band for DM on either side of the arch. The DM band is generally wider flanking the Michigan Basin than that on the Illinois Basin side. This can be accounted for by the smaller dip angle into the Michigan Basin (Fig. 5C).

On the practical side certain economic resources such as oil and gas, coal, gypsum, limestone, etc. are related to rocks of certain ages (Fig. 2), e.g., Pennsylvanian coal, Mississippian gypsum, Ordovician oil and gas, etc. If one were to explore for these through a study of surface geology and/or a drilling exploratory program, knowledge of the bedrock geology can be very important. A well started over Pennsylvanian terrain would generally assure one that Mississippian, Devonian, Silurian, Ordovician, Cambrian, and Precambrian rocks will be encountered in descending order assuming that the well is drilled deep enough to penetrate the basement. Projected depths can be interpolated from generalized thickness estimates in Fig. 2 and structure contour maps, Figures 6C and 7B. On the other hand a well drilled on the axis of the Arch over Silurian terrain will automatically eliminate Devonian and younger rocks as objectives; however one could expect to drill through Ordovician and Cambrian rocks into the Precambrian basement.

Deviations from the normal bedrock pattern are rare in Indiana but two anomalies which interrupt the pattern are called to your attention. One structure is the Mt. Carmel Fault in south-central Indiana east of Bloomington and the other is the Kentland crypto-explosion structure shown as a small Ordovician inlier surrounded by DM strata in northwestern Indiana about 35 miles northwest of Lafayette (Fig. 3).

The Mt. Carmel Fault is known to extend about 50 miles in length in a NNW-SSE trend (Fig. 3). The fault dips steeply to the west and drops very gently dipping Paleozoic rocks 80 to 175 feet down on the west side relative to the east block. The relationships are illustrated in Figures 7C and 7D.

Detailed knowledge of the Kentland structural anomaly comes from a quarry located three miles east of Kentland in Newton County where steeply dipping and fractured Ordovician rocks are quarried directly below a thin glacial drift mantle. Bedrock in the surrounding area is normally Devonian-Mississippian strata which is almost flat-lying (dip less than 1° towards the southwest). Four Ordovician rock formations with aggregate thickness greater than 500 feet are recognized in the quarry within 200 feet of the bedrock surface; yet the same formations are present in wells at Kentland and Goodland below 1000 feet depth (Fig. 7E). Several explanations have been suggested to account for the origin of this unusual structure. These include deep-seated volcanic explosion, meteorite impact, and faulting. The high pressure and temperature mineral coesite ($SiO_2$) commonly found in meteorite impact areas has been reported from within the St. Peter Sandstone at Kentland. Conical rock fractures ("shattercones") ranging in size from a few inches to more than 10 feet are found at Kentland and these features indicate sudden shock. No volcanic materials have been recognized in the quarry. Neither the areal extent, details of the structure at depth, nor the mechanics of deformation are fully known. Much more geological and geophysical study is needed before the origin of this structure can be determined with confidence.

### Bedrock—Depth and Time

Enough has been said concerning the interpretation of the bedrock geology map to realize that we are dealing with a three-dimensional block of the earth's crust which has the areal size and shape of Indiana and the variable vertical depth (thickness) to the Precambrian basement. Within this block of rocks is contained the geological history of over one billion years, many millions of dollars of natural resources much of which is yet to be discovered, and need for many man-hours of concentrated study for future knowledge of the geological

Fig. 6—A—Block diagram to illustrate bedrock relations for horizontal strata.
B—Bedrock superposition relations of a sequence of uniformly dipping strata. The geometry of strike (measured in horizontal plane) and dip (measured in vertical plane) is illustrated.
C—Contour map to delineate structure of layered sedimentary rocks across Indiana. Zero line shows position of intersection of plane of sealevel (horizontal) and warped bedding surface. Other lines are traces of sub-sealevel horizontal planes with same bedding surface (after Dawson, 1952, Misc. Map 3).
D—Block diagram model of example of bedrock formational thinning in southern Indiana (after Deiss, 1952, p. 15).
E—Geological cross-section along line SW-NE (figure 6C) to show arrangement of rock systems below surface diagonally across Indiana. The margins of two basins are separated by a pronounced arch in the upper block; however note the thin lower block drawn to the same vertical scale as the horizontal. Gross effects of vertical exaggeration often gives one a false perspective.

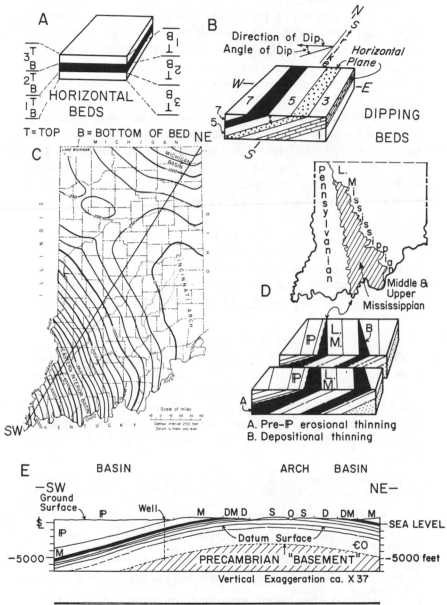

A

HORIZONTAL BEDS

T = TOP    B = BOTTOM OF BED

B

Direction of Dip
Angle of Dip

Horizontal Plane

DIPPING BEDS

C

D

Middle & Upper Mississippian

A. Pre-℗ erosional thinning
B. Depositional thinning

E

BASIN    ARCH    BASIN

—SW

NE—

Ground Surface    Well    M  DM D    S  OS  D  DM  M

SEA LEVEL

Datum Surface

—5000    PRECAMBRIAN "BASEMENT"    —5000 feet

Vertical Exaggeration ca. X 37

Horizontal = Vertical Scale for block above (Cross-Section)

history, exploration, discovery, and exploitation of the mineral resources of our state.

The gross volume of Paleozoic sedimentary rocks deposited in Indiana during the past one-half billion years can be calculated from the data. Estimates from integration of variable thickness contour maps can be made for rocks above sealevel using Figure 4B added to estimates of rocks below sealevel down to the basement shown in Figure 7B. The area of the state of Indiana is 36,291 square miles. The total volume of Paleozoic crustal rocks in Indiana is believed to be somewhere between 40,000 to 50,000 cubic miles. It should be noted that only about 10 wells in the state drilled through the Paleozoic sequence into the Precambrian basement; however there is additional control on depth of the basement from indirect geophysical measurements.

The reason for emphasizing the great bulk of bedrock beneath our state is that our mineral wealth will be derived directly from these rocks either as raw materials or fluid reservoirs. Subsequent papers on Ground Water and Mineral Resources will discuss the production and potential of bedrock wealth.

## Future Bedrock Studies

The major aspects of the bedrock surface map of Indiana have already been determined by geologists.[4] Significant new discoveries will continue to be made in the next few decades. Further refinements of the bedrock geology will be made from outcrop and quarry exposures, but most progress will be made through geophysical studies and exploratory drilling operations.

Fig. 7—A—Indiana's position in the regional crustal structural framework. Diagram is simplification of figure 7B. Compare with figures 6C and 6E.
B—Contour map showing geometric configuration on top of basement complex. Lines represent depths below sealevel (sealevel = O) of top of Pre-cambrian "Basement", see figure 6E (after Rudman, Summerson, and Hinze, 1965, p. 896).
C—Cross-section to illustrate break in bedrock surface caused by the Mt. Carmel Fault.
D—Block diagram to illustrate geometry and mechanics of the Mt. Carmel Fault.
E—Cross-section of structural anomaly 3 miles east of Kentland, Indiana, which shows the major structural disruption of normal stratified sequence between Kentland and Goodland. Rocks in the quarry have been catastrophically raised more than 1000 feet above their normal position.

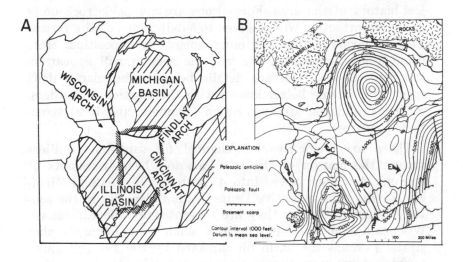

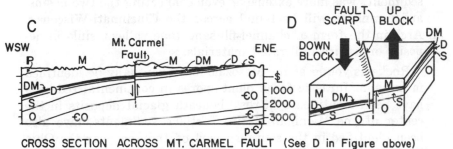

CROSS SECTION ACROSS MT. CARMEL FAULT (See D in Figure above)

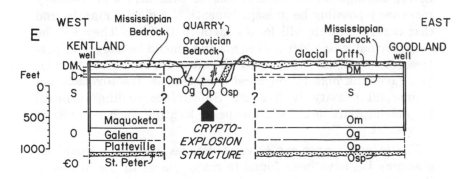

The geologic map is an important tool to decipher the geological history of the area. Formations are mappable rock units and more attention will be given to subdivisions of the formations in terms of different environments of deposition. More detailed subdivisions of the geologic section will appear on the map. Bedrock surface details beneath the glacial drift cover will become better known with the location of outliers, inliers, pre-glacial stream erosion channels, and local structural features.

There are Pennsylvanian channel fill sandstone outliers around the margin of the late Paleozoic basin remnants of streams that once flowed into it. Both the Illinois and Michigan Basins have extensive Pennsylvanian deposits in the center of them; however they are separated by the Cincinnati-Wisconsin Arch which is truncated much below Pennsylvanian strata. Perhaps the basin fill climaxed by the Pennsylvanian sediments was more extensive, even connecting the two basins, and remnants will be found across the Cincinnati-Wisconsin Arch in the form of channel-fill sandstone valleys, sink-fill deposits or fissure infiltrated materials.

Rocks as young as the Mesozoic may eventually be identified in Indiana. Jurassic fossil plant spores in continental red-beds have been identified by Cross[1] beneath glacial deposits in the center of the Michigan Basin. Tertiary sediments have also been identified in the southern part of Indiana near the Ohio River. Perhaps other occurrences of Mesozoic and Tertiary rocks may possibly be present beneath the glacial mantle, and that careful search will locate them in Indiana. They will be unconformable on older sediments and should be sought in pre-Mesozoic erosional topography as valley fill, or related to solution cave-sink hole fill on karst surfaces, or fracture-solution fissure fill gravity infiltration. Subsurface drilling beneath the glacial drift offers some hope of locating such deposits if they exist.

Faults and crypto-explosive structures, whatever their origins may be, have been found in many places in the Midwest. Geophysical maps reflecting the seismic, magnetic, and gravitational properties of the bedrock suggest the possibility of other anomalous structures. It is reasonable to assume that more than one of each structure exists in the state possibly buried by a thick cover of mantle rock. Careful observation and imagination should be used in the search for these bedrock features.

It is most probable that the obvious surface outcrop-quarry exposures have already revealed the most significant bedrock geological features. Other finds are waiting to be discovered beneath the surface mantle where they are concealed. Unfortunately they will require expensive means to locate and identify them; progress will be slow in this direction.

The Precambrian basement offers promise for economic resources but there is little incentive to explore this deeply because of the great costs and high risk involved. Much of the North American continent mineral wealth, in gold, copper, iron, nickel, silver, uranium, and many others, come from the Precambrian Shield area not too many miles to the north. In effect the Precambrian Shield and its ancient crystalline rock outcrops represent the exposure of our basement. Rock types encountered in the few deep wells that have been drilled to the Precambrian basement in Indiana are similar to those present in the Canadian Shield. It is this geological evidence which offers hope for the future.

Finally we need to work out the most detailed chronological outline of the geological history of Indiana from the latest information available. This includes preparation of a comprehensive graphic composite columnar section similar to one recently published by the Michigan stratigraphic committee.[5] This history will record as completely as possible events such as marine and continental sedimentation with its complex changing panorama of environments; uplift and downwarp of the earth's crust; times of erosion (unconformities), structural deformation (folding and faulting), and mineralization. The history for the Precambrian will involve igneous intrusion and extrusion( volcanism) along with metamorphism.

Bedrock maps have been prepared from geologic field data for most of the states in the Union. Recent generalized composite geological maps are also available for the United States and for the North American continent. Geological maps (large and small scale) have been prepared for most land areas of the world. In some cases available geological data enabled construction of very detailed maps, whereas in less explored regions, the maps are composed from meager reconnaissance information. State and federal geological surveys and geological societies are sources for published geology maps.*

The same geological principles outlined in this paper and applied to the bedrock geology of Indiana can be universally applied to any area in the world. It should be noted that Indiana's geology may be less complex than many areas throughout the world and that additional concepts will be required for the latter.

In conclusion, the study of the bedrock geology of Indiana makes a fine practical exercise for students of the earth sciences in secondary education and at the college level. The study can be augmented with field trips to bedrock exposures depending upon the location in the state. It can also be expanded using library resources through publications of the Indiana Geological Survey.[8,13]

## LITERATURE

1. COHEE, G. V. 1965. Geologic history of the Michigan Basin. Jour. Wash. Acad. Sci. 55:211-223.
2. DAWSON, T. A. 1952. Map showing generalized structure of Trenton Limestone in Indiana. Ind. Geol. Survey Misc. Map 3.
3. DEISS, C. F. 1952. Geologic formations on which and with which Indiana's roads are built. Ind. Geol. Survey Circ. 1:1-17, 9 pls., 3 figs.
4. _____ (J. B. Patton-chrmn.). 1956. Geologic Map of Indiana. Atlas of Mineral Resources of Indiana. Ind. Geol. Survey Map 9.
5. ELLS, G. D. (chrmn.). 1964. Stratigraphic Succession in Michigan, Chart 1, Mich. Geol. Survey.
6. HOWELL, J. V. and J. M. WELLER (chrmn.). 1960. Glossary of Geology and Related Sciences with Supplement. Amer. Geol. Inst., 2nd. ed., 325+72 pp.
7. LOGAN, W. N., R. LEIBER, S. S. VISHER, C. A. MALOTT, W. M. TUCKER, AND E. R. CUMINGS. 1922. Handbook of Indiana Geology. Ind. Dept. of Conserv. Div. Geology, Publ. 21:1-1120, 180 pls., 120 figs.
8. NEVERS, G. M., and R. D. WALKER. 1962. Annotated bibliography of Indiana geology through 1955. Ind. Geol. Survey Bull. 24:1-486.
9. PATTON, J. B. 1955. Underground storage of liquid hydrocarbons in Indiana. Ind. Geol. Survey Rept. Progress 9:1-19, fig. 1.
10. RUDMAN, A. J., C. H. SUMMERSON, and W. J. HINZE, 1965, Geology of basement in Midwestern United States. Bull. Amer. Assoc. Petroleum Geologists 49:894-904, 12 figs.
11. WAYNE, W. J. 1956. Thickness of drift and bedrock physiography of Indiana north of the Wisconsin Glacial Boundary. Ind. Geol. Survey Rept. Progress 7:1-70, 10 text-figs., map.
12. _____ 1958. Let's look at some rocks. Ind. Geol. Survey Circ. 5:1-36.
13. Woodard, G. S. 1957. List of geologic publications and maps of Indiana. Ind. Geol. Survey, 103 pp.

* State of Indiana Department of Natural Resources Geological Survey, 611 North Walnut Grove, Bloomington, Indiana, 47401.
United States Geological Survey, Washington, D. C.
American Geological Institute, 1444 N Street, N.W., Washington, D. C. 20005.
The Geological Society of America, Inc., 231 East 46 Street, New York, N. Y. 10017.

# 2

# Ice and Land

## A Review of the Tertiary and Pleistocene History of Indiana*

WILLIAM J. WAYNE

Indiana Geological Survey

### Introduction

Indiana was enriched during the past half-million or so years by glaciers that developed in the upland east of Hudson Bay and spread out across the northeastern part of North America. Continental glaciers reached farther south in the Wabash and Ohio Valleys — south of the 38th parallel — than anywhere else in the northern hemisphere during the Pleistocene Epoch. In the northern two-thirds of Indiana (Fig. 8) virtually all the landscape was constructed by the glaciers. Between the Wisconsin glacial boundary and the greatest extent of glaciation, bedrock features are intimately mixed with those of glacial deposition. South of the glacial boundary, valleys cut in bedrock have been partly filled with outwash gravel and sand and with the silt and clay of glacial lakes; a veneer of dust, called loess, blankets almost the entire unglaciated part of the State.

During the Pleistocene Epoch, glacial ice extended into Indiana at least three times. Each of the cold periods was followed by a warmer interglacial episode, during which the glaciers melted. The total effect of these several glaciations on the landscape and resources of northern Indiana as well as all of northeastern North America was vast. Shale lowlands, trenched limestone plains, and sandstone-capped escarpments, which made up the preglacial surface features of the State, were buried beneath a great volume of rock debris carried and dumped by the glacier. The present relief in much of central and northern Indiana is slight, if compared to that of the buried rock surface.

The impression gained by many a casual visitor who speeds across the State may be that central and northern Indiana is

*Publication authorized by the State Geologist, Department of Natural Resources, Geological Survey.

merely a flat midwestern cornfield. The huge glacially built plain is much more than that; it has many distinctive features and it is made up of many distinctive kinds of materials. The geologic study of these features has made possible both the recognition of many usable resources left by the extinct glaciers and the interpretation of events that took place during the Ice Age, as this part of geologic time often is called.

A century and a half ago, at the time Indiana became a State, the idea of continental glaciation had not yet been conceived. One of the origins offered then for the boulders, loose materials, and nearly flat plains of the northeastern states

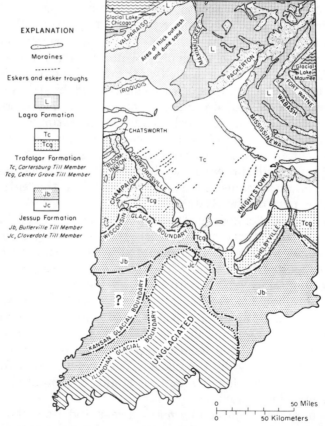

Fig. 8. Map of Indiana showing extent of ice-laid sediments and principal moraines of the Wisconsin drift sheets (modified from Wayne and Zumberge, 1965). The altered Kansan drift boundary has resulted from reinterpretation of existing data.

and northern Europe was a flood — the Noachian Deluge — hence the name "drift" that still is used for glacial deposits as a whole. In the early 1820's though, Venetz, a Swiss engineer, suggested that the accumulations of rock debris on piedmont plains and in valleys below the Alps had been left by formerly more extensive glaciers. Later, Louis Agassiz became convinced it was the correct explanation for the features he had observed in England and northern Europe, and did much to develop and spread the idea of continental glaciation. After Agassiz came to the United States in 1846, the glacial theory gained in acceptance in this country. Some opponents to it remained for many decades, but most geologists began to interpret the drift in the light of the theory of glacial origin.[6]

Early authors on the geology of Indiana described the drift but generally skirted well any discussion of its origin. The first clear reference to glacial action as a source for the surface materials in northern Indiana came in 1874, as a part of some work done under Cox, a state geologist who fully endorsed the glacial theory. Acceptance of a glacial origin for the drift became almost complete among geologists in the United States after the publication in 1883 of a report on the terminal moraines by T. C. Chamberlin.[1] The task of working out details in the complex glacial stratigraphy and Pleistocene history, however, has kept three generations of glacial geologists occupied. The early work of Leverett[10] was monumental; Malott[11] and Thornbury[13] supplied important supplemental work; development of new research techniques and the uncovering of new exposures assure that the task is far from complete.

### Origin of Ice Age Glaciers

A glacier is a large mass of ice made up of recrystallized snow and refrozen meltwater that lies primarily on land and that moves or has moved. Glaciers develop wherever snow accumulates faster than it melts. The snow particles in a perennial snow field become snow granules and the snow granules become ice by recrystallization and compaction. The final phase in the conversion to glacial ice comes when the ice begins to deform under the stress of its own weight; it becomes then an ice mass in motion, or a glacier.

Most glacier motion probably takes place by sliding of the ice over the rock beneath it and by internal shearing or sliding within ice crystals. Bands of clear ice along and nearly parallel to the base of a glacier represent zones of shearing within the ice. Movement along these shear planes, which resemble thrust faults in miniature, probably accounts for the very rapid forward motion sometimes observed in modern glaciers. Ice thickness needed for motion in temperate climate glaciers is not great, probably about 100 feet, although much greater thickness is needed in a polar climate. The Ice Age glaciers that extended into Indiana probably responded readily to minor changes in snowfall and temperature.

The Pleistocene Epoch was characterized by great climatic changes and large scale expansions and contractions of the earth's ice cover. Causes of these glaciations still is not known and no single theory adequately explains the growth and decline of the Ice Age glaciers. Several hypotheses have been advanced, and one or more of them may be valid.[6]

a. Cyclic variations in the kind and amount of solar radiation are known to produce short term changes in climate on the earth, such as increases in precipitation and fluctuations in temperature. Long range variations may have caused the sustained changes of glacial and interglacial times.

b. Creation of new highlands that had not existed until late Cenozoic time contributed to the conditions that allowed the development of Pleistocene glaciers but could not, in themselves, have been the cause of the glaciations. Along with the new highlands, a large percentage of the earth's crust — more than during most of pre-Pleistocene geologic time — has been above sea level during the Pleistocene.

In combined form these two suggested causes, solar variation and increased land and highlands, provide a possible theory for the cause of multiple glaciations;[6] it is not, however, the only one that has been offered. The most recent one suggests that during interglacial times of high sea level, full exchange of warm water with the Arctic Ocean across a threshold in the North Atlantic would melt the Arctic ice pack and lower the temperature of the Atlantic. An open Arctic sea would increase the moisture available for precipitation in northeastern Canada. Thus would glaciers begin to grow in the highlands east of Hudson Bay. Lowered sea level, caused by the glacial cover, would expose the threshold and stop the exchange of Atlantic and Arctic water. The Arctic Ocean would then refreeze and shut off the nourishment to the centers of glaciation; the Atlantic would increase in warmth; the overall effect would be to end the glacial part of the cycle.[4]

Regardless of the actual mechanism needed to trigger a glaciation, a long period of colder climate than the present would be necessary before glaciers could form in Canada and Scandinavia. But once formed, the glaciers themselves would have modified atmospheric circulation so that they would have tended to be self-perpetuating until world-wide temperatures increased enough to melt them.[12]

### Tertiary Geomorphic History and Deposits

After the land that was to become Indiana rose above sea level late in the Paleozoic Era, it probably underwent almost continuous weathering and erosion until the first of the Ice Age glaciers spread across it. Direct evidence of the Mesozoic physiographic history of Indiana is missing, but the Ohio River Formation, a sand unit in southern Indiana (Fig. 9), probably represents a depositional record from the early part of the Tertiary Period.[16] The basal part of the Ohio River Formation is a thick bed of cherty clay, now compacted and somewhat altered because of burial, but otherwise similar to the present residual soils on the adjacent limestone plain. Such a buried soil signifies that when it formed — probably during the last part of the Mesozoic Era — Indiana probably was a stable surface of low relief, in effect, a peneplain. Exactly how far the early Tertiary sea extended into Indiana is no longer determinable, but scattered deposits of the Ohio River Formation have been found as far north as Salem.

In the rest of Indiana, weathering and erosion continued throughout Tertiary and early Quaternary time. At least once during the Tertiary the surface probably was one of little relief.[14] Thick reddish-brown cherty clay soils are preserved in some areas on the Mitchell Plain where underground drainage has reduced the amount of water available to remove materials from the surface. Elsewhere, particularly on shales and sandstones, the soil cover over the rock is relatively thin.

Scattered deposits of weathered gravel now perched near ridge tops in unglaciated Indiana are the remains of old stream deposits. Called the Lafayette Gravel, they are thought to be middle to late Tertiary in age, but probably represent deposits of more than one episode of erosion and deposition. Younger floodplain sediments, found now on terraces outside the glaciated area in southern Indiana, are represented by the Prospect Formation (Fig. 10). The Prospect gravelly silts were

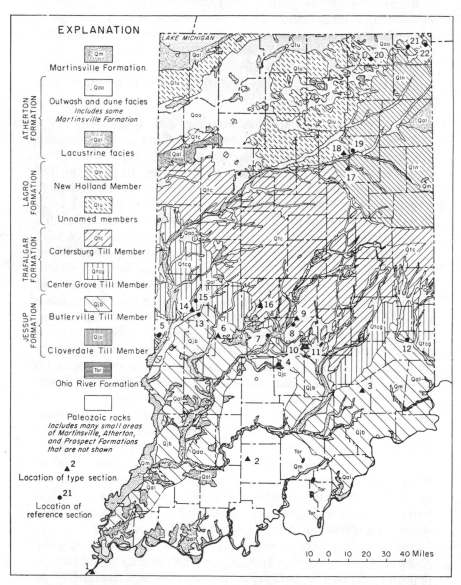

Fig. 9. Map of Indiana showing distribution of Pleistocene and Tertiary Formations, and the locations of type and reference sections (modified from Wayne, 1963).

deposited by streams that flowed across Indiana in late Tertiary to mid-Pleistocene time.

Shortly before the first Pleistocene glaciers buried northern Indiana, the bedrock landscape of the State had been carved to almost its present shape. The surface of Indiana was a series of limestone plains, shale lowlands, and sandstone uplands that trended from northwest to southeast. These terranes were trenched by the master stream of the region, Teays River, and its tributaries (Fig. 11).

Much of the drainage history of the Teays Valley has been worked out from studies of the sediments that fill its abandoned valley in Ohio and West Virginia, and from studies of the buried bedrock topography of Ohio, Indiana, and Illinois. The Teays was dammed by glacial ice during the early part of the Pleistocene, and overflow waters from the ice marginal lake followed a new course; thus was the Ohio River created.[15]

Glacial ice advanced first into the bedrock lowlands, and, when it became thick enough, protruded across the uplands. Lobes of ice reached farthest south in Indiana in the Scottsburg and Wabash Lowlands (Fig. 14). The triangular unglaciated area stood too high for glacial ice to cover.

Total thickness of the ice that spread out into central Indiana may never be known, but both estimates and measurements have been made of the marginal zone thickness. To have topped the Knobstone Escarpment near White River, the Illinoian glacier probably had to have stood at least 100 feet above the escarpment, thus its total thickness at that place was no less than 400 feet. More precise figures were found for the ice that left the upper till of the Trafalgar Formation. It thickened abruptly north of the margin and was about 1,700 feet thick 28 miles from the edge.[8]

The thick mass of ice depressed the surface beneath it. Over the Great Lakes and northward, postglacial uplift has been recognized by tilted beaches.[10,19] Even in central Indiana some depression and postglacial uplift took place, but it was relatively slight.

## History of Ice Age Events

Glaciations define the Pleistocene Epoch. The appearance, fluctuation, and disappearance of ice caps on the European and North American mainlands, as recorded by the sediments

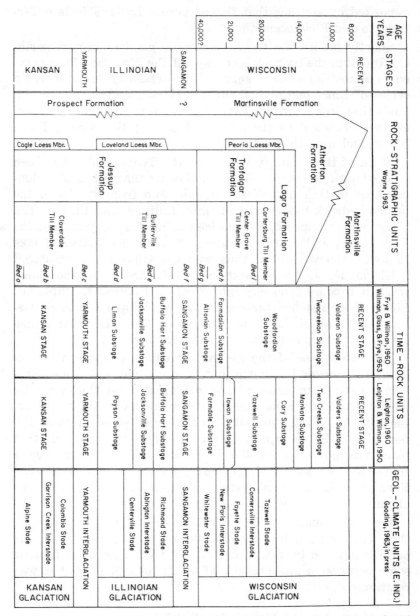

Fig. 10. Chart showing relationships of names used in the study of Pleistocene history and stratigraphy (from Wayne and Zumberge, 1965).

they left, have become the basis for working out a history of Ice Age events.

Layers of buried vegetation, or "forest beds", were recognized early in the study of the glacial drift. They were correctly thought of as signifying a warmer period between two glaciations. Recognition that some till sheets had more deeply weathered soils than others helped bring out the idea of multiple glaciation. Discovery of buried soils, or paleosols, added another significant step in the study of Pleistocene stratigraphy.[13]

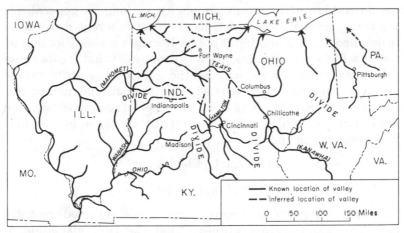

Fig. 11. Map of Indiana and adjacent states showing late Tertiary drainage (from Wayne, 1956).

Until 1950, all figures offered for the amount of time involved in the Pleistocene were estimates based on rates of deposition, of erosion, and of weathering. However inaccurate, these estimates did provide a rough time scale. In 1950 the disintegration rate of a recently discovered radioactive isotope of carbon — carbon 14 — was first used in an effort to date events of the Ice Age. It has become a most effective tool for studying the history of the last 40,000 years.

Radioactive carbon is formed in the upper atmosphere when nitrogen 14 atoms are bombarded by radioactive neutrons produced by the impact of cosmic rays on atmospheric atoms. Each new $C^{14}$ atom is oxidized to $CO_2$ and mixed completely with other atmospheric $CO_2$. Through respiration, all living matter maintains a constant ratio of $C^{14}$ to $C^{13}$ and $C^{12}$

atoms. When the organism dies, the exchange ceases, but the C[14] it contained at death continues to disintegrate at a steady rate; its half-life is 5730 years. A piece of wood, buried between two glacial drift layers, can be dated if it still contains a measurable amount of radiocarbon. Ages of events beyond the range of radiocarbon dating are still largely estimates based on rates of soil formation and marine deposition and extrapolated from the dated part of the record.[2,3,9]

Classification must accompany the accretion of knowledge. For many years stage and substage terminology has been used in the discussion of Pleistocene deposits, a system that has the advantage of apparent simplicity as long as generalities are being treated, but which has certain inherent drawbacks in detailed studies and in mapping. Recently a classification of Indiana Pleistocene sediments was proposed[17] that treats these sediments in the same way as the rest of the sedimentary rocks of Indiana are classified. The formational names are shown on Figure 10 along with all other stage, substage, and glaciation terminology that is currently in vogue among glacial geologists in Indiana.

## The Early Glaciations

### Nebraskan Age

Interpretation of sediments from cores collected recently from the ocean bottom suggests that the first glaciation of the Pleistocene may have taken place as long ago as 1½ million years.[3] Other interpretations place it considerably less than half a million years ago.[2] Of this ancient glaciation, perhaps represented in continental record by the Nebraskan Stage, no deposits have been found in Indiana. The most likely place for Nebraskan till to have been preserved, if in fact that glacier ever reached this State, would be in the buried valleys and lowlands in northeastern Indiana. Unfortunately, the total cover of glacial drift there is very thick, and records of holes drilled through it are not detailed enough to let such deposits be recognized.

### Kansan Age

The oldest glaciation for which any record has been found in Indiana took place during the Kansan Age. Although estimates for the beginning of the Kansan glacial age range from as recently as 200,000 to as far back as a million years ago, a good educated guess would put it around 350,000 to 400,000 years ago.

Kansan ice evidently came into central and southern Indiana from the northeast (Fig. 12A). The lobe that covered Indiana extended southward into the Scottsburg Lowland far enough to cross the Ohio River, but it was not thick enough to continue westward across the Knobstone Escarpment south of the East Fork of White River. North of the unglaciated triangle of southern Indiana, though, it spread across the Wabash Lowland into eastern Illinois. The till it deposited in Indiana is part of the Jessup Formation (Figs. 9, 10).

When the Kansan ice sheet lay across the Teays Valley in south-central Ohio it blocked the northwestward flow of the river and created a huge ice-marginal lake. Overflow water from the lake in Teays Valley is thought to have cut new channels through the divides between drainage basins to the west. The Teays drainage combined with meltwater from the glacier to create an outlet along the route now followed by the Ohio River.

A moderate volume of outwash must have been carried down the Wabash Valley during the Kansan glaciation, but it is not distinguishable from overlying younger sediments. Nor has loess of Kansan age been recognized along the lower Wabash. A single good exposure of Kansan loess has been found (Fig. 10, bed a). Highly fossiliferous, it represents silt blown from the valley of Raccoon Creek, the lower part of which is filled with outwash sand and gravel of Kansan age.

The Kansan ice margin fluctuated at least once while it lay near its maximum extent. In both eastern and western Indiana, a fossiliferous silt layer has been found between two tills of Kansan age (Fig. 10, bed b).

Even though no effort has been made to try to prove the relationship, all known gold panning sites in Indiana are within the limits of the Kansan ice sheet, as are all diamond finds. The general source of both is known to be Canada, but the exact source area is not known.

### Yarmouth Age

After the Kansan ice sheet had melted from Indiana, weathering of the new sediments began and streams started to strip

away and redeposit on floodplains the rock debris it had left.
The total volume of Kansan drift left in Indiana probably cannot be estimated, but many of the deeper valleys were partly
filled with glacially derived sediment, and a few shallower ones
were almost totally obscured by as much as 75 to 100 feet of
drift.

The interglacial Yarmouth Age that followed was long — it
probably lasted at least 200,000 years (although one extrapolation would give it a duration of more than 600,000 years)
— and warm. Soil development on Kansan tills indicates an
average interglacial climate in Indiana much like the present.
Carbonates were removed from the upper 9 to 12 feet of
Kansan till during this time.

A new level of erosion developed along the major rivers of
Indiana. Raccoon Creek valley, for example, had been excavated prior to Kansan glaciation to a depth 70 feet or more below
the present floodplain. Yarmouth floodplain sediments exposed along its present valley walls are almost the same level
as the present floodplain. Similar Yarmouth alluvial sediments
and flood-plain levels can be observed along several other
streams in southern Indiana. Thus the deepest valley cutting
clearly took place during Kansan or pre-Kansan time.

### Illinoian Age

About 125,000 years ago (by one estimate and 400,000 by
another), another glaciation, the Illinoian, began. The Illinoian ice sheet reached farther south in the lowlands along the
Wabash and in central Illinois — south of the 38th parallel —
than did any other continental glacier during the Pleistocene.

Unlike the earlier Kansan glacier, much of the ice that
covered western Indiana during the Illinoian Age came from
the north, out of the Lake Michigan lowland. Central and eastern Indiana was buried by ice from the northeast, though
(Fig. 12B).

The Illinoian glacier margin fluctuated at least twice while
Indiana lay buried under ice. An early advance reached west-
central Indiana and left a distinctively colored till. The marginal melting probably was minor, but a thin layer of fossiliferous silt (Fig. 10, bed d) recorded it. The readvance that spread
till over the Wabash and Scottsburg Lowlands evidently was
the big one. After the main advance had stalled and the ice

melted, a third short readvance of the ice margin buried the
snails and some vegetation that had begun to cover the new
surface (Fig. 10. bed e). The fossils in these intertill beds indicate a cool climate and open terrain. This sequence of tills
and other sediments is the upper part of the Jessup Formation.

The Illinoian glacier built few moraines in southern Indiana,
but it left an expansive record in the southwestern part of the
State of proglacial lakes and outwash plains. Part of the outwash that fills the major valleys of southern Indiana must be
Illinoian in age, but to recognize it now is virtually impossible.
Dust blown from that outwash was deposited along the banks
of the Wabash and Ohio Valleys, though, where it was later
buried beneath younger loess. Illinoian lake sediments fill all
the large valleys of southwestern Indiana.[5]

### Sangamon Age

Perhaps 105,000 years ago, the Illinoian ice disappeared.
Fossil pollen records from sediments deposited during the
warm spell that followed show that the vegetation changed
from a conifer cover to a hardwood forest, then toward the

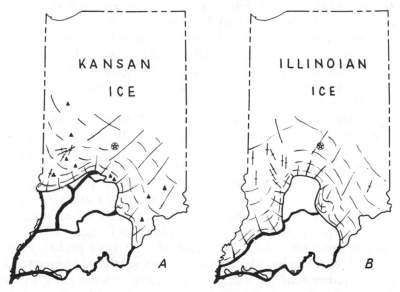

Fig. 12. Maximum extent of ice in Indiana during the Kansan and
Illinoian glacial ages, showing striation directions, inferred ice flowage,
drainage lines, and locations of significant exposures of Kansan till. A—
Kansan ice. B—Illinoian ice.

end of the ice-free age, conifer trees returned. The Sangamon was much shorter than Yarmouth. Colors of the buried soil profiles indicate that the climate must have been reasonably warm, but carbonates were dissolved from only about 5 feet of till before the next glacier buried the surface again.

Erosion levels were very similar to those of today along the Ohio and Wabash Rivers. The tops of buried Sangamon floodplain sediments lie at almost the same level as modern floodplain surfaces have developed. Radiocarbon dates show that new glacial sediments began to accumulate along the Ohio about 23,000 years ago.

## The Wisconsin Glaciation and Postglacial Time

### Wisconsin Age

Dated records from deep sea cores make it evident that the climatic beginnings of the last, or Wisconsin, glaciation were about 70,000 years ago.[9] How long it took for the ice cap to grow is still unknown, but early Wisconsin tills and intertill organic beds were being deposited in southern Ontario 40,000 to 50,000 years ago. Some sediments and radiocarbon dates suggest that this ice advance may have reached the upper reaches of the Wabash and Whitewater valleys.[7,19]

A somewhat weathered Wisconsin loess that underlies the main loess deposit along the Ohio and the lower Wabash may have resulted from this early Wisconsin glaciation. Radiocarbon dates from wood indicate that this loess was buried 20,000 to 23,000 years ago.

The main advance of ice during the Wisconsin Age covered about two-thirds of Indiana (Fig. 13A). It reached its maximum position at the Shelbyville Moraine about 21,000 years ago, then the marginal area melted almost immediately. About 1,000 years later the ice margin moved back southward to a new position a little short of the Shelbyville Moraine (Fig. 13B). The advance buried a thin bed of silt that covered the older till (Fig. 10, bed h). Fossil snails and plant remains in the silt show that central Indiana at that time probably was covered with tundra-like vegetation and scattered spruce trees. A few patches of permafrost may have existed close to the ice.[18] This advance of the ice is marked by the Crawfordsville Moraine. The group of tills deposited by these two glacial advances are the Trafalgar Formation.

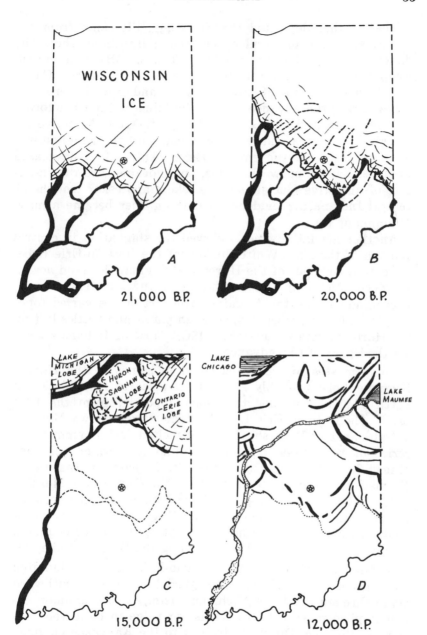

Fig. 13. Wisconsin glaciation of Indiana. A—Maximum extent of glacier (about 21,000 years ago). B—Wisconsin second maximum (about 20,000 years ago). C—Location of Wisconsin ice (about 15,000 years ago). D—Wisconsin morainal trends and extent of glacial Great Lakes (about 12,000 years ago).

The ice that deposited the Trafalgar tills came from the northeast; striations and esker trough lineations show the direction the glacier was moving (Figs. 8, 13B), and the till composition reflects the bedrock to the northeast into Canada.[8] Large amounts of outwash sand and gravel were laid down during the advance and the building of the Crawfordsville Moraine, and kames were abundant. After the active ice margin had melted and the glacier had built the Knightstown Moraine (Fig. 8), the entire lobe in central Indiana ceased to move. Kames, outwash plains, and moraines are the signature of an active glacier, but the eskers and esker troughs of central Indiana are evidence that the glacier became a mass of stagnant ice.

Another glacial advance followed the stagnation in central Indiana of the East White Sublobe of the Ontario-Erie Lobe. Ice moved first out of the Huron and Saginaw lowland across southern Michigan and north-central Indiana. The Maxinkuckee and Packerton Moraines are part of the varied topography of kames, moraines, outwash plains and kettles left by the Huron-Saginaw Lobe (Fig. 13C). Most of Indiana's lakes are the legacy of this advance.

Some masses of ice or ice-cored moraines of the Huron-Saginaw Lobe probably still lay in place to help block the north edge of the lobe that soon appeared from the Erie basin. The Ontario-Erie Lobe built the Mississinewa Moraine with its apex at Wabash, then as it melted, left a symmetrical series of recessional moraines around its former positions (Figs. 8, 13C). This till, clay-rich, is part of the Lagro Formation. After the ice melted from the Fort Wayne Moraine about 14,000 years ago, glacial Lake Maumee formed between the ice margin and the moraine (Fig. 13D). Its overflow spilled through the moraine and swept out a broad floodplain, now called the Maumee Terrace, along the Wabash Valley.[5][14]

At the same time that the Ontario-Erie Lobe was building its series of festooned moraines, glacial ice plowed southward again through the Lake Michigan basin. At its maximum extent it piled more till on an existing ridge to build the Valparaiso Moraine. Outwash drained to the Kankakee channel. As the ice margin melted, Lake Chicago came into existence between the glacier and the Valparaiso Moraine (Fig. 8, 13D) Old beaches and stable dunes now mark its former levels.

## *Recent Age*

Nonglacial sediments began to accumulate as soon as glacial ice had melted from the area. Except for changes in the fossils embedded in them, the earliest postglacial sediments can scarcely be distinguished from those of modern lakes and streams. These sediments of the Recent Stage include alluvial deposits along streams, colluvial accumulations on slopes, swamp and lake sediments, such as peat and marl, and sand dunes. All these deposits except the dunes are the various facies of the Martinsville Formation (Fig. 10).

Most rivers erode and redeposit their alluvial plains regularly. Thus few of the flood-plain deposits are more than about 7,000 years old. Peat and marl have accumulated mostly in ice-block depressions in central and northern Indiana. They contain a continuous record of the vegetation and faunal changes that have taken place in Indiana since the buried masses of ice melted and formed the depressions. The record from peat bogs shows that a cool climate conifer forest was followed, about 8,000 years ago, by a change to a deciduous forest. A comparable change shows up in the mollusk faunas of the marl lakes. Both kinds of sediments are fruitful materials for additional study.

Pleistocene vertebrates were many, but only a few — mostly the big ones — are known from Indiana. Someone remarked once that every bog that is bigger than an acre probably contains the bones of at least one mastodon. This may be true; certainly Indiana has been an exporter of mastodon and mammoth skeletons. Unfortunately, few of the elephantine fossils dug from bogs in Indiana can be found on display or for study in the State now. In addition to these behemoths, giant beavers, elk, muskox, and ground sloths roamed the area. Mice and other small vertebrates surely were abundant, too, but they are so tiny and unspectacular they have been overlooked almost completely so far.

### Special Pleistocene Problems

Even though much has been learned during the past century about the glacial deposits of Indiana, many problems, both large and small, remain to be solved. Any research toward solution of some of those problems would be a contribution to the knowledge of the glacial geology of the State. The following list includes some of the more pressing ones, and may provide a stimulus to those looking for ideas.

1. The glacial deposits of all of Indiana have been mapped, but most of that mapping is of a reconnaissance nature only. Only a few areas have been mapped carefully and in detail; much more is needed.

2. The general composition of the tills is known, but only a few studies have been made on the details of till lithology and mineralogy. Stratigraphically controlled size analyses and mineralogical studies will fill a large void in existing knowledge.

3. What direction did the ice move each time? Studies of till fabric — the orientation of the particles in till — are almost nonexistent.

4. Our knowledge of the details of the sediments that fill the buried valleys of Indiana as well as the shapes of those valleys is still very sketchy. The best source for this kind of information remains a careful study of all available well records.

5. Additional pollen profiles of bogs in central and northern Indiana would supply more data on the postglacial vegetational succession.

6. Many interglacial sediments never have been examined for pollen content or fossil seeds. The few that have been studied indicate that this could be a fertile subject.

7. Many postglacial lake sediments, particularly marls, are highly fossiliferous. Quantitative studies of cores for mollusks, ostracods, mites, and other invertebrate remains would add greatly to knowledge of zoogeography and postglacial ecology.

8. Late-glacial and interglacial floodplain sediments undoubtedly contain remains of small vertebrates, but few efforts have been made to recover them. Work on these fossils would help close a large gap in present paleontologic knowledge.

9. Examples of drainage diversions, small to large, abound throughout Indiana, but only a few have received any geomorphic analysis. Descriptions and interpretations of others would add considerably to the knowledge of details of the drainage history of Indiana.

10. Better knowledge of the internal stratigraphy of the

alluvial deposits of the larger rivers of Indiana would help immeasurably in the understanding of the process of alluviation and, in certain places, of prehistory.

This list is by no means exhaustive, but is offered merely as a group of ideas. If it serves to stimulate someone to start a research project on some aspect of the glacial geology of Indiana, it will have been successful.

## LITERATURE

1. CHAMBERLIN, T. C. 1883. Preliminary report on the terminal moraine of the second glacial epoch. U. S. Geol. Survey Ann. Rept. **3**: 291-402.
2. EMILIANI, CESARE. 1964. Paleotemperature analysis of the Caribbean Cores A254-BR-C and CP-28. Geol. Soc. Am. Bull. **75**: 129-144.
3. ERICSON, D. B., MAURICE EWING, and GOESTA WOLLIN. 1964. The Pleistocene Epoch in deep sea sediments. Science. **146** (3645): 723-732.
4. EWING, M., and W. L. DONN. 1956. A theory of Ice Ages. Science. **123** (3207): 1061-1066; also 1958. **127** (3307): 1159-1162.
5. FIDLAR, M. M. 1948. Physiography of the lower Wabash Valley. Indiana Geol. Survey Bull. **2**, 112 p.
6. FLINT, R. F. 1957. Glacial and Pleistocene geology. New York, John Wiley & Sons, Inc. 553 p.
7. GOODING, A. M. 1963. Illinoian and Wisconsin Glaciations in the Whitewater Basin, southeastern Indiana, and adacent areas. Jour. Geology **71**: 665-682.
8. HARRISON, WYMAN. 1963. Geology of Marion County, Indiana. Indiana Geol. Survey Bull. **28**. 78 p.
9. KU, TEH-LUNG, and W. S. BROECKER. 1966. Atlantic deep-sea stratigraphy: extension of absolute chronology to 320,000 years. Science. **151** (3709): 448-450.
10. LEVERETT, FRANK, and F. B. TAYLOR. 1915. The Pleistocene of Indiana and Michigan and the history of the Great Lakes. U. S. Geol. Survey Mono. 53, 529 p.
11. MALOTT, C. A. 1922. Physiography of Indiana, *in* Logan, W. N., and others, Handbook of Indiana Geology: Indiana Dept. of Conserv. Pub. No. **21**, Pt. 2, p. 59-256.
12. MITCHELL, J. M., Jr. 1965. Theoretical paleoclimatology, *in* Wright, H. E., and D. G. FREY. ed. Quaternary of the United States. Princeton Univ. Press. Princeton, N. Jer. p. 881 901.
13. THORNBURY, W. D. 1937. Glacial geology of southern and south-central Indiana. Indiana Div. Geology, 138 p.
14. _____ 1958. The geomorphic history of the upper Wabash Valley. Am. Jour. Sci. **256**: 449 469.
15. WAYNE, W. J. 1956. Thickness of drift and bedrock physiography north of the Wisconsin glacial boundary. Indiana Geol. Survey Rept. Prog. **7**. 70 p.
16. _____ 1960. Stratigraphy of the Ohio River Formation. Indiana Geol. Survey Bull. **21**. 44 p.
17. _____ 1963. Pleistocene Formations of Indiana. Indiana Geol. Survey Bull. **25**. 85 p.
18. _____ in press. Periglacial features and climatic gradient in Illinois, Indiana, and western Ohio, east-central United States, *in* Cushing, E. J., and H. E. Wright, ed., Contributions to Pleistocene Paleoecology.
19. _____ and J. H. ZUMBERGE. 1965. Pleistocene geology of Indiana and Michigan, *in* Wright, H. E., and D. G. Frey, ed. The Quaternary of the United States. Princeton Univ. Press., Princeton, N. Jer., p. 63-84.

# 3

# *Physiography*

Allan F. Schneider*
Indiana Geological Survey

## Introduction

In a summary of this nature, it is possible to discuss the physiography of our State only in general terms. Little attention can be devoted to specific landforms or even to the important subjects of landscape evolution and the geomorphic development of Indiana's scenery. One must paint a picture of Hoosier physiography with broad strokes, and in order to do so he finds it convenient to treat the subject descriptively in terms of physiographic units. Ideally, a physiographic unit is an area in which several topographic and geologic conditions, such as rock type and structure, are similar throughout, but in which one or more of these conditions is significantly different in adjoining units.

The basic physiographic divisions of Indiana were outlined and described in considerable detail more than 40 years ago by Prof. C. A. Malott.[6] Other classifications, such as those of Dryer[3] and Fenneman,[4,5] are either less applicable or less comprehensive. An important facet of Malott's classification is that the bedrock physiographic units of southern Indiana do not terminate at the Pleistocene glacial boundary (Fig. 14) but are carried northward through glaciated country as far as their physiographic character can be recognized. In the classical scheme of Fenneman, on the other hand, the maximum extent of glaciation serves as the boundary between the Till Plains Section of the Central Lowland Province and the Highland Rim Section of the Interior Low Plateau Province.[4,5] Some of Malott's boundaries and names were slightly modified about 10 years ago by Wayne,[11] who traced the bedrock physiographic units of southern Indiana northward beneath thicker glacial drift and also defined other bedrock physiographic units that are wholly buried and thus have no surficial expression. Additional modifications based on data accumulated during the past decade would be relatively minor.

*Publication authorized by the State Geologist, Department of Natural Resources, Geological Survey.

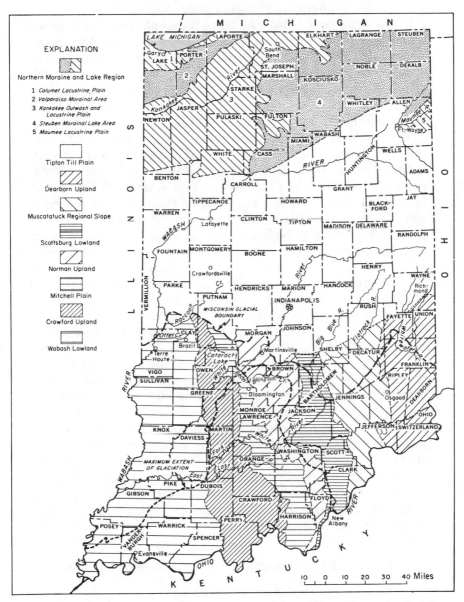

Fig. 14. Map of Indiana showing physiographic units and glacial boundaries. Modified from Indiana Geol. Survey Rept. Prog. 7, fig. 1.

## General Physiographic Aspect

Indiana can be divided into three broad physiographic zones that trend in a general east-west direction across the State. The central zone of about 12,000 square miles is a depositional plain of low relief, underlain largely by thick glacial till and modified only slightly by postglacial stream erosion. For many years it has been appropriately called the Central Drift Plain[3] or the Tipton Till Plain[6,11] (Fig. 14).

The northern and southern zones are generally characterized by greater relief than the central plain (Fig. 15) ; in fact, in many places these belts are very hilly — yet even in these areas the hilly uplands are broken by lowlands and plains of little relief. Hence the northern and southern zones offer much more topographic variety than does the Tipton Till Plain — a fact that is readily explained by significant differences in geomorphic history. Landforms in northern Indiana are mostly of glacial origin; a great variety of depositional forms is present, including end moraines, outwash plains, kames, lake plains, valley trains, and kettle holes, as well as many closely related postglacial features, such as lakes, sand dunes, and peat bogs. This northern zone of about 8,500 square miles is called the Northern Moraine and Lake Region.[3,6,11] Landforms in southern Indiana, on the other hand, are largely the result of normal degradational processes, such as weathering, stream erosion, and mass movement. The middle part of this belt was not glaciated during the Pleistocene Epoch (Fig. 14), and thus the topography strongly reflects the influence of bedrock structure, stratigraphy, and lithology; the lateral parts of the area were glaciated, but the drift blanket is sufficiently thin that the physiography is largely bedrock controlled. Seven physiographic units, all of which trend north-northwest in conformity with the strike of the bedrock formations, are recognized in this southern zone of 15,500 square miles (Fig. 14).

## Bedrock Physiographic Units of Southern Indiana

### Dearborn Upland

The name Dearborn Upland is applied to a dissected plateau north and west of the Ohio River in southeasternmost Indiana. The area is underlain by virtually flat-lying limestones and shales of late Ordovician age that outcrop along the crest of the Cincinnati Arch. These rocks are overlain by glacial drift, which increases in thickness from perhaps 15 or 20 feet on the average near the Ohio River to about 50 feet near the Wisconsin glacial boundary (Fig. 14); north of this boundary the glacial deposits are as much as 200 feet thick.[11]

The western boundary of the Dearborn Upland is the drainage divide between the general westward-flowing streams of the East Fork (White River) and Muscatatuck drainage basins and the southward- and eastward-flowing streams (Indian-Kentuck Creek, Laughery Creek, and Whitewater River) that discharge directly into the Ohio. These streams and most of their tributaries are deeply incised, generally occupying sharply defined steep V-shaped valleys, the floors of which are as much as 450 feet below the upland surface. Some parts of the plateau are so thoroughly dissected that the upland surface has been completely destroyed. Upland remnants are well preserved away from the main streams, however, and still farther removed are broad plains of virtually unmodified terrain. Most of these upland areas have nearly accordant summit elevations of about 1,000 feet above sea level. This fact prompted earlier workers[6,11] to consider the upland areas to be remnants of the Lexington or Highland Rim Peneplain, a postulated gently rolling erosion surface of the eastern interior United States that was formed only a few hundred feet above sea level and then uplifted to its present elevation in late Tertiary time.

The drainage divide at the west edge of the Dearborn Upland approaches or barely reaches 1,100 feet elevation in some places. It approximates the boundary between rocks of Ordovician and Silurian ages. The low ridge held up by the gently westward-dipping resistant basal Silurian limestone that forms the divide was named the Laughery Escarpment by Malott.[6]

### Muscatatuck Regional Slope

West of the Dearborn Upland is a gently sloping plain known as the Muscatatuck Regional Slope. At its northern end the plain slopes from 1,100 feet above sea level at its eastern margin to about 725 feet on the west; near the Ohio River the comparable elevations are about 225 feet lower.

The Muscatatuck Regional Slope is commonly interpreted as

a structural plain or stripped surface on the rather resistant westward-dipping Silurian and Devonian carbonate rocks that lie beneath. A recent study[10] covering the broad northern part of the slope and adjoining area to the north indicates that although the dip of the bedrock formations (about 20 feet per mile) is slightly greater than the slope of the bedrock surface (about 12 feet per mile), the slope directions correspond very closely, and one may safely conclude that the regional slope of the bedrock surface is structurally controlled. This study also indicates, however, that the present surface slope and drainage pattern strongly reflect the influence of Wisconsin glaciation: the modern drainage system is dominated by streams that flow in a south-southwestward direction, but several of the preglacial streams apparently flowed more nearly westward, or almost directly down the slope of the bedrock surface.

Although only the northern portion of the Muscatatuck Regional Slope was glaciated during the Wisconsin Age, the entire area was ice covered in earlier Pleistocene time (Fig. 14). Thus the middle Paleozoic carbonate rocks are nearly everywhere covered by a blanket of glacial drift. In many places the drift is thin, however; over preglacial upland tracts it may be no more than 5 or 10 feet thick. The average drift thickness is perhaps 20 or 25 feet, but the material thickens northward to a maximum of about 150 feet over buried valleys at the north edge of the slope.[10,11] The valleys of the Muscatatuck Regional Slope are commonly steep sided and moderately deep, the streams having downcut through the thin cover of unconsolidated deposits into the underlying limestones and dolomites. Stream entrenchment and drainage development are noticeably less advanced in the eastern or upstream part of the area than farther west. Upland areas are, in general, very broad and nearly flat to undulating. These features indicate that the region is still in the youthful stage of landform development.

### Scottsburg Lowland

The Muscatatuck Regional Slope passes westward with virtually no topographic break into a linear belt of low relief called the Scottsburg Lowland (Fig. 15). At its northern end the Scottsburg Lowland has been partially filled with glacial drift that is as much as 150 feet thick, and consequently the lowland is not well defined. Farther south, however, where the drift is thinner the lowland is more easily recognized as a distinct physiographic unit.

In geomorphic terminology, the Scottsburg Lowland is a strike valley — a lowland belt controlled by the structure and lithology of the underlying bedrock formation — because it follows the outcrop belt of relatively nonresistant shales of late Devonian and early Mississippian age. In cross section the lowland is a strongly asymmetric trough, with its more gentle eastern slope cutting obliquely across the gently westward-dipping shale beds at a low angle. The elevation of the trough is about 750 feet above sea level in the north and gradually drops to about 500 feet near the Ohio River.

### Norman Upland

The western boundary of the Scottsburg Lowland is drawn at the base of an east-facing cuesta scarp called the Knobstone Escarpment. This escarpment is the most prominent regional topographic feature in Indiana. Throughout much of its extent the Knobstone rises about 300 feet above the Scottsburg Lowland and thus forms one of the best physiographic boundaries in the State (Fig. 15). The escarpment is most prominent north of the Ohio River near New Albany, where its crest is 400 to 600 feet above the lowland valleys to the east. North of here the escarpment generally decreases in height, and about 100 miles north of the river it gradually disappears beneath the thick drift cover of the Tipton Till Plain.

The Knobstone Escarpment represents the eastern part of a dissected plateau known as the Norman Upland. This upland is underlain by relatively resistant siltstones and interbedded softer shales of the Borden Group of early to middle Mississippian age; present in some parts of the upland is the oldest of several middle Mississippian limestone formations that crop out in South-central Indiana. All these rocks dip about 25 feet per mile to the west-southwest (Fig. 15) and are succeeded by the more soluble younger limestones along the ill-defined western boundary of the upland.

An area of strong local relief, the Norman Upland is characterized generally by flat-topped narrow divides, steep slopes, and deep V-shaped valleys. Most of the shorter tributary streams have developed only incipient floodplains or none at all, but the larger streams are marked by conspicuous narrow valley flats. The area is nearly all in slope and is well drained by an almost perfect dendritic drainage system. These features are well displayed in Brown County State Park, which is in the heart of the Norman Upland. They clearly indicate that the area is in the mature stage of landform development.

Almost everywhere in the Norman Upland the skyline appears to be virtually flat. The nearly accordant summit levels at elevations of 900 to 1,000 feet are commonly interpreted as remnants of the Lexington or Highland Rim Peneplain. Flat surfaces at lower elevations may represent floodplain straths developed during the Lexington cycle of erosion, younger erosion surfaces, or simply stripped surfaces on more resistant rocks of the Borden Group.

### Mitchell Plain

Probably more has been said about the geology of the Mitchell Plain than any other physiographic division of the State. Formed on the dip slope of a moderately thick sequence of middle Mississippian limestones (Fig. 15), the Mitchell Plain exhibits some of the best karst topography in the world. One of these limestone formations is the Salem Limestone, from which is quarried in the Bloomington-Bedford area the famous Indiana Limestone that is used for building purposes throughout the country. Most of the solution features of the Mitchell Plain, however, are developed on the younger St. Louis and Ste. Genevieve Limestones.

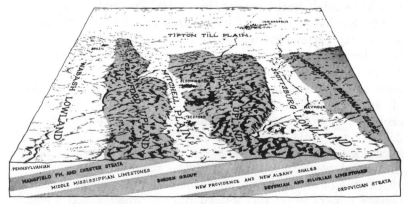

Fig. 15. Physiographic diagram of part of southern and central Indiana. From Indiana Geol. Survey Guidebook 12.

Except in its western part where it is marked by numerous outliers or detached hills of the adjacent Crawford Upland and in a few places where it is crossed by deeply entrenched surface streams, the Mitchell Plain is an area of low relief. To say that is flat or without relief would be quite erroneous, however, because the surface almost everywhere is pocked with sinkholes and other solution features. It has been estimated that as many as 300,000 sinks may be present in southern Indiana; 1,022 sinkholes were counted in a single square mile near Orleans.[7] The depressions are, of course, of many different shapes and sizes, but a typical sinkhole of the Mitchell Plain is 10 to 30 feet deep, and its diameter would approach half the length of a football field. Most sinks are more or less funnel shaped in cross section and form below the soil by the slow solution of limestone along vertical or inclined fractures. Once formed, these depressions — called dolines — and other larger depressions that open directly into bedrock — called swallow holes — serve as basins into which surface runoff readily drains. Thus, the drainage is mostly underground; surface streams are generally short and intermittent in character, traversing the surface for only short distances before disappearing into sinkholes; dry valleys and uvalas are common. In some places the vertical passageways have become plugged with soil or other debris, and the depressions are occupied by ponds or small lakes. The variety of karst features on the Mitchell Plain is almost endless,[7] and beneath the surface the limestone bedrock is punctured with an equally endless system of channels and caverns.[8]

## Crawford Upland

The middle Mississippian limestones that underlie the Mitchel Plain are overlain to the west, or downdip, by alternating sandstones, shales, and limestones of the Chester Series (upper Mississippian); these rocks in turn are unconformably overlapped by resistant sandstones and softer rocks in the Mansfield Formation (lower Pennsylvanian) (Fig. 15). Differential erosion of these diverse lithologic units has produced a deeply dissected upland marked by a great diversity of topographic features. Malott, in fact, considered the Crawford Upland to have a greater variety of landforms than any other physiographic division in the State.

The boundary between the Mitchell Plain and the Crawford Upland is generally irregular, although in some places — such as just north of the Ohio River — it is exceedingly sharp. It is drawn along the base of the Chester escarpment, an east-facing cuesta scarp (Fig. 15) capped by resistant sandstones. The face of the escarpment is commonly ragged, being marked by elongated upland spurs and karst valley reentrants that extend into the upland for several miles. The eastern part of the upland is also characterized by numerous springs and by many of Indiana's larger and best-known caverns — including Wyandotte and Marengo Caves[8] — formed in the soluble mid-Mississippian limestones beneath protective Chester or Mansfield caprocks.

The Crawford Upland is a maturely dissected westward-sloping plateau characterized by abundant stream valleys and a well-integrated drainage system. Most of the area is in slope, the drainage divides are generally flat topped but narrow, and the valley walls are steep. The bottoms of the larger valleys are occupied by moderately wide floodplains, and in some areas these floodplains are the only level tracts of land. In all these respects the topography of the Crawford Upland closely resembles that of the Norman Upland. Overall relief in the Crawford Upland is generally somewhat greater, however; local relief of 300 or 350 feet is not at all uncommon.

### Wabash Lowland

The Crawford Upland grades westward into the Wabash Lowland, the largest of the southern Indiana physiographic divisions (Fig. 14). This broad lowland tract has an average elevation of about 500 feet above sea level, some 300 to 400 feet below the crest of the Crawford Upland. It is underlain by relatively nonresistant siltstones and shales of Pennsylvanian age, which by the beginning of Pleistocene time had been carved into a lowland tract of moderate relief. This area, named the Sullivan Lowland (Fig. 16), was characterized by generally subdued landforms consisting of broad valleys and smoothly rounded hills with gentle bedrock slopes.[11] The invasion and consequent modification of much of this area by pre-Wisconsin glaciers is thus easily understood.

In addition to its partial blanket of glacial till (Fig. 14), the Wabash Lowland is underlain by widespread and in places thick lacustrine, outwash, and alluvial sediments. The most conspicuous deposits, of course, are the broad terraced valley-fill materials along the Ohio, Wabash, and White Rivers, but broad flat bottomlands underlain by slackwater sediments are present along many of the tributary streams. The presence of extensive aggraded valleys throughout the Wabash Lowland is, according to Malott,[6] the principal common denominator of the area.

Upland tracts of the Wabash Lowland are best described as undulating to rolling plains. In general, the topographic relief is lower in the glaciated northern portion of the lowland than farther south, where divides are commonly 100 to 150 feet above the valley floors. Deposits of windblown sand or silt (loess) blanket much of the upland surface and form the upper valley walls in some places, particularly along tributary valleys near the Wabash River. Sand dunes are also present, chiefly along the larger valleys. In general, the thickness of the eolian sediments decreases eastward, or away from the Wabash valley train, from which they were derived in late Wisconsin time. The wider valleys are also characterized by island-like masses of bedrock that range in size from small conical hills to massive upland outliers covering several square miles and ranging up to 100 feet or more in height.

### Tipton Till Plain

The southern margin of the Tipton Till Plain in western Indiana is relatively sharp. The Shelbyville Moraine, which marks the southern limit of Wisconsin glaciation, effectively truncates the various landforms associated with the physiographic belts of southern Indiana. In the eastern part of the State the boundary is drawn arbitrarily along the north edge of a broad transitional zone in which the topography is similar to that of the till plain but in which glacial drift is not sufficiently thick to completely obscure the general form of the bedrock physiographic units.

The Tipton Till Plain is a nearly flat to gently rolling glacial plain (Fig. 15), considered by many to be the most typical representation of Indiana landscape. Throughout much of its area the plain is virtually featureless — so monotonous, in fact, that one well-known student of Hoosier physiography stated that "the traveler may ride upon the railroad train for hours without seeing a greater elevation than a hay stack or a pile of saw dust".[2] Actually, the plain is crossed by several end moraines, but in most places these are so low and poorly developed that they modify only slightly the overall aspect of the landscape. The most prominent moraines are the Champaign, Bloomington, Crawfordsville, and Chatsworth Moraines in the west-central part of the State and a series of concentric moraines, including the Mississinewa, Wabash, and Fort Wayne Moraines, in east-central Indiana (Fig. 8).

The monotony of the Tipton Till Plain is also broken by low eskers, esker troughs (Fig. 8), and meltwater drainageways, most of which trend in a general northeast-southwest direction and form a conspicuous subparallel drainage pattern.[9,10] Many of the outwash-floored channels are now occupied by modern streams, but others carry no through drainage and are either swampy or partially filled with various mineral and organic sediments. In general, these channels are shallow, but in some places they have been deeply trenched by late glacial and postglacial stream erosion. The Wabash Valley across central Indiana, for example, was deepened by relatively clear waters escaping from glacial Lake Maumee. Some of the most spectacular scenery in the State is found in west-central Indiana, where tributaries to the Wabash have cut through the glacial drift and are entrenched in narrow precipitous bedrock valleys as much as 150 feet deep, such as at The Shades and Turkey Run State Parks.

### Northern Moraine and Lake Region

The Northern Moraine and Lake Region with its variety of glacial and associated postglacial landforms has been subdivided into five physiographic units[6,11]: the Calumet Lacustrine Plain, the Valparaiso Morainal Area, the Kankakee Outwash and Lacustrine Plain, the Steuben Morainal Lake Area, and the Maumee Lacustrine Plain (Fig. 14).

### *Calumet Lacustrine Plain*

The highly industrialized Calumet region at the south end of Lake Michigan is built largely on an abandoned lake bottom called the Calumet Lacustrine Plain. This plain is part of the former site of Lake Chicago, which occupied the southern part of the Lake Michigan basin in late glacial time (Fig. 13D). The Calumet Lacustrine Plain is not a simple lake plain but a compound lacustrine area in which successive stages of Lake Chicago are represented at step-like intervals between 640 feet and 590 feet elevation. The highest (640 feet) is about 60 feet above the present level of Lake Michigan and generally follows the boundary between the lake plain and the Valparaiso Moraine. Lower strandlines are represented by beaches at intermediate positions and elevations, particularly at 620 feet and 605 feet. Thus the topography of the lake plain is not everywhere flat and featureless but is marked by abundant low sand ridges. The principal shorelines are defined by nearly continuous beach ridges, which in many places are covered with stabilized sand dunes that rise as much as 40 feet above the adjoining lake bottom; offshore bars and spits, although much lower and less conspicuous, are common; and the massive high dunes along the modern lake shore, such as at Indiana Dunes State Park, are some of the finest shoreline dunes in North America.

### Valparaiso Morainal Area

The Calumet Lacustrine Plain is enclosed on the south by the Valparaiso Moraine, an arcuate end-moraine complex that can be traced for several hundred miles around the head of Lake Michigan from southern Wisconsin through northeastern Illinois and northwestern Indiana to west-central Michigan. The south edge of the moraine is generally considered to mark the terminal position of the Lake Michigan Lobe (Fig. 13C) during the Cary Subage of the Wisconsin Age, but this interpretation is questioned. Recent work indicates that the Valparaiso Moraine in Indiana (Fig. 8) is a compound moraine and probably represents more than a single stillstand of the ice front, but it is not possible to recognize the several discrete morainic ridges within the Valparaiso system that have been mapped in Illinois.

The Valparaiso Moraine is about 150 feet higher than the Calumet Lacustrine Plain. Much of the moraine is between 700 and 800 feet above sea level, but many of the higher knobs exceed 850 feet and some have an elevation as high as 950 feet. Between Valparaiso and the Michigan state line the moraine is generally higher and distinctly more rolling than the wider part farther west, which in some places closely resembles a gently undulating till plain. The more rugged part is definitely more complex in terms of both its material and landform composition. Ice-block depressions, for example —

some of which contain lakes and some of which are partially filled with peat — are found throughout the entire morainic belt, but they are more abundant, though perhaps somewhat smaller, in the distinctly knob-and-kettle topography that prevails in the northeast-southwest-trending part of the belt.

### Kankakee Outwash and Lacustrine Plain

South and southeast of the Valparaiso Moraine and also extending through northwestern Indiana from Illinois to Michigan is a vast area underlain mostly by sand. Much of this area is low and poorly drained, a fact that has suggested a lacustrine origin for much of the material. It seems more likely, however, that most of the sand was deposited as outwash by glacial meltwaters derived from melting ice at several different times during late Wisconsin time. Although some of the outwash was unquestionably dropped in standing water, most of the material was deposited in the form of broad valley trains and outwash plains, whose outlines are genetically related, at least in part, to the present St. Joseph, Kankakee, Tippecanoe, and Iroquois Rivers. Thick gravel deposits below or interbedded with the surficial sandy sediments partly confirm the outwash origin of the material.

Large parts of the original topography of the Kankakee Outwash and Lacustrine Plain have been substantially modified during the past 12,000 years or so. The greatest modification has been produced by the prevailing westerly winds blowing across the surface of the outwash deposits, reworking and redistributing the sand, in some places filling in ice-block depressions and depositing a veneer of eolian material atop the outwash to form virtually featureless sand plains, and in other places piling the sand into dunes of almost every conceivable size and shape.

### Steuben Morainal Lake Area

The Steuben Morainal Lake Area east of the Kankakee Outwash and Lacustrine Plain is more complex in its topographic expression and physiographic history than either the Valparaiso Moraine or the Kankakee plain. Local relief of 100 or 150 feet is not uncommon, and in some places it exceeds 200 feet; the topography in some areas is nearly as rugged as in the bedrock uplands of southern Indiana. The conception of many Indiana residents that the most obvious effect of continental glaciation was the reduction of relief and the creation of a vast till plain is certainly not supported by the overall character of the Steuben Morainal Lake Area.

Some areas within this physiographic unit are similar in topographic expression and origin to the ground-moraine topography of the Tipton Till Plain. Much more of the area, however, is a morainal lake area like that around Pokagon and Chain O'Lakes State Parks. All the landforms are of glacial (or postglacial) origin, having been produced by the advance and related activity of the Huron-Saginaw and Ontario-Erie Lobes of the Wisconsin ice sheet about 15,000 years ago (Fig. 13C). Knob-and-kettle type end-moraine topography is evident nearly everywhere in the massive Maxinkuckee, Packerton, and Mississinewa Moraines (Fig. 8). Most of the knobs are till knobs, but many are kames, composed entirely or largely of ice-contact sand and gravel deposits; in fact, much of the morainic topography in certain parts of the Steuben Morainal Lake Area consists of kame complexes. The kettles or ice-block depressions serve as basins for the thousands of lakes and peat bogs that characterize northeastern Indiana and thus set it apart from the rest of the State. Meltwater channels abound: some are floored with outwash deposits and some with organic sediments; some are occupied by elongate lakes, whereas others are completely dry; some are ditched and some are swampy; some are a mile or more in width with flat floors, but others are V-shaped and narrow; some are through flowing, but others are blind; some lead to broad valley trains and outwash plains, but others seem to end mysteriously, suggesting that the waters probably reentered stagnant ice masses. Small lacustrine plains are relatively common. Sand dunes are present in places but are not important features of the landscape. To the casual observer all these features may seem to be nothing more than a disorganized array of bottomlands, hills, and plains, but to the serious student of landforms there is no greater variety anywhere else in Indiana.

### Maumee Lacustrine Plain

Similar in topographic expression to the Calumet Lacustrine Plain of northwestern Indiana, the Maumee Lacustrine Plain is a nearly level plain at a general elevation of 750 feet above

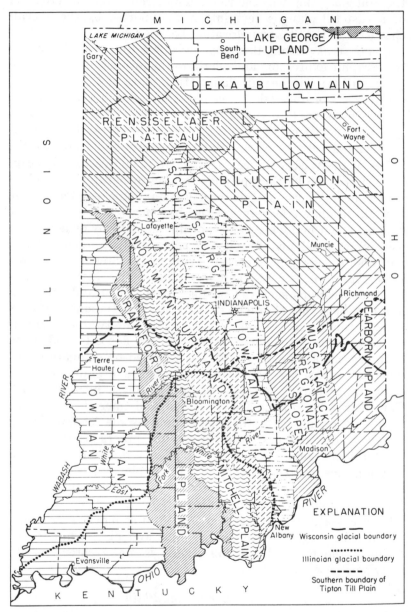

Fig. 16. Map of Indiana showing bedrock physiographic units. Slightly modified from Indiana Geol. Survey Rept. Prog. 7, fig. 3.

sea level. It represents a small part of the abandoned floor of Lake Maumee (Fig. 13D), which occupied the Lake Erie basin in late Pleistocene time and spread across northwestern Ohio into Indiana. Here it was dammed by the Fort Wayne Moraine, but its waters spilled through a gap in the moraine at Fort Wayne; abandoned shorelines diverge from the spillway and can be followed for many miles both northeastward and southeastward from the city. Except for these beaches, 10 to 20 feet high, and the narrow valley of the Maumee River, 20 to 40 feet deep, the lake plain is virtually featureless.

## Bedrock Physiography of Central and Northern Indiana

The bedrock physiographic units of southern Indiana do not terminate abruptly along the southern boundary of the Tipton Till Plain, as one might conclude from the accompanying figures. Along this line the units simply become unrecognizable as they are overlapped by the northward-thickening cover of glacial drift. Through the use of well records and geophysical data, much has been learned in recent years about the character of the bedrock surface in areas where it is covered with unconsolidated deposits, and several maps showing bedrock topography or preglacial drainage in Indiana have been prepared.[1,10,11]

The Dearborn Upland and the Muscatatuck Regional Slope have been traced northward as subsurface units only about 15 to 25 miles beyond the southern boundary of the Tipton Till Plain (Fig. 16). The Scottsburg Lowland, on the other hand, has been followed northwestward along the strike of upper Devonian and lower Mississippian shales for a distance of more than 100 miles from this boundary. The physiographic units farther west have also been traced northwestward along the regional strike through west-central Indiana, where their configurations closely reflect the controls of bedrock structure and lithology. The Mitchell Plain, for example, gradually narrows and finally terminates about 20 miles north of the Wisconsin glacial boundary (Fig. 16) as the middle Mississippian limestones are overlapped from the west by clastic rocks of the Mansfield Formation.

In his study of the bedrock physiography of Indiana, Wayne[11] defined four buried bedrock units that are not continuations of the southern Indiana physiographic belts; these he called the Bluffton Plain, the Rensselaer Plateau, the De-Kalb Lowland, and the Lake George Upland (Fig. 16). He also identified and traced many buried bedrock valleys, some of which have been cut completely through the thick sequence of Silurian dolomites that outcrop at the bedrock surface over much of the area. The deepest and broadest of these buried valleys is the Teays Valley, a generally east-west valley that extends across the entire State.[1,11] In late Tertiary time the Teays drainage system was one of the largest in the eastern United States and carried much of the discharge that now enters the Ohio River. The main stem of the Teays system probably headed in North Carolina or Virginia and flowed northwestward across West Virginia and Ohio. Near the Indiana state line the river turned westward, crossed Indiana and eastern Illinois, and thence angled southwestward toward the Mississippi River (Fig. 11). Where it crosses Indiana the buried valley of the Teays is filled with as much as 400 feet of drift. Much of the river's course can be followed on bedrock maps of the State, which show a sinuous outcrop pattern where the main river and its tributaries cut through the Silurian carbonate rocks, for example, into the underlying Ordovician shales.

## LITERATURE

1.  BURGER, A. M., S. J. KELLER, and W. J. WAYNE. 1966. Map showing bedrock topography of northern Indiana. Indiana Geol. Survey Misc. Map (in preparation).
2.  DRYER, C. R. 1908. General geography of Indiana. *In* C. R. Dryer, ed., Studies in Indiana geography. The Inland Publishing Co., Terre Haute, p. 17-27.
3.  DRYER, C. R. 1913. The geography of Indiana. *Supplement to* High School Geography by C. R. Dryer. American Book Co., New York, p. i-xl.
4.  FENNEMAN, N. M. 1917. Physiographic divisions of the United States. Annals Assoc. Am. Geog. **6**: 19-98.
5.  FENNEMAN, N. M. 1938. Physiography of the United States. McGraw-Hill Book Co., Inc., New York. 714 p.
6.  MALOTT, C. A. 1922. The physiography of Indiana. *In* Handbook of Indiana geology. Indiana Dept. Conserv. Pub. **21**, pt. 2: 59-256.
7.  MALOTT, C. A. 1945. Significant features of the Indiana karst. Proc. Indiana Acad. Sci. **54**: 8-24.
8.  POWELL, R. L. 1961. Caves of Indiana. Indiana Geol. Survey Circ. **8**. 127 p.
9.  SCHNEIDER, A. F., G. H. JOHNSON, and W. J. WAYNE. 1963, Some linear glacial features in west-central Indiana (Abstract). Proc. Indiana Acad. Sci. **72**: 172-173.
10. SCHNEIDER, A. F., and H. H. GRAY. 1966. Geology of the Upper East Fork Drainage Basin, Indiana. Indiana Geol. Survey Spec. Rept. **3**. 55 p.
11. WAYNE, W. J. 1956. Thickness of drift and bedrock physiography of Indiana north of the Wisconsin glacial boundary. Indiana Geol. Survey Rept. Prog. **7**. 70 p.

# 4

# Soils

H. P. ULRICH*

Agronomy Department, Purdue University

One of the greatest natural resources of Indiana is its soils. The combination of good soils with a high level of management and favorable climate has contributed to consistently rising crop yield levels and the highest state average corn yield in the nation in 1965—95 bushels per acre. This paper, based on numerous soil survey reports and other publications, will provide a brief description of the principal kinds of soils, their identification and classification. The distribution of the soils is shown on the General Soil Regions Map of Indiana. The characteristics, management problems, use and productivity of the principal soils of each region are discussed. A transect from west to east across southern Indiana will be shown. Here the more striking regional differences in soils, geology and physiography can be readily seen as well as the marked difference in age and characteristics of the younger and older soils. The soils in the rest of the state will be discussed alphabetically by soil regions.

A soil is a natural body made up of a sequence of layers or horizons that parallel the surface of the earth. Certain characteristics are developed over broad areas due to the influence of living organisms and climatic factors. These characteristics are modified locally due to differences in the parent material, and topography through its effect on soil moisture conditions as influenced by time. As illustrated in Fig. 17, soils are identified on the basis of the color, texture, structure, consistence, number, arrangement and thickness of horizons, depth of the soil body, and the character and composition of the parent material. These characteristics will be referred to throughout this article.

A soil is made up of 3 major horizons known as the surface or A horizon, subsoil or B horizon and parent material or C

*The author appreciates the assistance of Dr. A. L. Zachary in review of the manuscript, and figures provided by S. D. Alfred, Soil Conservation Service, and Harry Galloway, Purdue University.

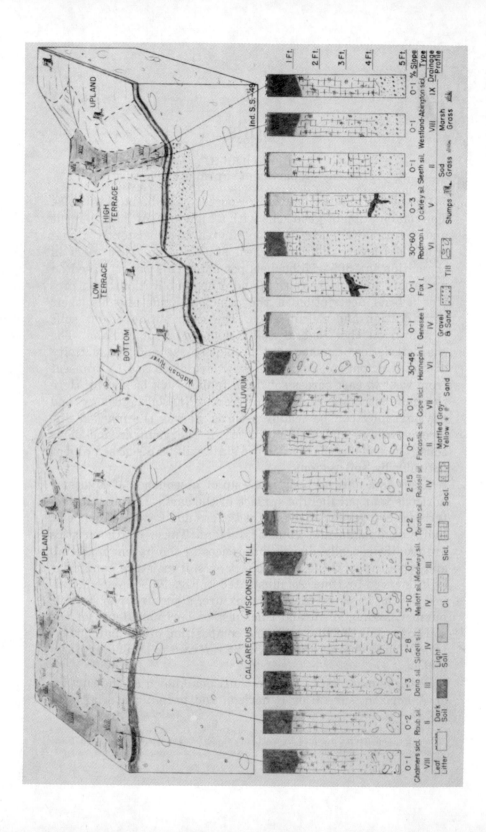

horizon which rest on the underlying geological material, D. This relationship is shown in Fig. 18, a photodiagram of a profile of Russell silt loam.

Plants growing in the soil return plant nutrients through the roots to the leaves, producing organic material. The leaves are returned to the earth to produce humus by bacterial decomposition and alteration. The A horizon or surface soil found under forest is made up of subhorizons: a thin layer of leaf mold or O horizon, a thin dark-colored mineral horizon enriched by leaf mold and earth-worm activity, the A1 horizon, a thicker lighter colored subsurface horizon or A2, which has lost organic matter, iron and clay through soil forming processes. The structure of the A2 is usually platy. In tillage these horizons are mixed to form the plow layer, or Ap horizon.

The subsoil or B horizon is finer in texture due to an accumulation of clay and iron oxides. On well drained sites the color is stronger or redder due to accumulation of these materials: in wet sites it may be lighter gray due to the loss of soluble iron. Changes in the parent material, through physical and chemical means, result in the formation of silicate clays of various kinds, loss of soluble materials, iron oxides, and the development of blocky or prismatic structure. Transition horizons may occur both at the top and bottom of the main B horizon.

The C horizon is nonconsolidated mineral material presumed to be the parent material from which the soil has been formed. The relation of soils to their environment or factors of soil formation are shown in Figures 17 and 20.

Each of the factors of soil formation will be treated briefly. The climate of Indiana is sufficiently warm and humid to result in moderate soil development and complete leaching of soluble materials from the soil body. Soil development is more intense in the warmer, more humid southern part of the state. Soil development has been influenced by grass and trees to a greater extent than by animals. Grass and some trees feed more richly on bases, thereby keeping the soil better supplied with bases such as calcium and magnesium. Bacteria and fungi

Fig. 17. Soils and their environment. Characteristics of representative soils in a cross section of the Wabash River Valley near Lafayette, Indiana, showing their relation to relief, parent materials, native vegetation and natural drainage.

convert the organic matter to humus. The forests that covered most of Indiana produced soils with a thin dark colored A1 horizon low in organic matter. Prairie grasses produced thick A1 horizons and may have been the principal contributor of organic matter to the marshland soils (Humic Gley group). The parent materials of Indiana soils are directly or indirectly related almost entirely to glaciation. Collectively known as drift, glacial deposits consist of (1) relatively unassorted ice laid deposits called till and (2) stratified materials such as stream and lake deposits called outwash. They vary in particle size from gravel to clay. Wind deposited materials were transported chiefly from the flood plains of streams when the meltwater receded; thus exposing the dried out material to the prevailing strong westerly winter winds. Wind carried the materials in a southeasterly direction depositing the sand at the upland break and carrying the silt or loess, many miles eastward. Bedrock, shale, siltstone, sandstone and limestone when exposed, form soil chiefly on the steep slopes. The ridge tops are usually covered with loess. Relief effects soil drainage

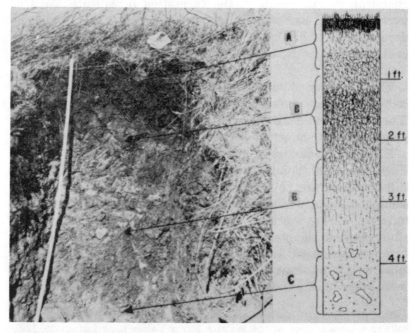

Fig. 18. Photodiagram showing the soil horizon relationship in a profile of Russell silt loam.

resulting (1) in rapid runoff of water, erosion and thinner soil on sloping areas (2) on less sloping to flat areas the internal drainage of the soil becomes poorer where the soil and parent materials are slowly permeable.

Time is important in soil formation only when soil materials remain in place a very long time. Soil movement on steep slopes or periodic deposits on flood plains result in young soil with little development other than organic matter accumulation. Age is reflected in development of "fragipan" horizons, soil acidity and variable depth of carbonate leaching. On level land surfaces which have been developed through the different glacial periods, depths of leaching range from 2 to 10 feet or more on the till plains of different ages (Fig. 17).

## The Principal Great Soil Groups and Their Distribution in Indiana

### Alluvial Soils

These soils are widely distributed and represent about 9 percent of the state. They occur on the formerly forested flood plains of major streams in Region H, and the bottoms of small streams common to all soil regions. They are forming in recently deposited alluvium resulting from irregular and periodic overflow. In some places the material is stratified, especially below 2 or 3 feet. The most noticeable difference is the darker color of the surface soil due to the accumulation of organic matter. In the wet areas the solution and loss of iron has resulted in gray or reduced colors in some parts of the profile. There are yellowish or reddish brown mottles where the iron has been redeposited and oxidized. The alluvial materials are usually fertile but vary in composition and quality depending on the geological materials of the watershed from which they are derived. Water assortment during flooding usually deposits the coarser and more permeable material on the slightly higher areas bordering the stream. In the lower backbottoms and swales the finer, less permeable materials are deposited. The materials may range in texture from sand to clay but silt loam, silty clay loam, and loam are the more common textures in this order. Alluvial soils, due to the hazards of overflow, are most often used for intensive grain farming, chiefly corn and soybeans. Narrow and stream dissected bottomlands are commonly used for hay or pasture.

## Gray Brown Podzolic Soils

This group of soils is widely distributed throughout the northern 2/3 of the state. They are well or moderately well drained, developed under a mixed hardwood forest resulting in a thin organic leaf mold, 0 horizon, and a dark mineral surface horizon, A1. Under field conditions they have a leached brown to dark grayish brown surface soil, 8 to 12 inches thick, in which the subsurface or A2 horizon is lighter colored and lower in organic matter content than the plow layer or Ap horizon. The subsoil or B horizon is yellowish brown to brown in color, higher in clay and has well developed block structure. Dissolved materials such as iron and clay are moved downward through the soil, with the clay deposited in thin films on the structural aggregates or peds. The soils are moderately acid and leached of carbonates, to the parent material, or C horizon, at a depth of 3 feet or more. Where soil development has occurred on heavier textured materials structure development and clay accumulation often occurs below the top of the C horizon. The Gray Brown Podzolic soils are moderately fertile, responsive to good management and suited to a variety of crops.

## Somewhat Poorly Drained Gray Brown Podzolic Soils

This group of soils is widely distributed, intermingled with and often more extensive than the well drained Gray Brown Podzolic group through Region G and northward. They are developed in an intermittently wet and dry environment on nearly level relief under a beech-maple forest cover. The plowed soil is dark grayish brown with a somewhat lighter colored subsurface. The subsoil is dominantly gray with many yellowish brown mottles. The gray color is due to loss of the iron oxides when in the reduced and soluble condition that prevailed during the time the soil was saturated with water. The subsoils are higher in clay than the A horizon and leached of bases. The structure and texture profiles are similar to but often a little more strongly developed than the associated well drained soils. These soils require drainage for most efficient cropping. When well managed they are often more productive than the well drained sloping soils that are susceptible to erosion. Crops such as wheat and alfalfa may suffer winter injury in the slightly depressed areas where water may stand.

## Humic Gley Soils

This group of soils is extensive in both the prairie and the timbered areas of the state, chiefly from Region G northward and southward along the major river valleys of Region H. Development of this group of soils requires a good lime source and high base status as they were formed mainly in calcareous glacial drift materials of Wisconsin Age. They occur in shallow depressions and seepy areas where waterlogged conditions prevailed much of the time.

These soils have thick, black to very dark gray A1 horizons that contain from 5 to 10 percent organic matter. The dark color is diffused through or into the dark gray subsoil that is mottled with olive and yellowish brown. The surface soils range in texture from loamy fine sand to clay. The subsoil may be heavier or lighter in texture than the surface layer. The evidence favoring significant clay movement under the prevailing neutral to alkaline subsoil conditions is contradictory.

The major soil forming processes are (1) accumulation of organic matter, (2) leaching of some soluble materials from the soil which remains in a highly base saturated condition, (3) development of gleyed or gray colors mottled with yellowish brown and olive indicative of poor natural drainage. In a few places lime concretions in the soil suggests the accumulation of carbonates under rising ground water conditions.

Most of these soils have been drained and are cropped. When adequately drained and properly managed they are highly productive and well suited to corn and soybean production.

## Brunizem Soils

The Brunizem or prairie soils occur principally in the northwestern quarter of the state in Region C. This is the eastern extremity of the Grand Prairie Region of the United States. Remnants of this group also occur in Regions A, I and H. They developed under moisture conditions that ranged from somewhat poorly drained to well drained under a tall grass prairie, chiefly big blue stem.

The Brunizem soils have very dark brown A1 horizons, 10 to 15 inches thick, that grade into the dark yellowish brown heavier textured subsoil. The solum, or A and B horizons, usually extends to the calcareous parent material at 30 to 50 inches. The soils are medium acid through the upper subsoil, below which they gradually approach neutrality. The organic content, about 5 percent in the suface soil, decreases gradually with depth as suggested by the soil color. The texture of the A horizons range from silt loam to loamy sand and the parent materials are moderately leached, usually limy and range in texture from silt loam to gravel and sand.

Soil forming processes include: (1) the accumulation of organic matter, (2) the leaching of bases and development of moderate acidity in the solum, (3) the formation of high cation exchange capacity clay that is related to the organic content and calcium supply and (4) the accumulation of clay in the subsoil.

The Brunizems are inherently fertile, occurring in a region of uniform and generally adequate rainfall distribution. They are primarily suited to grain farming and include some of the most productive soils of the corn belt.

## Planosols

Planosols are poorly and somewhat poorly drained soils in nearly level areas that have very strongly illuviated subsoils. In Indiana they are most extensively developed under a forest cover on the Illinoian till plains and other soil regions to the south, principally in Soil Regions I, J, N, L, M and Region H along the Ohio River Valley. The Planosols usually have a seasonally high and perched water table due to restricted subsoil permeability. However, some ponding may be present where there are slight depressions on the flats. Planosols may have either a heavy clay subsoil (Claypan Planosols) or a dense, brittle, cemented horizon with polygonal structure (Fragipan Planosol).

Fragipan planosols are more common to Indiana than claypan planosols. They typically have a grayish brown to gray silt loam Ap or A1 horizon, a light gray silt loam A2 horizon with thin platy structure and a fragipan B horizon consisting of gray and slightly mottled silt loam or silty clay loam texture (26-31% clay). The structure of the fragipan consists of compact or very firm sharp pointed prisms with broad indistinct bases. The prisms or peds are coated with light gray silt and clay streaks that wind along cracks for 20 to 40 inches.

These soils when properly managed are productive for most crops. Surface drainage either used alone, or in conjunction with tile, is the most effective. They are acid, strong leached and low in fertility. They respond well to lime and proper fertilization. The organic content is low. Crusts form readily on bare soil so special care must be taken to improve the physical condition.

## The Red-Yellow Podzolic Soils

This group of soils is best developed in the unglaciated Soils Regions L and M. Soils that have several but not all of the properties of the group occur in Regions I, J, and N and on stream terraces associated with these regions. This area has mean annual rainfall of 45 to 50 inches and annual temperatures of 55 to 58 degrees resulting in more intensive weathering of the soil materials. An oak-hickory forest cover is common. Such trees return less lime and other bases in the leaves than other deciduous trees, thus gradually making the soil more acid.

These soils have thinner, lighter colored A horizons, with less organic matter, more highly oxidized subsurface and subsoil horizons on well drained sites. The subsoils range from red, through yellowish red and a brighter yellowish brown silt loam to silty clay loam subsoil. In some soils there is a dense fragipan horizon in place of, or below, the textural B horizons. The fragipan on these sloping soils seems in some cases to be more strongly developed and more effective than in the Planosol group at restricting water supply to crops. This may be due in part to the higher proportion of runoff on the sloping soils.

The soils forming processes are chiefly: (1) leaching out of soluble materials and exchangeable bases, (2) the more thorough decomposition of the soil forming minerals to form secondary silicate clay minerals, (3) the breakdown of some clay particles and (4) the movement of clay deeper into the subsoil.

These soils are relatively low in fertility, require liberal liming and fertilization and other good management practices to secure moderately high yields.

### Sols Bruns Acides: (Acid Brown Forest Soils)

These soils are formed in a cool temperate humid climate under hardwood forests. They are formed in acid sandstone and shale materials which are the dominant forming materials on steep slopes in Region L. The soils have a brown to yellowish brown color and uniform texture from the surface down to and through stony material and to the bedrock. They are usually strongly to very strongly acid throughout. In places where they are less acid the soils are darker in color due to accumulation of moderate amounts of organic matter, chiefly in the surface soil. Due to the steep slopes as well as thin soil mantle, this group of soils is suitable mainly for forest.

### Lithosols

These soils are shallow soils usually less than 12 to 18" thick over bedrock. They are stony and typically have no genetically related horizons. The Lithosols in Indiana are formed on sandstone and shale under a hardwood forest cover. They vary in texture and thickness of the soil, character of the rock material and steepness of the slope. They usually intergrade in varying degrees to the Sols Bruns Acides. Lithosols are an important component in complexes of soils on steep slopes in Region L.

### Kinds of Soils and Their Characteristics by Regions

### Soils of the Flood Plains—Region H

The soils of Region H shown on the General Soil Map, include the flood plains of present day streams and the alluvial terraces of former glacial streams that were very much larger, as shown on Fig. 19. Soils of the flood plains are classified as Alluvial Soils; the higher terraces comprise several groups of soils. The common features of the Alluvial group will be discussed and then some of the main differences in the principal series will be presented.

The Alluvial soils may be grouped into soils that range in color from light to dark; in reaction from neutral to strongly acid; and into texture and particle size groups that range from silty clay loam through loam to silt loam.

The dark colored group of Alluvial soils are all neutral in reaction and includes the Allison, Armiesburg, Huntington, Huntsville, Ross and Abscota series. They range from heavy silty clay loam to light fine sandy loam respectively. They are developing most extensively in the larger river valleys and are best represented by Huntington silt loam.

Huntington soils occur throughout the Ohio River Valley. They consist of medium textured alluvial materials containing conspicuous amounts of mica. This mica was washed from soils that were developed in sandstone and shale that contained sufficient lime bearing materials to produce neutral alluvium. They are nearly level, well drained soils that are associated with the lighter colored, moderately well drained Lindside and the somewhat poorly drained Newark soils. The surface to a depth of about 20 inches is dark brown to black, heavy silt loam. The subsoil is brown to dark yellowish brown heavy silt loam that is moderately permeable to moisture. It has a high water supplying capacity. The substratum below 3 to 5 feet or more is often stratified with thin layers of fine sand, silt loam and light silty clay loam.

The Allison and Armiesburg soils are heavier in texture, a little less permeable and require more care in tillage in the preparation and maintaining of good seed beds.

Light colored soils are the most extensive and widely distributed of the Alluvial Soils. These include members of the Genesee, Haymond, Lindside and Morganfield cantenas that range from mildly alkaline to slightly acid, and the strongly acid Pope and Cuba catenas. The light colored neutral group is best represented by members of the Genesee catena, which occur as small bottoms throughout Regions D, E, F, and G and in the larger valleys shown as Region H.

The Genesee soils are forming from neutral to slight calcareous alluvium that has been washed from the calcareous Wisconsin glacial drift area. The materials are chiefly coarse silt loam and loam with thin strata of fine sand. The Genesee soils are the well drained member of drainage sequence that includes the moderately well drained Eel, the somewhat poorly drained Shoals and the poorly drained Sloan soils. The Genesee soils usually have brown to dark brown silt loam a horizon 8 to 12 inches thick. Silt loam and loam are the most common textures. The subsoils are dark yellowish brown of similar texture with weak blocky structure. Thin strata of fine sand may occur anywhere in the soil particularly on areas near the stream channel. On the broad areas, particularly in the back bottoms, sand strata are usually at 30 inches or more in depth. These soils drain freely but have good moisture supplying capacity for crop production. They are fertile and well supplied with organic matter and plant nutrients. Under intensive cropping, corn will respond well to supplementary nitrogen. Corn and soybeans are the crops least likely to be damaged by late spring floods.

The Eel and Shoals soils are not as well drained, and have mottled subsoils at 18 and 10 inches respectively.

Soils of the Morganfield and Haymond catenas are developed in silty materials washed from loess covered uplands. The Morganfield group consists of neutral deep silty soils containing less than 18 percent clay that occurs chiefly in Region P. The Haymond group ranges from neutral to medium acid, has more than 18 percent clay and is washed from the thinner silt mantled soils of Regions I, J, L, M, and K where the normally acid alluvium has been neutralized by a source of lime other than neutral loess, as is illustrated in Fig. 19.

The Cuba, Philo, Stendal and Atkins drainage sequence occur principally in Regions J and L, but they may be associated with strongly acid soils of Regions I and P. The soils are forming in alluvium of mixed origin from sandstone, siltstone, shale and Illinoian drift areas where the soils have a thin silt mantle. The soils are lighter in color but more silty and less productive than comparable members of the Genesee catena.

The Pope series include the sandy coarse textures soils of small bottoms in Region L.

### Region H—Soils of the Alluvial Terraces

Soil region H as previously noted includes both the flood plains of present day streams and the former flood plains of older glacial streams. This group occurs on 2 or more levels of terraces ascending stairstep fashion from the flood plains to the upland level as is illustrated in Figure 17. The terrace levels are nearly flat topped with short steep escarpments as contrasted with the longer more beveled slopes leading to the upland level.

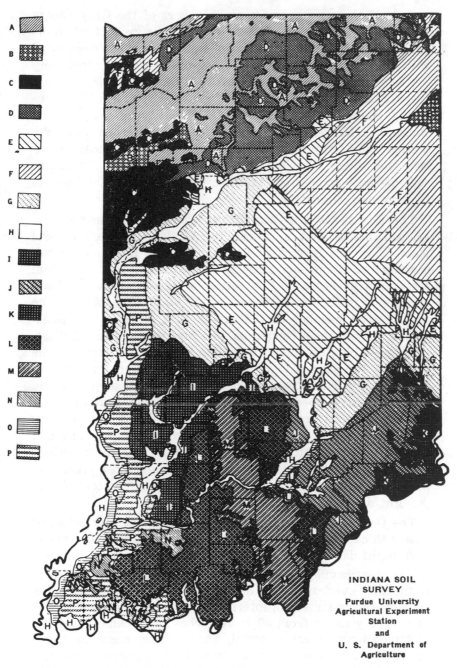

Fig. 19. General Soil Regions of Indiana showing the principal soil types of the regions.

Soils of the river terraces are members of the Gray Brown Podzolic, Brunizem and Red Yellow Podzolic group that intergrades to the Gray Brown Podzolic group of soils. Associated with these groups are some less well drained groups including the somewhat poorly drained Bray-Brown Podzolics, Humic Gleys, Planosols, and other soils of minor importance. The more poorly drained soils occur on the level and depressed positions where heavier textured, less permeable materials were deposited. The Gray Brown Podzolic group is the most extensive and widely distributed in Indiana. The more important soils of the terrace areas are Fox, Ockley, Rush, Martinsville, Camden and Elkinsville.

The Fox series are Gray Brown Podzolic soils usually developed on the first or lower, terrace level above the flood plain. They are formed in loamy materials that overlie calcareous gravel and sand at 24 to 42 inches. Silt loam and loam are dominant types of Fox series in Region H; sandy loam is common in the northern part of the state. Fox soils are the well drained member of the catena that includes the somewhat poorly drained Homer and the very poorly drained Westland and Abington series. Fox soils have brown surface soils and brown to dark reddish brown clay loam and gravelly clay loam subsoils. Near the contact with the calcareous gravel and sand the subsoil becomes darker in color and neutral in reaction. Fox soils are freely permeable. Moisture supplies are somewhat limited and consequently crops such as corn and soybeans may suffer some damage even during short periods of drought in the summer season. Although most crops can be grown, wheat and alfalfa are the least susceptible to drought damage.

The Ockley and Rush soils are similar to the Fox soils but have a thicker silt mantle, thicker sola and are less susceptible to drought damage.

The Martinsville and Camden soils differing in the thickness of the silty overburden are developed in silty and loamy materials overlying stratified, interbedded silts and fine sands. The sola usually range from 50 to 70 inches in thickness over the stratified limy parent material. They usually occur on broad outwash plains or downstream from the Fox soils and are less susceptible to drought hazard than the Fox soils.

The Mahalasville, Westland and Abington series are the principal dark colored soils of formerly marshy areas associated with the forested and prairie groups of soils in Region H: They are members of the Humic Gley group of soils.

The Mahalasville occur in elongated swales and depressions some of which were former glacial drainage ways. They have very dark gray silty clay loam surface soils that are 10 to 15 inches thick; mottled, gray, olive and yellowish brown silty clay loam subsoils that contain increasing amounts of sand in the deeper subsoil at 30 inches or more. The underlying material from 42 to 60 inches is calcareous stratified silt and fine sand. These soils are highly productive when drained and properly managed. Corn and soybeans are the principal crops.

The Westland and Abington soils are similar to the Mahalasville but are coarser textured throughout and are developed in calcareous gravel and sand at 42 to 60 inches.

The Elston, Warsaw and Wea soils are the principal representatives of the Brunizem group in Region H. As a group they are well drained, and have developed in or over relatively coarse texture materials. Crops are susceptible in varying degree to drought damage but crops such as corn responds well to irrigation.

The Wea soils have the best moisture potential of the group, are developed in silty and loamy materials 42 to 60 inches thick over limy gravel and sand. The silt mantle is usually less than 2 feet thick, although areas from Fountain County southward may have 3 feet of silt cover. Wea soils are the well drained member of the catena that includes the moderately well drained Tippecanoe, the somewhat poorly drained Crane and the very poorly drained Westland and Abington soils.

The strongly leached soils developed in alluvium of mixed origin include members of the Elkinsville and Wheeling catenas. The subgroup includes Red-Yellow Podzolic soils, Red-Yellow Podzolic integrades to Gray-Brown Podzolics, and Planosols.

Soils of the Elkinsville catena occur in the lower ends of the Wabash and White River Valleys on the lower terrace level adjoining the flood plains and in tributary stream valleys that rise in soil Regions L and J. They resemble soils of the Otwell catena, Region N, but have very weak profile development. The Pekin, Bartle and Peoga have incipient fragipans with

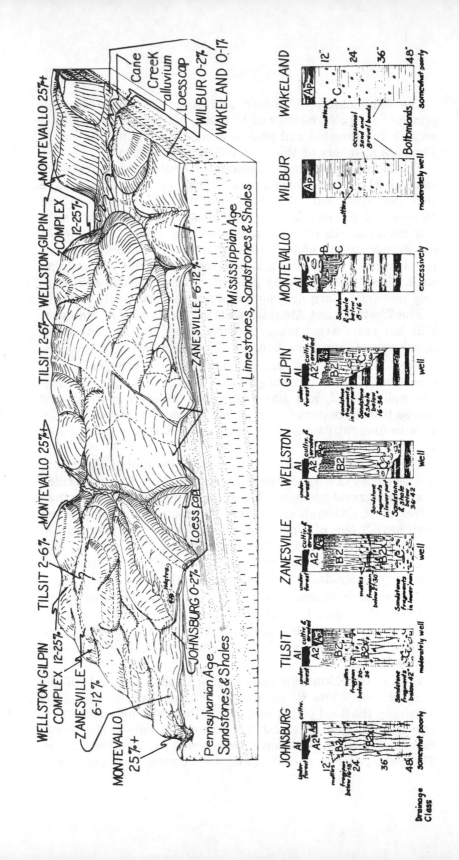

SOILS                                    73

little clay accumulation in the subsoil. The Elkinsville soils
have a weak textured B and no fragipan. They are developed
in deeply leached silty alluvium of mixed origin. These soils are
productive when adequately limed and liberally fertilized.

The Wheeling series represent the principal soils of the Ohio
River terraces. They are developed in silty and sandy alluvium
of mixed origin principally from micaceous sandstone and
shale materials. Below 50 to 70 inches or more the material is
stratified sand, silt and some fine gravel. The soils are low in
exchangeable bases and strongly to very strongly acid to a
depth of 10 feet. Wheeling soils are the well drained member
of the drainage sequence that includes the moderately well
drained Sciotoville, the somewhat poorly drained Weinbach
and poorly drained Ginat soils. Wheeling soils dominantly have
brown to dark brown silt loam surface soils, and yellowish
brown to strong brown silty clay loam subsoils to 40 inches
or more. Sola are 5 feet or more in thickness, the lower part of
which may be silt loam with thin strata of loam and fine sand.
Wheeling loam is a minor type. Wheeling soils, when adequately limed and liberally fertilized are highly productive.
All the crops common to the area may be grown.

The other members of the Wheeling drainage sequence have
compact slowly premeable horizons or fragipans and are classified as Planosols or planosolic soils.

### The Dune Belt or Soil Region O, Bloomfield— Princeton Association

The sand dune belt shown on the map as soil Region O is a
long narrow discontinuous strip of sandy soils that border the
east side of the larger river valleys in southern Indiana. The
sand was blown by the prevailing westerly winds from the
flood plains of former glacial rivers to the terrace-upland border of the valley. It occurs as low winding ridges and crescent-
shaped dunes with intervening depressions and swales. The
principal soils are the well drained Bloomfield and Chelsea
loamy fine sands, the heavier textured Princeton soils and the
more poorly drained Ayrshire and Lyles fine sandy loams.
These soils, with the exception of Lyles, were formed under a

Fig. 20. Soils of the Southern Indiana Forage Farm, Dubois County,
Indiana, related to parent materials and topography. The bottoms normally acid are neutral along Cane Creek due to the outcropping limestone.

hardwood forest cover and are light colored and low in organic matter.

The Bloomfield soils are members of the Gray-Brown Podzolic group. They have dark brown to brown loamy fine sand surface soils. At variable depths of 30 to 50 inches the subsoil consists of reddish brown wavy bands of loamy fine or heavier sand that contain an accumulation of clay and iron. The bands, separated by loose lighter colored fine sand, increase in thickness with depth from ⅛ to 4 inches or more and markedly increase the moisture supplying capacity of the soil. Below the banded subsoil at 40 to 80″ there is calcareous brown fine sand. Winter grain cover crops, liberally fertilized, are used to maintain the organic matter content; the plants bind the sand particles to reduce wind erosion, and increase the moisture supplying capacity. The commercial melon and peach orcharding industry of southwestern Indiana is centered in the area of Bloomfield soils.

The Chelsea soils are similar to the Bloomfield soils but have much weaker subsoil development, lower moisture supplying capacity, lack the limy parent material and are somewhat more acid.

The Princeton soils have heavier textures and continuous subsoils. The subsoil at depths of 12 to 40 inches or more is a brown to reddish sandy clay loam that may range to loam or heavy fine sandy loam. The parent material at depths of 3 to 5 feet or more is calcareous brown fine sand, that is often interbedded with silt. Due to the more favorable moisture supplying capacity crop adaption is wider. Peach orcharding is the dominant special crop.

### The Thick Loess or Windblown Silt Belt, Region P; Sylvan-Alford-Hosmer Association

Soils developed partially or entirely in silt occur in several regions through the southern 2/3 of the state. Silt deposits 5 to 25 feet thick are the soil forming material of Region P bordering the Wabash River Valley to the east of the dune belt from Attica southward. The materials consist of flour-size particles 80 per cent of which range from .002 to .05 millimeters in diameter. The particles are so small that it requires a cluster of 3 to 5 or more to be visible to the naked eye. The silt deposits are thicker near the bluff, and thin gradually in a southeasterly direction. This is an area of low relief, gently rolling and completely stream dissected. Flat-topped inter-stream divides occur on the till plains of Illinoian and Wisconsin Age but the level areas are larger in the northern half of Region P. Three groups of soils dominate this region: (1) Soils of the Sylvan catena which are relatively young, and medium acid, are developed in silt that is calcareous at a depth of 3 to 5 feet, (2) Soils of the Alford catena which are more strongly developed, more acid and are usually completely leached of carbonates and (3) Soils of the Hosmer catena which are developed in strongly acid silts 4 to 8 feet thick and have a slowly permeable fragipan that extends from about 30 inches to the weathered underlying rock or till.

The soils of the Sylvan catena consist of the well drained Sylvan, the moderately well drained Iona, the somewhat poorly drained Reesville, the poorly drained Whitson and the poorly to very poorly drained Ragsdale. This group of soils is developed in a long narrow upland strip near the bluff and back of the dunes in southwestern Indiana. In Knox County the topography is more rolling and the silts are somewhat coarser in texture. On the smoother parts of the Illinoian and Wisconsin till plains the more poorly drained soils are dominant and the belt is several miles in width. These soils are medium acid to a depth of 3 feet, have good structure, and are capable of intensive cropping. The Sylvan soils are well drained, occur on gently sloping to rolling topography where erodibility is the principal limitation on cropping. Most areas with favorable topography have been cleared of timber and are either grain cropped or used for forage. The Sylvan soils have grayish brown to brown silt loam surface soils, and brown to reddish brown heavy silt loam to light silty clay loam subsoils. They grade at 30 to 40 inches through brown to yellowish brown slightly acid silt loam into mottled limy silt loam that contains from 10 to 20 per cent or more calcium and magnesium carbonate. Due to the low clay content of the subsoil the physical condition of this soil when eroded is not very harmful to crops and the yield levels can be readily increased by farming methods that build up the organic matter content and restore the fertility.

The Iona soils are on gently sloping areas. They differ from the Sylvan soils chiefly in having gray and yellow mottled subsoils at 18 to 20 inches.

The Reelsville soils occur on level divides where they often intermingle with the black, poorly drained Ragsdale soils of the depressed areas. They have dark grayish brown silt loam surface soils and grayish brown to gray and yellow mottled silty clay loam subsoils. The subsoil at 30 inches or more becomes more yellowish in color, more silty and less acid in reaction. The calcareous silt loam parent material occurs at 30 to 50 inches and is near the minimum on the west side of the area and on the Wisconsin till plain. The Reelsville, Whitson and Ragsdale soils have usually been tile drained and are intensively cropped.

The soils of the Alford catena consist of the well drained Alford, the moderately well drained Muren, and the somewhat poorly drained Iva. They are extensive and occur over a wide belt that roughly parallels the Wabash River Valley. They differ from the Sylvan group of soils in having thicker, more acid sola to a depth of 5 feet or more. Where the Alford soils grade into the Hosmer soils they often have a thin brittle incipient fragipan horizon developed at 30 to 40 inches depth.

The Hosmer soils are well drained and moderately well drained soils that have some of the characteristics of both Gray Brown Podzolic and Red Yellow Podzolic soils. These soils occur in southwestern Indiana chiefly where loess deposits 4 to 8 feet or more in thickness have been deposited over residuum from sandstone, shale, and Illinoian drift. They often occur on gently sloping, broad ridge tops in association with Zanesville, Wellston or Gilpin soils on the steeper slopes. Hosmer soils are characterized by brown silt loam surface soils that have more highly oxidized subsurfaces. The subsoil at 10 inches is a brown to strong brown light silty clay loam having moderate angular blocky structure. At depths of 20 to 25 inches there is a compact, brittle horizon that breaks into coarse prisms a foot or more in height. The maximum clay content is about 31 per cent or less and decreases with depth. The pan rests on silty material, but where the loess thickness is at the minimum, it may extend into residuum from sandstone, shale and Illinoian drift materials.

The slow permeability and erosive character of the Hosmer soils limit their use to rotation crops on the less sloping areas and pasture on the more sloping and erosion areas. Liberal applications of lime and fertilizer are needed to secure good crop yields. Crops, such as corn and soybeans suffer readily from drought which is common during late June to September.

### Soils of the Sandstone and Shale Area, Region L; Zanesville-Gilpin-Montevallo Association

Region L is a highly dissected sandstone and shale upland characterized by narrow ridge tops, steep stony hillsides, and narrow V-shaped valleys, containing a small amount of bottom-land. This soil region consists of two parts. In the southwestern part the ridges are broader, the rocks are softer, and the soils are deeper. A higher proportion of the land is arable than is typical of Region L. In the rest of the western part stream dissection has exposed rocks of varying degrees of hardness and weatherability. Exposed strata of limestone and shale form hillside terraces; the hard sandstone forms crags and bluffs. This is a scenic area consisting of about 50 per cent woodland. In the eastern part the rocks weather uniformly resulting in uniformly steep valley walls and knife-edge ridge tops. The arable land occurs in small irregular-shaped ridge top fields and narrow bottomland fields. Three-fourths of the land is in timber. These soils have greater potential for forestry and grassland than grain farming. The principal soils are Zanesville and Tilsit on the broad ridges, Wellston on the narrow ridge tops and moderately steep slopes, and Gilpin, Muskingum, Berks, Montevallo and Ramsey on the steep nonarable slopes. The relationship of soils to the landscape is shown on Fig. 20 of the Southern Indiana Forage Farm Area.

The Zanesville, Tilsit and Johnsburg soils have slowly permeable fragipan subsoils that are progressively more poorly drained and occur on broader ridge tops. Zanesville differs from Hosmer in having part of the soil profile developed in the weathered rock residue.

The Wellston soils are similar to the Zanesville but are better drained internally because they lack a fragipan. They are developed on more sloping areas have a loess mantle of 2 feet and an average soil depth of 40 inches over hard rock.

The Gilpin soils are Red-Yellow Podzolic soils formed largely in residuum from the weathering of acid sandstone and shale. They occur on narrow ridge tops and moderately steep upper slopes. On the ridge tops where there is a thin silt mantle the common texture is silt loam. On the hillsides small fragments of sandstone and shale occur on the surface and increase through the brown silty clay loam subsoil. Hard relatively unweathered but fractured sandstone and shale usually occur at about 30 inches. The soil is very strongly acid and low in exchangeable bases. Tree roots penetrate the fractured rock and make good growth but on shale material tree growth is rather poor.

The steep stony soils are members of the Lithosol or Sols Brunes Acides groups of soils. Areas formerly classified as Muskingum have recently been subdivided into 4 series to better recognize the thickness of the soil, the degree of stoniness and the kinds of soil forming materials. New soil maps will show many of these slopes as complexes of two or more series because it will be difficult to separate them accurately. Muskingum and Berks are 20 inches or more thick with increasingly stony profiles; Montevallo and Ramsey are less than 20 inches and are very stony throughout.

### Soils of the Mitchell Plain, or Limestone Area, Region M; Crider-Frederick-Bedford Association

The Mitchell Plain is an undulating upland limestone area which extends in a southerly direction from Morgan through Harrison Counties to the Ohio River. In the vicinity of Mitchell, it is a gently undulating plain with large areas of level, somewhat poorly drained soils. Southwest of Salem there is a highly pitted sinkhole area on which the loess mantle is very thin. Elsewhere, the relief is moderate to steep with drainage provided by shallow surface streams that descend rapidly when they approach the major streams of the area.

The soils of Region M are formed in a thin silt cover on residuum from the weathering of two general kinds of limestone represented by the somewhat cherty St. Geniveve and St. Louis and the high grade Salem formation. The Bewleyville and Frederick, Bedford, Lawrence, Guthrie and Burgin drainage sequence is formed on the former and the Crider soils on the latter. The soils of this area are strongly acid, low in organic matter, nitrogen and phosphorus. Crops respond well to the liberal use of lime and fertilizer. This is an area of grain, grassland and livestock farming with some commercial orcharding, chiefly apples.

The Bewleyville series comprises well drained Red Yellow Podzolic soil formed in 18 to 40 inches of silty material over cherty red clay residuum from the weathering of limestone. They differ from the Crider soils chiefly in having a very cherty red clay subsoil that is streaked and mottled with brown and yellowish brown. They have brown to grayish brown silt loam surface soils with dark brown to yellowish red chert-free light silty clay loam subsoils that have well developed blocky structure. At 24 inches or more there is a thin transitional layer of strong brown cherty silty clay loam to the darker reddish brown clay that contains 30 per cent or more of cherty. This horizon is streaked, stained, and mottled on the faces of the blocky aggregates and through the matrix. Limestone underlays the soil at 5 to 10 feet or more. The Bewleyville soils occur on ridge tops and around drainage ways on slopes of 2 to 18 per cent. They are quite erosive under clean tillage and require the use of good conservation practices to protect them. The more sloping areas are best suited to pasture.

The Frederick soils are developed in less than 18 inches of silty material over cherty red clay residuum from the weathering of limestone at 5 to 10 feet or more. Where there is less than 8 inches of silty overburden, the soils are often cherty to the surface and closely resemble the Baxter soil of Kentucky. Where the red clay is close to the surface, permeability is slower and the soil is highly erosive. The Frederick soils are best suited to pasture.

The Bedford, Lawrence and Guthrie soils occur on gently sloping to nearly level areas. The soils in this sequence are increasingly gray and more poorly drained. As these soils are developed in silts and have a fragipan, they resemble the soils of the Tilsit sequence in the upper part of the profile. They differ in that the lower part is clay residuum from the weathering of limestone. They represent the better crop land of Region M because erosion is a less critical problem.

The Crider soils have browner upper subsoil and more reddish lower subsoil and lack of mottled colors and chert that is commonly present in the deep subsoil of the Bewleyville. They occur extensively on smoother topography where drainage is more often by streams than sinkholes. They are generally more productive and are more intensively farmed.

The Corydon soils are shallow, dark-colored, neutral soils developed in limestone residuum associated with both the Crider and Bewleyville groups. They are inextensive soils of the steep wooded slopes.

### Soils Developed on Ordovician Limestone Materials, Region K; Switzerland-Fairmount Association

This is a highly dissected upland area of southeastern Indiana that borders the Ohio River and extends northward to Richmond, Indiana. These soils are formed only on slopes near the valley as the upland is covered with glacial drift largely of Illinoian Age. On the unglaciated ridge tops the soils are formed from a thin mantle of loess usually less than 3 feet thick and from the interbedded flaggy limestone and soft shales that are highly calcareous and medium high in phosphates. The principal soils recognized in this region are the light-colored Switzerland and Allensville soils and the dark-colored Fairmount soil.

Switzerland soils are well drained, have dark grayish brown to brown silt loam surface soils, yellowish brown silty clay loam subsoils to 20 inches and olive colored clay lower subsoils. The parent material at 36 to 50 inches consists of thin flaggy, fossilifferous limestone and pale olive calcareous soft clay shale. The soil is strongly to very strongly acid to 40 inches or more. The clay content ranges from 37 to 60 per cent through the subsoil. Due to the strong relief and the erosive character under clean tillage, they are better suited to use for grass and meadow crops.

The Fairmount series comprises well drained, shallow Rendzina soils developed in flaggy limestone and calcareous clay shale of Ordovician Age. They occur on very steep upland slopes bordering the Ohio River and its tributaries. Fairmount soils have very dark grayish brown silty clay surface soil horizons 3 to 5 inches thick, that have strong granular structure are firm when moist, and plastic and sticky when wet. The subsoil at 5 to 8 inches or more is dark yellowish brown silty clay with strong angular blocky structure. The parent material at variable depths 7 to 20 inches is pale olive limy clay shale and limestone. The gentler foot slopes of this slope are often cropped to tobacco and alfalfa, from which it gets the name of "Black Tobacco land." When tilled erosion is severe,

Fairmount is best suited to pasture although most areas are so steep that they have never been cleared. Timber growth is very slow. The soils are fertile and produce good pasture in seasons of adequate moisture.

### Soils of the Western Lobe of the Illinoian Till Plain, Cincinnati-Vigo Soil Associations: Region I

The western lobe of the Illinoian glacial till plain differs from the eastern lobe by soils having formed in a thicker silt deposit, by the accumulation of clay in the upper subsoils, particularly on the nearly level areas, and by having very gently undulating topography on the divides. Part of this region with the thicker loess mantle and limited pan development is now classified as members of the Alford, Muren and Iva Catena. On the eastern side of Region I there are unglaciated island areas of shale and sandstone-derived soils that are members of the Zanesville and related soils.

The soils of this area are best represented by the well drained Cincinnati series, the moderately well drained Ava and the somewhat poorly drained Vigo. Soils of lesser importance are the Hickory, Cory, Pike, Parke, and Negley and Grayford series. The Cory soils are remnants of a prairie that once covered this region. They have dark colored plow layers but otherwise resemble the Iva soils.

The other soils are light in color, low in organic matter, and were developed under a mixed hardwood forest cover. The soils are generally strongly acid, deeply leached and low in fertility and exchangeable bases. They are developed in 3 to 5 feet or more of silty material and leached clay loam drift of Illinoian Age that is calcareous at 10 feet or more.

The Cincinnati series comprises well drained Red-Yellow Podzolics that intergrade to the Gray-Brown Podzolics. They are developed in 20 to 40 inches or more of silty material and residuum from the weathering of Illinoian Age till. They occur on slopes of 2 to 20 per cent or more on areas around most drainage ways. This series occurs in both the western and eastern lobe of the Illinoian region.

Cincinnati soils have brown silt loam A horizon and reddish brown to yellowish brown silty clay loam B horizons to a depth of 30 to 48 inches where a moderately strong fragipan occurs. Due to erosiveness this soil is best suited to permanent pasture or forestry. The soil is very strongly acid to 7 feet or more and low in exchangeable bases.

The Hickory soils are well drained and occur on very steep slopes around drainage ways, in association with the Cincinnati soils. Slopes range from 20 to 70 per cent. They differ from the Cincinnati in having a thinner silt mantle, a shallower solum, and in lacking a fragipan. The Hickory soils are used mainly for woodland.

The Ava series includes moderately well drained soils that occur on gently sloping areas around shallow drainage ways and bordering the nearly level Vigo soils. They are developed on 30 to 50 inches of silty material over residuum from the weathering of Illinoian till, and are calcareous at a depth of 10 feet or more. They have brown silt loam surface soils dark yellowish brown heavy silt loam upper subsoils and at 16 to 18″ change abruptly to mottled gray and yellow silty clay loam subsoils. At 24 to 48″ the subsoil is light brownish gray silty clay loam with weak to moderate prismatic structure. It has slow permeability to roots, air and moisture. Erosion control and adequate liming and liberal fertilization are needed to secure good crop yields. Most of it is under cultivation although the more sloping and eroded areas are better suited to pasture.

The Vigo soils are somewhat poorly drained Planosols that occur on nearly level to gently sloping areas. They are developed in a silt cover 40 to 60 inches thick over leached strongly acid clay loam till. They occur on the broad divides throughout the till plain area. They have a dark grayish brown silt loam plow layer and thick gray to nearly white silt loam subsurfaces that have platy structure. At about 24 inches there is an abrupt change to the gray silty clay loam subsoil that has many yellowish brown mottles, and a strong coarse prismatic structure. Light gray silt caps and coats the peds and fills the crevices that extend through the pan to a depth of 42″ or more. At lower depths the soil becomes more silty, lighter in texture and more permeable to moisture movement. Drainage is necessary for efficient cropping. Surface drainage can usually be more economically applied but tile drainage is also effective. This soil is highly productive when properly managed. It is almost entirely under cultivation chiefly to grain crops.

Distributed through the Illinoian glacial till plain are areas
of water-assorted sand and loamy sand on which three kinds
of well drained soils have been developed. The Pike and Parke
soils are more thickly silt mantled, the Negley has little silt
mantling. They are dark brown soils with reddish brown freely permeable subsoils.

The Parke soils developed in 18 to 40 inches of silt have
more sandy lower subsoils than the thickly silt-mantled Pike
soils. Arable areas of Parke and Pike soils are good crop land;
sloping areas are better suited to pasture. The Negley soils
developed largely in sandy materials and occuring on steep
slopes are suited chiefly to forestry.

The Grayford soils are well drained Red-Yellow Podzolics
that are intergrading to Gray Brown Podzolic soils. They are
developed in three kinds of materials; loess, very strongly
acid glacial till of Illinoian Age, and clay residuum from the
weathering of limestone. They occur chiefly on the glaciated
northern extension of the Mitchell plain in Morgan, Owen and
Putnam Counties. Small areas occur in Region J. This soil occurs chiefly as undulating pitted plains with level divides.
Grayford soils have brown surface and upper subsoil and dark
reddish brown clay lower subsoils extending from 30 or 40
inches to rock at 4 to 8 feet. They are productive soils under
good management.

*Soils of the Eastern Lobe of the Illinois Till Plain; Cincin-
nati, Avonburg-Jennings-Trappist Association, Region J*

This is a stream-dissected till plain that has broad flat divides. Streams have a gentle gradient in a southerly direction
across this region, but the valleys are deep, and the slopes
steep along the east, south and west sides. The thickness of
the glacial till of this region ranges from 5 to about 40 feet.
In places the till contains much rock material of local origin
or the soils are largely developed from the underlying rock
formations. The till-derived soils of this region are generally
more silty, lower in clay content and have a fragipan as compared with the clay pan character of the nearly level soils of
the western lobe. All of the soils of this region are strongly
acid, low in fertility, and are either erosive or require drainage. The principal soils of Region J are the well drained Cincinnati and Hickory soils, the moderately well drained Ross-

moyne, the somewhat poorly drained Avonburg, and the poorly drained Clermont. The Cincinnati and Hickory soils of this region are similar to those soils in the western lobe.

Rossmoyne soils occur on nearly level to gently sloping relief around drainage ways. They are similar to the Cincinnati soils but have mottled subsoils at about 18 inches. They differ from the Ava soils of Region I in having little clay accumulation above the fragipan at 30 inches and in having less clay accumulation in the pan. The lower subsoil of the two soils is similar. A small proportion of the Rossmoyne soils in the counties bordering Ohio have heavier subsoils and parent material till that contains a high proportion of clay derived from the Ordovician limestone material.

The somewhat poorly drained Avonburg and the poorly drained Clermont soils are classified as Planosols. They are silty soils that differ in the color and proportion of yellow mottles in the upper subsoil. The fragipan is the heaviest horizon in these soils. It ranges from silt loam to light silty clay loam of about 31% clay. The fragipan extends to 60 inches or more and is underlain by till that is calcareous at about 10 feet. These soils are strongly acid, low in fertility but respond well to good management. Drainage is essential particularly on the Clermont. Surface drainage is most effective as tile lines tend to fill with silt and require considerable maintenance. Avonburg is more intesively cropped than Clermont because the slight slope provides drainage. Where the Clermont occurs in large undrained areas it is usually in forest or low grade pasture. When adequately drained and properly managed it is highly productive.

The Jennings, Cana and Whitcomb constitute a catena developed in thin silt mantle 24-40" thick, and leached glacial till material overlying bituminous or "black oil shale" at 40 to 72 inches. These soils occur where the Illinoian glacier overrode Devonian Age oil-bearing shales but left only a thin deposit of glacial till on the shale. Where there is much weathered shale mixed with the till, the soil is likely to be very acid and low in exchangeable bases, and low in fertility.

The Colyer and Trappist soils are formed where the soil is completely developed in Devonian Shale or there is an insignificant amount of till to influence soil development. They occur in the same general area as the Jennings catena.

*Soils of the Glacial Border Lakes and Slackwater Fill of
Melt Water Streams, Region N; Otwell-Dubois-
Markland-Henshaw Association*

The glacial border lakes formed chiefly along the outer ice
margin of the Illinoian Glacier. The deposits consisted of stratified silt, silty clay loam and minor amounts of fine sand. A
loess mantle 2 to 5 feet in thickness is present in some areas.
Loess deposits are thicker on former lakes in southwestern
Indiana and decrease in thickness eastward. The principal
drainage sequence consists of the well drained Otwell, the moderately well drained Haubstadt, the somewhat poorly drained
Dubois and the poorly drained Robinson series. Some of these
soils have fragipans like the Cincinnati-Clermont group. Elsewhere, they have clay pans resembling the Cincinnati-Vigo
sequence. On glacial beaches and outlet channels, soils of the
Pike, Parke and Negley group may occur.

Slackwater clays of Wisconsin Age were deposited principally along the main stream courses in southern Indiana and the
adjacent tributary valleys. The drainage sequence consists of
the moderately well drained Markland, somewhat poorly
drained McGary, the poorly drained to very poorly drained
Zipp, Montgomery and Kings. The clay content of the subsoil
in this catena ranges from 40 to 55% or more and is highest
in the Kings clay developed in the deeper depressions.

The Uniontown, Henshaw and Patton catena represents a
group of soils developed on silty clay loam slackwater deposits
that frequently have a thin silt mantle of about 18 inches.
They occur chiefly among tributary streams where silty materials were washed into the lake. They have better structure
and are more easily managed than comparable soils of the
Markland sequence.

*Soils of Region A developed in sands and gravels of the
Kankakee Outwash and Lacustrine Plain and the Calumet
Lacustrine Plain: Plainfield, Oshtemo sands, Maumee,
Gilford sandy loams, Tracy, Door and Fox loams*

This is an area of low relief consisting of winding sand
dunes interspersed with long marshy swales and with extensive gravel terraces and broad flat depressions that were formerly marshes. The soils are all of recent origin but they vary

widely in characteristics and potential productivity due to difference in mineralogical composition. The loose sandy soils represented by Plainfield and Tyner are droughty and inherently low in fertility although the latter has fair moisture supplying capacity. The Fox, Casco, Kalamazoo and Oshtemo soils developed on calcareous gravel and sand, are arrayed in increasing sandiness and drought susceptibility. The Fox soils in this region are more sandy and less productive than those of Region H. The Tracy and Door soils developed on acid shaley and gravelly sand, are strongly acid, somewhat droughty and require good management to get high level crop yields. The most productive soils, represented by Maumee, Runnymede, Gilford and Westland series, are the black sandy and loamy soils of the former marshland areas, that are extensively developed throughout the region. They are used almost continuously for grain crops, chiefly corn, soybeans, oats and wheat. The organic soils chiefly Carlisle and Houghton mucks are extensively developed and used for special crops such as potatoes, mint, onions, carrots.

### Soils of Region B, Glacial Lake Areas of Northern Indiana; Jasper-Rensselaer-Hoytville-Nappanee Association

This region consists of two parts. The western area consists of a lake bed of calcareous clay that has been covered by outwash deposits of interbedded silt and fine sands. The soils are dark colored, developed under prairie grass, from interbedded silts and fine sands that are calcareous at 30 to 50 inches. The soils consist of the well drained Jasper, the moderately well drained Foresman, the somewhat poorly drained Darroch and the very poorly drained Rennsselaer. Silt loam and loam are the dominant surface textures. Minor areas of sandy loams soils of other series do occur. Where the underlying clay is at the surface to form soil, the Strole and Montgomery soils are developed. A cash grain system of farming is followed on these productive soils.

The eastern part of this region is a broad flat lake plain more than 80 per cent of which was a once forested marshland. The soils are developed chiefly in heavy till, but there are local deposits of stratified materials. Bordering the lake there are poorly assorted beachridge deposits, on which the Belmore soils are developed. The area is dominantly Hoytville silty clay, a dark gray poorly drained soil developed in heavy clay till, that is used mainly for corn and soybean production. Mixed with the Hoytville are small areas of light colored Nappanee and Haskins silt loam. Drainage and poor tilth are the principal management problems in use of this area. This is the most intensively drained area in the state in which uniformly distributed tile lines empty into a network of open ditches. Crop yields are high—corn normally exceeding 100 bushels per acre and soybeans 40 bushels per acre.

### Region C, the Prairie Till Plain; Sidell, Parr Elliott and Chalmers Association

Region C is the undulating to nearly level prairie region of the state in which the soils are dark in color, high in organic matter and natural fertility and are formed in moderately heavy limy glacial till deposits. Low knolls and ridges of erosive well drained soils are common but small in total extent. Forty per cent or more of the area consists of swales and depressions of former marshland areas that were drained in order to bring them under cultivation. This is an area of fertile, highly productive soils which is nearly all used in a grain system of farming. The principal groups of soils are (1) the silt-mantled loam till soils; members of the Sidell, Dana, Raub, Chalmers catena, (2) the Parr, Corwin and Odell catena which are silt mantle in southern Newton County but somewhat sandy on the morainic ridge extending northeastward across the center of Newton County, and (3) the Varna, Elliott, Ashkum group of soils in the Lake County area developed on silty clay loam or clay loam till. Small areas of Prairie soils also occur on outwash plains on stratified materials in Region C in widely scattered areas in Region H.

### Soils of Region D; the Miami-Crosby loams, Metea-Chelsea loamy sand Association

This is a rolling glaciated upland plain with numerous lakes, kettle holes, sandy and gravelly knolls and ridges and outwash plains. There are intricate variations in both topography and soils. The soils are predominantly Miami, Celina, Crosby loams and sandy loams and Brookston loam. There are many deposits of sandy materials, variable in thickness and irregular in shape of the areas. Soils that are increasingly sandy in texture and thickness range from the Hillsdale, Metea, Aubbee-naubee, Seward, and Rimer to the deep loose sandy Chelsea soils. The soils are predomiantly loam and sandy loams that are easily worked, well drained and of good productivity. However as the soils increase in the amount and thickness of sand the drought hazard increases. On sloping areas the soils are moderately erosive. Organic soils such as Carlisle muck are present in the numerous kettle holes throughout the area. They are suitable for special crops, corn and pasture. Because of the irregular topography the proportion of land used for meadow and forage crops is high and dairying and livestock raising are important farm enterprises.

### Soils of Region E; the Miami-Crosby silt loams Association

This region consists of a nearly level to very gently undulating till plain that is crossed by a few low morainic ridges and shallow drainage ways. The soils are developed in a thin silt mantle less than 18 inches thick, and clay loam till that has been leached of carbonates to a variable depth of 18 to 42 inches. The unweathered loam till occurs at an average depth of 32 inches, is very compact and ranges from 15 to 30 per cent in carbonate of lime. The soils consist of the well drained Miami, the moderately well drained Celina, the somewhat poorly drained Crosby and the poorly drained Bethel silt loams and the very poorly drained Brookston and Kokomo silty clay loams of the depressions. Bordering the deeper valley there are minor areas of the neutral, shallow Hennepin soils on the steep slopes. Brookston and Crosby soils commonly known as "Black and clay land" are the dominant soils of this region. Crosby silt loam, the more extensive, soil occurs on flat to very gently undulating areas intermingled with the dark colored Brookston silty clay loam of the depressions. Crosby has a grayish brown silt loam surface soil 8 to 10 inches thick that overlies a gray clay loam subsoil mottled with yellowish brown to a depth of about 30 inches. Near the contact with the limy till at average depth of 33 inches there is a dark mottled yellowish brown neutral clay loam layer. The clay content of the subsoil ranges from 30 to 40 per cent and averages about 34 per cent. The soils of this group are productive when properly managed. The principal problems are the control of erosion on sloping areas and maintaining an adequate drainage system on the level and depressed areas. A grain and live-stock system of farming is commonly followed with heavy hog production occurring throughout the area.

### Soils of Region F. Blount, Morley, Nappanee, Pewamo Association

This is a nearly level to gently undulating till plain marked by a number of low morainic ridges that beginning with the Union City moraine, extend eastward encircling the western end of Glacial Lake Maumee lying east of Fort Wayne. North-east of Fort Wayne the till plain is undulating to rolling, pitted with ponds and kettle holes. The soil forming material is ice-reworked lake-bed material that ranges from 33 to 50 per cent clay. The soils are light colored developed under forests with dark colored former marshland soils intermingled.

The principal soils developed in silty clay loam till consist of the well to moderately well drained Morley, the somewhat poorly drained Blount silt loams and the very poorly drained Pewamo silty clay. In color these soils resemble the Miami, Crosby, Brookston sequence of Region E but they are more permeable, dry out more slowly, have a little shorter growing season and are less productive. On the higher knolls and bordering Glacial Lake Maumee the Rawson and Haskins loams occur. They are developed in an overburden of loamy materials 15 to 36 inches thick on the heavy till. The heavier textured Nappanee soils occur in the northeastern part of the area. A general system of farming is followed in which a high proportion of pasture and leguminous hay crops are grown.

### Soils of Region G; the Russell-Fincastle Association

This region consists of the nearly level to sloping, moderately stream-dissected outer border of the Wisconsin till plain. The soils are developed in a thin covering of silt ranging from 18 to 40 inches and averaging about 28 inches. The lower part is clay loam till that becomes calcareous at 42 to 60 inches and averaging about 53 inches. The till is very compact, loam in texture and ranges from 17 to 35 per cent acid neutralizing value or carbonate of lime. The principal soils consist of the well drained Russell, the moderately well drained Xenia, the somewhat poorly drained Fincastle, the poorly drained Delmar silt loam and the poor to very poorly drained Cope and Brook-ston silty clay loams. Bordering the east side of the Wabash

River Valley and along the Champaign moraine the silt mantle may exceed 3 feet in thickness. The Manlove and Birkbeck soils are formed in leached silts 3 feet or more thick over calcareous till. The Iona and Reesville soils are formed in calcareous silts 3 to 5 feet or more in thickness.

This is a region of acid but productive soils that respond well to good management. A grain and livestock system of farming is followed with intensive row cropping on the level areas and pasture and meadow crops grown on the sloping areas to control erosion.

# 5

# *Lakes and Streams*

MALCOLM D. HALE

Indiana District, Water Resources Division

U. S. Geological Survey*

Water in the lakes and streams of Indiana is one of our most valuable resources. Where does it come from and where does it go? Is there too much of it or is there too little? Is it friend or is it foe? Perhaps the Hoosier, viewing his home and possessions covered with the slime and mud of a disastrous flood, would count it foe, as would the city fathers rationing water when the town reservoir becomes dangerously low. But surely the fishermen, the farmer irrigating his crops, the dusty little-leaguer quenching his thirst at a drinking fountain — all these and more — would say friend, and they would all be right. For water can be both friend and foe, and there is too much and there is too little.

## Hydrologic Cycle

Water on, under, and over the surface of Indiana is but a small fraction of the total amount of water in our world. Throughout the world this total remains almost constant. There is the same quantity here today as there was at the beginning of geologic time. Some of it is frozen in polar ice caps; some is in the oceans, rivers and lakes; some is stored in the ground; and some is held as vapor in the atmosphere.

Much of it moves in a never ending journey known as the hydrologic cycle. Water is evaporated from the ocean and carried over land by the winds. Here it condenses and falls to earth as rain or snow. Part of this is evaporated back to the atmosphere, part soaks into the ground, and part is used by trees and plants. The rest returns eventually to the sea through rivers and streams to start yet another journey through the cycle.

This cycle moves at a varying pace. One drop of water may return to the ocean in minutes as a rainshower directly on the sea. Another may fall in torrential rain and return through swollen rivers in a matter of days or weeks. Another may

*Approved for publication by the Director, U. S. Geological Survey

soak into the ground and travel through sands and gravels for years in its journey back to the ocean. Yet another may fall as a snowflake on polar ice caps and remain in frozen storage for centuries of time.

But the important thing is that the water does move and thus man's supply is constantly replenished.

### The Drainage System

Rain and snow falling on Indiana literally flow in all directions. The mighty Wabash River drains water from about two-thirds of the state, and flows generally south into the Ohio River. The Kankakee and its tributaries flow westward into Illinois and to the Mississippi through the Illinois River. The Maumee River, formed by the confluence of the St. Joseph and St. Marys Rivers, drains to the east through Ohio into Lake Erie.

The rivers, streams, ditches, and lakes forming the drainage system of Indiana are shown in Figure 21. The system has not always looked like this. Countless storms millions of years ago carved river valleys in the bedrock surface. Glaciers advancing and retreating filled old valleys, cut new channels, created lakes, and changed the face of the land. Following the glaciers, floods through thousands of years eroded river banks, changed location of channels, and created new waterways. Every drop of rain that falls changes infinitesimally the face of Indiana.

### Water in the System

#### *The Streams*

Rainfall is the primary source of all surface water in Indiana. The sullen drizzle on a gray winter's day, the torrential downpour from a spring thunderstorm, the gentle shower sweeping by on a hot summer's day — all these combine to constantly renew our water resources. Roughly one-third of this rainfall is carried away by the surface drainage system (Fig. 22A and 22B).[3]

The flow or discharge of a river is usually measured in cfs (cubic feet per second). One cfs is equivalent to approximately 450 gpm (gallons per minute) or two-thirds mgd (million gallons per day). Our streams in Indiana carry huge quantities of water (Fig. 23). For example, the average flow in the Wabash River at Mount Carmel, Illinois, is 26,480 cfs.[6] This

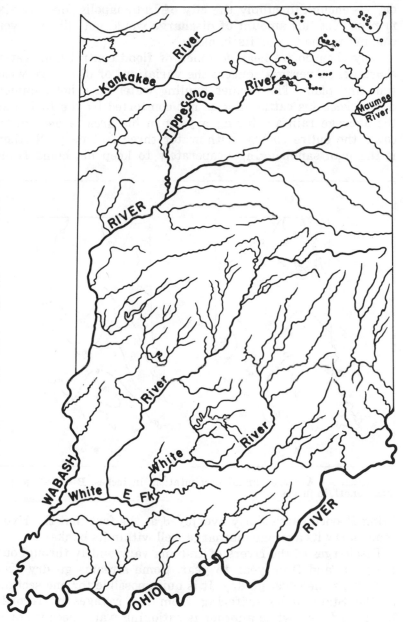

Fig. 21. The stream system in Indiana.

is equivalent to approximately 17,000 million gallons every day — enough to supply the city of Indianapolis for over six months. Yet this amount of discharge would not fill the river channel to the top of its banks.

Why then do we hear so much of flood control and water shortages? Averages conceal the variations of discharge with time and place. The farmer hauling water on a hot summer day to keep his cattle alive is not comforted by the fact that the average rainfall during a year in his area is enough to cover the entire county with water three feet deep. Neither is the man sandbagging desperately to keep his home from

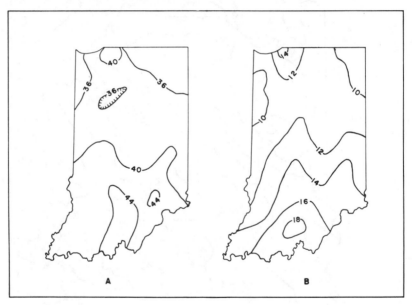

Fig. 22. A—Average annual precipitation, in inches. B—Average annual runoff, in inches.

being flooded particularly overjoyed at the fact that the river could carry its average discharge well within its banks.

Discharges of the rivers of Indiana vary widely throughout the year, and from year to year. Some streams go dry frequently; some never go dry. It is quite possible for one section of the State to be suffering from the ravages of record-breaking floods while another is rationing water because of a severe drought. In 1964, 23 counties in southern Indiana were declared disaster areas by the Federal government twice in

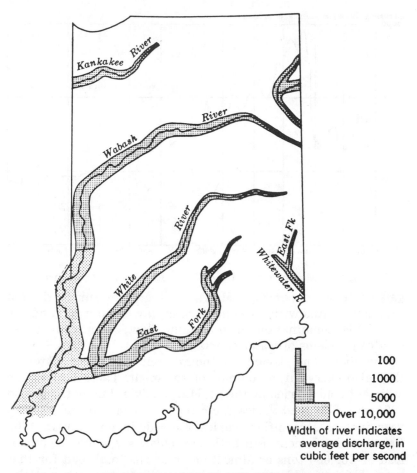

AVERAGE DISCHARGE OF THE PRINCIPAL RIVERS

Fig. 23. Average discharge of the principal rivers.

one year — once because of devastating flood damages and once because of a crippling drought. Figure 24 shows the variation in discharge of the White River near Petersburg during 1963. The higher discharges usually occur in the late winter and spring. At Petersburg over 75 percent of the total discharge in 1963 occurred in March and April.[6] Although floods can occur in any month in Indiana, it is unusual for severe floods to occur during the summer and fall. Usually this is the time of minimum flows. It is also the time of maximum use of water. Growing crops need huge quantities of water. For example, a single acre of corn transpires more than 3,000

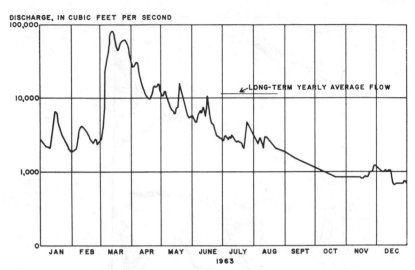

DISCHARGE, IN CUBIC FEET PER SECOND

Fig. 24. Variation of streamflow, White River near Petersburg, 1963.

gallons of water per day.[1] Man's use increases during the hot summer months with air-conditioning, lawn-watering, and the like. This combination of minimum flow — maximum use creates problems of water shortages.

The rivers and streams of Indiana not only carry water — they also carry large volumes of sediment. Table 1 gives the sediment load carried by the St. Marys River during the period 1954-63.[7] This load varies from season to season and year to year just as streamflow varies. Indeed, in one day in 1962 Raccoon Creek near Fincastle carried a suspended sediment load of 260,000 tons or almost one-half the total load for that year. This valuable top soil being carried away often settles in lakes and reservoirs, taking up space better used for the storage of water.

## Lakes and Reservoirs

The lakes and reservoirs of Indiana form a very important part of the water system. Although only a small portion of Lake Michigan is within the boundaries of Indiana, the industrial complex centered around the Gary-Hammond area depend upon it for their water supply. The lake counties of northeastern Indiana attract thousands of visitors each year. Flood control reservoirs dotting the state not only give protection from high waters but also offer recreation to a water-loving people.

TABLE 1. Suspended sediment, in tons, carried by
St. Marys River near Fort Wayne.

| Year | Total Suspended Sediment | Maximum daily load | Minimum daily load |
|---|---|---|---|
| 1954 | 78,816 | 3,980 | <0.5 |
| 1955 | 165,665 | 18,600 | <0.5 |
| 1956 | 157,243 | 26,000 | <0.5 |
| 1957 | 240,999 | 12,000 | <0.5 |
| 1958 | 154,533 | 10,900 | <0.5 |
| 1959 | 289,284 | 30,800 | 2 |
| 1960 | 107,056 | 9,540 | <0.5 |
| 1961 | 82,167 | 8,500 | <0.5 |
| 1962 | 90,021 | 8,610 | <0.5 |
| 1963 | 87,664 | 12,000 | <0.5 |

Most of the large cities in Indiana depend on storage in reservoirs for their water supply. The water system of Indianapolis is a good example. During low flows the streams nearby cannot furnish enough water for the city unless their surplus flow during floods is stored for future use. Two reservoirs serve the city. One is located on Fall Creek and the other on Cicero Creek. Their combined capacity is 13.8 billion gallons of water. When the natural flow of the White River is too low to supply the city, water is released from one or both of the reservoirs to supplement the flow in the river.

Many reservoirs store water for several purposes. Monroe Reservoir on Salt Creek is one of these. This reservoir, which is the largest single body of water within the state, can store over 440,000 acre feet (an acre foot of water will cover one acre a foot deep). Of this capacity, 258,800 acre feet is used to store flood waters and reduce floods downstream on Salt Creek and East Fork White River, and 159,900 acre feet of storage is reserved for use as water supply and to supplement the flow of the river downstream during times of drought. The lake behind the huge dam furnishes relaxation and recreation for thousands of people each year.

One of the interesting features of many of the deeper lakes in the state is the stratification that takes place with temperature changes in the water. During the winter the temperature is nearly uniform throughout the lake. The warm weather of spring increases temperature in the upper layer of water and as summer progresses the variation in temperature between the upper and lower levels of the lake becomes more pronounced. The colder weather of fall reverses the process and by winter the temperature is once more uniform. Figure 25 shows the marked difference in the temperature profile of Pretty Lake

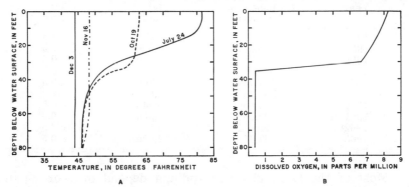

Fig. 25. Typical temperature and dissolved oxygen characteristics of Pretty Lake near Stroh. A—Water temperature profile during the summer and autumn of 1963; B—Relation of oxygen concentration to depth on July 17, 1963.

near Stroh during the summer and fall of 1963.[2] Since the density of water varies with temperature, the cool water at the bottom is heavier than the warmer water at the top. The marked difference in temperature between the upper layer and bottom layer forms a density barrier between the two. Because of this barrier the water in the two layers is quite different chemically. Figure 5B, showing the sharp decline in dissolved oxygen, illustrates this difference.

A tremendous volume of water is stored in our lakes and reservoirs. The natural lakes alone store more than 240,000 million gallons.

## Use

Water is used in everything man does. For example, 7,500 gallons of water are used in the manufacture of each automobile, 500 gallons to process each gallon of gasoline, 65,000 gallons to produce a ton of steel, and 90,000 gallons of water to manufacture one ton of paper board.[5] The estimated total surface water withdrawn in the state in 1960 was 5,400 mgd. Very little of this was actually consumed and much of it was used several times. For example, approximately three-fifths of the total water withdrawn was used in the generation of electrical power and was returned to the streams unchanged except in temperature.[4]

Our use of water has increased by leaps and bounds in recent years. As more and more homes are equipped with such water-using appliances as washing machines, dishwashers, and air-conditioners our individual use of water goes up and up. The public water supplies of Indiana in 1960 furnished an average of 126 gallons of water for each person every day.[4]

## Management

There are water problems in Indiana — many of them. We have floods and we have droughts. Some of our cities have reached the limit of their growth without seeking additional water. There are conflicts of interest. Some would like to see our rivers return to conditions that existed 150 years ago when presumably waters ran crystal clear and teemed with fish. Others see our stream system as natural drains for industrial and municipal wastes.

Are these insurmountable problems? They most certainly are not. But the solution depends on proper management. Proper management in turn means consideration of the needs and desires of all the people and consideration of the source and quantity of all the water, both surface and ground.

We can build reservoirs to control our floods and store water for use during times of scarcity. We can treat our water and use it over and over again before it finally leaves the State. In places we can supplement the flow of our rivers when needed by pumping from ground water storage and replenishing this storage during times of surplus rainfall and river flow.

In the total, Indiana has no shortage of water. With good management and careful planning there can be plenty of water for everyone wherever we want it and whenever we want it.

## LITERATURE

1. CALLAHAN, J. T., L. E. NEWCOMB and J. W. GEURIN, 1965. Water in Georgia. U. S. Geological Survey Water-Supply Paper **1762**: 5.
2. FICKE, JOHN F. 1965. Seasonal erasure of thermal stratification in Pretty Lake, Indiana. U. S. Geological Survey Professional Paper **525**-C: C199- C202.
3. HOGGATT, RICHARD E. 1962. Low-flow characteristics of Indiana streams. Indiana Pollution Control Board: 8,9.
4. MACKICHAN, K. A. and J. C. KAMMERER. Estimated use of water in the United States, 1960. U. S. Geological Survey Circular **456**: 5,26.
5. _____. 1956. Indiana water resources. Indiana Water Resources Study Committee: 25.
6. _____. 1963-64. Surface water records of Indiana. U. S. Geological Survey Basic Data Release.
7. _____. 1964. Water quality records in Indiana and Illinois. U. S. Geological Survey Basic Data Release.

# 6
## *Ground Water*

CHARLES H. BECHERT AND JOHN M. HECKARD
Division of Water, Indiana Department of Natural Resources

### What is Ground Water?

Ground water, as differentiated from surface water, is water that percolates or flows beneath the surface of the earth. The legal definition, as stated in Indiana's water law is, "all water filling the material openings under the earth's surface, including all underground streams, artesian basins, reservoirs, lakes and other bodies of water below the earth's surface."

Ground water is so closely related to surface water that it is often difficult to separate one from the other clearly. For instance, water flowing underground and discharging from a spring or into a stream is ground water while below the ground surface, but immediately becomes surface water as soon as it reaches the surface. The reverse is true when water flowing overland or in a stream finds its way into the underlying ground-water formations.

### Origin

As precipitation falls on the earth, one of three things happens to it: it runs off the land surface to rivers and streams, it is evaporated or transpired by plants, or it soaks through the ground and becomes ground water (Fig. 26). Eight to twenty per cent of Indiana's total annual precipitation (39.7") runs off the surface directly into our streams and eventually reaches the Atlantic Ocean, except for that which evaporates on its way. About 2/3 is lost by evaporation and transpiration, and the remaining 8 to 16% finds its way into the ground. That water which enters the ground also moves to lower elevations, but at a much slower rate. Upon entering the ground, this water percolates downward through the zone of aeration until it reaches the water table, or the zone of saturation. Here, under normal conditions, this ground water moves laterally through the earth to points of lower elevation and eventually to areas of ground-water discharge such as springs, rivers, and lakes. It thus leaves its habitat in the ground, and becomes surface water, where it ultimately will be evaporated back into the atmosphere.

This phenomenon is called the hydrologic or water cycle. During this cycle the water may be found in the ground, in streams, in plants, in food, and indeed, in almost everything, but it is always in the process of moving through the hydrologic cycle. The water we are using today is the same water that existed since the beginning of time.

## Mode of Occurrence

Ground water, by definition, occurs underground. It occupies the pore spaces and openings within the rock formations that make up the earth. Nearly all rock types, whether a compact shale or a loose sand, have porosity. The amount, size and distribution of pore spaces can range widely. In many rock types in Indiana, porosity accounts for about 20% of the total rock volume. This means that if the pore spaces could be filled with water, one cubic foot of water (7½ gallons) could be added to a piece of rock having a volume of five cubic feet.

There are no such things as underground lakes, and very few underground rivers. Nearly all underground rivers, such as Lost River, are found in the south-central part of the state and are the result of channels being formed in the rock by water flowing through it and dissolving the calcium in the rock.

Because it is impossible to see ground water in its native habitat, many erroneous ideas have been advanced about its behavior. However, ground water obeys the very same set of physical laws that surface water obeys. One of the most obvious facts about surface water is that it moves from one elevation to a lower elevation or flows downhill. The same is true for ground water. Equally obvious is that ground water cannot move uphill.

As water falling on the earth soaks into the soil, it percolates through the zone of aeration (Fig. 26). Its movement through this zone is essentially straight downward. The rate of movement is controlled to a large degree by the type of soil —it moves slowly through a clayey soil, and much faster through a sandy soil. It continues downward until it encounters the water table, or the top of the zone of saturation. This may be a distinct horizon, or it may be a gradational zone. Once in the zone of saturation, this water begins to move slowly through the water-bearing formation, called an aquifer.

Ground-water movement is seldom uniform in direction or

in velocity. Permeability of the aquifer, which in part determines the rate of movement, may vary greatly from place to place, even within short distances. Unlike surface water, movement of ground water is usually quite slow. In Indiana the rate of ground water movement is expressed in inches or feet per day. Velocities in the order of five feet per year to five feet per day are probably typical.

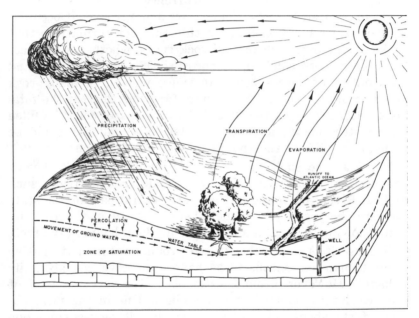

Fig. 26. The hydrologic cycle.

Figure 26 illustrates how water moves naturally through an aquifer. Under natural conditions, this water will "spill out" onto the earth's surface through a spring or into a lake or stream.

Ground water can be induced to move through the aquifer by discharge through a well. Withdrawal through the well has the effect of lowering the water level in the vicinity of the well, thus increasing the hydraulic gradient, causing the water in the aquifer to move toward the well at a higher velocity. This lowering, since it occurs in all directions around the well, is called a cone of depression. The size and shape of this cone is dependent upon the rate of well discharge, the permeability of the aquifer, and recharge to the aquifer.

## Recharge

A ground-water aquifer or reservoir may be likened to a bank vault. Just as the bank is a safe depository for large sums of money, an aquifer is capable of storing large volumes of water. Each may be tapped for withdrawal, and each must be replenished from time to time. This replenishment to an aquifer is called recharge.

There are two types of recharge, natural and artificial. Natural recharge occurs as precipitation falls on the earth and soaks into the ground. It also occurs when leakage from lakes and streams infiltrates the ground-water aquifer.

Artificial, or induced recharge, is defined as the process of replenishment of ground water through a works primarily designed for that purpose. Although no two projects are identical, all have the intent of inducing more surface water to enter the ground-water aquifer. This may be done through the use of pits, ditches, basins or stream beds which allow water to "leak" into the ground. Injection wells may also be used, into which water is pumped to the aquifer through wells.

There are several installations of this kind in Indiana although artificial recharge is not practiced to any large extent because the need for it has not arisen to date. At Anderson, a dam was constructed across Killbuck Creek for the sole purpose of impounding water behind it in order that it could seep into the ground and recharge the city's wells. Christiana Creek was rerouted through Elkhart's well field for the purpose of recharging that city's water wells. A pharmaceutical company in the northern part of the state discharges cooling water from its air conditioning equipment into a nearby pond, thereby recharging the aquifer from which it pumps water. While not designed as such, several cities and industries induce water into their well fields from nearby rivers by pumping large volumes of water and lowering the water table below the river level, thus causing water to flow from the river to their wells.

## Water Levels

Through the years many statements have been made to the effect that the water table in Indiana has dropped to dangerously low levels and that it is only a matter of time until the state will experience severe shortages of ground water. These statements generally have been made by individuals who had little knowledge of the facts or who knew little about the subject of ground water.

It is true that ground water levels have dropped in various parts of the state during the past century but this has occurred where man has either made changes in the surface of the land to accelerate the run off of surface water or by withdrawing water from the ground through wells. This has not necessarily been harmful, however, because ground-water levels often must be lowered to fully utilize the water resources that are available in a given area.

The water level in a well or aquifer is nearly always changing in response to the effects of natural and artificial influences. Water levels may be affected by precipitation, recharge from lakes and streams, by losses due to evaporation and transpiration, pumpage from wells, and by minor factors such as earthquakes, changes in barometric pressure, ocean tides, earth tides, etc. The potential effects of these factors must be considered in making an intelligent interpretation of water levels.

In order to determine the effects of these phenomena and to measure the long-term changes in water levels, or the water table as it is often called, a number of water-level observation wells have been established. The program, which started in 1935 with 46 wells, has grown to 145 wells.

It is the long-term trend of the ground-water levels as recorded by these observation wells that is important. This long-term trend is a function of the balance between recharge to the underground reservoir and discharge from it. In a situation where precipitation is above normal and discharge is minimal, water levels would be expected to rise. If, on the other hand, drought conditions exist and discharge is rather high, water levels would become lower.

Water levels in Indiana have fluctuated considerably since the first observations in 1935, but in no instance has there been any indication that water is being mined or that ground-water levels have continued on a downward trend since the first observations were made.

In a typical hydrograph of an observation well that is not affected by pumpage, the change in water level with time responds to changing conditions of recharge and discharge. In general, the water level rises in the spring when recharge is high due to thawing of the ground and heavy precipitation, and falls in the summer and autumn when evaporation and transpiration losses are high and rainfall is low. Both in that situation, and in a typical hydrograph of an observation well that is affected by nearby pumpage, there is essentially no overall lowering of the water level or water table from one normal year to another.

It is the long term trend of water levels in all the observation wells that is significant. As long as the water levels do not decline year after year there is no need for concern that water is being used at a rate greater than Mother Nature is replenishing it.

In addition to this value of water levels they are useful in determining the hydraulic characteristics of a given aquifer and its potential as a source of water.

### Springs and Flowing Wells

A spring is a concentrated discharge of ground water appearing at the ground surface as a current of flowing water. Seepage areas, as distinguished from springs, indicate a slower movement of water which may pond or evaporate as it emerges from the ground. There are many springs in Indiana, but the majority of them are found in the southern part of the state where water-filled caves and crevices in the rock come to the surface in the form of a "rise". Water in these cavities then issues forth as a spring. The largest spring in the state, Harrison Spring near Corydon, is of this type. A maximum discharge of 250,000 gallons per minute has been measured from this spring. Fifteen large springs in Indiana are listed in Table 2.

Most springs fluctuate in their rate of discharge in response to variations in the rate of recharge. Perennial springs discharge throughout the year while intermittent springs discharge only during portions of the year when sufficient ground water is recharged to maintain flow. Because of the variable flow of springs and the possibility of their being contaminated, they generally are not recommended for use as a water supply.

Flowing wells occur where ground water is confined at a pressure in excess of atmospheric pressure. Flowing wells are found in many counties, most of which are located in northern

TABLE 2. Minimum recorded flow of springs in 1960.

| NAME | COUNTY | MINIMUM FLOW |
|---|---|---|
| Harrison | Harrison | 12,375 gpm |
| Orangeville Rise | Orange | 2,848 gpm |
| Rise of Lost River | Orange | 2,745 gpm |
| Radcliff Springs | Washington | 2,745 gpm |
| Frank | Harrison | 1,600 gpm |
| Hunter | Washington | 1,552 gpm |
| Van Cleave | Orange | 1,237 gpm |
| Hamers Cave | Lawrence | 1,125 gpm |
| Blue Spring | Lawrence | 1,035 gpm |
| Avoca | Lawrence | 900 gpm |
| Craven's | Washington | 675 gpm |
| Organ Springs | Washington | 562 gpm |
| Marengo | Crawford | 450 gpm |
| Big Spring | Washington | 450 gpm |
| Beck's Mill | Washington | 450 gpm |

Indiana. These wells, when not put to beneficial use, constitute an unnecessary drain on the ground-water resources of the surrounding area. Artesian wells are the same as flowing wells except that the water level does not rise sufficiently high to flow. Contrary to popular belief, not all artesian wells produce mineralized water.

## Availability

In general, Indiana is blessed with a bountiful supply of ground water. With the exception of portions of southern Indiana, ground water may be depended upon to furnish an adequate supply of water for much of our populace. It is estimated that nearly one hundred thousand billion gallons of ground water are in reserve storage. This, plus the annual recharge from precipitation, if properly developed, can provide us with a dependable source of water to help meet our future needs.

Figure 27 is a generalized map showing the availability of ground water in Indiana. Four major ground-water provinces are defined.

In this report availability of ground water is defined as the average maximum amount of water that normally may be obtained from the water-bearing formations underlying a given area from a well which is properly sized and developed. The potential yield from this well will depend upon the geology of the area and the amount of recharge to the area. Because either or both of these conditions can vary with time or loca-

tion, it can be seen that this estimated yield is an approximation of the potential of the area based on several types of
available geologic and hydrologic data.

## Quality

In recent years it has been recognized that the quality of
ground water is nearly as important as the quantity. This is
particularly true of water used by industry because of the
effect certain minerals in the water may have on the product
being produced.

The quality of ground water varies considerably in various
parts of the state, but in general it is satisfactory for most
domestic and industrial uses. However, much of the ground
water has a relatively high iron and manganese content, and
a good percentage of it is considered as hard. This is borne
out by the fact that of the 350 public water supplies using
ground water and serving 39% of the state's population, 113
have facilities for removing the iron and manganese. There
are ten cities that soften their ground-water supplies and one
of the reasons that more do not is the expense involved in
softening it. Some individuals using city water as well as
those having individual wells, however, soften their water.

The U. S. Public Health Standards for drinking water limit
the iron and manganese content to 0.3 parts per million. No
standards for hardness have been established but generally
water containing 0 to 60 parts per million of hardness is considered soft; 61 to 120 ppm as moderately hard; 120-200 ppm
as hard and more than 200 ppm as very hard. It is not possible
to give an average figure of the iron and manganese content
of the ground waters of the state nor the average hardness
because of the wide variation in these qualities depending on
the location and depth of the well from which the water
is obtained. The iron and manganese content will vary from
zero as much as 20 ppm and the hardness from a few parts
per million to 1300 ppm.

Ground water contains other minerals such as chlorides,
nitrates, sulphates, carbonates, etc. In water obtained from
depths not exceeding 250 to 300 feet below the land surface,
the percentage of these minerals is generally below the standards established by the U. S. Public Health Service.

Table 3 contains representative chemical analyses of ground

waters found the various ground-water provinces outlined in Figure 27.

## Temperature

Although the temperature of ground water varies only slightly under natural conditions, it may change due to man-made influences such as returning cooling-water to the ground or recharging the ground surface water. Because of its rather constant low temperature, ground water is widely used for air-conditioning and cooling purposes. The low temperature is often one of the major considerations in the use of ground water by industry.

Fig. 27. Availability of ground water in Indiana. (Numbers refer to provinces designated on map.) (1) Wells with yield of several hundred gallons per minute can be developed in this area in the underlying sand or gravel formations; the wells generally are less than 100 feet deep. Most aquifers are hydraulically connected to a major stream and receive recharge from this stream. Yields as high as 2,000 gallons per minute have been reported, and there are more than 200 known wells each having production rated in excess of one million gallons per day. (2a) Water-bearing glacial drift attains thicknesses of 300 to 400 feet in much of this area. Wells are completed in sand or gravel forma-tions within the drift. Well depths range from less than fifty feet to more than 400 feet. Yields as high as 1,000 gallons per minute have been reported. (2b) Most wells are completed in glacial drift, although some penetrate bedrock. Well yields of several hundred gallons per minute have been reported in many instances. Depths of wells range from fifty to 400 feet, with an average depth of about 150 feet. (2c) The glacial drift is relatively thin in this area and most wells are completed in the underlying limestone. Yields of 300 to 500 gallons per minute are obtainable, and well depths range from 50 to 400 feet. As a rule of thumb, most large capacity wells are deep, while domestic wells are not. (3) In general, adequate supplies from wells can be obtained for domestic and light industrial uses ranging from 10 to 100 gallons per minute. Conditions exist locally where larger yields can be obtained, and also where minimal yields are reported. The glacial drift is relatively thin, and the underlying bedrock is not too productive. (4a) Most wells are completed in sandstone, although some are finished in coal or limestone. Wells are generally rated at less than 20 gallons per minute, and numerous wells have been abandoned due to insufficient water. Depths of wells range up to 400 feet, but average somewhat less than 200 feet. (4b) Due to the lack of water-bearing materials above the bedrock wells are completed in limestone. Because of the heterogeneous nature of the rock, erratic ground-water conditions exist. Although the average yield of water wells is about five gallons per minute, yields as high as 30 gpm have been reported. Springs are common in many parts of this area. (4c) With the exception of dug wells, wells are completed in shale and limestone. Because most wells are "seep" wells, diameters are greater than 8" in order to provide water storage in the well. The average yield of wells is probably less than two gallons per minute. Cisterns and dug wells are common.

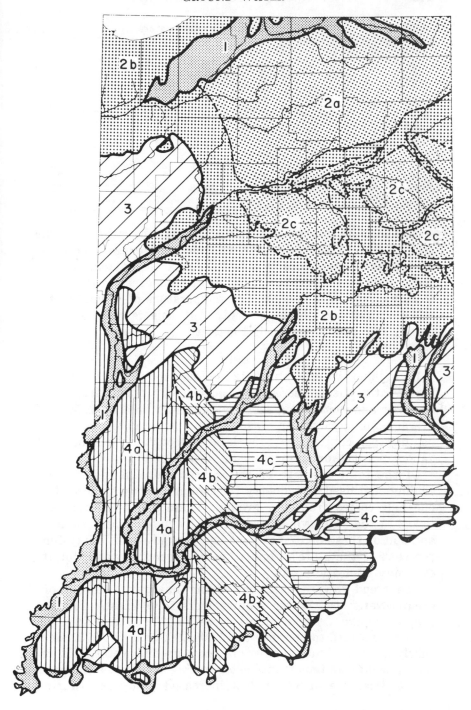

TABLE 3. Analysis of ground waters.

| Province | Hardness | Calcium | Magnesium | Sodium | Iron | Chloride | Sulfate |
|---|---|---|---|---|---|---|---|
| 1 | 339 | 90 | 24 | 14 | 2.0 | 16 | 79 |
| 2a | 294 | 74 | 26 | 10 | 1.3 | 3 | 20 |
| 2b | 274 | 61 | 23 | 42 | 1.1 | 20 | 31 |
| 2c | 425 | 107 | 38 | 27 | .8 | 7 | 218 |
| c | 375 | 92 | 37 | 24 | 2.0 | 6 | 103 |
| 4a | 168 | 40 | 26 | 213 | 2.8 | 60 | 33 |
| 4b | 410 | 92 | 50 | 39 | .6 | 23 | 253 |
| 4c | 289 | | | 39 | .5 | 49 | 95 |

Although there are exceptions, it may be said that the temperature of ground water will generally exceed the average annual temperature by 2 to 3 degrees. In Indiana, ground-water temperatures range from about 52 degrees in the north to 58 degrees in the south. The temperature of ground water will increase slightly with depth but this is only approximately one degree for each 100 feet.

### Uses

In Indiana, we use about 12 billion gallons of water each day. Water use is increasing because our population is increasing and demnadnig more water (Fig. 28). In 1950, the average municipal water consumption amounted to 120 gallons per day per capita; for 1750 is is expected to be about 174 gallons per day, or an increase of 45 per cent.

Of the total quantity of water used daily in Indiana, excluding that used by industry for cooling purposes, more than one half comes from the ground. There are 403 cities and towns in the state which are served by public water supplies and 350 of these or 87 per cent use ground-water. Sixty-four per cent of the state's population uses ground water for its everyday domestic needs.

The trend toward suburban living has resulted in more ground-water use. Water requirements for domestic supplies (not on public water system) were 75,000,000 gpd in 1954, and are expected to increase to 148,000,000 gpd by 1975. Since nearly all individual supplies are from ground water, this resource will be an important factor in this anticipated increase.

Industrial use of water has increased many fold during

the past decade or two as has domestic and other uses. New manufacturing processes requiring large volumes of water together with the rapid growth of the steel industry and the building of larger and larger steam generating plants, both of which require vast quantities of cooling water, is the reason for this rapid rise in water use. Most of this water comes from Lake Michigan, the Ohio and Wabash Rivers since it is used primarily for cooling purposes and does not have to meet rigid quality standards. However, many industrial concerns must have water of high quality, and in some cases of low temperatures, and consequently use ground water if it is available. Presently, industry in Indiana is using approximately 2.6 billion gallons of water per day of which about 175 million gallons is ground water.

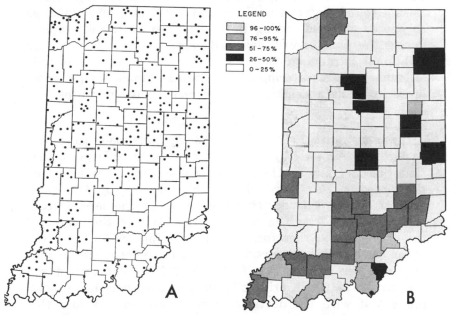

Fig. 28. A—Location of public water supplies obtaining water from a ground-water source. B—Percentage of population by county that uses ground water.

Ground water is an important source of water for irrigation. While rainfall throughout the state is generally sufficient during the growing season to produce good crops, there are years that this is not always true. In such instances, farmers have resorted to supplying supplemental irrigation. Both surface and ground waters have been used for this purpose and during the drought years of 1953 and 1954 about 325 million gallons of water was used daily for this purpose. Slightly less than half of this water came from the ground. Irrigation facilities have expanded since that time, but the use of water for this purpose has not increased as much as other uses because of more favorable rainfall conditions.

There are many other uses being made of ground water in addition to those already mentioned, and while the amounts being used for these purposes are considerably less, they are important in the overall development and production of this resource. Potable ground water is being used to a considerable extent in some parts of the state to increase the production of oil by injecting the water into oil-bearing formations. Ground water is used for heating homes and buildings as well as air conditioning them. This use has grown rapidly during the past several years. Recreation is also placing an additional burden on the use of ground water for private swimming pools, watering golf courses and maintaining water levels in ponds and lakes used for recreational purposes.

### Ground Water Rights

It was not until 1947 that any attempt was made to control or regulate the use of ground water by statute. Prior to that time the only law on the subject was common law based on the "English rule", brought to this country by the early settlers. Under this doctrine the owner of the land is considered to own from the center of the earth to the center of the heavens, and therefore has the absolute right to all the water beneath his property. Because of the inequities resulting from the application of the English rule, many of the eastern states which originally adopted that rule have today replaced it with the doctrine of reasonable use. Under this doctrine, withdrawals of ground water may be limited on a reasonable use basis. Litigation over the use of ground water in Indiana has been limited and because of this fact it is difficult to determine the state's position on this matter, although it is generally considered by some authorities to favor the reasonable use theory.

In 1947 the General Assembly passed its first law attempting to regulate the use of ground water by legislative action. This law made it unlawful for anyone to remove more than two hundred gallons per minute from the ground and use it for air conditioning or cooling of air, unless the water was circulated through cooling towers or other devices, returned to the ground through recharge wells, or a permit obtained as provided in the law.

The above law was repealed in 1951 and a more comprehensive ground-water law was passed to replace it. This new law was designed to conserve and protect the ground-water resources of the State, to prevent their loss and waste and to limit and allocate the use of ground waters in all areas of the state where it is found that their use may impair or exhaust the supply or render it unfit for use.

In 1957 a law was passed which provides authority to prevent the waste of water from flowing wells. It also provided a means of protecting the supply of potable ground water from being exhausted or depleted in areas where such waters are being used to pressure oil-bearing formations to increase oil production.

Still a further step in the regulation and control of ground waters was taken when the 1955 Water Resources Law was amended in 1959 to include ground water. This law states that the general welfare of the people of Indiana requires that the water resources of the state be put to beneficial use to their fullest extent and the use of water for non-beneficial use be prevented. It also states that the water resources are public waters and subject to control and regulation for the public welfare as hereafter determined by the General Assembly.

A more recent law pertaining to the ground waters of the state is the 1961 law which requires all water well drilling contractors to be licensed and to keep a complete record of every water well that is drilled and to file such record with the state.

As the need for ground water rises, undoubtedly there will be need for further legislation to assure the proper development and use of this vital resource. Looking forward to this need, the legislature in 1961 created a Water Resources Study Committee to study water rights, resources and management. This is a continuing committee, and wisely so, because the problems that lie ahead in clearly defining and establishing the rights of individuals and others in the use and development of the state's ground waters and in guiding the General Assembly in the enactment of legislation that may be needed to insure the orderly development and management of this resource are extremely complex and will require much thought and deliberation.

### Ground Water Program

Many early annual reports by the Indiana Geological Survey and the Department of Geology and Natural Resources contained reports on wells, springs, mineral waters and other aspects of the ground-water resources in various parts of the state. In more recent years, similar reports were published by the Division of Geology, Department of Conservation and in 1935 that Division published a report on Ground Water in Indiana. However, it was not in 1943 that the state had a formal program directed toward a state-wide study or investigation of its ground-water resources. At that time, the legislature passed a law authorizing the Department of Conservation to conduct an investigation and measurement of both the surface and ground waters of Indiana and appropriated funds for that purpose. It also authorized the Department to cooperate with the United States Geological Survey and other agencies in making this study.

The program has grown steadily since that time and a vast store of basic data needed to appraise and evaluate our ground-water resources has been accumulated. About 80,000 logs of water wells have been collected, and a network of 145 observation wells to obtain data on the fluctuation of ground-water levels throughout the state have been operated and maintained since 1935. Numerous aquifer-performance tests have been conducted to determine the hydraulic characteristic of different types of water-bearing formations at various locations. Detailed investigations have been made of the ground-water resources of 28 counties and reports of these studies have been published or are in the process of being published. These reports contain information on water levels, water quality, water sources, well records and the availability of water in the various water-bearing formations within each county.

Recently a program has been initiated to prepare and publish colored county maps showing the availability of ground water in the county. These maps will also contain information on water quality, water usage, geology and geography, climate and population.

Another part of the overall program is to make investigations of local problems throughout the state. These are made primarily to assist individuals, industrial concerns, cities and towns and others in solving their ground-water problems. Such diverse projects as deep-well waste disposal and oil-field water flooding with potable ground water are included in these surveys.

## Future

Quantitative studies are underway to determine how much ground water is available for use. Our increasing population is demanding more water, and because of contamination and the limited number of reservoir sites in our state, ground water affords the most dependable and the safest source of water. Since it is not vulnerable to radioactive fallout, it would play an important role in the event of a nuclear disaster. With new methods of water treatment, the vast supply of deep mineralized water (estimated to be greater than the reserve of potable water) may become a new source of supply. In addition to this potential supply there are still large quantities of untapped potable ground water that need only to be located and developed. In a world so acutely dependent upon water, we cannot afford to overlook this vital resource, our most dependable source of water.

### LITERATURE

1. BENNISON, E. W. 1947. Ground water, its development, uses and conservation, Edward C. Johnson, Inc.
2. Bulletin #SE 10, 1960. Data on Indiana Public Water Supplies, Indiana State Board of Health.
3. Ground Water Bulletins No. 7 through 27. Indiana Department of Conservation, U. S. Geological Survey.
4. Indiana Water Resources, Report by Indiana Water Resources Committee, 1956.
5. 1955 Yearbook on Water, U. S. Department of Agriculture.
6. POWELL, R. L. 1961. A geography of the springs of Indiana. Unpublished Master's thesis, Indiana University.
7. TODD, D. K. 1959. Ground water hydrology. John Wiley & Sons.
8. U. S. Geological Survey Circular 456.

*7*

# Caves

## Speleology and Karst Hydrology

RICHARD L. POWELL
Indiana Geological Survey*

### Introduction

Tales of endless caverns and of rivers swallowed by the earth were part of the earliest folklore of southern Indiana. Features now well known, such as Wyandotte Cave, were reported in somewhat exaggerated accounts by early visitors. Wyandotte Cave was a source of nitrate for gunpowder during the War of 1812, and nearby Harrison Spring, the largest in Indiana, was the site of a water mill owned by William Henry Harrison, the first territorial governor of Indiana. As of the present date, about 700 caves have been discovered in southern Indiana, and several sinking streams have been traced to their outlets from subterranean passages. The caves and associated karst features of Indiana have become known throughout the world. The longest mapped cave in Indiana, Blue Springs Cave in Lawrence County, is the fifth longest cavern in the United States and the eighth longest in the world.

### Cave and Karst Areas

Caverns, subterranean drainage, and associated karst features, such as sinking streams, sinkholes, and cave springs, are common in two areas of south-central Indiana: a glaciated area where limestones of Silurian and Devonian age crop out and a partly glaciated area where limestones of Mississippian age are the surface rocks (Fig. 29). Limestone, which can be dissolved by running water to form caves, underlies much of the bedrock surface of Indiana, but five-sixths of the State, including most of the eastern karst area in Indiana, is veneered with glacial drift which fills or obscures perhaps thousands of caverns formed before the advance of ice sheets. Evidence of these caverns is frequently found in drill holes and quarries.

There are some sinkholes, a few natural bridges, and about 30 known caves in the eastern karst in Indiana (Fig. 30).

*Published with permission of the State Geologist, Indiana Department of Natural Resources, Geological Survey.

The caves are mostly small and only a few have been mapped. The cave streams are tributary to surface streams, primarily the Muscatatuck, East Fork White, and Ohio Rivers, which are westward-flowing meandering streams entrenched into the carbonate strata, which dip to the west (Fig. 31). No sinking streams are known, but water enters the caves through sinkholes and groundwater from the glacial drift rather than from direct surface runoff.

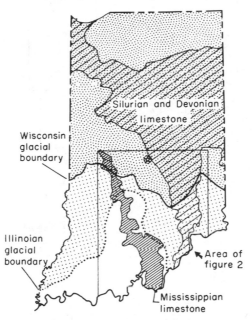

Fig. 29 Map of Indiana showing the areas of limestone bedrock and extent of Pleistocene glaciations.

The major cavern and karst region of Indiana, the area which has gained the attention of most speleological research, is in the south-central nonglaciated part of the State (Fig. 30.)[9] The karst features and most of Indiana's caverns, including the longest and largest ones, have been dissolved in limestones of the Sanders and Blue River Groups of middle Mississippian age. These rocks crop out in a belt extending northward from the Ohio River in Harrison County to northern Putnam County and southward into the cave region of Kentucky. The northern third of the belt of limestone is partly covered with glacial drift which has filled some caves and sinkholes. Some caves, but very few sinkholes, are situated in the thin limestones of the West Baden and Stephensport Groups of late Mississippian age. The rocks of all these groups

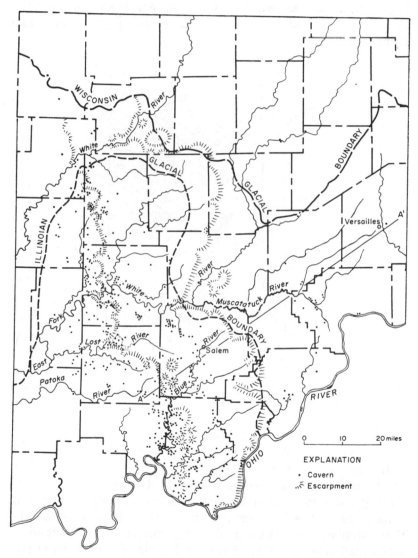

Fig. 30. Map of south-central Indiana showing the location of limestone caverns with respect to major drainage routes. Modified from Powell, 1961.

dip to the southwest at about 30 feet per mile, but local variations of the rate of dip are common (Fig. 31).

## Origin of the Mitchell Plain

The area of outcrop of the Sanders and Blue River Groups
is a westward-sloping sinkhole-pitted surface called the Mitchell Plain.[5] The Mitchell Plain is actually a low limestone plateau crossed by several major deeply entrenched streams:
the Ohio, Blue, East Fork White, and White Rivers. The
surface of the Mitchell Plain on the interfluves is an erosional
and depositional surface beveled before the late Tertiary and
early Pleistocene entrenchment of the surface streams and
development of sinkholes and other karst features. The upper
surface of the plateau is regionally inclined to the west and
locally toward the major streams. The general westward
slope of the Mitchell Plain is not as steep as the dip of limestone bedrock, but the structure of the bedrock has greatly
influenced the development of the surface and the configuration of the drainage routes across and beneath it (Fig. 31).[1]
Cavern development has been primarily down the dip of the
strata along joints in the limestone. The streams that shaped
the surface of the Mitchell Plain during Tertiary time headed
a few miles east of the plain where the slope extends onto
a belt of shales and siltstones of the Borden Group. These
streams, with a few exceptions, had much the same drainage
basins as at present. The sinkholes on the Mitchell Plain were
formed after the streams cut below the level of the adjacent
limestone plateau. Blue Springs Cave in Lawrence County is a
good example (Fig. 32) of cavern development beneath the
Mitchell Plain.

## Development of Karst Features

Although sinkholes and swallow holes are the primary openings through which surface water enters subterranean channels, the bedrock surface is nearly everywhere crisscrossed
with smaller openings developed by solutional widening of
joints.[6] These vertical channels, or grikes, are usually filled
with soil, but they form a subsoil drainage network that is
tributary to an underground solution channel or cave. Some
of the grikes extend into caves where they are seen as loosely
cemented cobbles and gravel in a clay matrix in the ceiling
of the passage. The irregular upward projections of the limestone bedrock are pinnacles or lapies.

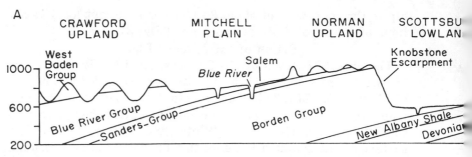

Fig. 31. Generalized geologic cross section showing relationship of physiographic units to bedrock geology. Line of section indicated on Figure 30.

Sinkholes form in places where the descending surface water most rapidly dissolves the bedrock. Some deep sinkholes in bedrock appear to be shallow because they contain large accumulations of soil; others contain ponds because their outlets are plugged. Collapse sinkholes are formed where the roofs of underlying caverns collapse to the surface. A large collapse sinkhole of this type is called a gulf or a uvala. Wesley Chapel Gulf near Lost River in Orange County covers 8 acres.[7] Karst windows, such as those at Twin and Bronson Caves in Spring Mill State Park, are collapse sinkholes opening into a cave passage from above or to the side to expose the upstream and downstream segments of the cave passage.

Solution of the limestone leaves insoluble particles of clay which accumulates in grikes and sinkholes or is washed into cave passages. This insoluble residue is generally termed terra rossa, although such material is yellow or brown as well as red. Large tracts of upland on the Mitchell Plain, generally remote from areas of entrenched surface drainage and cavern development, lack sinkholes and are covered with thick clayey soils. They are at least in part alluvial sediments derived from pre-Pleistocene surface streams which flowed across the upland surface of the Mitchell Plain. The soils include thin beds of chert gravel and cobbles and are overlain by loess of Pleistocene age. The chert was derived from beds near the base of the Sanders Group which cropped out to the east or from lenses near the middle of the Blue River Group. Some of these materials wash into the caves to form sedimentary deposits in the passages.

The relative local relief of the Mitchell Plain is greatest near

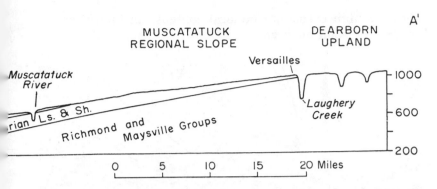

the major streams where it ranges from about 70 feet to as much as 200 feet. Some sinkholes adjacent to the streams are of comparable depth. Away from the major streams the sinkholes are much shallower and local relief is 50 feet per square mile or less in areas underlain by thick soil. The number of deep sinkholes commonly is greater above large caverns (Fig. 32).

## Development of Cave Passages

Acidic water that enters the bedrock through open joints, especially floodwater that fills the underground openings, drops rapidly to the water table and then flows laterally toward a surface outlet. The greater the velocity of the flowing water, the greater the amount of limestone that will be dissolved from the walls of the passage. The passage is enlarged most rapidly during flood periods when the acidic water comes in contact with the walls and ceiling of the solution channel or embryonic cave. The rate of enlargement decreases as the volume of floodwater becomes insufficient to fill the cavern. Climatic changes during the Tertiary and Pleistocene Periods have greatly influenced formation of caves in Indiana. Cold winter precipitation contains more carbon dioxide than warm summer precipitation and is therefore a more active solvent. That solution of the limestone is more effective than mechanical erosion is indicated by the fact that caves are the result of a stream piracy—that is, in limestone terraces many surface streams cannot downcut their channels as rapidly as subterranean channels can be formed beneath them by solution. Such easily eroded layers as thin shale beds project into cave passages as resistant ledges. Analysis of water from

caves shows a high carbonate mineral content, an indication
of the extent of solution involved.

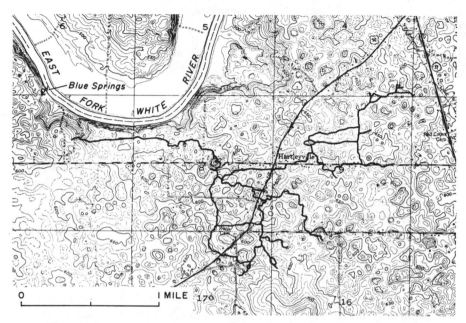

Fig. 32. Topographic map showing relationship of Blue Springs Cave
to sinkholes and local drainage. The passages are developed along joints
in the Salem Limestone, and the sinkholes are formed in the St. Louis
Limestone. Modified from Palmer, 1965.

## Development of Subterranean Drainage

Karst features formed on the upland surface of the Mitchell
Plain as the major streams and their tributaries downcut their
channels in several successive stages during late Tertiary and
early Pleistocene time. Some surface tributaries lost their
streams to interconnected joints which opened into the main
streams at lower elevations. The open joints became enlarged by solution as water continued to flow into them, and
became swallow holes or sinks in the old stream bed. Eventually these sinks took all but flood flows of the stream. These
swallow holes are usually choked with debris and sediments
from floods and generally lie several feet below the level of
the former surface channel or dry bed which carries surplus
floodwaters downstream. Lost River, a sinking stream in
Orange County, has along its dry bed five major swallow

holes, each of which receives the surplus floodwaters from those upstream.[7] Thus, rather than downcutting their channels, the former surface streams of the Mitchell Plain dissolved subterranean drainage routes as tributaries to the lower surface streams. The cavern passages developed headward beneath the former surface tributaries. Some of the cavern passages are developed at different levels and indicate that the downcutting of the surface streams was in progressive stages.

## Caverns formed by Subterranean Stream Piracy

Due west of the Mitchell Plain is the rugged Crawford Upland, a dissected cuesta with an eastward-facing escarpment broken in many places by through-flowing streams.[5] The hills of the upland are underlain by beds of sandstone, shale, and limestone of the West Baden and Stephensport Groups, but the streams along the eastern side have cut into the limestones of the Blue River Group (Fig. 31). Caverns are common along these valleys, especially where they receive underground drainage from the Mitchell Plain to the east. Generally the larger streams of the eastern margin of the Crawford Upland are about 100 feet lower than adjacent areas on the Mitchell Plain. Precipitation on the western part of the Mitchell Plain commonly is diverted westward through caverns trending down the dip of the strata into the surface streams at lower elevations. Many of the caverns have several levels which correlate with stages of downcutting in the valleys of the Crawford Upland. In places the cavern levels are superimposed and the cave passage is a high narrow subterranean canyon. This process of subterranean stream piracy has entirely diverted the headwaters of some ancient streams on the surface of the Mitchell Plain.[2] Sinkholes formed in the ancient valleys while caverns were dissolved beneath them. Similar streamless valleys in the Crawford Upland are situated at about the same level as the Mitchell Plain and are pitted with sinkholes. These karst valleys are a part of the former Tertiary drainage pattern.[11]

## Caverns Formed by Groundwater

The thin dense limestones of the West Baden and Stephensport Groups are commonly overlain by a permeable sandstone and underlain by impermeable shale. The rocks of the Craw-

ford Upland are greatly dissected and most of the outcrops
of the various strata are on hillsides well above the streams
in the deep valleys. Caves in the limestones have been dissolved almost entirely along sets of joints. In general the caves
closely parallel the outcrop of the limestone. Only in a few
places are sinkholes and other karst features found on the surface above the caves.

Precipitation and runoff from the hillside above the sandstone is absorbed and becomes a perched water body above
the limestone.[12] The release of the stored water is toward the
outcrop or into open joints in the underlying limestone. The
rate and volume of water release are controlled by the permeability of the sandstone and the size and location of open
joints in the limestone. The joints are enlarged by solution
in proportion to the amount of water which flows through
them. Thus, those joints that receive the greatest volume of
water enlarge most rapidly and, consequently, release more
water from the sandstone.

The water within the joints in the limestone is also a
perched water body above the underlying impermeable shale.
Discharge of water in the joints or caverns is generally down
the dip of the rock to the outcrop. The cave passages are commonly developed just above the level of the shale and extend
to the overlying sandstone through high narrow fissures or
domes that mark the points at which most groundwater enters
the cave. Speleothems are rare in these caves, apparently because the groundwater entering the passages has not passed
through overlying limestone beds where it could obtain calcium carbonate to carry in solution. Breakdown in the caves
commonly contains sandstone cobbles and boulders. Blocks
of limestone that fall into the cave stream from the ceiling
are dissolved by the flowing water.

### Development of Pits and Domes

Where the local relief and limestone thickness is sufficient,
water that enters the limestone bedrock may drop nearly vertically into a cave passage below. The water flowing down the
walls of the open joints dissolves vertical channels or grooves
which coalesce as they are widened and deepened. Vertical
pits and domes in caves appear to have been formed below
relatively impermeable strata, such as shale or less soluble

limestone beds. The insoluble strata may be overlain by permeable reservoir rock or exposed at the surface. The water above the cap rock flows into a joint which permits its descent to the top of the soluble limestone. The water then either directly penetrates open joints or flows laterally to enter open joints which permit its rapid descent to a lower level. A permeable rock above acts as an infiltration bed and absorbs water which would be lost as surface runoff, only to release it into joints or domes as rapidly as rock permeability and available openings allow. The presence of small waterfalls in some domes indicates that they may be fed by groundwater from overlying rocks and are not dependent entirely on direct precipitation and runoff. Collapse or solution of the roof of a dome may extend to the surface to form a pit or shaft, which may permit entry into cave passages, depending upon the amount of collapsed material or breakdown at the bottom of the pit.

## Cavern Collapse

The process of cavern development by solution creates a potential for collapse of the strata overlying the cavity. The occurrence and magnitude of roof and wall failure are mainly determined by width of the cave passage, closeness of jointing, and thickness and competence of the roof and wall strata. The collapsed material or breakdown is primarily of two types, blocks and slabs. Block breakdown is common in thick beds, whereas slab breakdown is formed by collapse of thin-bedded rock. Block breakdown is generally limited to the walls and lowest ceiling bed, whereas slab breakdown tends to affect numerous beds above the passage. Thin-bedded strata tend to sag above the cave passage and shear off near the walls to form slab breakdown. Each succeeding higher bed is better supported, so that the unsupported sagging layers over a cave passage form a tension dome. Collapse of the sagging layers usually results in a domed roof containing a mountain of breakdown, such as Rothrock's Cathedral and Monument Mountain in Wyandotte Cave. Obviously there are situations and conditions where the types are indistinguishable or mixed, particularly in wide passages where the failure may include numerous beds above the passage.

In some places roof failure extends to the bedrock surface

and forms a collapse sinkhole, karst window, or gulf. Frost action, which does not take place within cave passages, greatly accelerates collapse of the cave roof near the surface. Breakdown formed by mechanical weathering is composed of much small rubble and soil, commonly mixed with block and slab breakdown. These deposits commonly form a steep talus slope in the cave passage where the latter terminates at a hillside, such as the entrance to Wyandotte Cave, or in association with a sinkhole.

## Cave Deposits

Deposits in caves fall into two distinct groups, mechanical sediments and chemical mineral deposits. Mechanical deposits in caves include breakdown and alluvial, colluvial, or lacustrine sediments. The bedrock floors of few Indiana caves are exposed, for most of the caves are partly filled with clays, silts, sand, gravels, and cobbles deposited by the streams which flowed through them. Most of these materials appear to have been washed into the cave and limestone fragments are not dominant, nor common, as a constituent. Limestone that falls into the cave is easily removed by solution. The stream deposits are generally in irregular beds, although silts and clays may also be plastered onto the cave walls. Charcoal layers, perhaps derived from ancient forest fires, and finds of animal bones and plant remains are rare. Evidence from a few caves indicates that several feet of sediments have accumulated owing to erosion and slope wash that have resulted from poor land-use practices during the past 150 years. Most cave deposits, however, are of Tertiary or Pleistocene age. Many of the valleys to which caves are tributary are partly filled with deposits of Pleistocene age. Pleistocene lacustrine clays, including varved clay concretions, were deposited by glacial lakes which backed up into cave passages where contemporaneous sediments were deposited. Colluvial deposits, consisting of soil and rubble, are common in sinkholes that enter cave passages. Breakdown may rest on, be buried by, or be mixed with the sedimentary cave deposits or cavern fill materials.

Most chemical mineral deposits or speleothems in caves are accumulations of calcium carbonate as aragonite or calcite formed owing to a loss of carbon dioxide from calcium bicarbonate laden water that enters the air-filled cave passages.

The ultimate cause of deposition may have been a change in temperature, a loss of hydrostatic pressure, the presence of trace elements or organic agents, or a combination of these. Although most speleothems in Indiana caves are alternately banded calcite and aragonite or calcite pseudomorphs after aragonite, suggesting cyclic deposition, no method has been devised to interpret the deposition of speleothems. The cause of alteration of aragonite to calcite also is unknown. Although comparisons with Tertiary and Pleistocene climatic conditions would be desirable, the complicated mode of origin and unknown rate of growth have hindered any basis for such a study. But the deposition of speleothems is a great aid in the interpretation of the sequence of events in determining the depositional history of a cave, which in turn may be correlated with other known events in geomorphic history. Flowstone layers and stalagmites are in places buried by later mud deposits or suspended from the ceiling or wall where the unconsolidated fill has been eroded from beneath them.

## Indiana's Largest Caves and Cave Streams

When Indiana became a state 150 years ago, Wyandotte Cave was considered the largest cave in the State (Fig. 33). Additional passages discovered in 1851 led to the claim that the cave was the second largest cave in the United States. Although the size of the cave has been exaggerated, it is indeed a large cave.[3] Some of the passages in Wyandotte are the largest in Indiana, including the largest room, Rothrock's Cathedral, which contains Monument Mountain, the largest known pile of breakdown in an Indiana cavern. A remarkable feature of Wyandotte Cave is the dryness of its passages, for very little water or mud is found in them. Wyandotte Cave contains only one very small stream which flows for a very short distance through a side passage. A few seeps account for the other wet places. The stream that dissolved the passages of Wyandotte was probably diverted from Blue River about 2 miles to the northeast.[4] Blue River, then flowing at a much higher level than now, was captured through joints in the limestone. After passing through an underground route that was substantially shorter than the surface route, the stream reentered the lower Blue River valley at a much lower altitude. This large stream, of late Tertiary and early

Pleistocene age, was probably longer than that flowing through the Lost River Cave System in Orange County at the present time. Many of the passages of Wyandotte terminate at hillsides or valleys that postdate cavern development.

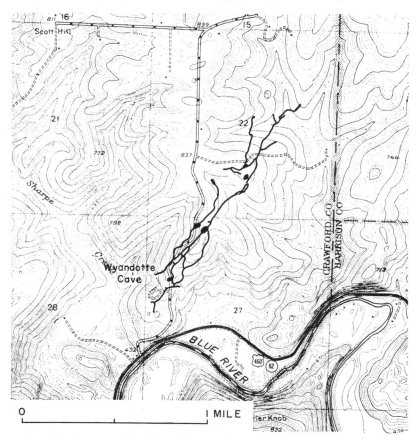

Fig. 33. Topographic map showing the mapped extent of Wyandotte Cave and its relationship to valleys in the Crawford Upland. The passages are developed in the Ste. Genevieve Limestone (Blue River Group). Base from Leavenworth Quadrangle, 1947.

Lost River is in direct contrast to Wyandotte Cave. Most of the passages are small and those that may be entered are wet and muddy.[7] The underground passages of Lost River are several times the length of Wyandotte, but most of them are flooded all of the time and the remainder flood with every light rain in the area. The parts of underground Lost River that may be entered indicate that the subterranean drainage route consists of a series of nearly parallel passages in a general east to west direction over a distance of about 7 miles. The surface channel or dry bed, which carries surplus floodwaters, is about 21 miles long between the uppermost swallow hole and the rise or artesian spring which discharges the cave stream back to the surface. The rise of Lost River, about 1 mile south of Orangeville, is a cave outlet which has been dammed by alluvial and lacustrine sediments of late Pleistocene age.[10] This cavern network was probably open during the late Tertiary when the major surface streams were downcutting their channels. Sinkholes and swallow holes developed simultaneously on the Mitchell Plain.

Blue Springs Cave, on the south side of the East Fork of White River near Bedford (Fig. 32), contains over 12.1 miles of mapped passages on several levels.[8] The downstream exit of the cave stream is a cave spring, but the dam across the East Fork at Williams has backed water up into the passage for a long distance. This cave stream is a small river which requires a boat to traverse the cave passage containing it. Side passages contain smaller streams and some at higher levels are dryer. The passages of this cave are fed entirely by drainage from sinkholes and a few short sinking streams on the overlying Mitchell Plain. Several deep sinkholes lie immediately adjacent to the cave passages, but no dry bed or surface channels are prominent. The cave stream is under heavy hydrostatic pressure when the passages are completely flooded, for water is known to fill some of the surface sinkholes to a level of about 100 feet above the adjacent river level. In spite of the dangers of exploring and surveying this cavern with its subterranean river, plans to map an estimated 5 miles of additional passages have been made.

### Future Studies

Spelunkers and speleologists in Indiana will search for longer and larger caverns, not merely to establish new records of size, but also to better understand how caves are formed and how they are related to local hydrology and geology. Caves will be studied in greater detail with respect to their geochemistry, meteorology, and biology to determine their effect on water supply, pollution, and engineering problems. Speleology is expanding from a field of casual interest to geologists, biologists and hydrologists to one dominated by the speleologist, an individual specifically trained for research on caverns and related phenomena.

## LITERATURE

1.  ASHLEY, G. H. and E. M. KINDLE. 1903. The geology of the Lower Carboniferous area of southern Indiana. Indiana Dept. Geology and Nat. Resources, Ann. Rept. **27**, pp. 49-122.

2.  BEEDE, J. W. 1911. The cycle of subterranean drainage as illustrated in the Bloomington, Indiana, Quadrangle. Indiana Acad. Sci. Proc. **20**:81-111.

3.  BLATCHLEY, W. S. 1897. Indiana Caves and their fauna. Indiana Dept. Geology and Nat. Resources, Ann. Rept. **21**, pp. 121-212.

4.  GRAY, H. H. and R. L. POWELL. 1965. Geomorphology and groundwater hydrology of the Mitchell Plain and Crawford Upland in southern Indiana. Indiana Geological Survey Field Conference Guidebook No. 11, 26 p., 20 figs.

5.  MALOTT, C. A. 1922. The physiography of Indiana *in* Handbook of Indiana Geology. Ind. Dept. Conserv. Pub. **21**, pt. 2., p. 59-256, 3 pls., 51 figs.

6.  _____ 1945. Significant features of Indiana karst. Indiana Acad. Sci. Proc. **54**: 8-24.

7.  _____ 1952. The swallow-holes of Lost River, Orange County, Indiana. Indiana Acad. Sci. Proc. **61**: 187-231.

8.  PALMER, A. N. 1965. The occurrence of ground water in limestone. Compass **42**: 246-255.

9.  POWELL, R. L. 1961. Caves of Indiana. Indiana Geological Survey Circ. **8**, 127 p., 4 pls., 58 figs., 1 table.

10.  _____ 1963. Alluviated cave springs in south-central Indiana. Indiana Acad. Sci. Proc. **72**: 182-189.

11.  _____ 1965. Development of a karst valley in Monroe County, Indiana (abs.): Indiana Acad. Sci. Proc. **74**: 222.

12.  _____ 1966. Groundwater movement and cavern development in the Chester Series of Indiana. In progress, Indiana Acad. Sci. Proc. **75**:

# 8

# Mineral Resources

CHARLES E. WIER* AND JOHN B. PATTON**
Indiana Geological Survey and Indiana University

## Introduction

The mineral resources of Indiana can best be understood when viewed within the regional framework of the State's geology. Indiana lies in the stable region of the eastern United States and Canada, and it has been subject to little structural disturbance during the last half billion years. The sedimentary bedrock, consisting of Paleozoic systems ranging from Cambrian through Pennsylvanian, overlies Precambrian igneous and metamorphic rocks. The Cambrian and Precambrian rocks are not exposed and have not thus far been the source of any mineral production. All the other systems are productive of some mineral commodity.

Land emergence, probably late in the Paleozoic Era, exposed the bedrock to weathering and erosion that have resulted in the present stratigraphic distribution pattern (Fig. 3), in which the oldest rocks (Ordovician) are exposed in southeastern Indiana, high on the Cincinnati Arch, and the younger Paleozoic systems are progressively exposed westward into the Illinois Basin, and northward into the Michigan Basin. About eighty percent of the State has been over-ridden by Pleistocene ice sheets ranging from Nebraskan to Wisconsin in age, and varying thicknesses of glacial drift lie above the bedrock in much of the State. The Pleistocene drift has also been the source of extensive mineral production.

Mineral resources are commonly classified as fuels, metals, and industrial minerals (nonmetals). In Indiana there are few deposits of metals and these are too small or too impure or both to be of commercial importance. The State does, however, contain large deposits of the mineral fuels—coal and oil— and the industrial minerals—sand and gravel, clay and shale, limestone, sandstone and gypsum. Minor deposits include marl,

*Assoc. Prof. Indiana University, and Head, Coal Section, Indiana Geological Survey.
**Chairman, Dept. of Geology, Indiana University, and State Geologist.
Published with permission of the State Geologist, Indiana Department of Natural Resources, Geological Survey.

peat, industrial sands, quartz pebble conglomerate, and natural gas.

To review the developed mineral resources in gross stratigraphic terms, the Ordovician System has produced oil and gas, crushed stone, and dimension stone (Fig. 34) ; the Silurian System has produced crushed stone, building stone, and raw material for lime, mineral wool, and cement; the Devonian System has produced oil, gas, crushed stone, dimension stone, and limestone for cement and lime; the Mississippian System has produced oil and gas, dimension stone, crushed stone, shale, gypsum and anhydrite, and raw material for lime and cement; the Pennsylvanian System has produced coal, oil and gas, building stone, clay and shale, and crushed stone; and the Quaternary System has produced sand and gravel, peat, calcareous marl, and clay.

## Mineral Fuels

Potential sources of energy that can be harnessed by man are coal, petroleum, natural gas, wood, water power, solar energy, and nuclear energy. During 1964 mineral fuels provided the lion's share of energy demands in the United States. Natural gas and petroleum each furnished slightly more than a third and coal provided slightly less than a third of the energy requirements. Water power continued to furnish four per cent. Nuclear energy, despite the tremendous amount of progress being made in its utilization, provided only a tenth of a per cent of our energy requirements in 1964. In Indiana, essentially all of the energy is supplied by mineral fuels.

### Coal

Indiana is indeed fortunate to possess large quantities of coal. It ranks 14th among the states in coal reserves and 7th in annual coal production. Nearly a fifth of the State is underlain by coal-bearing rocks (Fig. 35). Most of the available coal is in Gibson, Knox, Pike, Posey, Sullivan, Vanderburgh, Vigo, and Warrick Counties.

The coals were deposited in a structural and sedimentary basin that now is called the Illinois Basin. This area also is known as the Eastern Interior coal region and includes Illinois, southwestern Indiana, and western Kentucky. The coal beds in Indiana dip to the southwest 30 feet per mile. They crop out in the southwestern part of the State on the east

| System | Series | Formation or group | Mineral resources |
|--------|--------|--------------------|-------------------|
| Quaternary | Pleistocene | | P SG S IS |
| Tertiary | | | IS |
| Pennsylvanian | Conemaugh | McLeansboro Group | G CS S |
| Pennsylvanian | Allegheny | Carbondale Group | C G CS S IS |
| Pennsylvanian | Pottsville | Raccoon Creek Group | C O G D S |
| Mississippian | Chester | Unnamed group | O G |
| Mississippian | Chester | Stephensport Group | O G D CS |
| Mississippian | Chester | West Baden Group | O G CS |
| Mississippian | Chester | Paoli Ls. | O G CS |
| Mississippian | Meramec | Ste. Genevieve Ls. | O G D CS |
| Mississippian | Meramec | St. Louis Ls. | O CS Gy |
| Mississippian | Meramec | Salem Ls. | O G D CS |
| Mississippian | Meramec | Harrodsburg Ls. | O CS |
| Mississippian | Osage | Borden Group | O S |
| Mississippian | Kinderhook | Rockford Ls. | |
| Devonian | Kinderhook | New Albany Sh. | G |
| Devonian | | North Vernon Ls. | O G CS |
| Devonian | | Jeffersonville Ls. | O G CS |
| Devonian | | Pendleton Ss. | IS |
| Devonian | | Geneva Dol. | O G D CS |
| Silurian | | | D CS |
| Ordovician | Cincinnatian | | G D CS |
| Ordovician | Mohawkian | Trenton Ls. | O G |
| Ordovician | Mohawkian | Black River Ls. | O G |
| Ordovician | | | |
| Cambrian | St. Croixan | | |
| Precambrian | | | |

C-Coal, O-Oil, G-Natural gas, D-Dimension stone, CS-Crushed stone,
SG-Sand and gravel, S-Clay and shale, Gy-Gypsum, P-Peat and marl,
IS-Industrial sand.

**Fig. 34. Stratigraphic position of produced major mineral resources.**

side of the basin and are deepest in the center of the basin in southern Illinois. The coal-bearing rocks are Pennsylvanian in age and are 1500 feet thick in Indiana. Only the middle 500 feet, the Carbondale Group, contains coals that are widely distributed, fairly thick, and of considerable commercial importance. A lesser amount of coal is produced from the lower third, the Raccoon Creek Group, but these lower coals are less regular in thickness, and an area of thick coal large enough for a modern mine is difficult to find. Except for small mines in a few localities the coal beds in the upper third of the rocks are not considered commercial. The coals in the Carbondale Group that are mined range from 2½ to 10 feet in thickness and are underlain and overlain by 50 to 100 feet of shale and sandstone plus minor amounts of limestone and clay.

TABLE 4. Mineral production in Indiana in 1964.*

| Mineral | Quantity | Value |
|---|---|---|
| Mineral fuels | | |
| Coal | 15,075,000 tons | $ 57,246.000 |
| Petroleum | 11,283,000 barrels | 32,157,000 |
| Natural gas | 200,000,000 cubic feet | 47,000 |
| Industrial minerals | | |
| Dimension stone | 567,500 tons | 12,690,000 |
| Crushed stone | 21,664,000 tons | 27,236,000 |
| Sand and gravel | 24,416,000 tons | 21,811,000 |
| Clay and shale | 1,545,000 tons | 2,264,000 |
| Cement, Portland | 15,038,000 barrels | 48,695,000 |
| Peat | 66,568 tons | 543,000 |
| Marl | 86,500 tons | 52,000 |
| Abrasives | 5 tons | 16,000 |
| Gypsum and misc. | | 9,026,000 |
| TOTAL | | $211,783,000 |

*Data modified from Klyce and Fox, 1965, tables 1, 6, and 7.

Coal mining in Indiana is distributed through the center part of the Pennsylvanian outcrop area and extends in a nearly north-south direction. Where the middle Pennsylvanian coal beds are close to the surface large strip mines are in operation. They remove from 10 to more than 100 feet of shale, sandstone, and unconsolidated materials from above the coal seam before they can produce it. These strip mines are noticeable in Vigo, Clay, Sullivan, Greene, Pike, and Warrick Counties (Fig. 35). Underground mines are present to the westward where these coals are deep. The deepest underground mine now in operation in Indiana is in Gibson County and is 450 feet deep. Table 4 shows 1964 production.

All of the coal produced in Indiana is classified as high volatile bituminous coal. Three types of bituminous coal have been mined—cannel, block, and bright banded coal. Cannel and block coals have been mined on a small scale and are consumed by the domestic market, especially as a fireplace fuel. Cannel coal is no longer mined, but block coals are mined and are used, to small extent, in the industrial market. Most of the coal produced is the bright banded coal which is commonly burned to produce steam. Seventy per cent of the coal is consumed by the large electricity-generating power plants.

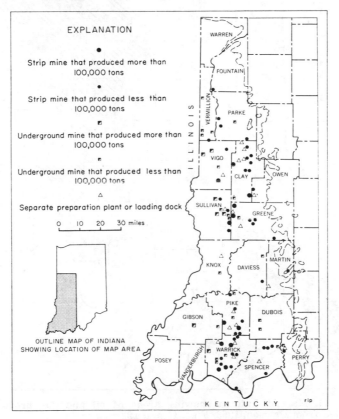

Fig. 35. Map of southwestern Indiana showing active coal mines in 1965. Modified from Wier, 1964, Fig. 2.

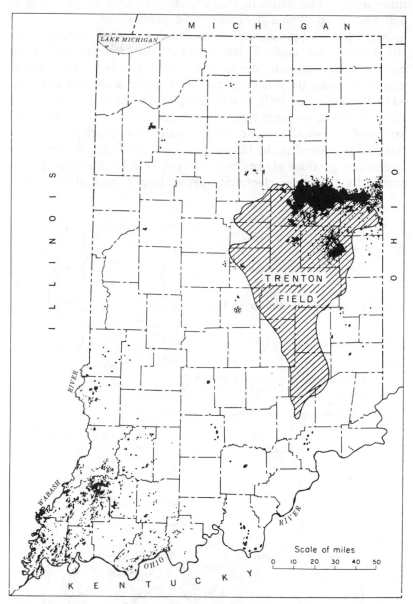

Fig. 36. Map of Indiana showing areas of oil and gas production. Compiled from Dawson, 1963, Figs. 11 and 12.

## *Petroleum*

Production of petroleum plays an important role in the economy of Indiana. About 370 million barrels have been produced since commercial production began in Indiana in 1889. Exploration and drilling for oil and gas have furnished a large and comprehensive set of records that geologists have used as a basis for understanding the origin and distribution of the Paleozoic rocks in the State.

Most of the oil production in Indiana has come from two different areas that have entirely different geologic settings and were developed at different times—the Trenton Field in east-central Indiana and the southwestern Indiana area (Fig. 36). The Trenton oilfield was developed during the years from 1889, when oil was first discovered, to 1904, when peak production from the Trenton Field was equivalent to the present annual production of the State.

The Trenton oilfield is on the northern end of a positive structural area called the Cincinnati Arch. The oil comes from a dolomitic zone about 1000 feet deep that is in the Trenton Limestone of the Ordovician System. The area where this limestone has high porosity and permeability is a single nearly continuous reservoir including nearly a million acres in Indiana and Ohio. Less than half of this area is in Indiana. The Trenton Field is included among the world's largest oilfields. Annual crude oil production in the Trenton oilfield rapidly declined until in 1912 it was less than a million barrels. Annual State production remained at about this level until 1939 when high-grade petroleum was found in Gibson County and the southwestern area was developed.

The southwestern area is on the east flank of the Illinois Basin. The Trenton Limestone dips southwestward about 30 feet per mile from the Trenton oilfield and, in the southwestern area, is about 6,500 feet deep. It is therefore below and is older than most of the oil-producing rocks in the southwestern area where production comes from sandstone, limestone, and dolomite beds that are 1,000 to 3,000 feet deep. In the southwestern area oil production comes from about 300 separate fields and 20 different formations. Most of the production comes from rocks of Mississippian age but significant amounts are produced from Devonian and Pennsylvanian rocks. Oil is trapped in a variety of structures. Structural traps, some of which are called domes, are common in Devonian, Mississippian, and Pennsylvanian rocks, but stratigraphic traps are restricted to upper Mississippian and to Pennsylvanian rocks.

Although primary production of oil has been decreasing since 1951, total annual production has not decreased because secondary production is increasing. Commonly only 20 to 25 per cent of the available crude oil may be produced from Indiana fields by normal pumping methods. This amount is called primary production. Secondary recovery refers to additional oil produced from this remaining 75 to 80 per cent that is left in the rock reservoir. During the life of an oilfield the amount of secondary production ranges from one to three times as much as primary production but still some of the oil is not recoverable. A common method of secondary recovery in Indiana is called waterflooding. By this method water is injected into the reservoir under pressure. The water forces the oil through the pores in the rocks into a lower pressure area that feeds a pumping well. About a fourth of the wells drilled last year in Indiana were associated with waterflooding of known fields.

## Natural Gas

Natural gas in Indiana is in much the same area and under much the same conditions as oil. In fact natural gas commonly provides the pressure to help push the oil through the pores of the rock and into position at the bottom of the well so that it may be easily pumped out. Much of this gas, although it is a significant amount for the entire State, is too small in quantity in many individual fields to be recovered economically, and it is flared (burned) at the wellhead. The large gas-producing area in Indiana, one of the largest in the world, was the Trenton Oil Field which also produced oil. It includes several additional counties to the south (patterned area in Fig. 36). Much of the gas was wasted early in this century, and little production now comes from this area. Indiana now produces less than a per cent of the gas used in the State, and large amounts are pumped into the State through interstate pipelines from the Gulf Coast and Midcontinent areas. Because peak use of gas is seasonal, considerable attention has been given to storing large quantities of gas during the summertime and utilizing this gas during the winter months. Twenty-seven underground gas storage areas are now in operation in the State. These are developed in naturally occurring geologic structures that initially held varying amounts of water, gas, or oil and now have been prepared for underground storage of gas. Producing zones of natural gas and underground storage areas for gas are scattered throughout Paleozoic rocks younger than Cambrian (Fig. 34).

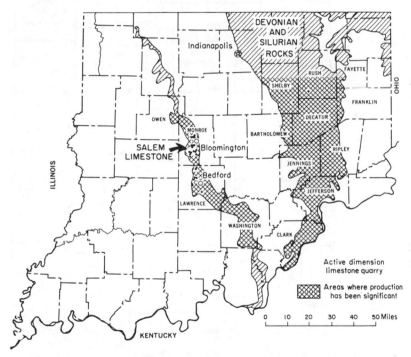

Fig. 37. Map of southern Indiana showing areas where dimension limestone has been and is being produced. From Rooney, 1965, Fig. 2.

## Industrial Minerals

Industrial minerals are not glamorous. Rarely is the average citizen impressed with their importance nor does he realize how dependent he is on many of the common ones. He lives in a house that uses gypsum in either plaster or plasterboard; the outside wall may be dimension stone cut from limestone or sandstone, brick made from clay and shale, or concrete made from cement and aggregate. He drives on roads that

are surfaced with gravel or crushed limestone or are concrete
that may use limestone as aggregate and in cement, and even

Fig. 38. Map of Indiana showing location of quarries producing
crushed stone.

the food he eats required some of these minerals for adequate growth.

In general, industrial minerals are abundant and are widely distributed. Where they are produced depends on many economic factors of which the cost of transportation to the consumer is likely to be the most important.

## Dimension Stone

The mineral industry in which Indiana leads United States production is building stone. A producing district now limited to Monroe and Lawrence Counties (Fig. 37) yields the greater part of the dimension limestone quarried in this country. The product comes from the stratigraphic unit named the Salem Limestone, which is found at the surface from Harrison County to Putnam County. Although the Salem contains several lithologies, it is best known for the granular, cross-bedded, massive calcarenite that is quarried for cut stone and veneer. In the region of Bloomington and Bedford such stone is produced in large quantities by companies that quarry, saw, mill, split, and otherwise fabricate dimension stone products. The part of the Salem that is quarried for dimension limestone is relatively soft and can be economically and effectively milled. It has little preferential direction of splitting and can, if desired, be turned out in tremendous monoliths. The color of most of the stone is some variant of gray or buff and depends upon the position of the stone in relation to former water tables, as oxidation, or the lack of it, affects the color. Surface reserves of the stone are tremendous, although urbanization is removing much of the potential land from quarry development, and it would be feasible to quarry the stone underground, which would add enormously to the accessible reserves.

Another segment of the Indiana dimension stone industry, although one of much less magnitude, is found in sandstones of late Mississippian and Pennsylvanian age distributed through several counties in southwestern Indiana. Individual sandstone quarry operations tend to be ephemeral, because much of the demand for dimension sandstone is based on a desire for strong color tones, and these tend to be present only near the outcrop and to diminish as the quarry acquires greater depth. Only one of the active sandstone quarries has been long-lived, and this is near Ferdinand in Dubois County.

A third type of dimension stone is material removed in its natural bedding thickness and used principally for rustic effects in architecture and for flagging. The principal source is near Waldron in Shelby County, where Silurian and Devonian limestone and dolomite are quarried. Several other quarries operating principally for crushed stone in similar rocks produce small amounts of such slab stone for rough dimension purposes.

## Crushed Stone

The material crushed in Indiana for such purposes as concrete aggregate, road metal, riprap, filter beds, and agricultural limestone is produced from carbonate rocks that range from high calcium limestones to chemical dolomites and include rocks with intermediate calcium-magnesium ratios, and moderately impure limestones. Stratigraphically the materials are principally Mississippian, Silurian, and Devonian, in that order of production volume, but minor amounts of crushed stone come from both the Pennsylvanian and Ordovician Systems (Fig. 38).

The belt of Mississippian limestone exposed between Harrison, Crawford and Perry Counties and Putnam County, produces by far the greatest amount of crushed stone, principally from the Ste. Genevieve Limestone and immediately overlying and underlying beds.

Second most prolific are the middle Silurian (Niagaran) rocks quarried from Clark County along the Ohio River northward to Rush and Shelby Counties, where they are obscured by glacial drift, and at scattered localities considerably farther north where Silurian rocks of similar age and younger, principally near major drainage, lie beneath glacial drift thin enough to leave the bedrock accessible. Many of these Niagaran strata are dolomitic, and some are theoretical dolomites that could well be used for chemical dolomite purposes, but they are not.

A substantial crushed stone industry is also developed in limestones and dolomites of middle Devonian age distributed through a belt extending from the Ohio River in Clark County northward to Rush County. Localities in northern Indiana, near Rensselaer in Jasper County and near Logansport in

Cass County, have production from Devonian limestones. The basal Devonian unit from Scott County northward to Rush County is the Geneva Dolomite, which would be generally suitable for chemical dolomite purposes but is utilized only as crushed stone.

Most of the Ordovician limestones in southeastern Indiana are interbedded with shale to an extent that makes production for crushed stone purposes impractical, but the uppermost beds of the Cincinnatian Series (upper Ordovician) are produced and crushed along with overlying Brassfield Limestone (Silurian) in Switzerland County.

### Sand and Gravel

Gravel and sand for aggregate (construction) purposes are produced almost entirely from glacial drift of later Pleistocene (Wisconsin) age in Indiana. Minor production is obtained from the alluvium of present stream valleys or by dredging of stream channels, but even these materials are principally reworked glacio-fluviatile deposits. Thus to a considerable extent the distribution pattern of commercial sands and gravels is essentially a map of Wisconsin valley trains, outwash plains, and kames and eskers (Fig. 39).

The quality of the materials is variable and closely related to the terrane over which the ice sheets moved immediately before the outwash materials were released. Deleterious materials are found in and adjacent to regions in which the bedrock includes undesirable constituents for construction gravels. Such constituents diminish in the direction of glacial movement and tend to be reduced sharply by transport in the meltwater sluiceways. Hence a tendency exists for the materials to improve in the direction of transport, but the average grain size diminishes, leading eventually to excessive sand-gravel ratios, and certain durable but undesirable constituents, notably chert, may ultimately increase in proportional abundance to an unacceptable percentage.

In summary of the availability of aggregates in general, it can be said that glaciation has yielded an abundant supply of useful aggregates and has distributed such materials more uniformly over the State than they could be if crushed stone were the only source.

### Clay and Shale

In both character and utilization Indiana clays and shales are diverse. Shales of early Mississippian age lead in production volume. They are produced as raw materials for brick, drain tile, lightweight aggregate, and cement raw materials

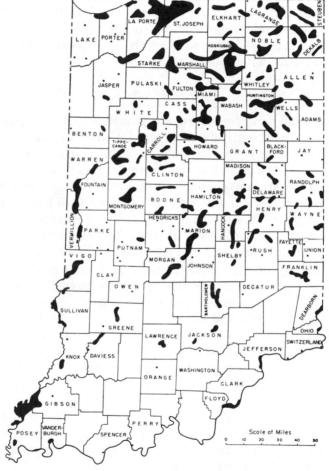

Fig. 39. Map of Indiana showing areas producing sand and gravel.

in localities extending from Clark County northwestward to Montgomery County (Fig. 40).

Second in abundance, and possibly first in product value, are shales and clays including coal underclays from the lower and middle parts of the Pennsylvanian System throughout its distribution in western Indiana. The Pennsylvanian clays in general are more refractory and better suited for vitrified products than are the Mississippian argillaceous materials. The products include sewer pipe, structural tile, brick, and insulators, and Pennsylvanian materials supply the alumina-silica portion of cement raw materials at one operation.

Glacial drift of late Pleistocene age, including both lacustrine clays and clay tills, are used for ceramic raw materials to make drain tile and brick at a few localities in northern

EXPLANATION

⊠  Pleistocene clay
✕  Pennsylvanian clay and shale
●  Mississippian shale
+  Silurian shale

Fig. 40. Map of Indiana showing location of pits and mines producing clay and shale in Indiana.

Indiana, although in general only the shallow surficial layer that has been leached of calcium carbonate may be so used. Pleistocene till and modern soils supply part of the alumina-silica materials for three cement plants.

## Gypsum

Evaporite beds that include gypsum are known at two localities in Indiana, and of these the only commercial development has been near Shoals in Martin County (Fig. 41), although

Fig. 41. Map of Indiana showing location of cement, gypsum, high silica sand, expanded shale, and whetstone plants, and area underlain by gypsum.

other localities in nearby counties are underlain by evaporite sequences with probable commercial potentiality. In this southern region gypsum is present at several levels in the St. Louis Limstone, but only one of the levels has been developed commercially in the two active mines, and the other gypsum zones may be too thin for exploitation. Updip from the known areas of exploitable gypsum beds, the gypsum diminishes in thickness and disappears in a relatively short distance, probably because it has been dissolved by ground water. Downdip the ratio of anhydrite to gypsum increases beyond the point of usability.

Both of the existing gypsum mines are captive operations of major companies that manufacture most of the raw material at the site into plaster and plasterboard products.

A lobe of the Michigan Basin extending into northern Indiana contains an evaporite sequence that includes apparently commercial thicknesses of gypsum in places, and particularly in LaPorte County. Mining has not taken place, but the advantageous location makes such development probable.

## Cement Raw Materials

A review of raw materials for manufacture of portland cement and natural cement is, to a considerable extent, a repetition of information already presented. Five cement plants are operative in the State (Fig. 41), and of these one, at Indiana Harbor in Lake County, uses blast furnace slag as the principal ingredient. Additive material, such as limestone and iron ore, are brought in by Great Lakes freighters, and thus little, if any, Indiana raw material is used.

The four other plants use Paleozoic limestone as the principal raw material and obtain some of the accessory materials close at hand and import others from considerable distances.

A plant at Speed in Clark County utilizes raw material from the Jeffersonville and North Vernon Limestones (middle Devonian), and includes a small amount of the immediately underlying Louisville Limestone of Silurian age. At this plant natural cement rock from the Silver Creek Member, a lithofacies of the North Vernon Limestone, is used to manufacture mortar. The earliest cement operations in Indiana were in this locality and were based entirely on the natural cement rock. Argillaceous material for the portland cement production in

Clark County has been obtained from the New Providence Shale (lower Mississippian) and the New Albany Shale (Devonian and Mississippian), but now it comes wholly from soil. Gypsum for retarder is imported into the region, as are various types of iron oxide. Sands from the Ohio River supply supplemented silica when needed. A plant at Mitchell in Lawrence County utilizes material from the Harrodsburg and Salem Limestones (middle Mississippian) for the calcium carbonate requirement and brings New Providence Shale by rail from Jackson County for the necessary alumina and silica components. Sand from Jackson and Knox Counties has been used for supplemental silica, and a variety of materials including Lake Superior iron ores, mill scale, and burned pyrites, has been used for iron surfaces.

At Limedale in Putnam County a quarry in the Ste. Genevieve Limestone and parts of overlying and underlying formations supplies the calcium carbonate. Argillaceous materials have included Mississippian and Pennsylvanian shales and Pleistocene clays, including Recent soils. Gypsum and iron-bearing materials are imported.

The newest cement plant in Indiana is west of Logansport in Cass County. It utilizes stone from the Kenneth Limestone Member of the Salina Formation (Silurian). Argillaceous materials are obtained from Pleistocene till and soil. Gypsum, iron-bearing materials, and aluminum dross are imported.

## Lime

For many years burned lime was produced from both limestones and dolomites, but commercial lime production ceased in 1953. Because of the requirements of the basic oxygen process for steel manufacture, new lime-burning capacity is being developed in Lake County. The raw limestone will be imported by Great Lakes freighters, probably from Michigan.

## Lightweight Aggregate

At Brooklyn in Morgan County a plant utilizing rotary kilns manufactures lightweight aggregate from lower Mississippian shale within the Borden Group (Fig. 41). Materials for this type of aggregate are found at numerous places in the State, and the increasing use of lightweight aggregates indicates that other manufacturing plants will be installed.

Substantial production also takes place at Indiana Harbor, where slag from the iron and steel industry is frothed into a widely used product. Other lightweight aggregates, for use in plaster and insulation, are made in the State by expansion of perlite imported from New Mexico.

## Industrial Sands

Numerous types of industrial sands have been produced from varied sources in Indiana. Many of the former operations have become defunct, largely because of tightened specifications for glass and foundry sands, but one new source and use has been recently developed. The State's extensive glass industry once utilized major amounts of domestic sands from such sources as the dunes along the south shore of Lake Michigan and from Pennsylvanian sandstones at various localities in western Indiana. A small amount of glass sand was produced from a Devonian sandstone at Pendleton in Madison County, and glass was formerly manufactured at New Albany from sands in adjacent Harrison County. Lowered tolerances, particularly in iron content, removed these sands from the glass field, but new beneficiation methods applied to the Harrison County sands (Fig. 41), which are probably Tertiary in age, have recently yielded materials that would meet glass sand specifications, although the new product is used principally as abrasive and for other non-glass uses.

Engine sands and foundry sands are still produced from the dunes in Porter and LaPorte Counties.

## Quartz Pebble

A single captive operation south of Shoals in Martin County produces quartz pebble for refractory purposes from conglomerate at the base of the Pennsylvanian rocks. The conglomerate is apparently a channel-filling material in drainageways that developed on the post-Mississippian land surface, and it was formerly quarried at other localities in Martin and Lawrence Counties for road metal. The washed and sized pebble from the modern operation is shipped to western Illinois for manufacture of silica brick.

## Whetstones

Thin-bedded siltstones of early Pennsylvanian age have been

quarried for more than 150 years in Orange County (Fig. 41) and cut and ground into whetstones. Only one quarry and fabricating plant has operated in recent years and the plant is now idle or closed. These stones have been widely marketed under the name Hindostan whetstone but they no longer compete with the less expensive mass-produced artificial abrasives.

### Peat

Late Pleistocene bogs containing peat of commercial quality are present at various localities from Indianapolis northward (Fig. 42). The material is produced sporadically from pits in Grant, Hamilton, Kosciusko, Marion, Marshall, Porter, Warren, and Wells Counties, and is used for horticultural purposes.

### Marl

Late Pleistocene lakes were filled with calcareous marl in numerous counties of northern Indiana (Fig. 42). The marl

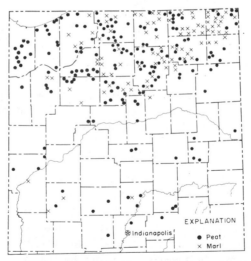

Fig. 42. Map of northern Indiana showing pits that have produced peat and marl. Data on marl furnished by W. J. Wayne and on peat by A. F. Schneider.

probably was deposited by biochemical precipitation and is noticeably thicker around the margins of the lakes. A marl-producing industry directed toward agricultural and soil conditioning uses operates intermittently in Elkhart, Fulton, Kosciusko, LaGrange, LaPorte, Marshall, Noble, St. Joseph, and Steuben Counties. Early production was utilized in mortar, in portland cement, and as a flux in the early iron furnaces that used bog iron ore.

## Metals

Although Indiana is well known for large production of pig iron and steel in the vicinity of East Chicago and Gary and, to a lesser extent, for the smelting of aluminum in a plant on the Ohio River in Warrick County, the State does not produce the ores that go into this production. Metals are not common in the sedimentary rocks in Indiana because the appropriate geologic conditions needed for such mineralization have not been present during geologic time in the accessible rocks. Copper, gold, lead in the mineral galena, and silver have been found in the Pleistocene unconsolidated materials, especially in the outwash sands and gravels in front of moraines along the glacial sluiceways.

Nuggets of copper that have been transported by the ice and melt water from the Lake Superior Copper District have been found along some of the larger glacial sluiceways. These fragments of native copper have been reported from at least 18 counties in the State, and the pieces appear to be larger in the north and diminish in size to the south. Early explorers noted that the Indians were using fragments of copper to make various ornaments. Copper nuggets are now much sought by rock and mineral collectors.

The presence of gold has been highly publicized in Indiana, but it too has been found only in water-sorted glacial material. Gold has been found in at least 25 counties but the richest deposits are in Brown and Morgan Counties. Probably as much as $40,000 worth of gold has been found in Indiana, and much of it has gone into private collections. It is reported that during the depression years some enterprising people in Brown and Morgan Counties earned as much as $5 a day panning gold. Most of the gold is small rounded grain or flattened flakes less than 3 mm across, but one find was reported to have weighed 8½ grams.

Lead and silver mines that presumably were worked by the Indians and early settlers and whose locations have been lost have been reported from many areas of the state during the last 50 years. It is probable that lead and silver mines never existed in Indiana and that such finds were isolated fragments found in sand and gravel.

Iron deposits in Indiana were given a great deal of attention by the early geologists and, in fact, several iron furnaces were in operation in Indiana before 1900. None are now operating. Most of these furnaces used the residual limonite that weathered from lower Pennsylvanian and upper Mississippian sandstones where it was originally deposited as lenses and concretions. Commonly these limonitic rocks were picked up on the hillsides, collected in a horse-drawn wagon, and hauled to the furnace. Other sources of iron include bog iron that occurs in the peat and marl bogs in northern Indiana where bands of mud and limonite more than a foot thick line the bottom of some of the bogs. Other potential sources of iron include the bands and nodules of pyrite that commonly are associated with coal. Pyrite that has oxidized to limonite may have been used in the past as a source of iron, but a more recent use of pyrite has been the production of sulphuric acid from the pyrite refuse in coal mining.

## Conclusions

The kind and amount of mineral resources affect the kind and amount of industry and, to a great extent, the well-being of the people in the State. When Indiana was admitted to the Union in 1816 other natural resources—the towering trees, the black rich soil, and the clear pure water—were being exploited. The State's mineral resources, however, were almost unknown. Because of the small amount of industrialization and the relatively small population there was little need for mineral fuels and industrial minerals. During the first 75 years after Statehood, exploration, production, and utilization of mineral resources progressed slowly, but during the past 75 years a great amount of drilling and mining activity has taken place that has furnished the geologic data necessary to understand the origin and distribution of each mineral commodity. We can now look back 150 years at our record of rapidly increasing production and consumption of our mineral resources and look forward to a continuing and more rapid utilization of our mineral resources in the next 150 years. In 1964 the total value of mineral resources produced in Indiana was nearly $212 million (Table 4). Because much of this production was utilized as raw material in other industries the value was increased many fold and the production and utilization of mineral resources in Indiana affects every family.

Mineral resources are exhaustible and are not renewable; they are harvested but one time and then they are gone. Thus it seems possible to predict how long each will last. One can establish a rate of production and divide it into the total reserves and the answer will be years of production remaining. It is difficult to make an accurate evaluation of the amount of a mineral commodity present in an area but much more difficult to know what will be usable in the future years. The quality of fuels and industrial minerals shows significant variation in the State, and the ease or difficulty with which they may be produced at any one place obviously affects the price for which they may be sold. We have produced them where they are of highest quality, thickest, closest to the surface, and most desirable. We are taking the cream. Comparable material is becoming harder to find and more expensive to produce. Future production depends on improvements of mining equipment and technology, more efficient and cheaper methods of preparing the raw commodity for use, and competition from other deposits of similar nature elsewhere and from other kinds of natural or synthetic materials that can be used for the same purpose.

Because the number of people is steadily increasing and because each family wants and gets more of the material things in each generation, the State's mineral resources will continue to be used at an ever-increasing rate until each resource is nearly consumed or until a cheaper substitute is found.

More than 33 billion tons of coal is available for mining. At least half of this can be produced under present economic conditions and is a sufficient quantity to last a thousand years if the rate of production stays the same. Increases of 10 per cent each year would leave only enough for 50 years. Proved reserves of petroleum are calculated at 61 million barrels and would last only 6 more years at the present rate, but estimated reserves would extend this production to, perhaps, 50 years.

When petroleum becomes in short supply, coal may be used

to make gasoline. It is now possible to make gasoline from coal at a cost of 11 cents per gallon.

Probably in a few decades nuclear energy will replace the fossil fuels in the energy market. Proposed legislation that limits the amount of sulphur in coal and oil would make these fuels more expensive and speed up the change. Then both coal and oil could be used in a more efficient manner—as a source of chemical raw material.

The State's supply of dimension stone seems almost inexhaustible, but this does not guarantee the industry's future. Competition is keen not only from stone in other states but from synthetic building materials. As tastes and architectural styles change, buildings have tended to use more aluminum and glass and other manufactured materials. It is likely, however, that as long as the industry continues to seek ways of improving its efficiency the price will be competitive and production will continue at the same or an increased rate.

Reserves of limestone and dolomite for crushed stone aggregate, agricultural lime, cement raw materials, and lime will last almost indefinitely. As long as more and wider roads and more and higher buildings are built the amount of limestone quarried must increase. It is difficult to visualize an effective substitute.

Gravel and sand for general aggregate use is also in large supply but a too rigid specification imposed by the consumer might make it difficult to compete with other kinds of aggregates. Deleterious materials—chert, sandstone, siltstone, and shale—range from 3 to 85 per cent in the various gravel deposits scattered throughout the State. In general, the gravel deposits that contain the least per cent of deleterious material will be produced first.

Clay and shale suitable for making brick, drain tile, and lightweight aggregate are present in great abundance, but refractory clays are more difficult to find. Although large reserves of refractory clays likely are available beneath the coals in southwestern Indiana it will continue to be more expensive to find suitable deposits and produce the clay.

The amount of gypsum available is not precisely known but large areas (Fig. 41) are known to be underlain by gypsum. If demand continues the gypsum industry will develop the purer deposits, and a shortage is not anticipated.

Adequate information is not available to calculate tons or cubic yards of peat and marl but the amount already produced is surely less than a per cent of available supply. It is likely that both peat and marl will continue to be used for agricultural purposes and will continue to be produced at about the same or a slightly accelerated rate.

In conclusion, our supply of mineral fuel is limited and economists are already predicting the year when the entire supply will be consumed. The supply of industrial minerals, on the other hand, is nearly inexhaustible and the industrial minerals now being produced and utilized in Indiana will likely still be an important part of our economy when the State is twice as old.

## LITERATURE

1. DAWSON, T. A. and G. L. CARPENTER 1963. Underground storage of natural gas in Indiana. Indiana Geol. Survey Spec. Rept. No. 1.
2. KLYCE, D. F. and M. B. Fox. 1965. The mineral industry of Indiana. U. S. Bureau of Minerals Yearbook, 1964.
3. PATTON, J. B. 1955. Underground storage of liquid hydrocarbons in Indiana. Indiana Geol. Survey Rept. Progress 9.
4. ROONEY, L. F. 1965. Indiana's dimension limestone industry. Indiana Business Review, Sept., 1965.
5. WIER, C. E. 1964. The history and future of State's coal industry. Indiana Business Review, July 1964.

# 9

# *Climate*

LAWRENCE A. SCHAAL*
Department of Agronomy, Purdue University

## Introduction

Hoosiers have come a long way in understanding the climatology of Indiana, and they have taken advantage of its fine climate in many ways. In the early years settlers coming from the east had experience in coping with the weather of the eastern states but knew very little about the climate of the new land in Indiana. Even their experience was a composite of a few years in their life—still a tendency of mankind today to the exclusion of past accumulated knowledge. Today the Hoosier is several times better informed—thanks to extensive communications and broad knowledge resulting from research, experience and accumulation of data and information.

Consider that in early times our citizens seldom knew what was beyond the horizon in weather. Now, we have the circling satellites which are capable of picturing in one snapshot half the territory of the United States. At a time when meteorological research has become global, we find that micrometeorology, the weather of our immediate environment, is taking on new importance in research.

As Indiana celebrates its sesquicentennial, climatological research moves toward defining what goes on at the earth's surface and in the atmosphere above.

## Rainfall Heritage

Indiana has a great heritage in the rainfall it receives. The first settlers did not know how reliable the rains were. (Fig. 43). Our widespread network of over 160 rainfall stations in the state shows the adequacy of distribution by area and in the seasons. Admittedly summer distribution is not always the best. (Fig. 44). We are made acutely aware of this by the high measurements of moisture loss by evaporation in the summer when rainfall demands for our crops are the greatest of any

*Weather Bureau State Climotologist, Environmental Science Services Administration, United States Department of Commerce.

time of the year. (Fig. 45). If it were possible to revamp our weather we would schedule more summer rain or a better dis-

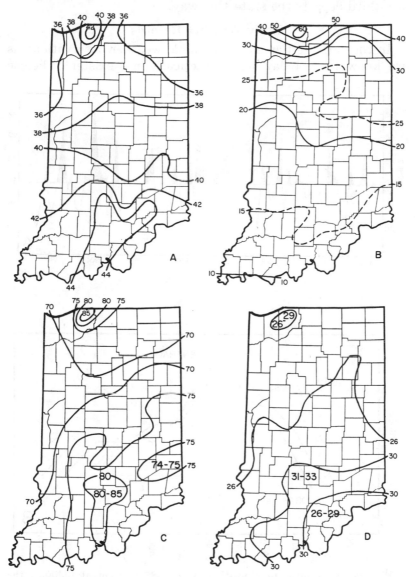

Fig. 43. A—Normal annual precipitation (1931-1960); B—Mean annual snowfall (inches) (1931-1960); C—Mean annual number of days precipitation exceeds 0.1 inch (1951-1960); D—Mean annual number of days precipitation exceeds 0.5 inch (1951-1960).

tribution and do with less rain and snow in the winter. Much winter and spring precipitation flows down the rivers; about one-third departs the state this way.

## Early Weather Records

In the early settlement of Indiana, weather observations as we know them today were practically non-existent. People

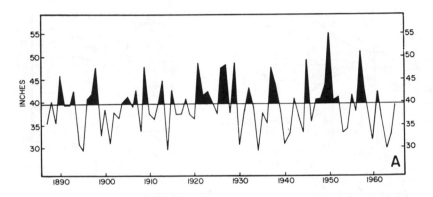

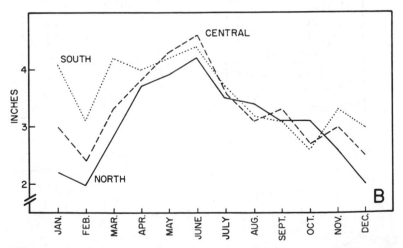

Fig. 44. A—Annual precipitation since 1887 in Central Indiana; the variability of annual precipitation is indicated. B—Normal monthly precipitation in Indiana (average of 1931-1960). Late summer and fall rainfall averages about the same but in other seasons southern Indiana has considerably more rain than northern Indiana.

were very busy gathering the essentials of life to survive the winters. They no doubt worried that some summers would be too dry and hot and crops would be lost. Climatology now indicates this is very unlikely. Early citizens realized the value of a weather history to determine the likelihood of such an event and enhance their knowledge of climate. Several Hoosiers took it upon themselves to record weather data religiously.

In the years ahead Indiana climate will be probed further, both at the surface and above. Measurements will involve soil temperatures, soil moisture, solar radiation, evaporation, and wind. Climatological analyses will show these parameters fluctuate in a few hours, in a day, from season to season, from low elevation to high elevation, and from north to south across the state.[7] Specialists in many fields of endeavor will seek explanations of the weather vagaries. This will involve synoptic climatology or a climatology of our weather systems derived from weather maps of the surface and above.

### High Speed Data Processing

Indiana climatology has been thrust ahead by rapid advances in the technology of data processing. No longer can we say that several thousand solutions to an equation is impossible on account of time; rather the work can be given over to present-day electronic computers for rapid computation. Practically every weather observation taken in Indiana since 1948 has been placed on punched cards. This means that observations, some hourly, and others daily, can be transferred to computers, and bioclimatic relationships in our environment can be expeditiously determined.

### Data Publishing

Several publications of Indiana climatological data facilitate use of such information by specialists in science, agriculture, and industry.[5,7,8,15] For example, we now find that hourly and daily precipitation for approximately 160 stations in Indiana are published monthly.[9,10] The daily extremes of temperature are published for 100 Indiana localities (Fig. 46 and 47). Data are routinely collected, summarized, and published for nine soil temperature measuring sites. At some of these stations soil temperatures for several soil depths under both bare and sodded surfaces are published. Evaporation of water from

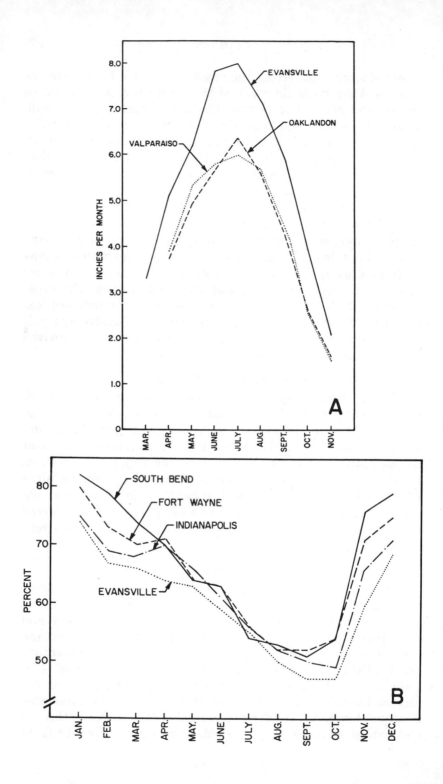

a W.B. Class A evaporation pan (4-foot tank) is recorded daily
and published for eight stations in Hoosierland. More detailed
meteorological information is recorded almost minutely at our
U.S. Weather Bureau manned stations such as South Bend,
Fort Wayne, Indianapolis, and Evansville. The hourly observations for a 10-year period at these stations have been summarized and provide frequency tables of temperature, hourly precipitation, humidity, cloud heights, wind, and visibility.[14] The
potentiality of these data has barely been scratched. Scientific
expansion will require increased use of data especially collected and summarized to best fit and relate to the information the scientist has collected. Requirements may indicate increased raw data availability at the expense of routine summarization which may serve only a minority.

## Needed Climatological Measurements

How enthusiastically should we compliment ourselves for
150 years of progress? Many meteorological variables that
need to be measured still are unmeasured. We should have a
history of soil temperatures and soil moisture. Solar radiation
is measured at only one place in the state. Net radiation is not
measured at all. Our ideas of how extreme weather in a day or
week affects a crop is relatively unknown. When the time comes
that a week of harmful weather can be forecast will we know
the magnitude of the results before the fact? Will we have
remedies or prescriptions at hand? To help answer such questions a phenology study has been initiated which involves the
growing of shrubs of great variety and of the same species at
several points throughout the state adjacent to climatological
stations. The variability of plant growth will be watched closely. A plant is one of our best integrators of climate, even over
short periods. First leafing, first flowering, first fruiting of
various shrubs and other observations through several seasons
are some of the factors to be studied.[2,4] In the future we will
have a better idea of what some of the usual and unusual segments of a growing season brings in plant life development.

Fig. 45. A—Mean monthly evaporation from WB class A pan. Southern Indiana has considerably higher evaporation from a free water surface than northern Indiana. B—Daytime cloudiness, average percent of
sky covered. Many months of the year are cloudier in northern Indiana
than in southern Indiana.

## Untimely Freezing Temperatures

A series of years from 1921 through 1950 was studied thoroughly for the frequency of late spring and early fall freezes

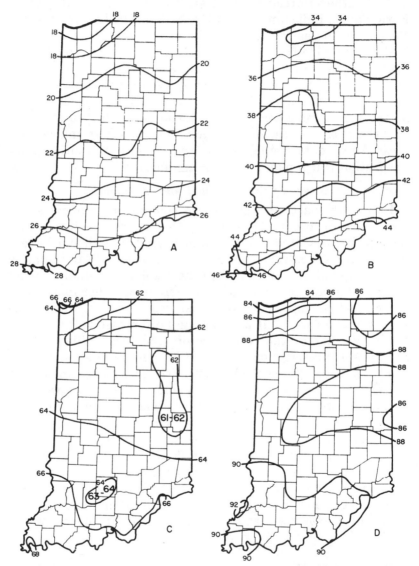

Fig. 46. A—Mean daily minimum temperature (°F.), January (1931-1960). B—Mean daily maximum temperature (°F.), January (1931-1960). C—Mean daily minimum temperature (°F.), July (1931-1960). D—Mean daily maximum temperature (°F.), July (1931-1960).

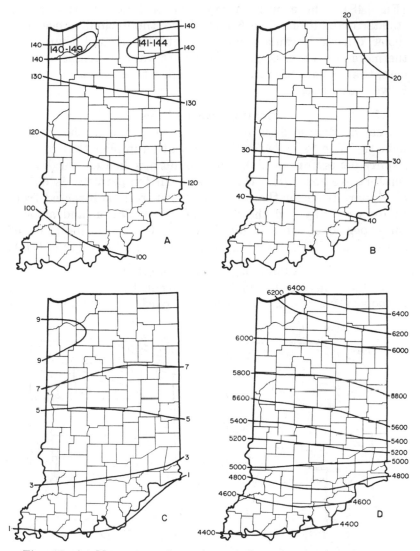

Fig. 47. A—Mean annual number of days temperature 32° F. or lower (1951-1960). Isopleths are highly smoothed to eliminate local differences. B—Mean annual number of days temperatures 90° F. or higher (1951-1960). C—Mean annual number of days temperatures 0° F. or lower (1951-1960). D—Mean annual heating degree days (base 65° F.). The daily sum is obtained by subtracting the daily mean temperature from 65°. If the mean is 65 or higher the value is zero. These values when accumulated daily over a period of time are useful in comparing heating requirements at different times in the seasons, in different localities, and for different structures.

(Fig. 48). These were temperatures taken mostly under standard conditions 5 to 6 feet above the ground. Since it is cooler during a radiational frost at the ground than in a thermometer shelter, and since plants vary in freeze tenderness, the probabilities for other temperatures from 16° to 40° F. were calculated.[7]

## Heating Degree Days

Heating degree days have a popular usage in the heating industry. The formula for this calculation implies that heating requirements for dwellings and buildings heated for human comfort are zero when the day's mean temperature is 65° F. or higher. If cooler the mean temperature is subtracted from 65 for each day and their rate of accumulation and amount for a period of time is highly correlated to consumption of heating fuel. These data[9] are calculated regularly (Fig. 47D).

## Climatological Probabilities

Purdue University and U.S. Weather Bureau researchers, in cooperative effort, have placed on cards and magnetic com-

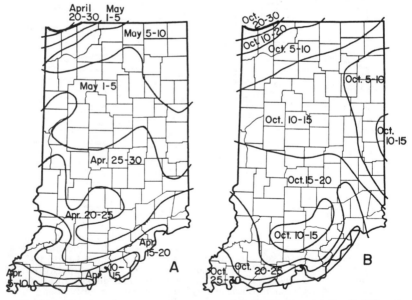

Fig. 48. A—Average date of last temperature of 32° F. or lower in spring (1921-1950); these temperatures taken 5.5 feet above grass in a thermometer shelter are often warmer than at ground level on a cloudless, windless night. B—Average date of first temperature of 32° F. or lower in fall (1921-1950).

puter input tape old climatological records dating well back
into the 19th century. The first study using these punch cards
was the summarization of rainfall on a weekly basis.[1] For 10
stations in Indiana, based on 50 years of record, the probability for both common and rare amounts of precipitation for any
one week of the calendar year has been calculated. We have
the probability of receiving no measurable precipitation in a
week or various amounts up to 6 inches or more in a week.
This type of information primarily has helped those who are
studying various degrees of drought. We must rely upon this
type of information for rainfall probability forecasting for any
time period beyond the immediate future (one to four weeks).

Just available is another type of climatological prediction.[3]
This study answers the question, if it has rained on some specific date, what is the probability of rain on the following day.
And then in the opposite sense, this question is answered for
those days following a no-rain day. Many operations in our
busy world will utilize this type of information. Consider the
farmer and his need for three days of no rain for the harvesting of top quality hay. A builder may need a two-day period to
complete a job—such as outside concrete pouring—under limited weather circumstances. The risk of loss due to weather
is being used more and more in the development of decision
techniques. Such work may require other inputs of temperature, sunshine, humidity, and wind. At this relatively early
stage in the development and meaningful utilization of climatological information it is important that we have the data
for the future.

## Geographic Variability of the Climate

We have already learned much about Indiana climatology
after these years of observation and work. I doubt if the pioneer in Indiana 150 years ago would have realized that Indiana winters or Indiana summers could vary so much from year
to year. In some winters snow cover is negligible in central
Indiana but in other winters snow may cover the ground some
30 or 40 days. Southern Indiana is much less susceptible to
snow cover. In fact, the long term average of daily minimum
air temperatures does not drop to freezing along the Ohio
River.

## Lake Michigan Effects

We now have an approximate idea of the effect of Lake Michigan on the weather in northwestern Indiana. Snowfall is much heavier than anywhere else in the state (Fig. 43B). The result is higher annual precipitation. Many agricultural activities in that part of the state are geared to take advantage of the modifying effect of Lake Michigan. Those areas near the lake are warmed in the wintertime and cooled in the summertime. We now know that extreme northwestern Indiana experiences extreme snowfall in just a few square miles—unheard of elsewhere in the state. Climatological data document and show how temperatures in different months of the year are affected by Lake Michigan. If it were not for the Great Lakes influence, extreme northern Indiana would be colder than anywhere else in the state. Since this is not true the coldest sections are farther south toward the central area of Indiana. Greatest climatic change in short horizontal distances must certainly be greatest between the sandy shores of Lake Michigan and a few miles southeastward. It is indeed a complex area with respect to climatology with its complexity aggravated in the last few years by industrial growth along the shore east of Chicago. Urban development has altered the local climate and perhaps to some degree the mesoclimate with increased airborne nuclei and energy modification.

## Intense Rain Storms

The investigation of shower activity, both in time and area, continues and need is unabating. The city dweller who is flooded out of his house with a two-inch rain in an hour is just as interested in the probabilities of the recurrence of this event and the necessity for the planning of water removal from streets, as the farmer who experiences a five-inch rain in 24 hours and loses his crop by a flooding river. Statistical theory has helped us to work out probabilities of such events for periods beyond 100 years even though such lengthy records are scarce.[10,12,13]

## Cloudiness

We now know that Indiana cloudiness is greater in the north than in the central and southern parts of the state (Fig. 45B). Again, this is mainly due to influence of the lakes. This difference is most pronounced in the winter and spring. Evaporation is greater in the south than in the north and also the growing season is longer (Fig. 45A). There are more days with temperatures below zero in the north (Fig. 47C). Indiana's recorded lowest temperature is –35° F. This occurred at Greensburg on February 2, 1951. Two nearby stations, Scottsburg and Salem recorded –32° F. The highest temperature of record is held by the Collegeville Station, where 116° F. was observed July 14, 1936.

## Ohio River—Storm Alley

After these many years of observing Indiana weather, we find that the state lies in the main path of storms or low pressure centers moving across the plains to the Atlantic Ocean. It was a long time before our forefathers knew about this migration pattern. The movement of these storms and the centers of high pressure with the contrasting and sunny weather result in great and frequent changes in the daily and weekly weather in Indiana. They impart a more uniform pattern of precipitation through the year than enjoyed in states to the west, and an invigorating climate. During a large part of some seasons these storms may travel at one time to the north over the Great Lakes region with warm tropical air flowing over the state, and at another time, rapidly through the Southern states attracting cool air flow over Indiana from Canada. The result is two completely different regimes of weather. Many variables these storms induce in our climate scarcely have been studied and offer a gold mine for future exploitation in years ahead.

## Summer Storms and Tornadoes

In the summer Indiana is highly dependent on rainfall from thunderstorms. They can be generated by daytime convective activity or storm frontal activity near or in the state, and sometimes create severe weather. Occasionally in midsummer a moist air mass and rapid convective activity from solar radiation will induce a scattered development of these storms in the afternoon. Occasionally a weather front passes through the state in midsummer without leaving precipitation. Some summers would be very dry if it were not for these thundershowers which are usually quite local in nature. There are slightly more thunderstorms in the south than in the north.

Tornadoes are sometimes associated with severe thunderstorms. Indiana climatology reveals the paths and direction that many of these tornadoes have taken. Although the quality of tornado data leaves much to be desired, information points to a higher incidence of tornadoes in the southwest than in northeastern Indiana, and also a higher count in the west than in the east.

Fig. 49. Double jeopardy! On Palm Sunday, April 11, 1965, twin tornadoes were caught, in this rare photograph by Paul Huffman at 6:30 P.M., approaching Dunlap, Elkhart County, Indiana. They were moving northeast and about a quarter-mile distant. Golf-ball size hail was falling in this scene. Twenty-two persons were killed in Dunlap, and 92 house trailers in one court were destroyed. At least 15 tornadoes occurred in Indiana on this same day.

Tornadoes have taken the lives of 418 Indiana residents since the turn of the twentieth Century.[6,16] Of these 137 were from the Palm Sunday Tornadoes of April 11, 1965 (Fig. 49). The second greatest disastrous tornado day in Indiana took place March 18, 1925 when 70 persons were killed in Posey, Gibson and Pike Counties. Among states, Indiana ranks from 7th to 12th in number of tornadoes, or number of days with tornadoes, depending on data used. Generally, states in the central plains west and southwest of Indiana rank higher. The April 11, 1965, tornadoes increased the rate of deaths from tornadoes for the recent period but fatalities were higher in the 1916 to 1925 period—205 in ten years. March and April seem to have the most severe tornadoes, but the frequency of all tornadoes is higher in May and June. Tornado frequency declines to nearly zero in late fall and early winter. Only one death from tornadoes has occurred in the last half of the year. Two-thirds of the tornadoes have occurred in the afternoon or early evening hours. In the last 50 years Indiana has averaged nine reported tornadoes a year; these have occurred on five days a year. Recent improved reporting data indicates these averages are actually much too low.

### Surface Winds
The average speed of surface winds differs very little over the state except as caused by local exposures, like the top of a hill, in a valley, or near a large body of water like Lake Michigan. Winds from Lake Michigan are considerably higher than off land winds because of the diminished drag over water surfaces. The prevailing wind direction over Indiana is southwest in most all months except in the winter. Northwest is the predominant direction in the winter months. Gusty surface winds commonly occur with thunderstorms. They are most numerous in the spring and summer and quite scarce in the winter. Most are related to the advance of cold or warm fronts across the state.

### Relative Humidity
The common expression for amount of moisture in the air is relative humidity—per cent of moisture in the air compared to the maximum possible at the same temperature. This has great variability during a typical day as air temperatures change about 20 degrees and cause the maximum possible moisture term to vary greatly. We then find that relative humidity in Indiana often ranges during a typical sunny day from a per cent in the 40's in mid-afternoon at the time of maximum air temperature, to the 90's early in the morning at the time of minimum temperature. If there is a night breeze the percentage will not be so high. Also cloudiness may prevent by 10 to 30 per cent the usual drop of relative humidity at the time of maximum temperature. The areal variability of

relative humidity in Indiana seems to be small.[11] Moisture content per unit of volume or weight of air is usually greatest in the south where temperatures and thus moisture capacities are higher.

## Forecast: Favorable

The future is bright as intelligent beings apply their skills toward understanding weather and its effects on the enterprises of the people. To this day much of our thinking is single tracked. For many of us climate is just rainfall and temperature and how it comes in a year. When our new young scientists start to think and work in terms of selecting and defining the distributions of weather variables pertinent to a specific operation, great advances in climatology, and the application of such information, will have taken a giant stride.

## LITERATURE

1. BARGER, G. L., R. H. SHAW, and R. F. DALE. 1959. Chances of receiving selected amounts of precipitation in the North Central Region of the U. S. Iowa State University, Agricultural and Home Economics Experiment Station.
2. BLAIR, B. O., Purdue University Personal Communication.
3. FEYERHERM, A. M., L. D. BARK and W. C. BURROWS. 1965. Probabilities of sequences of wet dry days in Indiana. North Central Regional Research Publication 161. Agricultural Experiment Station, Kansas State University and Purdue University.
4. LINDSEY, A. A., J. E. NEWMAN. 1956. Use of official weather data in spring time. Temperature Analysis of an Indiana phenological record. Ecology **37** :812-823.
5. SCHAAL, L. A., Climatological summary, climatography of the United States No. 20-12. 1956-1965. U. S. Weather Bureau. One sheet summary for each city such as: Albion, Anderson, Angola, etc.
6. _____. Indiana tornado fact sheet. 1966. L.S. 6101, U.S. Department of Commerce, Environmental Science Services Administration, Weather Bureau.
7. _____, J. E. NEWMAN, and F. H. EMERSON. Risks of freezing temperatures — spring and fall in Indiana. 1961. Purdue University Agricultural Experiment Station Research Bulletin No. **721**, June 1961.
8. WEATHER BUREAU, Environmental Science Services Administration, U. S. Department of Commerce. Climatography of the U. S. No. 86-10, decennial census of the United States Climate — Climatic summary of the United States — Supplement for 1951 through 1960, Indiana. 1964.
9. _____. Climatological data — Indiana, Monthly, 1900 to present.
10. _____. Hourly precipitation data, Monthly, 1951 to present.
11. _____. Mean relative humidity, ($\%$), Monthly and Annual. 1961. National atlas of the United States.
12. _____. Rainfall frequency atlas of the United States for durations from 30 minutes to 24 hours and return periods from 1 to 100 years. Technical Paper No. **40**.
13. _____. Rainfall intensity - duration - frequency curves, for selected stations in the U. S. Technical Paper No. **25**.
14. _____. Summary of hourly observations. 1951-1960. Climatography of the U. S. No. 82-12, Decennial Census of United States Climate. 1963.
15. VISHER, S. S., Climate of Indiana. 1944. Indiana University.
16. WOLFORD, L. V. 1960. Tornado occurrences in the United States. Technical Paper No. **20**, U. S. Department of Commerce, ESSA, Weather Bureau.

# 10
# *Bioclimate*

JAMES E. NEWMAN
Department of Agronomy, Purdue University*

## Introduction

The term bioclimate denotes climatic effects and controls on living things. In this brief discourse, some features of Indiana's climate and its effect on various forms of life are discussed.

The weather, the most universal topic of conversation among men the world over, affects man in many ways. It could be that this universal use of the weather topic is deeply rooted in man's subconscious concern, rather than in his lack of knowledge of another topic.

Climate, the aggregate of all weather changes over a period of time for a given place, has been a subject of man's concern since the beginning of written history. In Western literature, perhaps the earliest scientific treatment of climatic effects on man is that of Hippocrates, written about 400 B.C. Therefore, it is clear that scientific study of daily weather events and their accumulated effects on living things is among the oldest of man's concerns.

## Macro-Scale Climates

According to Koppen's[1] world-wide designation of climates, Indiana has a humid, mesothermal-microthermal, continental climate. The key words in this description are "humid" and "continental." Indiana has no definite dry period or season with an average humidity less than 50%, thus it is humid in all seasons. The seasonal changes exhibit the continental influence, namely the extreme cold periods in winter and the extreme hot periods in summer. Indiana's climate is definitely transitional from south to north. The southern half falls within Koppen's mesothermal (Caf) type meaning a warm temperature climate similar to those found in the South and East. The northern half falls within a microthermal (Daf) type meaning a cool temperature climate similar to those found in the North and East.

* Journal paper 2807, Agricultural Experimental Station

The transitional nature of Indiana's climate is manifest in many ways. Perhaps, the common expression among Hoosiers is well founded: "If you don't like our weather, just wait a few minutes." This transitional nature also is evident in the length of the growing season. As illustrated in Fig. 50 the so-called normal frost-free growing season varies from 150 days in the northeastern counties to well over 200 days in parts of Posey County in the extreme southwest.[5] Perhaps the most dramatic transition in the state is found in the areas bordering Lake Michigan. Here the normal frost-free growing season varies from approximately 190 days near the shoreline to less than 160 days in the Kankakee River basin 15 to 20 miles to the south. The dramatic change in the local climate for the

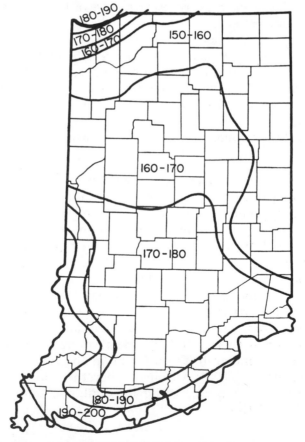

Fig. 50. Average length of frost-free seasons in days.

lakeshore area of northwestern Indiana is further evident in summer temperatures, cloudiness, and winter snowfall.

### Agricultural Seasons

In a mid-latitude temperature transitional climate like Indiana's, the astronomy-based concept of four equal-length seasons does not accurately coincide with the observed facts. As any native Hoosier well knows, spring does not automatically appear on March 21 each year. Further, it is plain that plant growth does not follow the classical four season concept very well either.

For many native species of vegetation and cool-season agricultural crops, the growing season is not confined to the frost-free period of the year. In fact, the total array of agricultural crops conforms to the concept of six-seasons far better than the conventional four seasons. For example, the calendar year can be subdivided into known crop-response periods referred to as "agricultural seasons."[4] In Indiana, such seasons can be defined in the following manner: (1) Winter—all crops are dormant. (2) Early spring—cool season perennial crops such as bluegrass begin to grow. (3) Late spring—warm season crops, such as dent corn, are planted. (4) Summer—warm season crops grow rapidly and cool season crops, such as small grains, are harvested. (5) Early autumn—cool season crops, such as winter wheat, are planted and warm season crops, such as soybeans, are harvested. (6) Late autumn—cool season crops continue to grow throughout the autumn harvest season.

The average length in days, as well as the onsetting date, for these six agricultural seasons are presented in Table 5, for Evansville, Indiana. Here daily maximum temperatures were used to depict these seasons. There are other approaches using mean daily temperatures, minimum temperatures and mean diurnal changes in temperatures, but all these methods yield similar results.[4]

### Local Climatic Influences

Shifts in climatic conditions related to a major change in the earth's surface are normally referred to as meso-climates. There are several landform features within Indiana that create unique meso-scale climates. They include all of the major river valleys, the shore area around large lakes, and exceedingly high plateau areas. Further, major man-made changes such as large cities and large artificial lakes create unique meso-climates.

TABLE 5. The average beginning and ending date of the six agricultural seasons as determined by 5 years of daily maximum temperature levels (1949-54) at Evansville, Indiana.[7]

| WINTER (all plants dormant) | EARLY SPRING (cool season plants grow) | LATE SPRING (warm season plants grow) | SUMMER (cool season plants dormant) | EARLY AUTUMN (warm season plants mature) | LATE AUTUMN (cool season plants grow) |
|---|---|---|---|---|---|
| Below 50°F | 51° to 70°F | 71° to 80°F | Above 81°F | 71° to 80°F | 51° to 70°F |
| Dec. 13 to Mar. 4 | Mar. 5 to Apr. 21 | Apr. 22 to June 16 | June 17 to Sept. 11 | Sept. 12 to Oct. 21 | Oct. 22 to Dec. 12 |
| 81 Days | 48 Days | 57 Days | 87 Days | 40 Days | 52 Days |
| Heavy Freezes | Frequent Frosts | Frost Free but Cool Nights | Hot Nights | Frost Free but Cool Nights | Frequent Frosts |

The immediate topographic features such as slope, forest cover, large buildings, large areas of concrete, major wind obstructions, etc., modify climatic conditions on still a smaller scale. These modifications, usually confined to areas of a few hundred square feet to an acre or so, are normally referred to as "local climates." However, modifications in climatic factors related to the immediate soil or water surface are normally thought of as "micro-climates." These influences are usually restricted to within a few inches or a few feet in the vertical immediately above such surfaces.

Meso-scale climates are controlled mainly by the *wind*. Major features of the earth's surface as river valleys, lake shores, and large cities create unique patterns of wind flow. The classical example here is the reversal of winds between day and night along major shore lines or the so-called sea-breeze phenomenon.

The major control for local climates is that of slope. The amount of solar energy received per unit area at the earth's surface depends on the angle of incidence. The quantity of solar heat received on any unit area may be approximated by the following formula:

$$I = I_s \cdot \sin h$$

where I is the amount of heat per unit area of the earth's surface at any given slope, $I_s$ is the intensity of the solar heat if the surface is perpendicular to the sun's rays, and h is the

angle on the solar incidence at a given time. The values for
h depend on the height of the sun in the sky which is determined by the time of year, the latitude, and time of day. The
value of $I_s$ is related to the solar constant and the atmospheric
transmission at a given value for h.

Another influence on "local climate" is that of major variations in winds due to obstructions. These influences can be
observed around buildings, trees or within vegetative cover
such as a forest. Here man has learned to exert considerable
control over winds, thus creating and controlling local climates
by the construction of shelter-belts. Fig. 51 illustrates in
a dimensionless manner how a properly arranged shelter-belt
can change and control winds in a local area.[2]

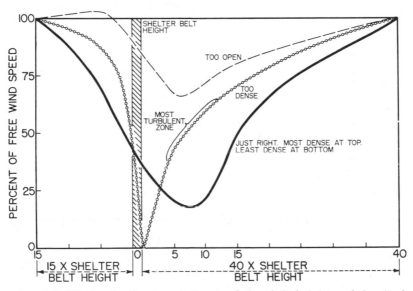

Fig. 51. Wind reduction in relation to shelter-belt height and density.[2]

Micro-climate is a product of the interactions of heat exchanges between the major physical components that make
up any given environment. In an out-of-doors plant environment these major components consist of the soil body, the
vegetable cover, and the air layer immediately above. The
diurnal organization of sensible temperature variations within
a micro-climate related to a plant environment is idealistically
illustrated in Fig. 52.

Micro-climates are created by the concentration of energy exchanges that takes place at a radiating surface. At any one instant in time the state of these energy exchanges or the so-called "energy balance" can be assessed as follows:

$$R_n = (R_i + R_l) - (R_{re} + R_b)$$

Where $R_n$ is the net radiant balance, $R_i$ is incoming solar insolation, $R_l$ is long wave infrared sky radiation, $R_{re}$ is the reflected solar incidence and $R_b$ is the back radiation at the terrestrial surface.

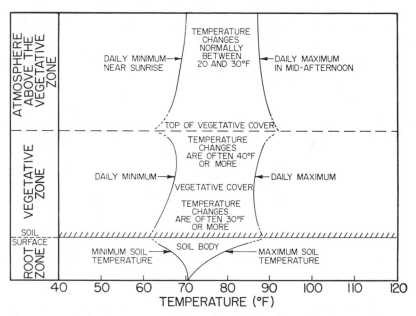

Fig. 52. Daily temperature changes within the soil, the vegetative cover, and in the atmosphere immediately above the vegetative cover.

Further, the "net energy balance" ($R_n$) at the receiving surface is dissipated in the following manner:

$$R_n = S + E + A + P$$

where S is the stored heat within the body of the mass forming the receiving surface, E is the heat used in evaporating water, A is the heat used in heating the air immediately surrounding the receiving surface and P is the light energy used in photosynthesis if growing plants form part of the receiving surface.

All micro-climates are a product of unique radiant energy exchanges and their resulting energy balances.

## Climate and Human Comfort

Recent research relates human comfort outside to four environmental factors or weather elements. They are (1) the temperature, (2) the humidity, (3) the amount of sunshine or solar heat striking a person, and (4) the amount of wind.[6]

Fig. 53 diagrams how these four major climatic elements interact to produce an environment under which various out-of-doors human activities can take place in comfort. Most

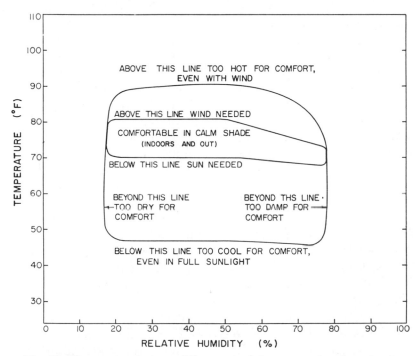

Fig. 53. Human comfort conditions out-of-doors as related to the four environmental factors of sensible temperature, relative humidity, solar radiation and wind.[3]

individuals are comfortable in a shaded area, out of the wind, with temperatures between 70 and 80 degrees F., and relative humidity between 20 and 80 per cent. These combinations of sensible temperatures and relative humidities, in the absence of direct sunlight and wind, are known as the "human comfort zone."[6] This zone is the same indoors and out. It is represented by a heavy, dark line surrounding the above stated combination of temperatures and humidities in Fig. 53.

Ideal human comfort in average household or street dress covers a range of temperatures and humidities. This is proof that individuals vary in their response to environmental factors. Some are so-called warm-blooded, while others are more cold-blooded. Thus, each person may require somewhat different combinations of temperatures and humidities for comfort. This is particularly true when the individual is at rest or relaxing.

When temperatures rise into the 80's and 90's, a fan or air conditioning is needed indoors. Light winds add to human comfort outside. In fact, a wind is necessary for comfort when temperatures climb into the 80's if humidity stays above 50 per cent and the sun is shining. As temperatures drop below 70 degrees, heat must be added indoors and some direct solar heat is necessary outside for comfort. Temperatures between 50 and 60 degrees under full sunlight with little or no wind are nearly ideal for active sports out-of-doors. Further, the comfort zone in normal street clothing can drop as low as 45 degrees under full sunshine with little or no wind. Then, too, the comfort zone can shift up to the low 90's at night under clear skies with light winds and low humidities.

Fig. 54 illustrates the average percentage of time during the year that temperatures and humidity relationships can be expected to fall within the *human comfort range* at Indianapolis, Indiana.[8] Such illustrations, relating how temperature and humidity vary throughout the year, are referred to as *climographs*.

The human comfort range, as outlined by the double dark lines, between 45 and 90 degrees F. and 20 to 80 per cent humidity, occurs 39% of the time during the year. Additional calculations show that about 20% of these hourly values falling within this human comfort zone were unfit for human activities out-of-doors due to other inclement weather conditions. These additional reductions are due to precipitation and high winds for the most part. Therefore, about 30% of all hours in the year are within the human comfort zone in central Indiana. This compares very favorably to other north-central regions of continental United States.

As any Hoosier will testify, human comfort out-of-doors changes greatly with the seasons. Most of nearly 5 months are too cold. This period begins by mid-November and extends to mid-April on the average. Another period averaging nearly two months long, is too hot and humid, particularly during

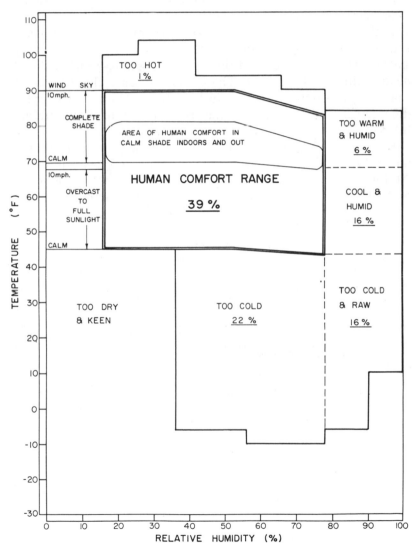

Fig. 54. Climograph for Indianapolis, Indiana. The total distribution of hourly temperature and relative humidity values (1951-60).[8]

the afternoon hours. This period begins around mid-June and often extends well into September. But the remaining 5 months of late Spring and early Autumn are nearly ideal for out-of-door activities during a high percentage of the time.

## Summary

Indiana has a humid, continental climate that is transitional from south to north. Native plant growth, as well as annual agricultural crop-responses, conform to six seasons rather than to four equal-length seasons. There are many smaller scale climates within the large-scale, humid, continental climate of Indiana. These smaller scale climatic shifts are related to major changes in land forms, local topographic differences, and the physical nature of the immediate surface intercepting radiant energy.

Human comfort out-of-doors is determined by temperature, humidity, wind, and the intensity of solar and sky radiation. At Indianapolis, a person can be comfortable out of doors in normal street dress about 30% of the time during the year.

## LITERATURE

1. KOPPEN, W. 1931. Grundriss der Klimakunde. Walter de Guyter Co., Berlin.
2. MINISTRY OF AGRICULTURE, FISHERIES AND FOOD. 1964. Farmer's weather. Bull. **165**, Her Majesty's Stationery Office, London.
3. NEWMAN, J. E. 1964. Human comfort out-of-doors. Proc. Turf Conference, Midwest Regional Turf Foundation, Purdue Univ., Lafayette, Indiana.
4. _____ and Jen-Yu Wang. 1959. Defining agricultural seasons in the middle latitudes. Agronomy Jour. **51**: 579-582.
5. SCHAAL, L. A., J. E. NEWMAN and F. H. EMERSON. 1961. Risks of freezing temperatures — spring and fall in Indiana. Purdue Univ. AES Res. Bull. **721**.
6. TROMP, S. W. (Ed.). 1962. Biometeorology. Proc. Second International Bioclimatological Congress. Pergamon Press, New York.
7. WEATHER BUREAU. 1900. Climatology of the United States No. 30-12. Summary of Hourly Observations, Evansville, Indiana, (1949-1954). U. S. Dept. of Commerce.
8. WEATHER BUREAU. 1900. Climatology of the United States No. 82-12. Summary of Hourly Observations, Indianapolis, Indiana, (1951-60). U. S. Dept. of Commerce.

# *11*
# *Algae*

WILLIAM A. DAILY AND FAY KENOYER DAILY
Lilly Research Laboratories and Butler University

Algae, "the grass of many waters", abound in Indiana where many favorable growing places are found. Numerous species have been reported and all but one major class are represented. They do not constitute a natural group, but range from one-celled to many-celled plants of varying complexity. Some have been called the "gems of the plant world", and are beautiful, microscopic, bright green crescents and crowns! Some algae are attached and motionless or oscillate. Others float freely with the water currents and are called phytoplankton or "the wanderers". The most rapidly moving algae propel themselves by means of flagella. Less spectacularly, movement may be the result of slime secretion. Microscopic forms may be seen with the unaided eye only when they clump together to form floating pond scums or produce cushions and mats on the soil. The plant body may be several feet long, however, and form vast "aquatic meadows" over the bottom of a lake.

## Representative Kinds

Based primarily on pigments and morphology, the algae are divided into several major classes. Nearly all contain the pigment, chlorophyll, and are green in color. Others have additional pigments such as carotenes, xanthophylls and phycocyanins which render them shades of blue, green, purple and red. Some representatives of each major class of algae found in Indiana follow:

*The grass-green algae (Chlorophyceae)* (Fig. 55: 1, 2, 4, 9, 11, 12, 14, 19). These are abundant in Indiana. *Protococcus,* a single spherical-celled organism is often seen growing as a green coating on trees, stones, fences, old fence rails and shingled roofs. Barnyard pools rich in nitrogenous compounds, ditches and ponds may be colored green because of microscopic single-celled and colonial forms. They are flagellated, hence swimmers, and represent species of *Chlamydom-*

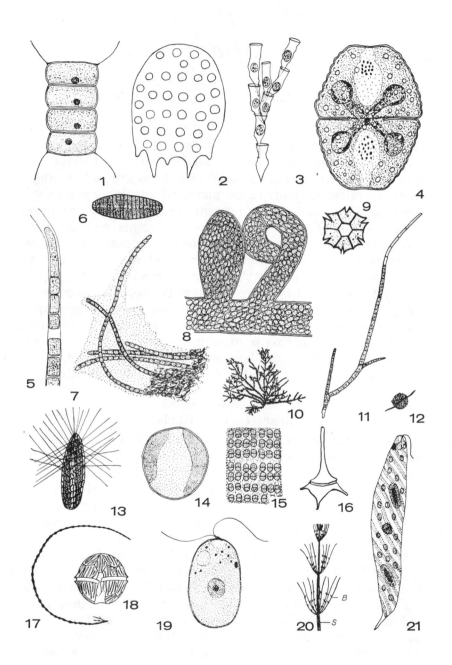

*onas, Eudorina, Platydorina* and *Volvox*. A rare form, *Volvox Carteri*, about the size of a head of a pin, was found as a waterbloom (floating scum) in an Indianapolis Fish Hatchery Pond.[11] It had not been reported previously in this country!

Filamentous species, the most conspicuous of the greens, are seen in almost all bodies of water. *Spirogyra,* a thread-like plant, slimy to the touch, has been referred to as "water silk" or "frog spittle" and is very abundant in the spring. Small streams and rivulets may teem with clumps of *Cladophora, Tetraspora, Chaetophora* and *Stigeoclonium.* Some are attached to stones in water and even to the inside of watering troughs. A rare green algal species *(Cladophora holsatica)* forms "cladophora balls." Some of these hollow green balls, an inch in diameter, were found along the shore of Long Lake in Steuben County.[4] The spherical shape is attributed to the wave action along the shore. Cladophora balls the size of small grapefruits grow in Lake Akan in Japan and are protected by the government as a "National Treasure." A stamp was issued in 1956 depicting this unusual alga.

The common "water net" *(Hydrodictyon reticulatum)* resembles a hairnet in structure and often the individual cells are large enough to be readily seen with the naked eye. It is found along small streams, the shores of permanent ponds and lakes.

*The charophytes or stoneworts (Charophyceae)* (Fig. 55:20). [3,5,6] This group of algae is closely allied to the foregoing, but because of the complexity of the plant body is classed separate-

Fig. 55:1-21. A few Indiana algae greatly enlarged except for figures 10, 12, 17 and 20 which are ½ natural size. 1. *Scenedesmus,* a floating, planktonic green alga. 2. *Platydorina* (flagella not shown); a green colonial alga. 3. *Dinobryon,* a golden-brown floating alga. 4. *Cosmarium,* a planktonic green alga. 5 & 7. *Phormidium,* a blue-green alga showing the detail of a single filament and several filaments in a gelatinous mass. 6. *Diatoma,* a diatom, which was entangled in other algae on a stone from a creek. 8. *Vaucheria,* a yellow-green alga which was floating in quiet water. A small part of the plant shown. 9. *Pediastrum,* a floating green alga. 10. *Batrachospermum,* a red alga shown in a clump which was attached. 11 & 12. *Chaetophora,* an attached green alga. A branch is shown in detail and a gelatinous mass of plants is attached to a higher aquatic plant stem. 13. *Mallomonas,* a free-swimming golden-brown alga. 14. *Chlorella,* a one-celled green alga. 15. *Agmenellum,* a blue-green planktonic alga. 16. *Ceratium,* an armored flagellate, planktonic. 17. *Lemanea,* an attached red alga. 18. *Peridinium,* an armored flagellate, planktonic. 19. *Chlamydomonas,* a green free-swimming alga. 20. *Chara.* a charophyte, an attached alga. B = branchlet, S = stem. 21. *Euglena,* a euglenoid, a free swimming alga.

ly. The plant is composed of the rhizoidal (root-like) portion, the stem and whorls of branchlets (of differing complexity). Superficially, some of the charophytes resemble the horsetail rushes. There are three genera found in the state: *Chara, Nitella and Tolypella* (four if one admits *Charopsis*). *Chara contraria* is found in the greatest variety of habitats and may form "aquatic meadows" over the bottom of some lakes and gravel pit ponds. It probably forms the largest volume and weight of the algae in Indiana. Adding to the weight, is the calcareous deposit found on the surface of the alga and deposited in some of the cells when growing where calcium carbonate is abundant in the water.

*Chara Brittonii* is a rare alga and known only from the type specimen until found here again. The specimens from the Cabin Creek Raised Bog have been studied with respect to their chromosomes and morphology and they represent a unique type among the charophytes of the world.

The genus, *Nitella,* is not found often in Indiana, but *Nitella flexilis* is the most common and may cover large parts of ponds and lakes with black, mucky areas on the bottom (usually near a stream inlet). The large cells in this alga make it ideal for investigation of its cytology, physiology and ultrastructure.

The *genus, Tolypella,* differs from the other two by producing widely divergent and tangled branchlets in distinctive nest-like heads. It was first discovered in Indiana in the Display Ponds of Pokagon State Park, Steuben Co. Other collecting spots are near that area.

*The euglenoids (Euglenophyceae)* (Fig. 55: 21). Most of the genera in this class are free-swimming cells, grass-green to colorless and may exhibit both animal and plant characteristics. *Euglena* is probably the most common and, at times, a very beautiful one-celled plant. It may reproduce in such quantities as to completely cover the surface of a pond, farmyard ditch, or wet soil bordering ponds or streams. The individuals may continually change their shape (metaboly) while in motion. Five of the eight known genera in the United States are reported for Indiana.

*The golden-brown algae (Chrysophyceae)* (Fig. 55: 3, 13). *Dinobryon* is the most prevalent genus of this class in Indiana and at least six species have been collected from some of our glacial and soft water lakes. The dendroid (tree-like) colonies are composed of cells each of which is enclosed in a rigid, urn-shaped envelope attenuated at the base. *Mallomonas* is a free-swimming, solitary cell covered with scales and spines. *Synura,* another common genus, is colonial with pear-shaped cells covered with scales.

The diatoms *(Bacillariophyceae)* (Fig. 55: 6). *Asterionella, Melosira, Synedra* and *Diatoma* are some Indiana genera. Almost all bodies of water and most soils have representatives of this class. They are also found as epiphytes (attached to) on many filamentous green algae especially *Cladophora, Rhizoclonium* and *Vaucheria.* The yellowish to brownish diatoms are not only the most ubiquitous of Indiana algae but perhaps the easiest recognized because of the highly silicified cell walls composed of two overlapping parts as in a pill box. Identification to species is based chiefly upon the wall structure and ornamentation of these glass-like walls.

The *"armored"* flagellates *(Dinophyceae)* (Fig. 55: 16, 18). These single-celled ovoid-shaped swimming algae possess a firm wall which maintains its form even after death. The "armor" is composed of a definite number of plates whose arrangement and sculpturing is significant in identification.

Many species of *Peridinium* have been reported here. However, very seldom are they abundant in collections taken with a plankton net (a cone-shaped net of silk through which water is strained). An extremely rare species, *Peridinium volzii* var. *vancouverense* was recently found in Round Lake, near Bristol in Elkhart County. The Frisz Lagoon in the Shades State Park contains, at least, three other genera in this class.

*Ceratium hirundinella* is one of the most commonly collected free-floating wanderers in our lakes. These strange, usually 3 to 4-horned cells are quite variable in the number and size (length) of the horns. It is thought that seasonal changes in the environment may control this phenomenon.

Yellow-green algae *(Xanthophyceae)* (Fig. 55: 8.) These plants are predominantly yellow-green in color and grow on soil and in water. *Botrydium granulatum,* a tiny balloon-like alga which can be seen with the unaided eye, was found growing on the bank of White River in Johnson County for a distance of, at least, ⅓ mile and covering many square yards. It is attached in mud by a colorless underground rhizoidal portion.

*Vaucheria* ("green felt"), a filamentous form, is both aquatic and terrestrial and found as dark-green felty mats. Botanical laboratories often employ this alga to demonstrate the production of exceedingly large and prolific asexual zoospores (spherical swimming bodies). This is easily accomplished by placing mats of the alga from the soil into battery jars filled with water. These are held about 12 hours in artificial light.

*Botryococcus Braunii,* a true open-water planktonic form, is often in collections from our northern Indiana glacial lakes. The orange-colored irregularly-shaped many-celled plants are easily distinguished from all other algae.

*The red algae (Rhodophyceae)* (Fig. 55: 10, 17). The red algae differ from all other algae in modes of reproduction. The plant body may be fairly simple to very complex. Paradoxically, only one of the six genera in Indiana, *Porphyridium,* is a bright red color. The remainder have the red pigment phycoerythrin partially obscured by other pigments, chiefly chlorophyll and phycocyanin. *Porphyridium cruentum* is seen here only in greenhouses and grows as a thin gelatinous blood-red layer on the damp soil. *Asterocytis smaragdina,* a simple or branched filament is very brilliant blue-green in color and found sparingly in the muddy terraces of Kickapoo Falls near Attica. It has also been found on *Cladophora* attached to stones in the Calumet River, Lake County. *Compsopogon coeruleus,* a blue-green, many-celled broad filament, was found growing in an Indianapolis indoor fish bowl, but was thought to have been imported from a more southern state. *Audouinella violacea* resembles a filamentous blue-green alga when growing attached to limestone (at Vinegar Mill, Muscatatuck State Park, Jennings County) and sandstone (in canyon falls of Turkey Run State Park).

*Batrachospermum* (the frog-spawn alga) and *Lemanea* are the two best known red algae in Indiana. The former is generally attached to stones, snail shells and wood. The blackish-red, bead-like filaments are enclosed in a gelatinous mass. *Lemanea,* restricted to the southern portion of Indiana and observed on limestone subtstrata in swiftly flowing water, is typically olive-green in color.[18] These small (2 to 5 inches in length) plants, consisting of cartilaginous, thread-like, frequently simple filaments with alternate swellings and contractions are common in the rapids of Cataract Falls, Owen County, and streams in Bartholomew, Jennings and Jefferson Counties. Recently, several unusually large (about 20 inches long) *Lemanea* plants were found growing in dripping water and were attached to a concrete sluiceway on the Avoca State Fish Hatchery dam in Lawrence County.

*The blue-green algae (Myxophyceae)* (Fig. 55: 5, 7, 15). The blue-green algae, very widely distributed in Indiana, are one- to many-celled, spherical to filamentous and found floating in the water or as visible gelatinous masses on moist soil, rocks, wood or other materials. They are distinct from other algae because of the usually prevailing blue-green pigment which is dispersed throughout the peripheral protoplasm, the formation of heterocysts (large colorless bodies) and the presence of a primitive nucleus. Many of the species superficially resemble bacteria in shape, size and organization and are sometimes mistaken for them. These are the most primitive of the algae.

Some of the planktonic forms *(Anacystis, Gomphosphaeria, Anabaena* and *Aphanizomenon* are responsible for the production of "water blooms." [9,14] *Phormidium* forms a gelatinous covering on damp soil. One should be able to distinguish *Aphanizomenon* without a microscope because it resembles small bits of grass floating on the water.

For a complete list of algae reported from Indiana some check lists are available.[16,17,23] Some general references are helpful, too, in identification of Indiana algae.[24,26] A file of the published names of Indiana algae and their distribution by county was prepared by C. M. Palmer at Butler University. This has been the basis of his check lists. It is being kept up-to-date and another check list should appear soon (by F. K. Daily).

## Collecting Algae

Perhaps because the collection of algae from water requires specialized equipment and because many algae are in the greatest abundance during the hot, humid summer months, comparatively little has been done on the large bulk of algal classes in Indiana. This makes the study of this group of plants especially rewarding.

For sampling plankton, a collecting net can be obtained from biological supply houses or made from a fine mesh bolting cloth. One must have a long line, preferably of nylon cord (about 50 ft. long) attached by a swivel to three short cords about a foot long. These in turn are tied in three places equidistantly to a metal hoop of about a ten-inch diameter. A piece of silk bolting cloth (Number 20 with 173 meshes to the inch usually used) is cut into a triangular shape (a square yard is cut along the diagonal from corner to opposite corner). The two equal sides are then stitched together forming a cone. The top of the cone is fitted and sewn to a bias piece of muslin which forms a binding to be sewed around the metal hoop. The small end of the cone is cut to insert and fasten (tied in place with a drawstring) a piece of rubber tubing which can be opened or closed by means of a pinch clamp. The net is towed through the water until the plankton is concentrated in the bottom of the net. This can be removed into a bottle by opening the clamp.

Forceps are desirable to pick up shallow water forms to guard against attack by giant water bugs that may be lurking there.

A simple dredge can be made to collect charophytes by cutting several lengths from coat hanger wire, doubling them and twisting the looped portions together leaving an "eye" through which a piece of nylon cord about 50 feet long can be attached. Fine wire can also be dispersed through the coarse wire prongs made by bending out the loose ends of the coat hanger wire. The tangle of fine wire adds to the efficiency of the dredge which has the advantage over rigid metal dredges in that if it is caught on stones or other submerged objects, the wire will straighten out and the dredge can be pulled free. The dredge can either be tossed into the water and pulled back to shore to obtain charophytes or it can be towed from a boat.

Indiana lakes of glacial origin are usually clear enough that one may drift in a boat on a calm day over shallow water areas and see the bottom flora without benefit of special equipment. However, when it is windy, a glass-bottomed bucket may be inserted in the water through which a better view is obtained.

If one can scuba dive or deep dive, it is very helpful in collecting and studying the bottom flora.

A hunting knife is useful to scrape algae from soil and wet rock.

After collecting the algae, various ways are available for

keeping them. Of course, some forms must be kept living, cultured, and their life cycle studied for identification. Two per cent formalin is a good preservative for most algae. Soil algae and shallow water forms can be dried on newspaper and placed in packets. Some algae may be placed temporarily in plastic bags in the field and examined and preserved in the laboratory. Others may be pressed between absorbent sheets of paper in a plant press. Charophytes lend themselves to either method very well. Phytoplankton is conveniently dried on mica slips or glass slides. A drop of water and cover glass is all that is needed to observe them under the microscope. They will keep over a hundred years this way.

Pertinent information about the environment and the location should be recorded for a permanent record about each specimen. Specimens with the collection data should be available in herbaria for consultation by the student of the algae.

### Habitats

Over a thousand lakes and ponds left by the late Wisconsin glaciation over much of northern Indiana affords an ideal location for microscopic and larger forms of algae. Most of these lakes are hard or alkaline in nature. Soft water or acid reservoirs, lakes and ponds may occur in areas poor in dissolved minerals and boggy areas. Man-made lakes in the leached soils of southern Indiana or ponds without inlet or outlet (chiefly rain water catch basins) are soft water lakes. We owe the large number of permanent bodies of water in Indiana in part to the humidity of the region.

There are two general groups of algae in our lakes, the open-water or free-flowing (euplankton) and the shallow water (benthos) or shore and bottom forms. Occasionally the shallow water species will be found mixed with the phytoplankton especially when the water has been roiled. Many of the open-water forms are adapted to this mode of life by possessing wide gelatinous sheaths, long bristle-like appendages, flattened appendages, flattened colonies or coiled filaments which help to keep them afloat.

Some natural features influencing the occurrence of the various algae in Indiana waters have been observed. Lakes or lake systems afford differing habitats for algae because of their origin, shape of lake basin, bottom composition, pH, dissolved gases, depth, bottom slope (affects light intensity), natural wind barriers at water's edge, shape of margin, size, geographic location (growing season, temperature gradient, lake turnover), age of lake and consequent effect of accumulated organic matter, algae and other organisms on lake, presence or absence of inlets and outlets, minerals from springs emptying into the lake or other sources, any material washed in from the surrounding area, etc. Each factor may or may not influence the occurrence of an alga depending upon its tolerance to the factor in question.

The algae of flowing water differ with the nature of the habitat, too. The swiftness of the current, light transmission (is it muddy or clear), temperature, minerals available, pH, dissolved oxygen, depth, nature of the bottom, etc., are a few important factors. Pollution is a grave factor influencing rivers and streams. Some species of algae are not found in rivers and streams, but are found in lakes of glacial origin. Other species are rheophiles, (river-living), although they may be found in lakes and ponds, too, near the inlet from a stream, or in artificial lakes made by damming a stream.

In rapids and waterfalls, there are representatives of nearly all the classes of algae. They may form crusts on rocks or project out into the current. In slower portions of streams, they are found attached to rocks and bottom or floating in water. Oxbows and marginal ponds of streams offer quieter habitats for algae which may be brittle or delicate and cannot withstand strong currents.

Our Indiana soils are often completely covered by algal growths in some places. A study of the distribution of soil algae with reference to factors in the habitat has not been made in Indiana. However, undoubtedly one would find that certain algae grow almost anywhere on moist soil where they are dispersed, but others may be influenced by soil leaching and consequently the availability of minerals in the soil, pH, amount of organic matter, geographic location, temperature, slope of ground (facing sun or shaded), amount of moisture in the soil, etc.

Some algae adapt to a transitional type of habitat between strictly terrestrial and aquatic and live in a subaerial environment; that is, partly submerged, or completely exposed but in very moist soil. *Chara contraria*, the charophyte, was found on the bank of Lake Freeman growing in moist gravel continuously drenched by water from a spring. Other charophytes, *Chara Keukensis* and *Chara hydropitys* var. *septentrionalis* occurred on moist sand in seepage at the dam of Starve Hollow Lake, Jackson County. The last two species were found on wet muck at the edge of Lake Cicott, in Cass County, too. *Chara Brittonii* was collected from rather dry though moist peat at the Cabin Creek Raised Bog in Randolph County.

It has been supposed that aquatic algae were the most primitive plants and the origin of land plants was associated with the development of cortication which supported plants in an aerial habitat. No such correlation is seen in the charophytes mentioned above. *Chara Brittonii* is entirely without corticating cells (outer layer), *Chara contraria* has both the stem and part of the branchlets corticated, and the other two have the stem corticated but have differing degrees of cortication on the branchlets with *Chara Keukensis* devoid of it. They grow normally in an aquatic habitat but may grow subaerially without change in morphology. In fact, the charophyte with the least cortication grows in the driest habitat. Although there is good evidence that food and water is normally exchanged through the cell wall of these algae in an aquatic habitat, the above examples show that the rhizoidal portion of the plants can supply the nutritional demands if necessary.

Many other habitats for algae have been noted. For instance, nearly everyone is familiar with a greenish coating usually on the north side of tree trunks. This is *Protococcus,* a unicellular alga. Sometimes the backs of turtles may be covered with a green, "hairy" growth of a green alga. *Basicladia chelonum.* Air may contain spores and/or vegetative cells of algae. A recent demonstration of this occurred when popcorn plants were covered securely with new, previously unopened, plastic bags after the tassels formed in an experiment.[12] Algae were discovered in the moist bags. They undoubtedly settled on the corn before covering. Other unique habitats include cemetery urns, flower pots, tree pockets (depressions on the trunks or limbs of trees which may catch rain-water) in lichens, on dead snail and mussel shells, and bird baths. The Cabin Creek Raised Bog, Randolph County, is another fascinating habitat for algae.[10,20] Rivulets fed by artesian springs flow through the marly peat which has produced a mound above the surrounding field.

### Algae and Human Welfare

Algae have been rediscovered in recent years as a field of importance in medical research. Schwimmer and Schwimmer (1955) described the role of algae and plankton in medicine as a subject as old as recorded medical history yet so new that medical investigators do not realize its existence.[21]

Perhaps the upsurge in interest in this group of plants came about as the food supply reached the critical stage during World War II. The interest has continued since the possibility of growing a high-protein plant food in large quantities is of paramount importance in connection with the long-range planning for the feeding of an ever-expanding world population. The space race has also contributed its share to investigation of cultivation of algae as a source of oxygen, food, and elimination of wastes during space travel. An article in Collier's magazine with the frontispiece showing a hand reaching out of the sea grasping a loaf of bread and with the inscription "bread from the sea, now we have a new source of food and energy— a basic step to world peace," dramatizes the quest for growing algae successfully in large amounts for a food supply.[13] Algal culture from the laboratory to the pilot plant was investigated extensively in such laboratories as the Carnegie Institute of Washington and the Stanford Research Institute.

The advantage of using algae over other plants man has used as a source of food and medical products is considerable. Generally, only a small portion of the other plants is usable. The primary manufactory of the plant is the green leaves. It is here that synthesizing processes occur which produce food stuffs or products used in medicine, but the organic materials must migrate to other parts of the plant to be laid down in seeds and tubers as storage materials. This process depends upon the seasons and is not continuous. The shortcomings of higher plants as photosynthesizers seems obvious then. In contrast, lower forms of plant life present advantages. Unicellular green algae are relatively highly efficient in making food. One of the common forms studied is *Chlorella,* an Indiana alga described earlier in this chapter. This alga contains a large amount of pigments essential to photosynthesis. The

organic material formed in the process is stored within each
cell. The growth of the plant takes place through division of
each cell into 4, 8 or 16 new cells, each of which is capable of
photosynthsis and further division every 12 hours under favorable conditions.

For cultivating *Chlorella,* requirements are simple: inorganic salts dissolved in water, carbon dioxide as the only
source of carbon, light to carry forward the process of photosynthesis (may be fluorescent light-red to violet range of color
used), and a temperature of about 25°C. The materials syn-
thesized consist mainly of proteins, carbohydrates, lipids,
sterols, vitamins and other metabolic complexes. The chief
difficulties in algal mass culture are engineering in nature, but
it has been shown that large-scale culture is technically feasible.[2]

For the easy cultivation of an alga for food, the common
blue-green alga, *Nostoc commune,* or witch's butter might be
of interest. It is served as food regularly in China and is known
as Fat Choy. In Indiana, it is often seen in the grass or bare
soil and looks like a piece of lettuce.

The mounting interest in bacteria-free cultures of the algae
has developed along with the study of mass culturing. There
is an increasing awareness of the use of algal cultures for physiological and genetic research. Due to the simplicity of structure and large cell size, these simple plants are extremely useful in fundamental research.

Bacteria-free, unialgal cultures have been obtained sometimes with great difficulty, but during the last 20 years a large
number of algae have been isolated and maintained as in the
culture collection at Indiana University under the supervision
of Dr. Richard C. Starr. One of the chief difficulties in obtaining pure cultures of algae is that they usually have a gelatinous
covering. Other organisms cling to this or have been incorporated into it. Use of dilution and washing as well as treatment
with antibiotics and other agents have met with some success.

To keep cultures living after obtaining germ-free unialgal
cultures· one can repeatedly transfer the algae to fresh media
(which is time consuming) or put them away for a short time
in cool storage. For maintaining them for a longer period of
time, freeze-drying (lyophilization) can be used successfully

(for, at least, 2 years).[8] A more recent method is quick-freezing and storing in liquid nitrogen.

The study of the physiology of the algae is in its infancy. Difficulties in identifying minute algae showing morphological similarities are as great as in the bacteria. With the advent of pure culture methods, an opportunity is opened to the study of the physiology of these organisms. Cultural characteristics will now be known to relate to a single organism and not to probable contaminants. Classification on the basis of physiology is therefore possible. This also opens the way for investigation of the algae for possible industrial products, because of the feasibility of mass culture and greater control of a product containing only materials from a single kind of organism.

Although algal products of this sort have not met with great success as yet, it has been shown that they are of potential interest in medicine. An antibiotic has been obtained from *Chlorella* known as *Chlorellin*. Since other antibiotics, already in production, were active against the same organisms, *Chlorellin* has not been marketed.

Microscopic algae have been investigated in other ways from a medical standpoint. Algal "soups" have been tried in the treatment of leprosy.[13] No ill effects resulted from it and there was a marked improvement in the energy, weight and general health of the patients.

A laboratory technique has been devised making use of the fact that *Euglena,* another common Indiana alga, must have vitamin $B_{12}$ for growth. The blood from an anaemic person will not support growth of the alga. Therefore, if *Euglena* is grown in the presence of an unknown and compared with control cultures supplied with varying amounts of $B_{12}$, the state of anaemia can be determined.

Algae can be a source of Vitamin A, $B_1$, riboflavin, $B_{12}$, and ascorbic acid, but synthetic methods have so far proven more economical as a source of vitamin concentrates. The quantities of vitamins, however, are eminently adequate for the algae to be used as food.

Sterols have been obtained from most of the algal groups.[15] Chondrillasterol is the principal sterol in *Scenedesmus obliquus* and was favorably considered as a starting point for cortisone synthesis.[1] *Scenedesmus obliquus* is found in Indiana.

The following substances have been produced by some blue-green algae: acids, amino acids, peptids, carbohydrates, antibiotics, vitamins and growth substances.[15]

The interest in mosquitoes as vectors in disease and their eradication led to an investigation of the alga, *Chara*, as having a possible role in the absence of mosquito larvae from waters in which it grew. It was thought that this alga might produce a toxic substance with larvicidal action. It has been rather well established, though, that there is no larvicidal substance produced, but that *Chara* provides a haven for predators on mosquito larvae.

Both *Chlorella* and *Scenedesmus*, have been used as screening tools in the search for anti-cancer agents. A species of *Scenedesmus* has been found to convert a plant alkaloid into, at least, one new alkaloidal compound.

Some algae may be very useful as teaching aids, because they can be cultured or occur in nature when other plants might not be available. Some possibilities in teaching are evident in the exercises included in an outline of *Laboratory Exercises for Biology* given by Dr. Vernon Proctor, Texas Technological College. His studies were carried out on the genus, *Chara*, alone and the following listed: structure and the life cycle, preparation of keys, introduction to limnological methods, determination of chromosome counts, dispersal of *Chara* oospores (fruiting structures) by birds, emasculation and experimental crossing of *Chara* clones, tolerance of *Chara* to salinity, temperature and drying, uptake of ammonium and nitrate ions by *Chara*, chromatographic separation of pigments from *Chara*, estimation of productivity by *Chara*, collection and examination of fossil charophytes, seasonal changes in lakes, how far can *Chara* sperm swim, introduction to research.

Charophytes without a heavy lime coating provide a good food supply and maintain clear water in aquaria. The convenient whorls are often devoured by fish until only stems remain.

Out in nature, the algae of Indiana affect human welfare by adding to the fertility of the soil. They may influence chemical changes and the blue-green alga, "witch's butter" *(Nostoc commune)* fixes atmospheric nitrogen. Species of *Schizothrix*, *Nostoc* and *Scytonema* are also useful in retarding erosion on bare surfaces and often are the first colonizers on denuded soil areas. One-celled, colonial and filamentous green algae as well as some blue-greens may be the first colonizers in new aquatic habitats. They hold the soil and add some organic matter. *Charophytes* may follow after simpler algae have paved the way. Clearing of the water is helped by settling of algal remains to the bottom and then by trapping of particles in charophyte whorls when charophytes develop. The necessity of some organic matter in the habitat to initiate growth of the charophytes has been observed and demonstrated. [28, 6] Algae may help purify water by using organic matter and carbon dioxide in their metabolism and releasing oxygen which helps in putrefaction of organic matter.

Dried charophyte remains are useful in agriculture. *Chara contraria* grows in quantity in Indiana and should be a good source of lime for acid soil and could contribute friability to clayey soil. Since this alga is a common aquatic in recreational waters, occasionally, it must be dredged out to make way for boat docking and swimming. In fish hatcheries, it must be disposed of occasionally to retrieve the fish. The unsightly mounds of rotting material created may be mixed with nearby soils for enrichment. As far as is known, this is not done at present.

Algae are of basic importance to the aquatic fauna of Indiana. They may provide food directly to waterfowl, fish, crustacea or mussels. Larger algae also may provide a place of attachment and a haven for minute flora and fauna which are used as food for fishes. Large aquatic algae may also provide a haven for the fish and larger fauna. Because algae take up radioactive materials and subsequently are used as food for fish, their role in the food chain can be traced. In the case of a nuclear explosion, this involvement as food for fish and waterfowl may provide a threat to human beings who may eat such exposed animals.

In other countries, charophytes have been used as food for farm stock. Perhaps this potential use might prove of value here. A word of caution should be given in using charophytic remains. *Clostridium botulinum*, the causative organism, has been found in decaying plant remains including charophytes when there were epidemics of botulism among waterfowl.[29] For this reason, one should be sure the source of charophytes was uncontaminated.

Often, the algae become noticeable to us only when they are a nuisance. Blooms of algae may clog the filters and produce disagreeable tastes and odors in the water supply.[19, 25] For instance, *Uroglena* has produced a bad, fishy taste and odor in an Indiana water supply. *Mallomonas, Synura* and *Dinobryon* have also been associated with fishy tastes and odors.

Most Hoosiers are probably familiar with algae because they may produce unsightly discolorations (and contribute to deterioration) of bird baths, swimming pools, drinking fountains and all sorts of masonry. You may need a bleach to remove stains from the bird bath. Swimming pool ads may provide pertinent information on chemical treatments to rid your new pool of algae.

An epidemic among fish in Huffman's Lake was thought to be due to a blue-green alga.[22] The poison was thought to be derived from the metabolism or decay of the organism. The latter could have depleted the oxygen supply, too. It is sometimes necessary to rid a lake of a large quantity of decaying algae because of the latter reason. Such an occurrence was found at Lake Pappakeechie in Kosciusko County where "seeding" had been carried out by conservation authorities to remove a heavy growth of *Chara contraria* which had become entangled in a mixed filamentous algal growth. The whole lake was choked by the decaying mass.

### Fossil Algae

Algae are useful in tracing the distribution of plants in the world, i.e., in "phytogeography." It has been noted that Indiana is on the borderline of distribution of some northern and southern plants and the algae are no exception. Aiding in interpretation of plant migration and the ecological conditions of the past, reference to fossil algae is very useful. Two algal groups, the diatoms and charophytes, offer good fossil evidence because of the deposition of minerals in the living plant. Little study has been made of fossil algae in Indiana, however.

Some fossil diatoms were obtained from the Lakeville bog.[27] Their silicified walls remained unaltered as the plants were deposited in the sediment of the aquatic habitat upon death. They were preserved in stratigraphic order, so the diatoms from this lake provided indicators of ecological conditions. Representative kinds were seen as the bog developed from an open lake to maturity (filled with peat). The sequence unfolded in the samples taken at varying depths.

Parts of charophytes may be preserved as fossils. The outer cell wall of the plant may persist as a glossy ribbon on the surface of stone as it is split. Stems and branchlets may deposit lime on the cell wall or be silicified and remain unchanged after death. Fruiting structures (oogonia) may deposit calcium carbonate in some of the cells providing a "lime-shell" which is unique and is an easily recognized fossil organ. At the interior of the fruiting body, another structure (oospore) may be found covered with a leathery membrane, or in older fossils an internal cast may be found. The membrane may retain sculpture and the oospore (or cast) may have shape and striations of taxonomic value.

Some fossil charophytes of Indiana have been studied which could be identified to living species and which gave pertinent information about the habitat and early distribution of charophytes in the state.[7]

Thus, it is seen that a group of plants comparatively little known in Indiana and often considered of little economic importance, are really of considerable significance in our lives and are of potential use in a number of untried ways.

## LITERATURE

1. BERGMANN, W. and R. J. FEENEY. 1950. Sterols of algae I. The occurrence of chondrillasterol in *Scenedesmus obliquus*. Jour. Org. Chemistry **15**:812-814.
2. BURLEW, J. S. (Editor). 1953. Algal culture from laboratory to pilot plant. Carnegie Inst. of Washington, D. C.
3. DAILY, F. K. 1950. *Tolypella prolifera* Leonh. in Indiana. Butler Univ. Bot. Stud. **9**:273-276.
4. _____ 1952. Cladophora balls collected in Steuben County, Indiana. Butler Univ. Bot. Stud. **10**:141-143.
5. _____. 1953. The Characeae of Indiana. Butler Univ. Bot. Stud. **11**:5-49.
6. _____. 1958. Some observations on the occurrence and distribution of the Characeae of Indiana. Proc. Indiana Acad. Sci. **68**:95-107.
7. _____. 1961. Glacial and post-glacial charophytes from New York and Indiana. Butler Univ. Bot. Stud. **14**(1):39-72.
8. DAILY, W. A. and J. M. McGUIRE. 1954. Preservation of some algal cultures by lyophilization. Butler Univ. Bot. Stud. **11**:139-143.
9. DAILY, W. A. 1958. In search of some blue-green wanderers- an ecological study of Indiana planktonic Myxophyceae. Proc. Indiana Acad. Sci. **68**:43-57.
10. _____. 1961. Some algae of the Cabin Creek Raised Bog, Randolph County, Indiana. Proc. Indiana Acad. Sci. **71**:298-301.
11. _____. 1962. Notes on some algae found in Indiana. Proc. Indiana Acad. Sci. **72**:279-281.
12. _____ and R. T. Everly. 1963. Algae found growing in plastic enclosures covering ears of popcorn plants. Proc. Indiana Acad. Sci. **73**:219.
13. DAVIDSON, BILL. 1954. Bread from the sea. Collier's Apr. 16. p. 62-66.
14. DROUET, F. and W. A. DAILY. 1956. Revision of the coccoid Myxophyceae. Butler Univ. Bot. Stud. **12**:1-218.

15. LEWIN, R. A. (Editor). 1962. Physiology and biochemistry of algae. Academic Press, New York.
16. PALMER, C. M. 1928. Algae of Indiana - a classified check list of those published between 1875 and 1928. Proc. Indiana Acad. Sci. **38**:109-121.
17. _____. 1930. Algae of Indiana- additions to the 1875-1928 check list. Proc. Indiana Acad. Sci. **40**:107-109.
18. _____. 1941. A study of *Lemanea* in Indiana with notes on its distribution in North America. Butler Univ. Bot. Stud. **5**(1):1-26.
19. _____. 1959. Algae in water supplies. Public Health Serv. Publ. No. **657**.
20. REIMER, C. W. 1961. Some aspects of the diatom flora of Cabin Creek Raised Bog, Randolph County, Indiana. Proc. Indiana Acad. Sci. **71**:305-319.
21. SCHWIMMER, M. and D. SCHWIMMER. 1955. The role of algae and plankton in medicine. Grune and Stratton, Inc., New York.
22. SCOTT, WILL. 1917. An epidemic among the fishes of Huffman's Lake. Proc. Indiana Acad. Sci. p. 67-71.
23. SMITH, B. H. 1931. The algae of Indiana. Proc. Indiana Acad. Sci. **41**:177-206.
24. SMITH, G. M. 1950. Fresh-water algae of the United States. 2nd Ed. The McGraw Hill Book Co.
25. TAFT, C. E. 1965. Water and algae — world problems. Educational Publishers, Inc. Chicago, Ill.
26. TIFFANY, L. H. 1958. Algae, the grass of many waters. 2nd Ed. Charles C. Thomas, Springfield, Ill.
27. WEAVER, J. 1948. Fossil diatoms from Lakeville Bog, Indiana. Butler Univ. Bot. Stud. **8**:126-138.
28. WOHLSCHLAG, DONALD E. 1950. Vegetation and invertebrate life in a marl lake. Invest. of Indiana Lakes and Streams **3**:321-372.
29. WOOD, R. D. 1951. The Characeae. Bot Rev. **18**(5):317-353.

# 12
# *Fleshy Fungi*

JOE F. HENNEN
Indiana State University

The vast majority of fungi, including the molds, mildews, rusts, smuts, and many other types, are microscopic in size. These are not dealt with here. This paper discusses those fungi which produce fruiting bodies that are large enough to be seen readily with the naked eye. The texture of the fruiting bodies in different species is fleshy, leathery, woody, or gelatinous. The general term *fleshy fungi* is used to indicate all of these types.

A number of common names are applied to different groups of fleshy fungi. Mushrooms, sponge mushrooms, toadstools, puffballs (or devil's snuff boxes), earthstars, bracket or shelf fungi (sometimes called conks or punks), coral fungi, tooth fungi (or bear's heads), stink horns, birds' nest fungi, and cup fungi are some of the names used for the major groups. A few species have common names, but most have only scientific names. Since the application of common names is quite variable, most students of the fleshy fungi prefer to use scientific names.

No one knows the number of different kinds of fleshy fungi in Indiana. Only a few mycologists (students of fungi) have ever studied these plants in our state and, compared with other plant groups, there are few publications dealing with them. From the publications available, however, one can assume that Indiana has many species of fleshy fungi.

The central area of Indiana has been studied much more thoroughly than any other part of the state [6,15,16,17] more than 380 species having been reported from Marion County alone. If the rest of the state were to be investigated more thoroughly, many other species of fleshy fungi would probably be added to those which are known to occur in Indiana.

Although it is possible to find fruiting bodies of fleshy fungi throughout the year in Indiana, they are commonest during the summer and fall, especially if rainfall has been abundant. Areas with plenty of woodland usually yield the largest numbers. There are few if any unique features about the fleshy fungi as they occur in Indiana. Indiana has a fungus flora similar to that of the surrounding states because it has a similar climate and vegetation type (the two most important factors that determine the kinds of fleshy fungi which will be present).

### General Features of Fleshy Fungi

Green plants have chlorophyll which enables them to make their own food from carbon dioxide and water, with sunlight as an energy source for the process. Since fleshy fungi do not have chlorophyll, they cannot manufacture their own food. Most fleshy fungi use wood and other plant products for food. When plenty of moisture and food material are available and a favorable temperature prevails, the fleshy fungi are abundant.

Most often, only the fruiting, or reproductive, structures of the fungus are seen. The vegetable body is usually not observed because it is composed of microscopic thread-like strands (hyphae), which usually grow within the material upon which the fungus is living. The strands interconnect in a web-like mass and form what is called the mycelium or the vegetative body. Masses of whitish mycelium may be seen where they penetrate the soil at the base of a mushroom stalk. Sometimes a mass of mycelium grows together in root-like strands which are large enough to be readily seen. The strands, called rhizomorphs, are found in the forest duff, under the bark of rotting logs, and on rotting planks and boards. Rhizomorphs may be white, orange, or black in color. The honey mushroom, *Armillaria mellea,* forms long black rhizomorphs underneath the bark of rotting logs. Because of this characteristic, it is also called the shoe string fungus.

Digestive enzymes are produced by the mycelium and are secreted into the surrounding food supply. The digested food is then absorbed back into the mycelium where it is used for energy and growth of the fungus. The reproductive structures —forms such as mushrooms, puffballs, or stink horns—are produced only after the mycelium has grown for a period of time and has accumulated a sufficient food reserve.

Physiological and environmental factors must interact in a particular way before a fungus will form fruiting bodies.

This probably accounts for the fact that most kinds of fleshy fungi are found only during certain seasons or in particular years. For example, the sponge mushroom or morel produces fruit bodies for only a few weeks in the spring. Yearly fluctuations in temperature, light, and rainfall interact with the internal physiology of the fungus to control the formation of reproductive structures. The specific interaction of factors required is as yet unknown for most of the species of fleshy fungi.

Fruiting bodies are important to the fungus because they produce spores which are "seeds" of the fungus world. Spores are microscopic, dust-like particles that can be spread easily by wind. If they land in a suitable environment, the spores may germinate and grow into a new mycelium which will produce more fruiting bodies under favorable conditions. Spores are produced on special parts of the fruiting bodies. In a typical mushroom, for example, the spores are produced on microscopic structures which form the outer layer of the gills. The gills are the numerous flap-like structures on the under side of the mushroom cap. In the bracket fungi there are numerous small pores on the lower side of the fruit body. Each pore is lined with a microscopic layer of spore-producing cells. When the spores of the mushroom or shelf fungus are ripe, they fall from the gills or pores and are carried away by air currents.

Puffball spores are produced inside special structures and are released only after the puffball breaks open. Some puffballs and earthstars develop a small hole at the top of the fruiting body through which spores may be dispersed. Clouds of spores are puffed through these openings when raindrops splash onto the sides of the fruiting body. Other puffballs do not develop holes but crack open irregularly as they age. Puffball spores are not dispersed all at once because the internal spongy network of the puffball tends to retain the spores. This lengthening of the dispersal season increases the chance for at least some of the spores to be spread at a time when conditions for their germination and growth will be favorable.

The birds' nest fungi are also aided in their spore dispersal by raindrops.[5] Their fruiting bodies simulate minute birds' nests complete with tiny "eggs." These "eggs" are really parcels of spores. The "nest" is shaped so that when a raindrop makes a direct hit, the "eggs" are knocked out of the "nest" for a considerable distance.

Some fungi depend upon insects for dispersal. For example, the foul smelling, sticky mass in which the stink horns produce their spores attract flies and other insects which then carry the spores to new localities.[1] The cup fungi and morels have evolved a type of "spore gun" which shoots their spores into the air for a few inches. Wind and convection currents carry the dust-like spores far away from their origin. Individual spores are too small to be seen with the naked eye, but when a cup fungus is shooting spores there are often so many "guns" being shot simultaneously that a small cloud may be seen arising from the cup.

Spores of mushrooms are microscopic in size also, but they too can be seen in mass. For accurate identification of mushrooms it is often necessary to determine the color of the spores. Spore colors that are found in different species of mushrooms are white, cream, pink, green, brown, purple, and black. In order to determine the color, a spore print must be made. To make a print, a fresh cap of the mushroom is placed flat on a small glass plate or on a piece of white or black paper. Direct air currents should not be allowed to blow on the cap. After a few hours enough spores will have been deposited so that their color in mass can be easily seen. The spore print will also provide an outline of the gill pattern of the mushroom species being studied, since the spores fall between the gills. Mycologists have discovered that the various ways in which spores are produced, some of which have been described above, are useful in showing natural relationships and are of major importance in the classification of the various groups of fungi.

"Cold light," or bio-luminescence, is produced by a number of different kinds of living organisms, including the lightning bug. Not so well known as this example is the phenomenon called "fox fire." "Fox fire" is a weird glow produced by the mycelia of certain fleshy fungi growing in leaf mold and rotting wood. The rhizomorphs of the honey mushroom and the fresh fruiting bodies of the Jack-O-Lantern toadstool are also luminous.

Some mushrooms that grow in grassy places such as lawns and pastures may produce formations of fruiting bodies called "fairy rings" or "witches' rings" (hexenringe in Germany).

Superstitious people imagined that fairies or witches were responsible for the springing up overnight of the mushroom growth. Fairy rings have a point of origin at the center of the ring, and each year they increase in diameter a small amount. Rings are often imperfect, with small or large sections of the circle missing. Most fairy rings are rather small but some attain a large diameter. A fairy ring of *Lepiota molybdites* that was more than one-hundred feet in diameter was observed on the Purdue University campus in 1953. It was undoubtedly a very old ring. It has not been seen in recent years.

Individual specimens of some fleshy fungi may grow to rather large size. Giant puffballs *(Calvatia maxima)* and the bracket fungus *Ganoderma applanata* produce the largest fruiting bodies known among the fleshy fungi. Giant puffballs have been found in Indiana which measured sixteen inches in diameter[11] and specimens of *Ganoderma applanata* are known which were more than three feet across.[12] These specimens fall far short of the largest fruiting body on record which was a giant puffball from New York State that measured five feet four inches long, four feet six inches wide, and ten inches high. It was estimated that this puffball produced 160,000,000,000-000 spores.[4]

### Ecological Function of Fleshy Fungi

The most important function that the fleshy fungi have in the ecology of Indiana is that of decay, or the breaking down of dead organic matter (primarily woody and herbaceous plants) into simple compounds. Although other organisms are involved in the process of wood decay, the fleshy fungi are the most important. Because of decay, essential mineral elements are returned to the soil. The humus that is formed from the rotted plant material adds desirable properties to the soil, such as improved aeration and water and mineral-holding capacity. Try to imagine what our woods and fields would be like if there were no decay and you will gain an appreciation of the importance of the function of these fungi. An accumulation of stems, leaves, twigs, logs, and stumps would form an impenetrable litter on the ground. To some extent, excessive accumulation of dead organic matter does occur in the forests of the far north where rotting is slowed down because of the very low temperature.

Fleshy fungi have another important function in woodland ecology. Some occur closely associated with particular species of trees. The fungal mycelia grow in or around the young roots of the tree, forming associations called mycorhizae (fungus roots). Many trees do not thrive unless the proper mycorhizal fungus is present. Evidently, the mycorhizae help the trees to obtain mineral nutrients from the soil. Probably most of the native trees and shrubs in Indiana form mycorhizae but the specific fungus species involved is unknown in most instances. Mycorhizae have been found in Indiana in beech, cottonwood, several of the hickories, basswood, redbud, ironwood, hop hornbean, hazel, red maple, boxelder, a number of different oaks, and American ash.[8]

## The Use of Fleshy Fungi as Food

Sports are seasonal in Indiana with football following closely after baseball, and basketball after football. After the late winter basketball tournaments many Hoosiers begin thinking about another sport—mushroom hunting. The sponge mushroom or morel is in season for only a few weeks in early spring. Hunting these delicious delicacies can be a rewarding experience even if few or none at all are found. Getting out into the country at this time of year, when spring wild flowers abound and the trees are bursting with new growth, is reward enough for most people. If one finds mushrooms they are an extra bonus.

Unfortunately, public places for mushroom hunting are few. With increasing population pressures the few that are available are becoming overcrowded. New grounds that would be open to the public for this activity would be a great asset to Indiana. Advertisement of such areas would surely bring many city dwellers and out-of-state tourists. Here is an untapped attraction that should be given serious consideration.

The sponge mushroom or morel *(Morchella esculenta)* is undoubtedly the most popular wild mushroom in Indiana. It has often been said that a fortune awaits the person who learns how to grow the morel under domestication. Attempts have been made by many people, but commercial success has not yet been obtained. A recent attempt, which probably came as close to success as any other, was made by a high school student from Terre Haute. For her efforts, she won a first place in the National Science Fair competition in 1965.[3]

Six different kinds of morels *(Morchella* sp.) are known to grow in Indiana. Since they are all good to eat, the average mushroom hunter makes little effort to distinguish among them. It is important to be able to distinguish morels from other fleshy fungi, however, because some similar species can be harmful. One closely related form, the false morel *(Gyromitra esculenta)*, is especially confusing. This species fruits at about the same time as the true morels. Although many people have eaten the false morel without ill effect, it is known to have caused serious illness and even death.

The reason for different reactions to mushrooms in different people is not definitely known. Possibly, food allergies are involved. In addition to actual poisons which are found in certain species of mushrooms, other species which are usually considered to be edible contain various chemical substances which can cause allergies in some individuals. Some mushrooms which are normally nonpoisonous may become so if alcoholic beverages are drunk within an hour or so after they have been eaten. A few species of *Coprinus*, the inky cap and shaggy mane mushrooms, have been often implicated in such cases of poisoning. A recent report stated that common morels can cause stomach pains, diarrhea, and vomitting if alcoholic drinks are taken soon after eating them.[10]

A number of wild mushrooms other than the morels are eaten by the more confident hunters. Actually, most wild mushrooms are not poisonous, but some of the ones which are may cause death. Among the more easily identified edible mushrooms that are found in Indiana are the shaggy mane *(Coprinus comatus)*, the oyster mushroom *(Pleuortus ostreatus)*, the common meadow mushroom *(Agaricus campestris)*, and the sulphur mushroom *(Polyporus sulfureus)*. The field guides listed in the bibliography give details about the hunting, identification and cooking of wild mushrooms.[9,13,14]

Probably less than a dozen different kinds of dangerously poisonous mushrooms occur in Indiana. The most infamous is the deadly Amanita *(Amanita verna)*. When one first sees this beautiful mushroom growing in open woodland he may quite understandably remark, "It looks good enough to eat", but its common name, destroying angel, indicates precisely the consequences one may expect from eating just a small piece of it. It has been estimated that one cubic centimeter is sufficient to cause death. Every year the newspapers report about people who have died from mushroom poisoning. Some species of *Amanita* is usually responsible for the fatal cases of poisoning. The red *Amanita muscaria* grows abundantly around the campground at Turkey Run State Park. Some of the other toxic mushrooms found in Indiana are *Lepiota molybdites, Clitocybe illudens,* and *Hygrophorus conicus.*

The question naturally arises as to how to distinguish poisonous mushrooms from edible ones. A popular notion is that the word mushroom designates only edible kinds and the rest are "toadstools". Because of lack of knowledge, however, many people call some perfectly edible species "toadstools". On the other hand, some people may be calling certain species which have been harmless to them "mushrooms", but these species may prove to be poisonous to others. Of course there are many nonpoisonous species which are not particularly palatable. The only way to discover for sure whether a mushroom is poisonous to you or not is to eat a portion of it, but the consequences of that procedure may be very undesirable! It is from such trial and error methods, however, that knowledge of the poisonous nature of various mushrooms has been gained. Now that there is such a body of knowledge, if one knows the identity of a mushroom he can predict whether it will be poisonous or nonpoisonous. The *only* reasonable procedure is to identify the fungus and then find out what information is available about its poisonous or edible qualities. There are no safe short cut methods to determine the poisonous nature of mushrooms. Old wives' tales which advocate the use of simple tests such as "a poisonous mushroom has a cap that peels readily" or "darkens a silver spoon" are completely false. Relying upon such methods of distinction can be fatal.

After the mushrooms and toadstools the conks or bracket fungi are probably the best known fungi. The fruiting bodies of most of these species are leathery or woody, and they frequently persist from season to season. They often attract attention because of their relatively large size, and because they usually grow in rather prominent places, such as on trees or fallen logs. A few types are brightly colored, such as the sulphur mushroom or sulphur conk which is yellow or yellowish orange. The sulphur mushroom is rather common, particularly on oak trees, in late summer and early fall. If gathered while it is still young, the sulphur mushroom is soft enough to be eaten. Most of the other conks are too tough for eating. None of them are known to be poisonous, however.

## Harmful Activities of Fleshy Fungi

The deterioration of wood is a beneficial process when it helps to get rid of the litter in a forest, but when it happens to lumber or wood products useful to man it is undesirable. Indiana lumbermen, sawmill operators, carpenters, fence post and utility pole producers, and all others who deal in wood products must be aware of the always-present possibility of wood decay. Climatic conditions in Indiana are very favorable for the growth of wood rotting fungi. As a result, industries utilizing wood have developed their operations so as to prevent decay as much as possible.

Wood is subject to decay from even before the time that the timber is harvested until the time that steps are taken to prevent rot. The most common preventative is to dry the wood and keep it dry. Even if relatively low amounts of moisture are present there is danger of dry rot by certain fleshy fungi. Much of the practical value of painting wood is due to the fact that painted wood does not absorb as much moisture as unpainted wood; it is thus less vulnerable to attack by fungi. Various chemicals are used as preservatives for wood products. In Indiana, there are a number of companies that treat raliroad ties, utility poles, fence posts, and other items with creosote or other chemicals.

## Useful Drugs from Fleshy Fungi

Various species of molds and yeasts are used to produce chemicals such as alcohol, antibiotics, and organic acids. The fleshy fungi have not been used in this way until recently. Potentially useful drugs derived from species of mushrooms and puffballs are now being investigated. One of these drugs comes from a group of mushrooms from Mexico which have been used for centuries by Indians in some of the religious ceremonies. These "sacred mushrooms" contain the rare drug psilocybin which produces ecstatic and hallucinatory conditions when the mushrooms are eaten in sufficient amounts. Perhaps scientific investigations involving psilocybin will add to the knowledge of mental disorders and their treatment.

Another potentially important chemical is calvacin, which is found in the giant puffball.[2] It has been tested thoroughly as an anti-cancer drug in various animals and in humans, and has been found to inhibit the growth of many different types of tumors. Continued use in dogs and monkeys has produced what is apparently an allergic reaction, however. Possibly, the chemical structure of calvacin can be modified in such a way as to retain its anti-cancer properties while eliminating the undesirable allergenic characteristics.

These are but two examples of the kinds of useful drugs that may be produced by fleshy fungi. Since there are literally hundreds of different kinds of fleshy fungi, we can expect that they harbor many as yet undiscovered useful products.

Just a beginning has been made in trying to find out all there is to know about Indiana fleshy fungi. As mentioned earlier, there is no complete inventory of the kinds that occur in our state. The few species which have been studied thoroughly were usually chosen for research because of some obvious economic reason, such as the association of the fungus with wood decay. Since little is known about the natural history of most species, studies along this line would be useful. A college degree in mycology is not necessary for all of this work. An amateur seriously interested in the fleshy fungi could carry out worth-while projects in his own locality. With the assistance of professional mycologists in industry and at our state and private colleges and universities, laymen could make many contributions to our knowledge of the fleshy fungi.

## LITERATURE

1. BECHTEL, A. R. 1935. Rare Gasteromycetes in Indiana. Proc. Indiana Acad. Sci. **44**:79-80.
2. BENEKE, E. S. 1963. Calvatia, calvacin and cancer. Mycologia **55**:257-270.
3. BENNETT, BARBARA. 1965. Mushroom production by tissue culturing and fermentation with related nutritional studies. A project entered in the 16th Annual Naional Science Fair-International, St. Louis, Mo.
4. BESSEY, C. E. 1884. An enormous puffball. Am. Naturalist **18**:530.
5. BRODIE, H. J. 1957. Raindrops as plant dispersal agents. Proc. Indiana Acad. **66**:65-73.
6. COTTINGHAM, J. O. 1957. Higher fungi of Marion County, Indiana, VIII. Proc. Indiana Acad. **66**:305.
7. CHRISTENSON, C. M. 1965. Common fleshy fungi. Burgess Publishing Company, Minneapolis, Minnesota, 237p.
8. DOAK, K. D. 1928. Mycorhiza bearing species in the vicinity of Lafayette, Indiana. Proc. Indiana Acad. Sci. **37**:427-439.
9. GROVES, J. W. 1962. Edible and poisonous mushrooms of Canada. Canada Department of Agriculture, publication **1112**, Ottawa, Ont. Canada I-IX, 298p.
10. GROVES, J. W. 1964. Poisoning by morels when taken with alcohol. Mycologia **56**:779-778.

11. KERN, F. D. 1913. Notes on some puffballs of Indiana. Proc. Indiana Acad. Sci. 1912:105-115.
12. PORTER, CHARLES M. 1966. Personal communication.
13. THOMAS, W. S. 1948. Field book of common mushrooms. G. P. Putnams' Sons, New York, London, 369p.
14. SMITH, A. H. 1958. The mushroom hunter's field guide. Univ. of Mich. Press, Ann Arbor, Mich. 197p.
15. UNDERWOOD, L. M. 1894. Report of botanical division of the Indiana biological survey. Proc. Indiana Acad. Sci. 1893:13-67.
16. UNDERWOOD, L. M. 1897. Additions to the published lists of Indiana cryptogams. Proc. Indiana Acad. Sci. 1896:171-172.
17. VAN HOOK, J. M. 1935. Indiana fungi. XIII. Proc. Indiana Acad. Sci. 44:55-64.

# 13
# Plant Diseases

RALPH J. GREEN, JR.
Department of Botany and Plant Pathology
Purdue University

The condition in plants that we call disease results when one organism lives at the expense of another. In the ecology of living organisms, it is doubtful that any plant or animal has escaped from one or more disease-producing parasites. Fossil records show evidence of plant diseases long before the coming of Man. Thus, plant diseases are an integral part of the "natural features" of any area or plant community.

As Man evolved from a nomadic gatherer of food and began to tend crops, he became acutely aware of the effects of plant pests. The suddenness and devastation with which the pestilence often struck made him look to his gods for protection and mercy. Only time and painstaking trial and error unraveled the mysteries of the causes of the diseases of Man, animals and plants and permitted an objective approach to the control of disease.

The practices of modern agriculture tend to concentrate vast populations of crop plants of the same species or varieties in limited geographic areas where soil, temperature, rainfall and other factors are especially favorable. In Nature, this condition occurs less frequently, but is not uncommon. In either event, the results are often disastrous when a destructive disease or insect pest appears.

Indiana has experienced major disease epidemics in both the natural flora and in important economic crops. The following examples are chosen from many to illustrate plant diseases of singular importance in Indiana or instances in which Indiana scientists have made significant contributions in the etiology and control of plant diseases.

## Diseases of Natural Flora

There are more than 4.1 million acres of forests in Indiana. The oaks are the most numerous species of trees in the State and are commercially the most important. Seventeen species are listed as native to Indiana by Deam.[2]

The destructive disease Oak Wilt was first reported in Indiana in 1949 but evidence indicates that the disease has been present for a much longer period, especially in the extreme northwestern counties of the State.[7]

Oak Wilt is a fatal systemic disease caused by the fungus *Ceratocystis fagacearum* (Bretz) Hunt. The symptoms include a bronzing and wilting of the foliage and a brown streaking of the current years sapwood. All species of oaks are susceptible but the red-black oak group is usually killed within a few weeks after symptoms appear while the white-burr oak group shows a progressive dieback of branches that may continue for several years.

The causal fungus is spread over long distances mainly by insects, especially certain of the Nitidulid or sap beetles. Once an infection is established, all oaks of the same group are in danger of infection through root grafts between infected and healthy trees (Fig. 56).

Extensive ground and aerial surveys of the entire state of Indiana during 1949-1957 showed that there are 2 distinct areas of Oak Wilt infection.[3] Most of the counties in the northwestern section of the state exhibit from moderate to severe infection. In many wood lots, the red-black oak group has been eliminated by this disease. In the vast oak stands of south-central Indiana the incidence of Oak Wilt is low, indicating a more recent introduction of the disease. The remainder of the state is essentially free from the disease (Fig. 57).

Since more than two thirds of the forest lands in Indiana are in the southern part of the State, the potential destructiveness of Oak Wilt to this priceless natural resource is considerable. Careful study of the disease by comparing the actual and potential rates of spread in the heavily infected counties in the northwestern region and the lightly infected areas in the south shows that there is little difference in the rate of spread of the disease.[3] This strongly suggests that Oak Wilt, if left unchecked, will continue to increase in southern Indiana and may eventually deplete vast acreages of native oaks in that area.

Control of this disease is possible, especially in the lightly infected areas of southern Indiana. Rapid surveys can be made from the air and suspected infection centers located and marked. Ground crews visit the site to confirm the infection and initiate control procedures. This includes the poisoning of all infected trees and all oaks within root-grafting range (35-50 ft.) of the infection center. This prevents further spread of the disease-causing fungus. The eradication sites are checked periodically to be certain that no further spread occurs.

Fig. 56. Airphoto of oak wilt infection center in Scott County showing progressive infection through root grafts between infected and healthy trees.

If this control program could be initiated in the oak stands of southern Indiana the threat of Oak Wilt could be greatly reduced.

The native elms in Indiana have been subjected to two devastating diseases within a quarter of a century. Prior to 1940, the elms were the leading shade tree species in this country and were tenth in value for lumber. Today, the elms have practically disappeared from our streets, parks and woodlands as the result of diseases that could not be effectively controlled.

The two diseases responsible for the disappearance of the elms are the virus disease Phloem Necrosis and the fungus disease known as Dutch Elm disease.

Phloem Necrosis of elms was first identified as a virus disease in 1938, following an outbreak of the disease in Ohio.[9] The origin of the disease has never been clearly established but there are reports of similar outbreaks in other parts of the Ohio River valley dating back to the late 1880's.

The symptoms of Phloem Necrosis include a sudden and rapid collapse of the leaves, which quickly yellow and fall. The inner bark and phloem of the root collar and lower trunk show a characteristic yellow-orange discoloration with a faint wintergreen odor. A tree may be infected from several months to years before symptoms appear but the tree is killed within a few weeks after the onset of symptoms.

The virus causing Phloem Necrosis is spread from tree to tree by leaf hopper insects that feed directly from the sap stream of the plant. As the insect feeds from an infected tree it may take the virus into its body and later it is injected into other plants. The other means of spread of the virus is through root grafts between infected and healthy trees.

The American Elm, *Ulmus americana* L., and all of its varieties are highly susceptible to this disease but the red or slippery elm, *U. rubra* Muhl., and other elm species are more resistant.

Phloem Necrosis extended over much of the lower Ohio River valley from 1938 to 1950 and was widespread in the southern half of Indiana, Illinois and Ohio. It also invaded southeastern Missouri, Kentucky and northwestern Tennessee. Many cities and towns in southern Indiana lost many of their American elms during a 5 year period after 1940.

In addition to the direct losses of elms from Phloem Necrosis, the existence of great numbers of dead, standing elms favored a buildup of the native and European elm bark beetle insects. These insects were to play a vital role in the spread of the second major disease to strike the elms in the past 3 decades.

Indiana figured in the very first discoveries of Dutch Elm disease in the United States.[5] Because of their unusual grain patterns, elm burl logs were imported from Europe to Indiana for use in the veneering of furniture. The first imports were made during 1925-27 to veneer mills in the Indianapolis and Evansville, Indiana, areas. Dutch Elm disease was first reported from near Dayton and Cincinnati, Ohio, in 1930 and by 1933 was known to exist in Indianapolis, Indiana, and around the port area in New York City. It was shown that the elm logs imported from Europe carried the fungus causing Dutch Elm disease and at least one species of the elm bark beetle responsible for its spread.

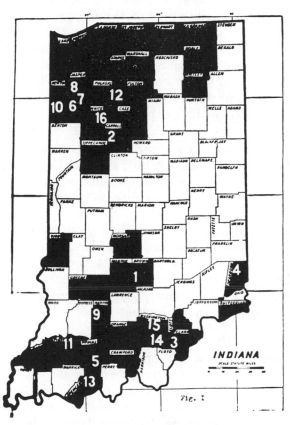

Fig. 57. Distribution of oak wilt in Indiana by counties. Numbers indicate infection centers used in studies of rate of spread of the disease.

Attempts were made to eradicate the disease from the United States by cutting and destroying every known infected elm and as many dead or dying elms as possible, regardless of the cause of death. The eradication program was unsuccessful and the disease was soon to ravage most of the elms in the northeast quarter of the United States and the contiguous areas in Canada.

The fungus causing Dutch Elm disease *(Ceratocystis ulmi* (Buis) Hunt) is spread by two species of elm bark beetles, one of which is also a pest introduced into this country from Europe. The life cycle of the fungus is uniquely integrated into the life cycle of the bark beetles, which lay eggs and overwinter only in dead and dying elms but feed in trees of high vigor. The only other means of spread of the disease is through root grafts between healthy and infected trees. The vast number of dead elms that existed as the result of the Phloem Necrosis disease provided the ideal habitat for the buildup of the elm bark beetle population. Thus, when the Dutch Elm disease was introduced there was already present an abundant and efficient carrier for the fungus causing the disease.

All native species of elms and their varieties are susceptible to the Dutch Elm disease. Only the Asiatic species, *Ulmus pumila* L., the Siberian or so-called Chinese elm, and *U. parvifolia* L., are resistant to this disease and these two species are not immune.

Dutch Elm disease is now or has been epidemic in every county in Indiana. Dead elms, debarked and bleached by the elements, mark almost every stream and watershed. The elms have been practically eliminated as a major species in a disease epidemic that rivals the devastation of the American Chesnut after the turn of the century.

### Diseases of Economic Crops

There are nearly 15 million acres of croplands in Indiana and more than 10 million acres are devoted to corn, soybeans and wheat—the three major crops of Indiana. Our State has long been a leader both in crop production and crop improvement in these three crops. In 1965, Indiana led the nation in the average yield per acre of corn, producing 94 bushels per acre on nearly 5 million acres. Though tenth in the Nation in wheat acreage, Indiana was second only to her sister state Illinois in the average yield per acre of this vital crop.

Indiana's climate and soil are well suited for the production of high quality soft red winter wheat. Wheats of this type go into the fine quality flours used in baked goods, pastries, and other products. There is a ready market for Indiana's wheat and there has never been a surplus of this crop.

The Purdue Agriculture Experiment Station, in cooperation with the U. S. Department of Agriculture and other agencies, has been concerned with improvement of varieties of soft red winter wheats through increased yields, winter hardiness, grain quality and resistance to diseases and insects.

Wheat and its near relatives rice and corn are the main-stay in the diet of most of the World's population. More than 75% of the World's food diet comes from these three crops. The famine and disease that have marked Man's recorded history usually followed failure of one of these essential food crops. Wheat's prime enemies are the dreaded Rust Diseases that shrivel the grain and reduce the yields of the promised harvest.

Throughout much of the winter wheat growing areas of the World, the Leaf Rust disease, caused by the fungus *Puccinia recondita* Rob., is a major disease. Leaf Rust attacks the leaf blade and sheaths, reducing the yield and quality of the grain. Young plants that are heavily rusted are severely weakened and are more subject to winter kill and other diseases. The fungus causing this disease does not survive well in Indiana during the Winter, but each Spring great clouds of spores may ride the winds from areas to the south of Indiana to infect the new crops as growth begins.

The complicating factor in the control of this disease is that the causal fungus exists as many different subgroups or strains that vary in ability to attack different varieties of wheat. This was the challenge to the scientists who undertook the task of developing new and more productive wheat varieties that would resist the ravages of diseases and insect pests. Wheat varieties and their wild parents and near relatives were collected from throughout the World and the tedious task of incorporating desirable genetic characters into adapted varieties was begun. The program was initiated in the late 1920's on the campus of Purdue University in cooperation with the Bureau of Plant Industry, U. S. Department of Agriculture. More than 20 years were to pass before the first truly new wheat variety was introduced that incorporated the sought for qualities that make up a superior wheat variety. The release of the wheat variety Vigo in 1946 marked a new era in the production of soft red winter wheats in Indiana and throughout the eastern part of the United States. Indiana became the leader in the development of wheat varieties of superior quality and characteristics. The scientists at the Purdue Agriculture Experiment Station realized that changing demands of the wheat-using industry, changing farming practices and the variability of the disease-causing organisms meant that each success was only temporary. This program has been marked by the development and release of such well known wheat varieties as Dual, Knox, LaPorte, Knox 62, Monon, Redcoat, Reed and Riley. These varieties incorporate the characteristics of superior yield, quality and adaptation and are resistant to all or some of the major diseases of wheat, as Leaf Rust, Loose Smut, Powdery Mildew, Black Stem Rust and the insect Hessian Fly.[8]

Perhaps the greatest tribute to the leadership of Indiana scientists in the development of superior wheat varieties can be found in the statistics of the U. S. Department of Agriculture on wheat production.[6] In 1964, the variety Monon, released in Indiana in 1959, was grown on nearly 60% of the more than 9 million acres of soft red winter wheat grown in the United States. Similar successes have been recorded with the other grain crops oats and barley.

As indicated earlier, more than 10 million acres in Indiana are devoted to corn, soybeans and wheat. An additional 1.5 million acres are planted to various forage crops and the remaining 3.5 million acres to various fruit, vegetable and special crops. Among the special crops in which Indiana has been a leader is the production of peppermint and spearmint for their essential oils. The choice oils from the crops grown on the mucklands of northern Indiana are considered to be of superior quality and flavor and industry users pay premium prices for these oils. They are used primarily in chewing gum, quality candies and in toothpaste. Indiana currently grows some ten to twelve thousand acres of peppermint and spearmint and is the leading producer in the midwest.

The mints were first grown in Michigan as early as 1835 and that state was leading producer until 1945. Indiana assumed the major acreage after this period and there was an increase in production in the Pacific Northwest.

Growers of peppermint and spearmint are confronted with numerous disease and insect pests. One disease was primarily responsible for the decline of the mint industry in Michigan and has seriously threatened continued production of these crops in Indiana.[4] The disease is called Verticillium Wilt and is caused by the soilborne fungus *Verticillium albo-atrum* Rke. & Berth. Symptoms of the disease include wilting, stunting and premature death of the infected plant, with accompanying reduction in yield of the essential oils.

Since the mints do not produce seed, they must be propagated by stolons dug from established fields. The fungus causing the wilt disease is readily spread by soil and infected plant material and many growers soon found that their lands were no longer suitable for mint production because of this disease. Early attempts at control through the development of disease-resistant hybrids or by chemical means were unsuccessful and many growers were forced to abandon mint production. Smaller growers were especially hard hit by this disease and the major mint acreages were taken over by larger growers who were able to continue crop production through more efficient methods of handling the crop. However, losses from the wilt disease increased and acreage in Indiana declined.

The mint-using industries of the United States wanted to be assured of a continued supply of the mint oils from the Midwest region. Through the cooperation of these industries and the Purdue Agricultural Experiment Station, a research program was initiated to study the problems associated with the control of the principal diseases of the mint crops, especially the destructive wilt disease. As a result of this program, Indiana mint growers now can continue production of peppermint and spearmint. The control includes the use of a selected long term crop rotation whereby corn and other related crops are grown in rotation with the peppermint and spearmint. It is essential that only the specified crops be grown to reduce the carryover of the wilt fungus. In addition, growers now maintain sources of planting stock in isolated locations to be assured of disease-free stolons for transplanting. Improved chemical soil fumigants are also available for use. New growers are provided with indexed and known disease-free plants so they can establish plantings on new land free from the wilt disease. Plantings are inspected periodically, at the growers request, to guard against the introduction of disease and insect pests.

Through this program, Indiana mint growers have been

able to maintain mint acreage at the present level for the past 3 years. In so doing, they remain the leading growers in the Midwest and produce the choicest flavored mint oils of any in the World.

Although Indiana produces a number of different vegetable crops for market and processing, only tomatoes have been grown on such acreage to make the State one of the leading producers in the United States. Indiana is currently the third largest producer of tomatoes for processing in this country. As early as 1918, the State acreage was 53,000 acres and the peak production was recorded in 1935 when nearly 100,000 acres were planted. The acreage has gradually declined until today about 18,000 acres are grown. The interesting fact is, however, that Indiana growers now produce almost as many tons of tomatoes on 18,000 acres as were grown on 100,000 acres in 1935! The average yield per acre in 1935 was 3.3 tons per acre and in 1965 Indiana growers averaged 16.5 tons per acre. Yield increases have been realized through better varieties, improved cultural practices and more effective disease and insect control.

The tomato crop is subject to numerous diseases and the fruit is especially vulnerable to infection and decay. There are two specific disease problems that have played an important role in tomato production in Indiana. The first of these is Fusarium Wilt, a soil-borne fungus disease. This disease caused a shift in the major tomato producing area of the State from the southern counties to the central and northern counties where the disease is less severe because of less favorable soil conditions for infection. The tomato processing industry has been able to "escape" the major effects of this disease by shifting to areas of the state where disease losses are negligible. There are numerous tomato varieties now available that are resistant to Fusarium Wilt disease but the growers and processing industry have chosen to retain proven varieties and to avoid areas where Fusarium Wilt causes heavy losses.

Another disease problem that is often a limiting factor in tomato production both to the grower and the processor is the disease called Tomato Anthracnose. This disease is caused by the imperfect fungus *Colletotrichum phomoides* (Sass.) Chester and develops mainly on the ripening fruit. The infected fruit is rejected by the processor because of problems of quality control in the processed tomato products. Thus, the grower may be forced to terminate harvest because of an unsalable crop.

The disease does not develop rapidly until late in the growing season and the grower may neglect the necessary steps for effective control. Heavy rains disseminate the fungus in the field and the fluctuations in soil moisture that follow heavy rains often causes the ripening fruits to crack or split and makes them more vulnerable to infection.

The successful grower must follow a careful spray program during the period that the crop is developing if he is to reduce losses from Tomato Anthracnose disease and other diseases of the tomato fruit.

Plant diseases continue to play an important role in the production of economic crops in Indiana and in the entire country. In spite of significant progress in disease control, plant disease losses are still a staggering 3.2 billion dollars annually in the United States.[1] Additional losses from other sources brings the total losses in crop production to more than 11.2 billion dollars. Current increases in population and the conversion of agricultural lands to other uses makes it imperative that these losses be reduced.

The natural flora of Indiana may also be seriously threatened by disease outbreak. Of particular significance is the danger of the introduction of disease organisms from other parts of the world. The rapidity and increasing volume of intercontinental travel increases the possibility of the introduction of a destructive plant pest. Such pests are a particular menace to the natural flora because native species are often extremely susceptible to the disease-producing organisms and there are few natural enemies of the plant pest in the new environment to help hold it in check. A rapid and destructive outbreak of the disease often results, that may threaten an entire species. The loss incurred by the native elms in Indiana and elsewhere is an example of this type.

Indiana plant scientists have accepted the challenge of protecting the economic crops and natural flora of the State from destructive plant diseases. The search will continue for more effective means to reduce losses to our essential food and feed crops and to our natural flora.

## LITERATURE

1. Anonymous 1965. Losses in agriculture. Agr. Handbook **291** ARS. USDA.
2. DEAM, C. C. 1953. Trees of Indiana. 3rd ed. Dept. of Conservation, State of Indiana.
3. GREEN, R. J., JR. and L. R. SCHREIBER. 1961. Studies of the control of oak wilt disease in Southern Indiana. Proc. Indiana Acad. Sci. **70**:87-90.
4. GREEN, R. J., Jr. 1963. Mint farming. Agr. Inf. Bull. **212**. ARS USDA.
5. MAY, C. 1934. Outbreaks of the dutch elm disease in the United States. USDA Circ. **640**.
6. REITZ, L. P. and L. W. BRIGGLE. 1965. Preliminary results of the 1964 wheat variety survey in the Eastern United States. Bakers Digest pp. 82-84.
7. SCHREIBER, L. R. and R. J. GREEN, JR. 1958. The occurrence and prevalence of oak wilt in Indiana. Proc. Indiana Acad. Sci. **58**:110-115.
8. STIVERS, R. K., F. L. PATTERSON, O. W. LUETKEMEIER, M. L. SWEARINGIN, L. E. COMPTON, R. M. CALDWELL, J. F. SCHAFER, R. L. GALLUN AND D. R. GRIFFITH. 1966. Small Grain Varieties for Indiana. Res. Bull. **805**.
9. SWINGLE, R. U. 1942. Phloem necrosis, a virus disease of american elm. USDA Circ. **640**.

# 14

# Lower Green Land Plants

WINONA H. WELCH
DePauw University

## Lichens

A layman would regard a lichen as one plant. But a botanist knows that a lichen body is composed of two kinds of plants living together, algae and fungi. In the examination of a bit of lichen thallus, with a compound microscope, many one-celled green plants (algae) are seen, scattered through a mesh of colorless fungus threads or hyphae. Microscopic observations of a thin transverse section show that the algal cells are in a layer, more or less, just below the upper surface.

The cells of the algae, containing chlorophyll, manufacture their own carbohydrates by the process of photosynthesis. The non-green cells of the fungus obtain their food from the green cells of the algae. In turn, the fungus provides water for the alga and itself. This partnership living is known as symbiosis. The fungus modifies some of its hyphae for the penetration of the algal cells. These modifications are called haustoria. They absorb the manufactured food from the algal cells for the use of the fungus. The mycelium (mass of hyphae or fungus threads) holds the absorbed water and protects the algal cells from drying out. Also, the fungus protects the algal cells from exposure to an excessive amount of light and from mechanical injury. In addition, the fungus in its disintegration of the rock substratum may release minerals for the use of the algal cells. The fungal hyphae are believed to synthesize proteins for use by both components of the lichen. The partnership enables the algae to live in a larger variety of habitats because lichens have a wider distribution than ony other group of plants. Under very adverse conditions for all other plants, the lichens are sturdy. Many, if not all, of the algae which occur in the lichen thallus can grow independently, also. The fungi, however, normally occur only in lichens.

Lichens belong to the Thallophytes, the lowest of the largest divisions of the Plant Kingdom. (Thallus plants are those in which the bodies are not differentiated into roots, stems, and leaves.) The Thallophytes or thallus plants precede the division known as Bryophytes (liverworts and mosses) in the development of the Plant Kingdom.

The alga has two scientific names, genus and species. The fungus has two, likewise. The composite plant body of algal cells and fungal hyphae also has a generic and specific name, as though it were a single organism.

There are 15,000 - 20,000, or more, kinds of lichens on the surface of the earth. About 166 species, varieties, and forms have been published for Indiana. Probably only a small part of the total lichen flora of the Hoosier state is known. Southern Indiana as well as the Indiana Dunes along Lake Michigan should yield a great variety of additional lichens for the state records. The study of the lichens in our state has been neglected, in comparison with publications in other plant groups. The first known lichen records for Indiana were published in 1893.

The fungus determines the form or shape, size, and strength of the lichen body. The three common forms of lichens in Indiana, as well as elsewhere, are crustose, foliose, and fruticose. The crustose lichen thalli resemble a thin crust because the plant body is flat and grows closely attached to the substratum, which is generally a rock or a tree trunk. The foliose thalli are flattened flakes or sheets of tissue and are more or less leaflike. The fruticose plant body is shrublike or bushlike in form.

Two genera of the foliose group in Indiana, *Collema* and *Leptogium,* are called the Jelly Lichens because, when wet, they appear gelatinous. They are dark green or black, colors which distinguish them from the bright green thallose liverworts. Eleven species of Jelly Lichens have been collected in the state.

Probably the crustose lichens are collected less often than the foliose and fruticose forms because they are rarely noticed except by a lichenologist (student of lichens). Also they are infrequently collected by botanists because of the difficulty in removal of the thallus if on a rock substratum (requiring hammer and chisel). Rarely can they be removed in one piece or without breaking the thallus. In the publications which include Indiana lichens, the author has noted 15 genera of the crustose forms. Probably the most interesting to the layman is *Graphis scripta*. The plant resembles pale blotches on the trunks of trees, their only substratum. The name is very informative and descriptive, resembling lead pencil writing. Its common name is Script Lichen. The crustose thallus is whitish, yellowish, greenish gray, or olive green. The small blackish or frosted gray fruits (1-5 mm long by 0.1-0.3 mm wide) are shaped and arranged on the thallus in variously curved or angled lines, like Arabic writing or like shorthand. Another crustose lichen on Indiana rock which may attract the attention of a layman is *Rhizocarpon concentricum*. The thallus is thin and circular. The dull black apothecia (open disc-shaped fruiting structures), although small to the unaided eye (0.3-1.5 mm in diameter), are in a distinct concentric arrangement. Thus the specific name *concentricum*.

The foliose bodies are usually much larger than the crustose and grow on the substratum more loosely, generally being attached at a single point. The most common genera of foliose lichens in the state are *Parmelia, Physcia, Peltigera,* and *Xanthoria* (*Teloschistes* formerly). The latter genus is readily recognized by its yellow to orange thallus and fruiting structures, on tree trunks. In Indiana there have been reported 21 species, varieties, and forms in the Parmeliaceae, 15 in Physciaceae, 10 in Peltigeraceae, and 4 in Teloschistaceae, common lichen families. The Wafer Lichen or Cliff Wafer, *Dermatocarpon*, is represented in the state by two species, *D. miniatum* and *D. hepaticum*. As the common name suggests, the plants resemble a wafer, to 3 cm in diameter. The thallus is umbilicate or attached to the substratum at one approximately central point, to rock in *D. miniatum* and to soil in *D. hepaticum*.

In the fruticose forms, the thallus grows at right angles to the substratum. These lichens either may grow upright from the substratum or be pendent, hanging from the branches of trees. It is in this group that the so-called Reindeer Moss of the Arctic region is classified. It is not like a moss in color or structure, occurs in sponge-like tufts, and is a species of *Cladonia*. The goblet-shaped lichens, on the ground, are also species of *Cladonia*. The family, Cladoniaceae, contains approximately 52 species, varieties, and forms in the state. The erect species are to 2.5 cm high. The pendent lichens of the world vary from a few millimeters to many centimeters in length. Some species of *Usnea* are pendent, although the common species in Indiana, *U. florida*, is erect.

Sometimes a lichen body does not have the forms described above but occurs in shapeless powdery masses, which, under favorable conditions, will produce new plants or thalli. They are called soredia and consist of a little fungus tissue and a number of algal cells. These powdery masses or soredia occur on the upper surfaces of many lichens, often in quantity, and are scattered from the thallus by wind and rain.

In Indiana the colors of lichen thalli are dark green, grayish green, greenish gray, yellowish, yellowish orange, whitish, grayish, brown, lead-colored to black, and reddish. In some of the species of *Cladonia* the fruiting discs are scarlet, brick red, or brown.

Lichens grow in a variety of habitats: on bare soil, rock, tree trunks and dead branches, logs, fence posts, shingles of roofs, and other objects of dead wood, cement walks, stone chimneys, outdoor fireplaces, stone benches or seats, tombstones, and, in tropical areas, on leaves exposed to the sun. The inscriptions on tombstones and monuments may be disfigured or obliterated, eventually, by the presence and by the abundance of lichen thalli. Although the kinds of habitats are numerous, lichens most frequently occur in exposed and dry situations. They thrive in bogs, habitats with daily fog, spray, or dew, barren areas, unburned sites, and in unplowed fields. Very few lichens occur in rich soil where other plants commonly grow best. They inhabit the waste places. Apparently smoke and fire are their worst enemies.

Lichens are probably the slowest growing of all living things. The foliose lichens are some of the most rapidly growing kinds and their growth rate may be about 1-10 mm in diameter, per year. Some fruticose lichens grow rapidly enough to become nuisances and sometimes to damage trees, especially fruit trees. The crustose lichens have the slowest growth rate of the three types, to about 0.9 mm per year in some species. It has been suggested by lichenologists that the slow rate of growth may imply that the organism has the ability to exist on little food, water, oxygen, and minerals.

Lichens do die even though they have very few natural enemies. They survive alternate extreme cold and heat, as well as soaking and drought. They become saturated with water, much as a sponge, on moist or rainy days. When wet their bodies are soft, pliable, and tough. When dry, a lichen does not wither, but becomes rigid and brittle.

Even though lichens are resistant to changes in temperature and moisture, they seem to be very intolerant of or sensitive to chemical and physical impurities in the air. They are absent or not abundant in cities and small towns. Apparently their thalli do not develop well in the presence of smoke, soot, coal gases, carbon monoxide gas from automobiles, and gases from industries. Some lichenologists have suggested that the sensitivity of lichens to foul air may be used, sometime, as an indicator of healthful air conditions for humans.

Lichens are unique in determination or identification methods. Some of them require color changes for recognition. These are brought about by chemical reactions. Various chemicals are used. The color reactions are combined with morphological characters for the determination of the species. In the tests, usually each reagent is applied separately, but in some plants, for example, potassium hydroxide is applied and followed by calcium hypochlorite. A positive test with one or more reagents indicates the presence of certain lichen acids. Iodine solution is used as a carbohydrate test.

Tree lichens generally occur on the trunks, occasionally on the lower branches. Foliose and fruticose thalli are more common on rough bark. The crustose species usually grow on trees with smooth bark. Observations have shown that lichens are not confined, commonly, to a particular species of tree. Several kinds of rock are substrata for the rock lichens.

Some of the Indiana species of lichens occur in specific kinds of habitats and thus may serve man as plant indicators. *Dermatocarpon miniatum* grows on wet ledges and cliffs, especially limestone. *Lecidea russellii, Verrucaria sordida, V. calciseda, Caloplaca flavovirescens,* and *C. lactea* usually occur on limestone or calcareous rocks. *Verrucaria rupestris* has been found on rock, especially limestone, mortar, and bricks. In contrast, *Lecidea virginiensis* is commonly found on sandstone. Other lichens in Indiana grow only on bark of trees and shrubs; a few species of *Cladonia* occur usually on old and rotting wood; several species grow on rocks and/or trees but among mosses; and others occur only on earth or soil. *Thrombium epigaeum* inhabits damp bare earth, especially clay, as indicated by its specific name ana by its common name, Clay Lichen.

With one exception it seems that the lichens presently known in Indiana are of general distribution in the United States. In the 1958 foray of the American Bryological Society, the lichenologists collected *Baeomyces absolutus*. J. W. Thomson[1] stated that it was the most remarkable find of the foray. This is a tropical species, reported[2] from North Carolina, Florida, and Alabama. The species was collected on Mansfield sandstone at Fallen Rock in Parke County and in Hoosier Highlands in Putnam County. Apparently these localities greatly extend the range of distribution of this lichen.

As to usefulness to the residents of Indiana, the lichens have had an important role in soil formation over a long period of time. If there exists an extensive area of bare rock, 'it frequently has been produced by landslides or by erosion, either by water or by retreating glaciers. In Indiana, most of our rocks are granite, sandstone, limestone, and shale. Crustose lichens are the first plants to grow on some more or less horizontal bare rock surfaces and thus begin the formation of the first soil. In turn these primitive plants pave the way for the more advanced kinds of vegetation. These thalloid plants produce the organic acids which gradually disintegrate the surfaces of their rock substratum. Foliose lichens commonly succeed the crustose forms. To the rock particles, organic material is added as death and decomposition occur to portions of these lichens. As the wind carries bits of dead plant parts and dust, these may be deposited with the particles of rock and dead portions of the lichens. Thus the building of a soil is started. The small amount of humus retains more moisture than the disintegrated rock surface. The bodies of the lichens produce more shade than did the bare rock surface. Eventually there is a sufficient amount of soil and moisture for certain species of mosses to grow with the lichens. As more rock is disintegrated by the lichens and mosses and more soil, including humus, has accumulated, certain grasses and herbs appear on the rock. The greater the number of herbaceous plants, the more rapidly the soil accumulates. Eventually, shrubs appear. In due time there is enough soil with humus to support the growth of trees such as oaks and hickories, which may be followed by American beech and sugar maple.

When the writer was a graduate student in Botany, the late Bruce Fink, in conversation, informed the author of the neglect in Indiana in the collections and study of the lichens. He asked the writer to collect these plants for him, to be included in his Lichen Flora.[2] The promise was made. Academic work for degrees prevented the collecting before the death of Prof. Fink. However, the promise has been kept. The collections were determined by well-known lichenologists of our country. The writer is greatly indebted to the late A. W. C. T. Herre,[3] the late G. G. Nearing,[4] and to John W. Thomson[1] for the taxonomic data included in this treatise on Indiana lichens.

## Liverworts

Indiscriminately and frequently liverworts* are called mosses by the laymen. Probably they had a common ancestor in the development of the plant kingdom. But, it has not been established which, the Musci or the Hepaticae, is the more primitive group. Although there are likenesses between the plants of the two groups, there are also distinct differences. They probably are not directly related.

In comparison with the mosses, this group of bryophytes has a smaller estimated number of 8,000 - 8,500 kinds or species, throughout the world. In Indiana, there are approximately 75 species. The first known report of Indiana collections of hepatics was published in 1879.

Both the common name, liverworts, and the scientific name, Hepaticae, refer to the liver. Wort was a word, of earlier centuries, applied to a plant or herb of any kind. The vegetative portion (in contrast with the "fruit") or thallus (a plant body not differentiated into roots, stems, and leaves) of some of the hepatics is lobed, reminding one of the lobes of a liver. Long ago these liver-resembling plants became known as liverworts. Other theories as to the application of the term, hepatics, to these plants began in the historical period of the belief in the doctrine of signatures. One source states that the name, liverwort, was originally applied to *Marchantia* because of its fancied resemblance to the liver. According to this doc-

---

* The writer's collections (1500-2000) of Indiana liverworts were determined and taxonomically treated by two students in Botany who were candidates for the Master of Arts degree. DePauw University. The theses have not been published. In this manner the author expresses indebtedness to Kenneth A. Wagner8 and Larry A. Lantz9 for data from their theses which have been used in this account.

trine, this plant was supposed to provide a specific remedy for all liver ailments.

Among the liverworts there are two body or vegetative forms, thalloid and leafy. The thalloid body is flat on the substratum and resembles somewhat a narrow green ribbon, generally 2-forked near the growing tips, or branching twice, repeatedly, as the thallus or plant grows. The leafy forms resemble the prostrate moss plants, having stem-like and leaf-like parts or structures. Careful observation is necessary to distinguish between leafy liverworts, with leaves apparently in 2 rows and the species of mosses which have 2-ranked leaves. (In the majority of the foliose hepatics there is a third rudimentary row of leaves on the lower surface of the plant, known as underleaves.) A dissecting microscope and/or a compound microscope may be required instead of a hand-lens, to observe the absence or the presence of the costa (midvein, midrib, nerve) in the leaves. The hepatic leaf does not have a costa. The moss species with 2-ranked leaves have a midvein. Two common mosses, *Mnium* and *Fissidens,* are collected frequently by beginners for hepatics. The thalloid and leafy liverworts are anchored to the substratum by one-celled unbranched rhizoids.

In Indiana, there are two groups of thalloid liverworts, those known as the true liverworts and the hornworts. The capsules differ in shape. In the hornworts the small (1 mm - 3 cm), elongated, cylindrical sporecase is assumed to have reminded the discoverer of an animal's horn. The capsules of the true liverworts are more or less spherical. Four kinds of hornworts have been reported in the state. Twenty-one species of the thalloid true liverworts have been recognized. The leafy hepatics comprise the third and largest group in Indiana.

Occasionally pale thalloid liverworts may resemble the plant body of a foliose lichen, but the hepatics are always much greener.

The habitats of the liverworts are similar to those of the mosses: in wet or moist situations, generally shaded, on soil, bark of trees, especially in basal portion of trunk, decaying wood or logs, rock, in stagnant ponds, proximity of springs, swamps, bogs, and along streams and roadsides. (In tropical countries, liverworts often grow on the leaves and branches of the seed plants, as well as the stems, trunks, and roots.)

Mosses and liverworts frequently grow intermingled or in proximity of each other.

One very easily recognized thallose liverwort occurs only in greenhouses. Its name, *Lunularia*, is indicative of crescent or the shape of the moon in the first quarter, lunar. On the upper surface of the thallus are crescent shaped receptacles, containing numerous gemmae (vegetative bodies capable of reproducing the plant). This hepatic has been introduced into our country from Europe where it is not confined to greenhouses. Collections of *Lunularia* have been made in Indiana.

Probably *Conocephalum conicum* and *Marchantia polymorpha* are the most common and most widely distributed thallose liverworts in the state. The thalli of *Conocephalum* are yellow-green and have a fragrant odor. *Marchantia* thalli are green to deep green and lack an odor. Certainly any visitor at Turkey Run State Park has observed these liverworts on the faces of the sandstone canyons.

*Riccia fluitans* and *Ricciocarpus natans* are floating aquatic thalloid hepatics. *Riccia* also grows on mud. *Ricciocarpus* is a frequent liverwort in stagnant ponds. Another thalloid hepatic, *Pallavicinia lyellii*, grows with mosses, in swampy habitats, on soil and moist rocks, as well as on decayed logs and among decaying moss stems. This liverwort may occur in acid swamps or bogs, associated with Sphagnum.

*Riccardia pinguis* (thalloid) grows on wet humus and may occur submersed. In Indiana it is often a calciphyte (plant living in a habitat containing calcium). It was the only hepatic observed in the Cabin Creek Raised Bog, in Randolph County. There this hygrophytic liverwort occurs between the moss plants of *Campylium stellatum* and *Cratoneuron filicinum*, on soil at base of the higher plants, as well as on the crusty, alkaline soil at the margin of the stream and extending into the water. In Wayne County, it has been collected on tufa and damp limestone; in Steuben County, on soil in a swampy area; in Putnam County, on rotten log with mosses; in Monroe County, in Baxter's Bog.

The Horned Liverworts *Phaeoceros* (*Anthoceros*) *laevis* and *Notothylas orbicularis*, frequently occur along margins of streams and rivers, on shaded alluvial sandy soil, occasionally on soil at edges of paths, or in paths rarely used. The writer, upon coming to a bare area of soil in the woods, searches for thalli of the Horned Liverworts. One of the best habitats is the moist vertical sides of cattle tracks in fields or the woods.

One of the most slender leafy hepatics in Indiana is *Frullania eboracensis*. It grows on the bark of trees in the woods and forms dainty designs. The dark brownish green plants are especially conspicuous on the bark of the birch and the American beech trees. At a glance, a layman interested in bryophytes may think someone has been making pencil drawings on the tree trunks. In plant succession on bark, this liverwort is regarded as a pioneer. Occasionally it may be observed on bare rock surfaces. Other species of *Frullania* may grow with *F. eboracensis*.

A common genus of leafy liverworts in Indiana is *Porella*. The plants are much larger than those of *Frullania* and are green to brownish green. *Porella platyphylloidea* occurs throughout the state and may be found alone or growing with mosses or other liverworts. It is a pioneer species and occurs on dry bark of trees and on dry cliffs and ledges.

Other than species of *Porella,* probably the widest (3-5 mm) liverwort in the leafy group in Indiana is *Bazzania trilobata*. It grows in deep dense mats, in Turkey Run State Park on the shaded moist sandstone of the ravines, as well as on other substrata and in other parts of the state.

There are habitat indicators among the hepatics as well as the mosses. *Marchantia polymorpha* (thallose), like the moss *Funaria hygrometrica,* is a pioneer invader as well as a plant indicator of recently burned areas. Daubenmire[5] suggested that the success of these plants is due to their low nitrogen requirements which allow them a brief period of freedom from competition with other species which have higher nitrogen requirements. He also considered that the release of bases during the fire also benefits these pioneer bryophytes. The *Marchantia* thallus produces on its upper surface small cup-like structures which contain gemmae. The latter are splashed out of the cups by raindrops and fall upon the soil. By division of their cells the gemmae develop into a new thallus. The growth at the tips of the thalli and the gemmae provide the vegetative means of this liverwort eventually spreading over much of the burned area.

Schuster's[6,7] data, combined with the writer's observations, provide the habitat information for the liverworts of Indiana included in this treatise.

Some leafy liverworts are indicators of calcium-containing or calcareous rocks; e.g., *Pedinophyllum interruptum, Lophocolea heterophylla,* and *Frullania riparia. Jubula pennsylvanica* (leafy) is an epipetric oxylophyte, growing on non-calcareous rock, avoiding limestone, and thus becomes a good indicator of acidic substrata.

Other species are indicators of calcareous or subcalcareous sandstone and shale; e.g., *Chiloscyphus pallescens* (leafy), *Frullania riparia* (leafy), and *Mannia rupestris* (thallose). *Diplophyllum apiculatum* seems to be limited to non-calcareous shale and sandstone outcrops, and clayey or loamy soils, apparently avoiding decaying wood and soil rich in humus.

Another common leafy hepatic, in Indiana, is *Scapania nemorosa.* These plants grow on either calcareous or acid substrata but are nearly always epipetric (on rock).

*Pellia epiphylla* (thallose) grows on either acid or subcalcareous substrata. Its special requirement is a relatively constant supply of moisture, in relatively shaded sites. In contrast, some liverworts thrive in dry habitats and are classified as xerophytes, such as *Cephaloziella rubella* (leafy), *Mannia fragrans* (thallose), *Reboulia hemisphaerica* (thallose), and *Frullania inflata* (leafy).

Light and shade are decisive factors in habitats of at least one liverwort in the state. *Cephalozia media* (leafy) is a distinct mesophyte (plant requiring an average amount of moisture), and apparently must grow in the shade, because it tolerates very little direct light. In Indiana it occurs in very thin mats on moist shaded sandstone on decaying logs, and on loamy soil. *Trichocolea tomentella,* one of our most beautiful leafy hepatics, as its finely divided leaves are observed with the compound microscope, occurs in swamps, not bogs, forming thick mats on decaying stumps and on hummocks. It seems to require a constant supply of water and moderately diffuse light.

Probably the liverworts are the pioneers (the first to appear) before the mosses, on many bare areas, particularly on vertical substrata. A few species in the state will be presented.

*Fossombronia foveolata* (leafy) is a pioneer species, usually on inorganic substrata not previously colonized, and seems to be unable to compete with other plants.

*Porella platyphylla* and *P. platyphylloidea* (leafy) are pioneer species on exposed sites which have a very intermittent supply of water, such as dry tree bark, exposed roots, and dry cliffs and ledges. In contrast, *P. pinnata* requires a continual supply of water and, at times, is submerged or floating.

*Radula complanata* (leafy) is a pioneer on bark or on vertical faces of rocks and cliffs, where the water may run off and the evaporation rate is high. It grows in habitats of high humidity. *R. obconica* requires more moisture than *R. complanata* and occurs in nearly pure colonies or patches. The latter apparently indicates that it does not compete successfully with other species.

*Frullania inflata* (leafy) pioneers either on bark or on cliffs. *F. riparia* in the midwest is a pioneer on shaded, slightly moist rocks. *F. eboracensis,* one of the most abundant hepatics in the Temperate Zone, is a pioneer on the bark of living trees. In contrast, *Diplophyllum apiculatum* (leafy) is never a pioneer. It occurs only after colonization of the bare area by other species.

Most of the Indiana hepatics are those which occur in eastern United States and in the deciduous forests. *Frullania squarrosa*[7] is a cosmopolitan and widely distributed species which has an essentially southern range. In Indiana, it has been reported from Montgomery, Spencer, Scott, and Jefferson Counties, on dry exposed bark of trees and exposed faces of rocks.

The species may grow alone, in a pure colony, or several species of different genera or of the same genus may thrive together, in a mixed colony; e.g., species of the genera *Radula, Frullania,* and *Porella.* These associations of small plants are known as associules.

Mosses and liverworts may invade bare areas together, as *Funaria hygrometrica* and *Marchantia polymorpha* in burned areas. Denuded soil banks may be colonized by the thallose hepatics *Phaeoceros* (*Anthoceros*) *laevis, P. crispulus, Blasia, Pellia,* and *Notothylas,* and by the moss with the green felt-like persistent protonema, *Pogonatum pensilvanicum.* Such colonies are apparently important factors in preventing washouts on roads. The mats renew themselves each year.

Hepaticae are among the first plants to invade flooded areas. The terrestrial forms of *Riccia fluitans* and *Ricciocar-*

*pus natans,* as well as *Notothylas orbicularis* and *Phaeoceros* (*Anthoceros*) *laevis* are frequently present.

In consideration of the advancement or progression of the plant kingdom, one theory explains that the ferns had their ancestry in the horned liverworts, and that the liverworts and mosses had their origin in the green algae or Chlorophyta (mostly aquatic plants). Bryophytes have such delicate parts that they have not been found abundantly in fossil form. They are known to have been well developed plants millions of years ago: liverworts about 300 million, mosses about 250 million, and Sphagnum 60-80 million.

The author is not aware of any commercial value of liverworts. They are of scientific importance in the study of the development of the plant kingdom. The hepatics are very interesting plants for study and research. They are pioneers and colonizers on moist exposed rock surfaces, especially on the faces of sandstone canyons, probably more frequently than the mosses. They also grow upon bare moist soil, bark, and wood. Like the mosses, the hepatics play an important role in Indiana in the formation of soil from rock surface and in the prevention of soil erosion. If one considers the general contributions of the present and directs thoughts backward to the retreat of the glaciers, an inestimable value may be placed on the direct and indirect economic importance of bryophytes to man.

## Mosses

Mosses and liverworts are often considered together as bryophytes or moss-like plants. It has been estimated that there are 23,000 species of bryophytes in the world. About 14,000 of these species are true mosses. Although the first known Indiana collections of mosses were made in 1875, only 275 kinds are known to occur in the state. In contrast with the small number of species, their importance to the state as a natural feature is noteworthy.

Laymen often call other groups of plants mosses, such as algae and lichens. The presence of leaf-like and stem-like parts or structures in a true moss aids in recognizing these plants. Bryophyte leaves and stems differ greatly in internal structure from those, for example, in a fern, pine, or maple, and thus are not true leaves and stems even though there is a superficial resemblance. The species of *Sphagnum* are known as peat mosses, distinguishing these plants from the true mosses. Although both groups are known as mosses, the structure of the plant bodies differs in many respects. About 350 kinds of *Sphagnum* are known. Eleven species and varieties have been reported as growing in Indiana.

Mosses characteristically grow in moist shaded habitats. They also occur in drier exposed situations and in water. The substratum may be soil, rock, old shingle roofs, rotting logs and wood, bark of living or dead trees and shrubs, or decaying organic matter. In Indiana the mosses which inhabit rock substratum may grow on limestone, sandstone, or granite, as well as on concrete and brick structures of various kinds. There is usually some accumulation of soil and humus, in varying amounts, on the latter substrata.

Although many mosses grow on more than one kind of substratum, other species are selective, requiring certain kinds of rock, soil, and humus, or specific habitats, and may serve man as plant indicators. Knowledge of the genera and species of mosses often aids in a speedy general recognition of the acidity or alkalinity of the substratum. It seems that all species of *Sphagnum* (bog mosses) are oxylophytes (avoiding alkalinity or the slightest trace of calcium carbonate or lime), thus indicating acid or "sour" substratum or soil. The Cushion Moss or The White Moss, *Leucobryum glaucum*, and The Broom Moss, *Dicranum scoparium*, in many Indiana habitats may be regarded as plant indicators of acid soil. They have a pH range of 4.2-5.4. Certain species of the true mosses, such as *Campylium stellatum* and *Drepanocladus aduncus* either prefer or are tolerant of fens (alkaline bogs). The Indiana species of *Gymnostomum*, *Eucladium*, and *Seligeria* are calciphytes (growing in alkaline habitats, such as on damp or dripping ledges of limestone). The pH tests of soil in which mosses were growing, made by the author in the state, show a ranƒe from 3.8-8.

In addition to peat bogs and fens, there occurs in Randolph County, Indiana, six miles north of Modoc, a raised bog, known as Cabin Creek Raised Bog. This convex mass is at least 10 feet above the floodplain of Cabin Creek. This area of glaciated terrain dates to the activity of the Early Wisconsin glacier. The bog is about 50 miles south of the limits of the Late Wisconsin glaciation in Indiana. It is believed that Cabin Creek

Raised Bog has been caused by artesian spring water, high in calcium content, with mosses, sedges, and grasses as the chief peat formers. The author made 60 random collections of mosses in this fen. *Campylium stellatum* occurred in 37 of them. Apparently this moss has been the chief bryophytic factor in the present stage of development of the Cabin Creek Raised Bog. Another indicator of calcareous habitats, found in this fen with *Campylium stellatum,* was the moss *Cratoneuron filicinum.*

Some of the lithophytic (occurring on rock surfaces) mosses grow on the horizontal surfaces of more or less flattened rocks, such as our most common *Grimmia, G. apocarpa.* Others such as the Sword Moss, *Bryoxiphium norvegicum,* and *Hookeria acutifolia* occur on the almost vertical faces of sandstone.

In the state there are a few so-called crevice-mosses. These plants prefer to grow on moist shaded decomposing rocks. One of the best examples in Indiana is *Fissidens closteri.*

A collection of moss plants on sandstone may be recorded erroneously as oxylophytes because often sandstone contains lime compounds. Without chemical tests, this condition may not be evident to man. However, there are mosses which are excellent indicators of the presence of calcareous inclusions in the sandstone. A minute moss, *Desmatodon porteri,* is one of these indicators in Indiana.

The Cord Moss, *Funaria,* is a very reliable indicator of a habitat in which there has been a fire. Although cinders or charcoal may not be evident on the surface, fragments may be found in the soil.

The Knothole Moss has been so named because its habitat is decaying wood which is soaked with moisture much of the time, especially in knotholes in living deciduous trees and in forks of trees. However, other species than *Anacamptodon splachnoides* may grow in knotholes. In Indiana this very small moss has been collected in Montgomery and Parke Counties.

Some mosses are classified as aquatic in contrast with terrestrial. A student of water mosses observes that certain species grow in swiftly flowing streams and others in more quiet water, such as swamps, bogs, pools, etc. Apparently the rate of movement of the water influences the amount of mechanical action and affects the aeration of the water. A few examples of aquatic mosses in Indiana are species of *Fontinalis*, *Hygroamblystegium*, and *Drepanocladus*.

If one recognized the mosses on the land which he wished to purchase, he would know whether he was considering poor or good soil. *Aulacomnium heterostichum* grows on soil rich in humus and *Bryum caespiticium* occurs on soil lacking organic matter.

One of the most cosmopolitan mosses growing in Indiana is *Ceratodon purpureus*. It occurs in barren habitats, as a low dense sod of moss, often with little competition with other plants. If shingles on a roof or a platform over a well are rotting, probably this moss is abundantly present and assisting in the disintegrating process.

In ecological studies of Indiana mosses a series or succession occurs, beginning on a bare area of sandstone with small species of *Fissidens* and reaching a climax with dominant mosses such as *Polytrichum* and *Dicranum*. Likewise there is a succession on limestone. Another moss succession begins on living wood, passes to decayed wood, and thence to soil.

Certain of the hydrophytic (growing in wet habitats) mosses are tufa or travertine builders in small streams in the vicinity of Bloomington. The water is very alkaline, from 7.6 to 8.2 in pH. The streams carry calcium carbonate in solution, since they drain from the limestone beds and exposures. Several Indiana species of mosses have a part in tufa formation. Two of the important species are *Brachythecium rivulare* and *Cratoneuron filicinum*. Probably these plants act only indirectly in the precipitation of the calcium carbonate, especially by providing a larger surface for the evaporation of the calcareous water than the filaments of algae which are often present among the mosses. Another possibility is the penetration of the plant tissues by the chemical substances in solution in water, and, as the plants grow older, they resist decay and form a porous rocklike mass.

*Brachythecium rivulare* has also been associated with the formation of bog iron ore near Otis, Indiana. In this locality numerous springs are impregnated with iron compounds. The moss grows abundantly in the spring outlets. Apparently as the iron compounds penetrate the moss tissue, a hard porous tufa is formed which becomes a part of the accumulation of bog iron ore.

One of the most exciting moments on a bryological field trip is to discover the dwarf plants of the pygmy mosses. Several species occur in Indiana. They are more likely to be seen if in "fruit" (seta and capsule). Some of the Hoosier pygmies follow. *Fissidens closteri* is about 0.5 mm high, with 2-3 pairs of leaves. It is either very rare or it is overlooked because of its minute size and its habitat, in crevices of decomposing rock and on rock in stream beds, in woods. There are other *Fissidens* species which are also very small, 1-5 mm. Many of our dwarfs prefer moist soil, usually bare; e.g., *Acaulon rufescens*, plants 1-2 mm high, bulb-like or bud-like in shape, *Astomum muhlenbergianum*, to 5 mm, *Ephemerum serratum* and *E. spinulosum*, about 1 mm, *Pleuridium subulatum*, 2-6 mm, *Bruchia sullivantii*, to 2 mm, *Aphanorhegma serratum*, 1-5 mm, *Buxbaumia aphylla*, about 1 mm, and *Diphyscium foliosum*, 1-2 mm. The writer has found the early forenoon hours, preferably when the dew or rain drops are on the capsules, or the later afternoon, when the sun rays are oblique, to be the more profitable periods for locating these dwarf mosses. If one crawls on hands and knees, the search may be more successful. The published records of these species show that they are not frequently collected.

As in the ecological study of the seed plants, one finds among the mosses or among the mosses and the liverworts the frequent associations of certain species, in their respective habitats. Or, on a specific substratum within the state, one may anticipate finding certain species of mosses or of bryophytes growing together in the same clump, sod, mat, or restricted area.

Mosses are regarded as pioneer plants or as colonizers because they can thrive on bare rock, soil, and wood. In these habitats, seedlings of the seed plants fail. However, in a period of time, the mosses prepare a suitable substratum for the success of the more advanced forms of plant life.

In this decade as in previous years, the laymen inquire as to the uses of mosses or their economic importance. They are of scientific interest but as yet have a small financial value, unless one can consider the value of the soil which provides directly or indirectly the food, shelter, and clothing for man and food for the animals used as human food. People who collect and study mosses do so for the purpose of contributions to botanical knowledge rather than for financial or commercial benefits.

From an economic standpoint, it seems that the greatest value of the true mosses to mankind is based upon their conributions to the formation of soil from rock surfaces left bare upon the retreat of the last glaciers which extended over much of Indiana, the Illinois and the Wisconsin, and to the preparation of habitats favorable for the germination of the seeds of the herbs, shrubs, and trees, which succeed the mosses. Mosses colonize bare rock, following lichens. They also cover areas of soil made bare by erosion, fires, and landslides, and when firmly established, hold the particles of soil until the larger plants establish themselves.

In the stages of plant succession from a bare area of rock to the climax vegetation in Indiana, Sugar Maple and American Beech Forest, the mosses follow the first and second stages of crustose and foliose lichens, respectively, and precede the herbs which are succeeded by shrubs and trees. Each group of plants in turn has possession of a habitat, produces profound influences upon it, and makes conditions favorable for the next more advanced plant community by increasing the humus, accumulating soil, and producing a more moist habitat. The depth of soil in rock depressions and crevices, under a cushion of moss may be one inch or more.

In the Indiana Dunes area, sods of *Ceratodon purpureus* may be the pioneer in plant succession on a bare area of sand, followed by the Hair-Cap Mosses, *Polytrichum juniperinum* and *P. piliferum*. The latter plants are often successful pioneers on sandy soils because they readily anchor themselves by dense growths of rhizoids, and when covered by blown sand quickly produce long branched shoots which grow upward and out of the sand.

Moss-covered stones in Indiana streams frequently stop quantities of sand and gravel, preventing them from being carried away by the water.

Moss protonema, the green filamentous or thread-like phase of a moss plant, is one of the first vegetative growths on soil made bare by man or nature. This forms an attached cover over the loose soil, thus preventing the water of spring floods and summer showers from washing away the soil. Sods and mats of mosses are important in breaking the force of rain upon the substratum and in the prevention of soil erosion. Terrestrial mosses anchor particles of soil by means of their rhizoids (many-celled, branched, thread-like outgrowths, chiefly from the stem, which serve for anchoring the moss and perhaps for absorbing water and minerals dissolved in the water for the plant).

Occasionally bare areas on moist banks of ditches along roadsides or bare soil banks in woods are covered with the green felt-like persistent protonema of *Pogonatum*, especially if the soil has been recently disturbed. The protonema not only provides a large part of the nutrition and retains water for the leafy portion of the plants but also holds the soil in place, to a large extent preventing erosion.

Mosses have an important part in the conservation of water in forests even though they are short plants in mats and sods on the forest floor or on tree trunks. During rains and melting snows, mosses absorb water very rapidly through the thin cell walls of the leaves. In most mosses the leaves are very close together, overlapping each other. As the moisture decreases, the leaves close tightly to retain the moisture. This ability to absorb and keep the water is regarded as one of the important contributions of mosses to the forests. The water in their cells will leave the moss plants slowly by transpiration (loss of water from living plant tissue in the form of vapor) as the humidity of the atmosphere decreases. Thus the moss carpet provides a source of moisture for the forest plants of many kinds. The mats of mosses on the sides of canyons and on rocky slopes also conserve the water.

In northern Indiana along Lake Michigan, floating islands occur. They seem to have had their origin in a surface mat, formed over the water. As portions of the mats have broken loose from the shore, they have become floating islands. One of the most common mosses in those mats is *Campylium stellatum*. This moss also has a part in filling damp or wet depressions by its mats or tufts of plants, thus aiding in the development of habitats favorable to terrestrial plants such as herbs, shrubs, and trees.

Common species of Indiana mosses are of use to botany teachers, not only in the study of these particular plants and their parts in different courses, and in the study of the development and advancement of the Plant Kingdom, but also in the observation of chloroplasts, pits in cell walls, and stomata in the capsules of some species.

Due to a peculiar structure of leaves of Sphagnum, the species of peat mosses have uses which the true mosses cannot provide. The leaves have two kinds of cells. One type consists of large, colorless, empty cells open to the exterior by a pore. These empty cells make possible the absorbent and retaining qualities of these bog mosses. Sphagnum is the most efficient of all mosses in conserving water.

There are three species of *Sphagnum* growing in the state which were efficient in surgical dressings as a substitute for absorbent cotton in World War I. They are *S. imbricatum, S. magellanicum,* and *S. palustre.*

There is a factory in central Indiana which makes peat pots for growing garden seedlings and small plants for the market. The source of some of the peat for this process is Indiana bogs.

Peat mosses have helped to develop much of the muck land that produces garden truck in northern Indiana.

Pulverized peat moss is used by gardeners as a moisture retaining humus, and peat moss is used for a top-dressing for golf-course greens. There are several Indiana bogs which are being used as sources of this material.

The largest extension of one species of moss in Indiana is that of an aquatic moss, *Fontinalis duriaei,* collected by the late Charles C. Deam in Elkhart County, in 1949. His notes state that this moss was very common over an acre or two in the bed of a bayou of the St. Joseph River just below the bridge at Bristol.

The esthetic value of the mosses is also worthy of recognition. For example, consider the beautiful sandstone canyons at Turkey Run and The Shades State Parks, the forest floor, tree trunks and logs in dense woods, stones along the brooks, moist shaded soil banks, and roofs of disintegrating old buildings, without the mosses. It is the mosses and their beautiful shades of green which so quickly bring to our attention the beauty produced by these small and frequently unnoticed plants, which are present at all seasons of the year.

A new species of *Grimmia, G. indianensis,* was collected by the author in 1937, in Warren County, southwest of Rainesville. The writer knows of no other moss which was first discovered in Indiana. Presently this is the only known locality for this species.

Perhaps some nature lover may wish to recognize some common mosses which grow in our state. A few are included with brief distinguishing characteristics. The peat mosses are light grayish green with groups of leafy branches on the erect stem, some branches spreading and others drooping. Silvery Bryum (*Bryum argenteum*) plants are short, silvery white, and commonly grow on soil between bricks and stones of walks, between buildings and walks, in paths, and on old moist shaded shingles. The names describe other kinds such as Cushion or White Moss (*Leucobryum glaucum*), Fern Mosses (*Thuidium*), Hooked Moss (*Drepanocladus*), Sword Moss (*Bryoxiphium norvegicum*), and Tree Mosses (*Climacium*). Bug-on-a-Stick Moss (*Buxbaumia aphylla*), Grain-of-Wheat Moss (*Diphyscium foliosum*), Apple Moss (*Bartramia pomiformis*), and Urn Moss (*Physcomitrium turbinatum*) are so-named because of the shape of their capsules or spore cases. To find the names of the majority of mosses, one needs a hand lens, often a dissecting microscope and a compound microscope, and books with keys, descriptions, and illustrations. The search is fascinating and not difficult as the author has had a successful student who began the identification of Indiana mosses at 13 years of age.

The following mosses which occur in the state are cited because of their interesting ranges of distribution. *Fissidens polypodioides* has been reported from Florida, Georgia, Alabama, Louisiana, and Indiana. The only known state collection was made in Putnam County, at Fern, in the latter part of the 19th century. This moss, which occurs on moist shaded banks and ledges, has a distribution range of southern United States, Mexico, West Indies, Central America, and northern South America. *Fontinalis sphagnifolia* (formerly *F. biformis*) one of the water mosses, is known only from Ohio, Kentucky, Indiana, and Wisconsin. The state collections are from Owen and Putnam Counties. The earlier specific name characterizes the moss because it has leaves in the spring which differ from those produced in late summer or autumn. *Dichelyma capillaceum*, one of the water mosses, occurs in Western Europe and Eastern United States and Canada. No report of its occurrence west of the Mississippi River is known. The one Indiana collection was made in Porter County, in the Dunes State Park, in 1935, by the author.

Although Indiana bryophytes have been recognized in publications for almost a century, many bryologists (students of mosses and liverworts) have not considered the bryophyte flora of the state worthy of attention because Indiana is regarded as one of the best agricultural states in the United States, a general indication of poor habitats for bryophytes. However, especially the limestone and sandstone ledges and canyons, the many forested areas or wood lots, the Indiana Dunes, and the Wabash River and Ohio River counties have made the bryological study very interesting to the author. The writer published an illustrated manual, "Mosses of Indiana,"[10] with keys to the species based upon the vegetative characteristics, instead of the "fruits", so that the mosses could be identified during any season of the year, with or without capsules. In August 1958, the American Bryological Society (organized in 1898) held its first Indiana Foray in Putnam County. The members (from Canada and from numerous states) had two days of interesting and unexpectedly rich collecting of mosses, liverworts, and lichens in the Midwest.

### Ferns and closely related Plants

The ferns are herbaceous, terrestrial, non-flower-bearing plants. The feathery leaves of the true ferns cause a nature walk through the woods to be more lovely as well as interesting. The ferns are the most advanced spore-producing plants in comparison with the lichens, liverworts, and mosses. However, the fern group of plants, Pteridophytes, is the lowest in the development of the vascular plants in comparison with the flower-bearing plants. Ferns have true roots, stems, leaves, and vascular (specialized conductive) tissues. The stems are usually horizontally elongated, either on the surface of the substratum or in the ground. Their stems are known as rhizomes. The fern leaves are often called fronds. These vary in size from a few centimeters to about two meters in length and from entire to many times divided.

Related to the plants which the layman calls ferns are other plants which do not have the beautiful fronds of the ferns. Some have no leaves. Others have smaller leaves and the plants resemble mosses. Several kinds bear small cone-like structures at the ends of aerial stems. These related plants (allies) include, in Indiana, four genera: the Horsetails (*Equisetum*), Ground Pines or Larger Club Mosses (*Lycopodium*), Little Club Mosses or Club Mosses (*Selaginella*), and Quillworts (*Isoetes*).

For the world 8,000 - 10,000 species of ferns and their allies have been listed. Most of them are found in the tropics where they may grow to a height of about 15 meters. There are approximately 100 kinds of ferns and related genera in the midwest. Eight families, 24 genera, and about 75 species, varieties, forms, and hybrids occur in Indiana, according to C. C. Deam.[11] Wherever one goes in the state, one may find ferns, if the land is not under cultivation. However, they are most abundant in moist shaded places. There is a community in Putnam County known as Fern, because of the numerous species of ferns growing in this wooded sandstone area. Fern became known throughout the world as the result of the botanical collections made here and distributed by Lucien M. Underwood, a member of the Indiana Academy of Science in the latter part of the 19th century.

Although there is in the United States a species of climbing, twining, vinelike fern, *Lygodium palmatum*, it is not known to occur in Indiana. The tree ferns sometimes shown in large display windows are not native of the state but of the subtropics or the tropics. One species of fern which has been collected in at least seven Indiana counties, Resurrection Fern (*Polypodium polypodioides* var. *michauxianum*) is classified commonly as an epiphyte (air plant; growing on other plants but not parasitically), although Deam stated that he had seen only one specimen on a tree in Indiana. The writer has not seen it growing on a tree in the state.

In the development of the ferns and their allies (*Pteridophytes*), the Adder's Tongue Fern (*Ophioglossum*) and Grape Fern or Rattlesnake Fern (*Botrychium*) are regarded among the oldest of the true ferns. There are two species and one form of the first, and four species and four varieties of the second recorded for Indiana. *Ophioglossum vulgatum* is known as the Common Adder's Tongue. *Botrychium virginianum* is the most frequently collected Grape Fern. The sterile leaf resembles in shape the tongue of an adder, thus the origin of the common name, Adder's Tongue. The grapelike arrangement of the sporangia or spore cases on the fertile frond or spike suggested the name, Grape Fern.

One of the most interesting ferns in Indiana is the Walking Fern (*Camptosorus rhizophyllus*). Its simple, prostrate, lanceolate leaves are 10-22 cm long. They radiate from the rhizome or rootstock. The leaf apices are long attenuate, often filiform, and form adventitious roots at the tips. Thus a new plant may develop at the end of each leaf of the original plant. These new plants, in turn, may form at the tips of their fronds additional new plants. One may find several plants connected in this manner. Thus the name Walking Fern was given to the fern which spreads over the substratum in this way.

The ferns in the genus *Osmunda* are tall, with the leaves arranged in large crowns, suggesting the names regal and royal, the Royal Fern (*Osmunda regalis*). The spore cases of the fertile blade are cinnamon-colored in the Cinnamon Fern (*O. cinnamomea*). In the Interrupted Fern (*O. claytoniana*), the sterile frond is interrupted in the middle by a fertile (spore-producing) portion. The plants are tall and generally grow in lowlands; thus they are commonly known as marsh ferns.

Probably no one, other than a botanist, would search for a fern in the water. There are ferns in this habitat, appropriately named Water Ferns. *Azolla caroliniana* is the only one presently known to occur in Indiana. The plants and the delicate leaves, arranged in two rows, are minute. They are green if floating on water which is shaded, their usual habitat, and often red when floating in water exposed to the direct rays of the sun. When well established, this fern multiplies until the plants cover the surface of the water. It often grows with duckweeds. One looks for this fern in stagnant water along streams, in dredged ditches, on the surface of still ponds and backwater, and about lakes. If the water level lowers, the *Azolla* plants will grow on the muddy banks, or will grow several inches above the water level on wet mossy soil banks. Water fowl, particularly wading birds, are probably the disseminating agents. They can carry it to waters in which it has not been seen previously. *Azolla caroliniana* grows in Canada from Ontario to British Columbia, throughout the United States, in Mexico, and also in tropical America. The species was first reported in Indiana in 1839 by Prince Maximilian and was reported from six counties in 1940 by C. C. Deam.

Another Water Fern was once collected in the state. It is an excellent illustration of a transplant-experiment in which the historical record is known and was published by C. C. Deam. If the data were missing, a botanist would not know how to interpret the Putnam County collection in the DePauw Herbarium, made in 1905. *Marsilea quadrifolia* is a native of Europe and Asia, and is a marsh or aquatic fern. The 4-foliate leaves usually float on the surface of the water, perhaps suggesting a shamrock or clover to the layman. The Putnam County plants were transplanted from Connecticut to New York, thence to Ohio, and finally to a pond at the south edge of Greencastle, in 1903. It is assumed that drainage and encroaching vegetation caused the species to disappear. This water fern is known to have lived in Indiana in the old mill pond from 1903-1911. The date of disappearance is not known.

Diseased ferns rarely occur. But occasionally someone asks a botanist to examine a plant which is assumed to be diseased. Invariably the condition is that of sori on the lower surface of the frond. A sorus (singular) is a cluster of sporangia (spore sacs or cases) in ferns. They may be naked or they may be covered with a membranelike indusium (singular). The indusia of ferns vary in shape and position and are very useful in the identification of the genera and species. The sori may be kidney-shape, linear, in chainlike rows, straight or curved, cup-shaped or flat, near ends of veins, or along midrib or margin. In the Maidenhair Fern (*Adiantum*), for example, the sori are not covered by indusia but by the marginal lobes of the fronds. The Marginal Fern or Leather Woodfern (*Dryopteris marginalis*) was so-named because the sori develop along the margins of the divisions of the fronds.

One fern, the Bracken or Brake (*Pteridium latiusculum*) is a common, sturdy, coarse fern which grows in waste or neglected land. It appears early in the growing season, often in large colonies, and is usually over knee-high. The leaves are divided into three parts and are relatively horizontal. This fern thrives in full sun or semi-shaded areas in woods, in thickets, old pastures, and burned-over areas; it rarely grows in rich, moist areas so typical for the majority of ferns.

The Bracken is generally killed by the first frost and the brown patches of this fern are quite conspicuous in the autumn.

One of our delicate ferns may be distinguished from other Indiana ferns by the presence of large fleshy bulblets on the lower surface of the upper part of the long tapering fronds. The bulblets easily separate from the leaves. When they fall on a suitable substratum, they produce new plants. The common name, Bladder Fern, and the species name, *bulbifera*, are indicative of these bulblets. *Cystopteris bulbifera* grows in rocky ravines and in crevices of shaded cliffs, only in places which are constantly moist and shaded.

Some ferns, as some oaks, are hybrids. C. C. Deam has reported four hybrids among the Indiana ferns. These hybrids have resulted from a cross between two species or a variety and a species: a hybrid between Goldie Fern (*Dryopteris goldiana*) X Marginal Fern or Leather Woodfern (*D. marginalis*); a hybrid between Crested Shield-Fern (*D. cristata*) X Toothed Woodfern or Spinulose Shield-Fern (*D. spinulosa*); Boott Woodfern or Boott's Shield-Fern (*D. boottii*), a hybrid between Crested Shield-Fern (*D. cristata*) X Toothed Woodfern or Spinulose Shield-Fern (*D. spinulosa* var. *intermedia*); and Scott Spleenwort (*Asplenosorus ebenoides*), a hybrid between Ebony Spleenwort (*Asplenium platyneuron*) X Walking Fern (*Camptosorus rhizophyllus*). Apparently this is a rare fern in Indiana, reported by Deam from Lawrence and Jefferson Counties, although it occurs in the United States from Vermont to Missouri and Alabama.

Probably the rarest (or the least collected) Indiana ferns are: Wall-Rue (*Asplenium cryptolepis*), known from two counties; Pinnatifid Spleenwort (*A. pinnatifidum*), reported by Deam from seven counties and collected by the author in an additional one, Putnam County, at Hoosier Highlands; Maidenhair Spleenwort (*A. trichomanes*), from eight counties; Scott Spleenwort (*Asplenosorus ebenoides*), from three counties; Water Fern (*Azolla caroliniana*), from six counties; Hairy Lipfern (*Cheilanthes lanosa*), from two counties; Hayscented Fern (*Dennstaedtia punctilobula*), from four counties; Boott Woodfern (*Dryopteris Boottii*), from four counties; and Resurrection Fern (*Polypodium polypodioides* var. *michauxianum*), from nine counties. These plants should not be collected for other than an additional county record in the state and should be preserved in one of the established herbaria of the state or the United States.

Our largest ferns are Goldie Fern (*Dryopteris goldiana*) to 1.5 m high, Ostrich Fern (*Matteuccia struthiopteris*) to 2 m high. Cinnamon Fern (*Osmunda cinnamomea*) to 1.5 m high, and Royal Fern (*O. regalis*) to 2 m high.

There is one living genus, Horsetails or Scouring Rushes (*Equisetum*), the ancestors of which grew to 33 m high. The Equisetales is regarded by some botanists as the most primitive order in the Pteridophytes. The species are most numerous in the temperate zones. Approximately 25 species have been published for the world, and 10 for the northeast and midwest states. Eight herbaccous species grow in Indiana.

The stems of *Equisetum*, resembling rushes, are jointed. The furrowed and ridged stems may be pulled apart at the nodes or joints because of the especially delicate tissue in these locations. The early settlers in the state tied several of the internodes or segments together and used them for scouring pots, pans, and floors. For this reason they referred to these plants as Scouring Rushes. The cell walls of the epidermis are rough in texture, because they contain a glassy substance, silica. Indiana species vary in height from 15 to 150 cm or to 1.5 m high. The small cones, at the end of the fluted stems, characterize these fern allies. Some species of *Equisetum* have two kinds of aerial stems, the fertile appearing before the sterile. Others have all stems alike, sterile below, and bearing terminal cones. The leaves of *Equisetum* are inconspicuous and occur in whorls at the nodes.

In Indiana, the Field Horsetail (*Equisetum arvense*) is regarded as a weed because it is found with weeds, is weedlike in growth, and is difficult to exterminate. The plants thrive in any soil and are found on railroad embankments in the cinder beds, in fields, woods, and waste places. Apparently it prefers damp, sandy, semishaded areas. This horsetail produces from the horizontal underground stem or rhizome, first, the erect fertile shoots with a terminal cone on each and brown sheaths at the nodes. Later, there appear the erect green shoots bearing whorls of green 3-4-angled branches at the nodes. If the latter plants are inverted, one may observe a resemblance to the tail of a horse.

Five species of Club Moss or Ground Pine (*Lycopodium*) have been found in Indiana, although there are over 100 known species in the world. These relatives of the ferns are chiefly tropical and subtropical. In the tropics, some of the species are epiphytes. The characteristic habitat for the species which grow in the temperate regions is open woodlands. The Ground Pines are usually terrestrial, herbaceous, evergreen plants with both upright and prostrate stems. The leaves are numerous, small, crowded, simple, narrow, pointed, and arranged around the stem in 4-16 rows. These fern allies commonly grow in forested areas. The upright portions of the plants slightly resemble small seedling pines. They are called Club Mosses because of the resemblance to mosses (growing close to the ground and having small leaves) and because of the small spore-bearing cones or clubs. The spores are distributed by the wind. The prostrate stems (rhizomes) may be several meters long.

The Club Mosses known as *Selaginella* are distributed widely throughout the world. The usual habitat of *Selaginella* species is the wet tropics, although a few grow in the desert. In the United States, there are 35-40 species, mostly in the forests. In Deam's *Flora of Indiana,* two herbaceous species represent the genus, *Selaginella, S. apoda* (Basket Selaginella or Meadow Club Moss) and *S. rupestris* (Rock Selaginella). The delicate Meadow Club Moss creeps over the substratum in moist and shaded habitats. It resembles mosses and leafy liverworts and is often confused with them. The Rock Selaginella is a stiff plant and grows in drier and more rocky habitats. The so-called "resurrection plant" is a species of *Selaginella.* It has been given this common name because when sold, the dry stems and leaves are rolled inward, forming a ball. Then, when placed in moisture, the plant unrolls or unfolds.

The Quillworts are represented in Indiana by one species, *Isoetes engelmannii* (Engelmann Quillwort). This fern ally is usually partially emersed when mature. The plants resemble tufts of grass, small rushes, chive plants or young onions, with the leaves rising above the surface of the water. The leaves are slender, needlelike, simple, brittle, and usually less than 12 inches in length.

A plant ecologist is a botanist who studies plants in relationship to their environment, or the influence of the habitat upon the plants. An ecological study of the ferns and their allies shows that many of our Indiana Pteridophytes are associated in specific habitats instead of having a general distribution. Thus an ecologist is able to predict many of the genera and species as a particular kind of habitat is approached.

In a rich shady Indiana woods, with moist deep humus, the following ferns are usually growing: Goldie Fern (*Dryopteris goldiana*), Narrow-leaf Spleenwort (*Athyrium pycnocarpon*) especially in beech woods, Silvery Spleenwort (*A. thelypteroides*) particularly in beech, sugar maple, or white oak woods, Lady-Fern (*A. angustum*), and Maidenhair Fern (*Adiantum pedatum*).

In wet lands such as bogs, marshes, swamps, etc., one finds Royal Fern (*Osmunda regalis*), Cinnamon Fern (*O. cinnamomea*), Ostrich Fern (*Matteuccia struthiopteris*), Sensitive or Bead Fern (*Onoclea sensibilis*), Crested Fern (*Dryopteris cristata*), Marshfern (*D. thelypteris* var. *pubescens*), Spinulose Woodfern (*D. spinulosa*), Virginia Chainfern (*Woodwardia virginica*), Swamp Horsetail (*Equisetum fluviatile*), Bog Club Moss or Marsh Club Moss (*Lycopodium inundatum*), Tree Moss (*L. obscurum*) Meadow Club Moss or Basket Selaginella (*Selaginella apoda*), and Quillwort (*Isoetes engelmannii*).

The acidity and alkalinity of the substratum may be indicated in a general way by the presence of certain species of Pteridophytes. In acid, subacid, or non-calcareous substrata, the following ferns and allies occur: Pinnatifid or Lobed Spleenwort (*Asplenium pinnatifidum*), Leathery Grape Fern (*Botrychium multifidum*), Rattlesnake Fern (*B. virginianum*), Virginia Chainfern (*Woodwardia virginica*), Bog Club Moss or Bog Ground Pine or Marsh Club Moss (*Lycopodium inundatum*), Shining Club Moss or Ground Pine (*L. lucidulum*), and Rock Club Moss (*Selaginella rupestris*). The latter fern ally grows especially on thin dry soil on rocks and dry ledges of granite or gneiss, on mossy rocks, gravelly slopes, and in other exposed dry and thin-soiled locations.

On outcrops of sandstone or in nearby residual soils which are the products of the sandstone, the following grow: Walking Fern (*Camptosorus rhizophyllus*), Leather Woodfern or

Marginal Fern (*Dryopteris marginalis*), Common Polypody (*Polypodium virginianum*), and Rock Selaginella (*Selaginella rupestris*). This species of *Selaginella* grows on dry exposed sandstone, dry sand in the dune area, or in open sterile soil.

On calcareous sandstone, in limy soil, or on limestone rocks, the following are found: American Wall-rue Spleenwort (*Asplenium cryptolepis*), Scott's Spleenwort (*Asplenosorus ebenoides*), Walking Fern (*Camptosorus rhizophyllus*), Bulblet or Bladder Fern (*Cystopteris bulbifera*), Adder's Tongue Fern (*Ophioglossum engelmannii*), Purple-stemmed Cliffbrake (*Pellaea atropurpurea*), and Smooth Purple Cliffbrake (*P. glabella*). As well as on dry exposed limestone cliffs, the Purple-stemmed Cliffbrake grows in holes in masonry, at base of limestone boulders, and from crevices in limestone cliffs where there is little or no soil. In Wisconsin, this fern has been collected only on sandstone cliffs [probably calcareous sandstone].

The Bracken or Brake (*Pteridium latiusculum*), the Field Horsetail (*Equisetum arvense*), and the Smooth Scouring-rush (*E. laevigatum*) are indicators of soil which is poor in organic matter.

If the mass distribution of a species is north of a line connecting Connecticut and Kansas, and south only in the mountains, the species has been regarded as a more northern plant. If the mass distribution of a species is south of this line, it has been classified as a southern plant. The more northern species which occur in Indiana are Leathery Grape Fern (*Botrychium multifidum*), Dwarf Grape Fern (*B. simplex*), Brittle or Fragile Fern (*Cystopteris fragilis*), Smooth Purple Cliffbrake (*Pellaea glabella*), Swamp Horsetail (*Equisetum fluviatile*), Variegated Scouring Rush or Horsetail (*E. variegatum*), and Ground Pine (*Lycopodium obscurum*). The southern species growing in Indiana are Pinnatifid Spleenwort (*Asplenium pinnatifidum*), Purple Cliffbrake (*Pellaea atropurpurea*), Resurrection Fern (*Polypodium polypodioides* var. *michauxianum*), and Meadow Club Moss or Basket Selaginella (*Selaginella apoda*). The Resurrection Fern usually grows on trees, on trunks, along upper surface of old branches, on stumps, logs, and old wooden buildings; also on rocks in more northern areas, in subacid to acid soil pockets. In dry weather the leaves roll or curl and the plants appear dead.

With sufficient moisture the fronds unroll or uncurl and become green. Thus its common name is Resurrection Fern. It is widely distributed in tropical America and abundant in warmer, southern areas. This fern is local in southern Indiana and has a distribution range into Guatemala, with a wide distribution in tropical America. It grows abundantly in warmer southern areas.

Some of our most common ferns and allies, growing throughout the state, are Maidenhair Fern (*Adiantum pedatum*), Cut-Leaved Grape Fern (*Botrychium dissectum*), Rattlesnake Fern (*B. virginianum*), Brittle or Fragile Fern (*Cystopteris fragilis*), Winged Woodfern or Broad Beech Fern (*Dryopteris hexagonoptera*), Sensitive or Bead Fern (*Onoclea sensibilis*), Cinnamon Fern (*Osmunda cinnamomea*), Interrupted Fern (*O. claytoniana*), Royal Fern (*O. regalis*), Christmas Fern (*Polystichum acrostichoides*), Bracken or Brake (*Pteridium latiusculum*), Field Horsetail (*Equisetum arvense*), and Tall Scouring-Rush (*E. prealtum*).

It may surprise many laymen to know that ferns may be found in Indiana throughout the year. If the sterile fronds (without sori or spore cases) are evident during the winter months in the state, the plants are classified as evergreen. The following list includes the Indiana ferns and allies which are evergreen: American Wall-rue Spleenwort (*Asplenium cryptolepis*), Lobed Spleenwort (*A. pinnatifidum*), Ebony Spleenwort (*A. platyneuron*), Maidenhair Spleenwort (*A. trichomanes*), Scott's Spleenwort, (*Asplenosorus ebenoides*), Cut-Leaved Grape Fern (*Botrychium dissectum*) [which may be considered partially evergreen], Leathery Grape Fern (*B. multifidum*) Walking Fern (*Camptosorus rhizophyllus*), Crested Fern (*Dryopteris cristata*), Goldie's Fern (*D. goldiana*), Marginal Woodfern or Leatherleaf Woodfern (*D. marginalis*), Spinulose Woodfern (*D. spinulosa*), Purple-stemmed Cliffbrake (*Pellaea atropurpurea*), Resurrection Fern (*Polypodium polypodioides* var. *michauxianum*), Common Polypody (*P. virginianum*), Christmas Fern (*Polystichum acrostichoides*), Blunt-lobed Woodsia (*Woodsia obtusa*), Variegated Horsetail or Scouring Rush (*Equisetum variegatum*), Trailing Christmas-green (*Lycopodium flabelliforme*), Shining Ground Pine or Club Moss (*L. lucidulum*), Tree Club Moss (*L. obscurum*), Fir Ground Pine or Club

Moss (*L. selago* var. *patens*), Meadow Club Moss or Basket Selaginella (*Selaginella apoda*) [evergreen if given some protection], and Rock Club Moss (*S. rupestris*).

No one will dispute the aesthetic value of the ferns in our state, in the woods, in the canyons and ravines of Indiana State Parks, and as ornamentals among the shrubs of the lawn plantings, in greenhouses, in the windows of residences and public buildings, on the pulpit, and around a platform which has been decorated for a public occasion. But the economic value of the ferns and their allies may be decreasing.

The Spinulose Woodfern (*Dryopteris spinulosa*) is the "Greenery" which is so frequently used by the florists. It is one of our most common and most attractive ferns. One plant is often composed of a cluster of five to ten fronds. The leaves of the *Polystichum acrostichoides* are useful for Yuletide decorations and for this reason it is known as the Christmas Fern. The rhizomes of the Grape or Rattlesnake Fern (*Botrychium virginianum*) and Maidenhair Fern (*Adiantum pedatum*) have been used medicinally by the American Indians and the early white man. Among the white people, the leaves of the Grape Fern were valued for healing wounds. The rhizomes of the Maidenhair Fern contain tannin. The tender fronds of the Bracken or Brake (*Pteridium latiusculum*) have been boiled and used by the North American Indians to destroy tapeworm.

In areas in which the various species of Ground Pine (*Lycopodium*) grow abundantly, they are used for ornamental purposes, especially for Christmas decorations, such as wreaths. In Indiana the species are not abundant and the botanists keep secret the localities in which the plants occur. The Trailing Christmas-green, Ground-cedar, or Festoon-pine (*Lycopodium flabelliforme*) has prostrate and much elongated stems. The plants are wide-creeping, with numerous erect irregularly forked aerial stems. The branchlets are flattened, 2-3-forked and fan-like. This plant has been especially popular for Christmas wreaths. The spores of Ground Pines (*Lycopodium clavatum* and *L. obscurum*) are water-repellent. In the past they have been used in dusting powder. Also, druggists have used the spores in the preparation of pills. Formerly the spores of the Common Ground Pine (*Lycopodium clava-*

*tum*) were used to produce artificial lightning in the theater, and in manufacturing fireworks.

The Meadow Club Moss or Basket Selaginella (*Selaginella apoda*) is a delicate, weak, flat-growing or creeping evergreen plant. The minute, flat, sharp-pointed, translucent leaves and the threadlike branching stems form delicate and beautiful plants. Frequently this species is mistaken for a moss. The leaves are somewhat spirally arranged on the stems. Since the plants commonly grow in damp habitats and are characteristically tropical and evergreen, they are very good for ornamentals, of use in terraria or in greenhouses.

The ancestors of the twentieth century species of ferns and their allies were dominant plants and often treelike in the habitats of the Carboniferous period of the geological time table. They were transformed into the coal which is of use today. The Pteridophytes, also, have connected the past with the present in providing an important phase in the advancement of the plant kingdom, between their primitive ancestors and the seed plants which are dominant in the vegetation of today.

## LITERATURE

1. MILLER, HARVEY A. and JOHN W. THOMSON. 1958. The 1958 foray of the American Bryological Society. Bryologist **62**: 67-73.
2. FINK, BRUCE. 1935. The lichen flora of the United States. 426 pages.
3. HERRE, A. W. C. T. 1944. Lichens known from Indiana. Proc. Ind. Acad Sci. **53**: 81-95.
4. NEARING, G. G. 1947. The lichen book. 648 pages.
5. DAUBENMIRE, R. F. 1947. Plants and environment. Wiley, New York. (page 336).
6. SCHUSTER, RUDOLPH M. 1949. The ecology and distribution of Hepaticae in central and Western New York. Amer. Midland Naturalist **42**: 513-712.
7. _____ 1953. Boreal Hepaticae. A manual of liverworts of Minnesota and adjacent regions. Amer. Midland Naturalist **49**: 1-684.
8. WAGNER, KENNETH A. (1946) A taxonomic study of the Indiana species of Hepaticae. (Unpublished M. A. thesis, DePauw University.)
9. LANTZ, LARRY A. (1963) Acrogynous Jungermanniales: a taxonomic treatment of species occurring in Indiana. (Unpublished M. A. thesis, DePauw University.)
10. WELCH, WINONA, H. 1957. Mosses of Indiana. 478 pages.
11. DEAM, CHARLES C. 1940. Flora of Indiana. Department of Conservation, Indianapolis.

# 15

# *Higher Plants*

CHARLES B. HEISER, JR., AND JACK HUMBLES,
Indiana University

## Introduction

The number and kinds of plants that grow in any region are determined first of all by the climate of that region. Because of Indiana's relatively small size and the lack of mountains, the climate of the state does not vary a great deal from one region to another. The growing season, however, in the southern part of the state is more than a month longer than that in parts of the north; therefore, as might be expected, a number of southern species enter the state and many northern elements are found in the northern-most counties. The second factor controlling plant geography relates to the soils. This edaphic influence can readily be seen from the very different plants that may grow in sandy as opposed to clay soils, or from those that grow on acid soil in contrast to more basic soils. The numerous bogs, lakes, and swamps also provide special habitats for many species of plants which otherwise would not be found in the state. A third factor influencing plant distribution concerns the interactions of plants with other organisms, either plant or animal. In this connection one of the most important in historic times has been man himself, who has destroyed many plant communities and at the same time has made new ones. With large areas of the state now being devoted to cities or to agriculture, obviously the vegetation and flora have changed greatly in the last one hundred and fifty years. Some species which once occurred in the state are now extinct, although the vast majority which grew here when white man entered this region are still to be found often in greatly reduced numbers. Man has also strongly influenced the flora by his intentional introduction of many crop plants and ornamentals and his unintentional introduction of other plants, many native to Europe or Asia, which have become weeds. Our primary concern here, however, will be with the native species.

## Size of the Flora

In the northeastern United States and adjacent Canada ("Gray's Manual range") there are 817 native genera of seed plants with 4305 species.[5] Using the figures from Deam's Flora,[3] we find that Indiana has 563 genera and 1769 native species. If we examine other nearby states where figures are available, we find that Illinois has about 750 genera and 2334 species and Missouri 751 genera and 2396 species. These states are, of course, considerably larger than Indiana. If we turn to some of the western states, for example, Arizona, we find 893 genera and 3359 species. It is more than three times the size of Indiana, but the great increase in number of species results primarily from the greater variety of climates and more diverse edaphic conditions.

Although we can not claim a particularly rich flora, we can claim to have one of the best known floras of the 50 states which is chiefly the result of one man's labor. From the year 1896 until his death in 1953, Charles C. Deam of Bluffton studied the flora of Indiana and collected in every township of the state. The specimens, about 65,000, which he collected and which are deposited in the Herbarium of Indiana University, and his many books[1,2,3,4] remain as testimonial to his outstanding floristic work.

We, however, need make no apology for the flora of Indiana. Our spring flora, particularly in the woodlands of the southern part of the state with its bloodroot, hepatica, trout-lilies, Dutchman's-breeches, spring-beauties and many others, and the exceedingly interesting flora of our dunes, commands respect and admiration. In a brief survey such as this, only a small number of the many interesting higher plants can be mentioned; therefore, some readers may find some of their favorite plants omitted.

## Gymnosperms

Indiana falls within the deciduous forest zone of the eastern United States and it is not surprising, therefore, that there are only 7 genera and 10 species of gymnosperms. All of these, with the exception of larch and bald cypress, are evergreen. The greatest concentration of native gymnosperms occurs in the northern part of the state. Many species are quite rare. Only one gymnosperm, eastern red cedar (actually a juniper and not a true cedar) is really common in the state. Although large areas of the state are planted to pine, our three native pines occupy very limited natural areas. The northern white pine is found in eight counties, Jack pine is limited to the dunes area, and Virginia pine occurs in three of the southeastern counties. Yews are extremely rare but are found in two of our state parks, Turkey Run and Shades, where it is hoped they will be preserved. Even more rare is the eastern arborvitae which at last report was known only from an area just north of Mineral Springs in Porter County. The bald cypress, perhaps more familiar to most Hoosiers as the source of the cypress knees sold to tourists in Florida, is a southern species that at one time occupied vast areas in the southwestern part of the state. Today except for scattered trees it occurs only in two areas — at Hovey Lake in the southwestern corner of the state and at Cypress Ponds in southern Knox County. The former is now a state refuge; and in spite of the presence of oil, the areas have been maintained relatively undisturbed.* However, extensive clearing has been carried out at Cypress Ponds so that this magnificent stand is rapidly disappearing. Unfortunately no efforts have been made to preserve it. Tamarack, once fairly common in our northern counties, is becoming increasingly scarce as its habitat disappears. The eastern hemlock occurs in several stations, referred to as relic stands, but usually only a small number of trees is found in a given area.

## Flowering Plants

In point of number of genera the grass family is the largest in the state with 51 genera and 171 species, but the sedge family has a greater number of species, 215, although these represent only 15 genera. The Compositae, or sunflower family, with 46 genera and 202 species comes next, followed by the legumes (26 genera and 68 species) and members of the rose family (19 genera and 90 species). However, some of the most interesting plants occur in families less well represented.

## Orchids

Many non-botanists think of orchids as strictly tropical plants and may be somewhat surprised to learn that there are 16 native genera and 39 species of true orchids in Indiana. Almost every county in the state has one or more orchids with

*It is now reported to be threatened by engineering works on the Ohio River — Ed. note.

the northwestern counties having the greatest number of representatives. Some of the orchids, such as the ladies-tresses, have extremely inconspicuous small flowers, hardly meeting the layman's conception of an orchid whereas others, such as our lady slippers, are quite showy.

### Insectivorous Plants

Some people are also unaware that our flora includes several insectivorous plants. Two species of sundews and the pitcher-plant are found in many bogs in the northern third of the state. Bladderwort, another plant which traps insects, is well represented in many aquatic localities in the state.

### Trees

There are 101 trees native to Indiana. Although virgin stands of timber are now extremely rare (one may still be seen at Spring Mill State Park), our second growth deciduous forests are worthy of admiration; and our beautiful fall coloration provided by it is equalled by few other states. Many of the trees yield important commercial woods, and species giving edible nuts occur in some abundance. The black walnut falls into both categories; and the pecan, which is found in the southwestern part of the state, is certainly one of the best nut trees. Another species furnishing an edible fruit and found in the southern half of the state is the persimmon which enjoys special fame because of the annual persimmon festival held at Mitchell. The pawpaw, or Hoosier banana, as it is sometimes called, is still another species furnishing a fine fruit. Although its relatives are mostly tropical plants, it is found in virtually all areas of the state.

Among some of the rare trees, although they are common in some of the southern states, are magnolia and yellowwood. Two species of magnolia enter the state. The cucumber tree, which once must have been fairly widespread in the southern part of the state, is now limited to a few scattered trees and often to a single individual in some places. The umbrella magnolia is known only from one fairly large stand in Crawford County. The yellowwood as a native tree is limited to Ogle Hollow in Brown County, although it is a cultivated tree in many places.

### Miscellaneous Plants

Indiana has both parasites and saprophytes among its flowering plants. Of the former, dodder is one of the most common and cancer-root which grows in most parts of the state as a parasite is one of the most unusual. Some, perhaps, may not realize that mistletoe, probably best considered as only a semi-parasite, was once common in the southern counties, particularly on elm, and may still be found in some areas. Of the saprophytes, the Indian pipe with its ghostly-white color, is widely distributed, but at the most, only a few individuals are ever found growing in any one area, generally in deep woods. Poisonous plants are, of course, well represented, with poison ivy being found in all parts of the state. Poison sumac, which belongs to the same genus and is considered more objectionable by many people, is found in wet ground or bogs scattered throughout the state. Another objectionable plant, rather common in the state, is the stinging nettle. A number of species of Indiana plants at one time were collected by herb gatherers for medicinal use, the most noteworthy of which is ginseng, whose roots are still occasionally collected for sale. Although the extensive collecting of this species has nearly resulted in its extinction, it is still found in several areas. It should also be noted that one species of cactus, the prickly pear, is native to the state.

## Hybrids

Deam lists only 34 species hybrids among the higher plants of Indiana. Twelve of these are found among the violets and nine in the oaks. Among the latter, one of the best known is *Quercus deamii* which is believed to be a hybrid of chinquapin and bur oak. The land on which the tree stands was purchased by Deam and deeded to the state so that it might be preserved. Seedlings from the hybrid have been widely distributed "to perpetuate" the plant, but it should be obvious that if the plant is a hybrid the seedlings would hardly be expected to yield plants exactly like the parent.

The number of species hybrids now exceeds by far the number reported by Deam; for in recent years hybrids have been found in sunflowers, goldenrods, asters, *Tragopogon, Lespedeza,* and *Silphium*. More reports of hybrids may be expected with further study, for hybrids most frequently occur in disturbed areas of which Indiana has an increasing number.

## State Tree and State Flower

Although hardly a matter of scientific concern, some mention should be made of the official tree and flower of the state. The first state flower was the carnation, a native of Europe, and in 1923 the legislature voted to replace it with the flower of the tulip tree. It remained as the state flower until 1931 when the tulip tree was designated as the state tree; and the Zinnia, a native of Mexico, was made the state flower. Deam, who was somewhat incensed at this, wrote in 1940, "Out of our abundance of native flowers we should be able to select one for our state flower. I take this opportunity which may be my last to voice my protest against designating as a state flower one that is not a well-known native of the state nor even a native of the United States." It wasn't his last statement on the subject, however, for again in print in 1953 he "most heartily condemns" this act of the legislature. Matters so remained until the meeting of the General Assembly of 1957 when the subject of the state flower again was brought up, and this time it was changed to the peony. Although undeniably a beautiful flower and widely cultivated in Indiana, the peony is a native of China and Japan.

There can, however, be no quarrel with our choice of a state tree, for the tulip tree or yellow poplar as it is called by some people for unknown reasons, is a truly magnificent and valuable timber tree and is native to nearly all areas of the state. There is, of course, no reason why its blossom, as Deam wanted, could not serve as the official flower of the state as well.

## Pollination

A great number of the plants of Indiana are wind pollinated — all the gymnosperms, the grasses, the sedges, many of the trees, ragweed and a number of others. A few are pollinated by water, *Elodea* for example. The remainder, unless self-pollinated, are pollinated by animals. The insects are, of course the most important — from beetles which pollinate magnolias to butterflies, moths and bees which pollinate great numbers of species. Some interesting examples of the relation of flowers to their pollinators are seen in Dutchman's-pipe which is pollinated by small flies temporarily trapped in the flower, in shooting-star which is pollinated by bumble bees whose violent buzzing is necessary to dislodge the pollen from the anthers, and in yucca which is pollinated by the yucca-moth whose larvae feed on the developing seeds. Whether or not the yucca was ever native to Indiana is problematical, but today it is cultivated or escaped throughout the state and its pollination may be readily observed, although it sometimes takes a discerning eye to distinguish the moth from the flower because both are the same color.

The only other animal, unless one considers man's intentional pollination in plant breeding work, involved in pollination in Indiana is the hummingbird. The hummingbird pollinates mostly flowers having red colors, with columbine and trumpet creeper being good examples.

The interrelation of flowers and their pollinators, a popular area of investigation in the past century, has recently been the subject of renewed scientific interest and has been dignified by the name of floral ecology. Much important and interesting work remains to be done in the field, both from patient observation and actual experimentation.

## Plant Identification and Collecting

The identification of the trees is no difficult task and many books may be found, including Deam's excellent "Trees of Indiana," which serve quite adequately. The identification of the herbaceous plants, however, is a different matter. Although a number of picture books and simplified keys dealing with wild plants are available, these are usually incomplete and can hardly be recommended for the serious student who must therefore turn to one of the more scientific or technical manuals. Deam's "Flora of Indiana" is the ideal book, but unfortunately it is no longer in print. Copies of it, however, may be found in the libraries of all county seats in the state. The other two manuals which may be used are by Fernald[5] and by Gleason and Cronquist.[6] The latter is particularly recommended since its keys are easier for a beginner to master. Obviously the best way for one to learn to identify plants is to take a course in taxonomy at a university or college; but with patience and hard work, one will find that he can use these books to identify many plants on his own, although the more difficult groups such as the grasses, the sedges, and the composites, will require considerable effort.

Since most keys for identification are based on flower structure, the student will find that it is usually necessary to study the plant when it is in bloom. Some people find that making dried specimens by pressing plants is a good way to learn them. There is, of course, no great harm done if specimens are made of the common plants; but the rare ones should not be collected.

Deam's Flora gives records county by county for all of the higher plants, and new records for plant distribution are published periodically in the Proceedings of the Indiana Academy of Science. If a previously unreported wild species is found, a dried specimen of it should be sent to Indiana University, so that verification of the identification may be made and the specimen deposited in the Herbarium as a permanent record. Although the flora of Indiana is extremely well known scientifically, it is, of course, possible that new plants may become established in the state as weeds; and it is desirable to have records of them as well as of the native species.

## Future Work

As far as the advancement of scientific knowledge is concerned, there is little need for additional collecting of the Indiana flora. For the student who is interested in this phase of botany, *i.e.*, collection and identification, it should be mentioned that there are vast areas of the world, particularly in the tropics, and even parts of the United States, where such work is still needed. The above statement by no means should be taken to indicate that we have a complete knowledge of the taxonomy of the higher plants of Indiana. But the next advances in the understanding of these will not come from the types of studies conducted in the past but will involve studies of groups throughout their entire range, for plants have no respect for political boundaries, and the research will include the use of new approaches, including both cytogenetics and biochemistry.

### LITERATURE

1. DEAM, CHARLES C. 1929. Grasses of Indiana. State of Indiana Department of Conservation, Division of Forestry.
2. ———— 1932. Shrubs of Indiana. 2nd ed. State of Indiana Department of Conservation, Division of Forestry.
3. ———— 1940. Flora of Indiana. State of Indiana Department of Conservation, Division of Forestry.
4. DEAM, CHARLES, with the assistance of T. E. SHAW. 1953. Trees of Indiana. 3rd revised ed. State of Indiana Department of Conservation, Division of Forestry.
5. FERNALD, M. L. 1950. Gray's Manual of Botany. 8th ed. American Book Company.
6. GLEASON, HENRY and ARTHUR CRONQUIST. 1963. Manual of Vascular Plants of Northeastern United States and Adjacent Canada. D. Van Nostrand Company.

# 16

# Plant Communities

R. O. PETTY AND M. T. JACKSON
Wabash College and Indiana State University

Everyone knows what vegetation is until the day he asks, "Why are those plants *there?*" or more specifically, "Why are *those* plants there and not the many others familiar to us?" Why are certain plant species consistently found growing together and why are some species more abundant "there" than others? These questions of "why?" and "how many?" are where the study of vegetation begins.

There is a distinction between the flora of a region and its vegetation. It is the matter of numbers. In a floral list, which is an inventory of the plant species of an area, the presence of a single plant of a rather rare species is of equal importance to thousands of a more common one. Vegetation, on the other hand, is the impact which the plant species of an area make collectively. The nature of this sum of plant life is the subject of this chapter.

Botanists, and more particularly, plant ecologists, recognize within vegetation many categories of plant groupings from the most general sort of *plant formations* (deciduous forest, boreal forest, grassland, etc.) to more particular communities such as oak-hickory or beech-maple forest or bluestem prairie. Plant communities are often considered as characterizing broader *plant associations* which occupy particular geographic regions.[6] Such associations of plants develop in response to cumulative effects of particular environmental factors such as variations in amount and distribution of annual rainfall, mean temperatures and temperature extremes, the length of the days and the growing season, light intensity and soil conditions and the competition between organisms. Those plant communities which are in a "dynamic equilibrium" with such factors are called *climax communities,* and because the over-riding factors are commonly climatic, the principal community types are often referred to as being, or approaching, the "climatic climax."

While in reality, vegetation exists as individual stands or

*concrete communities* (into which one may throw an empty beer can) a useful idea of vegetation is the *community type* or abstract community based on the observed recurrent association of plant species and characterized by the dominant ones. It is in this sense that an ecologist speaks of a *beech-maple* community; it is the abstract sum of all the separate stands he has ever walked through in which beech and maple were predominant. The conditions which produced the stands were not identical but analogous and the resulting actual communities were enough similar to join his abstract notion.

While some ecologists believe that these groupings of plant species have evolved through their common requirements, tolerances and mutual interactions into rather definite recurrent and predictable communities[6, 24], others conclude that plant species are distributed across landscapes individually and independently of each other and that if certain species happen to be found growing together, it is because in that place their individual requirements happen to overlap.[23, 62] As with most disagreements among experts, this one results from a lack of proof or clear-cut evidence and perhaps also from a failure to recognize that the truth may include both situations. In spite of this, vegetation may be described and appreciated in terms of its functional composition, history of development, and on the basis of its dominant species.

### Plant Succession

Succession is, most simply, the change which vegetation undergoes. Over a period of time, successive plant species and community types occupy the same area, with one gradually replacing the other in response to changes in the environment. An abandoned field, for example, very quickly undergoes a series of changes, from bare soil to a first year assemblage of algae, mosses, lichens and dominating annual grasses, such as crabgrass and panic grass, and such forbs as lamb's quarter, smartweed, pigweed, carpetweed, cocklebur, ragweed and mullein. The second stage is characterized by increasing numbers of perennial forbs and turf-building perennial grasses, such as poverty grass, broom-sedge and blue grass. During this stage, asters and goldenrods are frequently associated with various briars, the most common being blackberry, dewberry, raspberry and wildrose. Normally, develop-

ing with the goldenrod-briar community are scattered tree
seedlings such as eastern red cedar, hawthorn and black
cherry which are rapidly disseminated by birds, plus such common wind-disseminated species as red maple, elm, ash, sycamore and tulip poplar. If the field has been previously pas-
tured, honey locust and hawthorn are often abundant. The developing saplings further modify the environment favoring
a ground cover of woodland forbs. Species intolerant of shade
are slowly replaced by tolerant ones and finally those forest
trees and forbs which are best adapted to the particular soil
and climate, terminate the sere and persist in a climax equilibrium. Each progressive stage in this succession results
in modifications of the environment in some way and these
changes continually favor more integrated and more stable
communities. All vegetation is at some stage of succession,
either terminal (climax) or developmental.

## Origins of Indiana's Plant Communities

Indiana is a critically located land area with respect to the
geography of plant life.[18] Approximately 45% of our flora is
comprised of species which are at the limits of their present
range. Only 10% of our tree species have a state-wide distribution (all floral areas).[31] Why should this be so? To understand this diversity within present vegetation we must
know something of the past. During the late Mesozoic era,
some 100-80 million years ago, North America was uniformly
low, warm-wet and densely timbered. Tropical palms and fig
trees grew up interspersed among ancestral species of certain
contemporary hardwoods such as magnolia, tulip poplar and
sassafras.[3] This great Cretaceous forest extended from Ice-
land to Alaska. By the mid Tertiary period (30 million years
ago) a mixed deciduous forest had developed which was much
like that found growing today in certain parts of the southern
Appalachians. It contained most of the tree species which are
found in Indiana at the present time.

During the late Tertiary, three changes occurred which
substantially affected the subsequent vegetational pattern of
the continent. One of these was the continued uplift of the
Rocky Mountains which produced the eastward rainshadow
and the eventual dry grassland formations of the western
interior, driving the mixed deciduous forest eastward and

segregating the oak forests of the Ozark mountains. The second was the onset of increasingly low mean annual temperatures over the whole northern hemisphere, which together with altered precipitation patterns, culminated in the glacial climates of the Quaternary in which we live today. A third factor was the rejuvenation of erosion cycles within the eastern landscape, which segregated the mixed Tertiary forest along physiographic lines.[6]

The most important recent geologic event in North America is continental glaciation. To it we owe the regenerative fertility of our best agricultural soils and the very nature of much of our landscape. Indiana's vegetation is still responding to the broad changes in soil and climate which accompanied the glacial advances and retreats. In the time since the last glacial ice removed from Indiana (between 13,000 and 8,000 B.C.) midwestern vegetation has undergone many changes. Plant communities arose only to be replaced as the climate changed. The vanished plant communities, however, left a permanent record in the form of pollen grains rained into the sediments of the many kettle-hole lakes which dotted the postglacial landscape. Most pollens preserved well under the conditions unique to bog deposits. The southern-most natural lakes in Indiana are completely filled with sediment and plant debris. From analysis of the pollen composition at various levels in the peat of these bogs and the sediments of more northern lakes, the history and succession of primeval vegetation in Indiana have been discerned.[10, 49, 55]

One general progression is consistently found in these pollen records: a cool-moist climate which favored a forest dominated by spruce and fir, gradually changed to one which allowed pine and then pine and oak to replace the boreal conifers. Some palynologists believe that prairie vegetation invaded Indiana and Ohio during this early post-glacial period.[2] During a time which began approximately 8,000 years B.C., a temporary return to a cooler moister climate allowed pine and hemlock to become prevalent once again in the regional forest. This second cold period (which corresponds to a minor re-advance of ice)[17] was closed by a gradual shift to a prolonged warm-dry climate. Throughout this warm-dry period, species of oak dominated the forests of Indiana. This oak peak, called the Xerothermic Period, which reached a maximum be-

tween 2,000 and 1·000 B.C., continued with only minor inter-
ruption until approximately 1,000-1,300 A.D. (still warm
enough at this time to allow Norsemen to settle and successfully cultivate crops in Greenland). From 1,300 to 1,800 A.D.
the general climate of North America was somewhat cooler
and moister than now. Our current vegetation is the product
of the myriad responses of plant species and communities to
these environmental variations and existing physiographic
patterns.

## Relict Communities

A *relict community* is one that persists in an area longer
than the climate which produced it. It is usually found in a
special habitat situation which compensates partially for the
climatic disadvantage and allows the species to exist within
the domain of the climatically favored types. Such communities are generally much fragmented and often are represented
by only a few or even a single species isolated within the more
recent vegetation. In Indiana there are various distinct relict
types. Prairie, chestnut oak and boreal relicts have been described. At present the best reported relict community occurs
in the Pine Hills Natural Area of the Shades State Park.[19]
This area shelters what has been interpreted as a remnant
of a post-glacial hemlock—white pine—hardwoods community
which is now a climax type in wide areas of the lake states.
Occasionally associated with the hemlock and white pine
relicts in Indiana are other boreal disjuncts such as Canadian
yew, rough-leaved dogwood, shinleaf, wintergreen and bush
honeysuckle. In one relict hemlock stand in Crawford County,
yellow birch trees thrive 250 miles south of their present day
range.[12]

## Birthplace of American Ecology

"The only thing the Lake Michigan Dunes are good for is
to get sand in your shoes," remarked an Indiana politician recently. To those unschooled in reading the landscape and in
interpreting the rich geological and ecological history that is
represented there, the Indiana Dunes may have little value.
However, studies at the dunes during the 1890's blew the
breath of life into the then embryonic science of ecology.

Dr. Henry C. Cowles, of the University of Chicago, pointed

to the shifting sand dunes as a unique case history of successional change in the landscape. His classic studies at the turn of the century culminated in a series of papers on physiographic ecology that lucidly outlined the natural processes whereby landforms and plant communities develop into stabilized units.[9, 10] His work focused the attention of American biologists on dynamic ecology and further pointed out the outstanding values of the dunes as outdoor laboratories in which to determine long-term changes in biological communities and soil development.

Dunes of almost pure quartz sand originally extended as a narrow belt around the entire "toe" of Lake Michigan from Chicago to the Indiana-Michigan line north of Michigan City. The dunes continued northward into Michigan nearly to Petosky. The Indiana dunes formerly extended inland from the lake for about 4 miles at the west end and for about ½ mile at the east end, with heights of advancing dunes ranging from a few to 200 feet or more. But the Indiana dunes, like the vast hardwood forests and "endless" prairies, have been largely removed by the inexorable advance of civilization.

Sand eroded from bedrock, glacial deposits and beaches on the western lake shore is the building material for the dunes. Selective transport first by water, then by wind, eliminates the coarser and finer particles, resulting in even-sized sediments. The westerly and northwesterly winds build the dunes on the lee side of the lake, dropping their load of sand when dune-binding vegetation is encountered. The age sequence and vegetation development progresses with distance from the lake. As plants develop, the shifting dune sands are stabilized and the dune stops growing. In this way, the plant communities and the dunes develop as a physiographic and ecologic unit, becoming increasingly complex with height, age and distance from the shore.

This ordered process of dune succession is frequently interrupted. When the wind gets a "foothold" and causes a "blowout," this breaks the successional chain. After a period of years the blowout area is stabilized by developing plant communities. In the past, natural, Indian and settler-induced fires complicated the successional trends and altered the successes of many dune communities.

Dune ages have been determined by growth cycles in dune

binding grasses, by tree ring analysis and radiocarbon dating. Ages range from a few months for foredunes to about 12,000 years for the older well-vegetated dunes.[33]

The flora of the dunes has a curious admixture of northern and southwestern elements, both of which have water-obtaining and retaining structures that are absent in plants of more equable habitats. Northern relict species, such as jack and white pines have persisted in this unique habitat since the Pleistocene glacial retreat. These colonies, disjunct from their range by about 100 miles, probably survived as a result of less competition from deciduous trees and the recurrent fires in the dunes.[33] Prairie and southwestern plant species of the dunes are relicts of the Xerothermic period. During that time, these more dry-adapted species extended their range greatly eastward and northward.

A series of wetland habitats occur in the peripheral dune areas, including river bottoms, lakes, swamps and bogs. The 165-acre Pinhook Bog, located in the area proposed for the Indiana Dunes National Lakeshore, is noted for its rich flora, including tamarack and white pine. The dune flora, collectively totaling more than a thousand species of flowering plants and ferns, makes the dunes one of the most interesting botanical areas of the United States.

The ideal successional sequence of foredune ridges in the Indiana dunes may be simplified as follows: pioneer grasses, with or without accompanying cottonwoods or dune-building shrubs, eventually lead to various types of black oak communities, often with an intervening stage of jack or white pine.[33]

These black oak dominated communities may persist for thousands of years. However, as soils mature they may eventually succeed to typical mesophytic forests, dominated first by basswood-maple or red oak-basswood and finally by beech-maple. These mesophytic forests may be found in certain locations in the dunes region· but no direct evidence indicates that they have followed the oak communities in successional sequence.[33]

The sequence of vegetation development depends upon whether the invasion substrate is a damp depression, active dune crest, blow-out area, upper-beach or leeward slope pocket. Plant stabilization of dunes typically begins near the landward beach margin where foredunes originate. Marram grass is the most common pioneer. It occurs in pure stands or in mixtures with sand reed or little blue stem grass.[9] The tenacity of marram grass in holding dune sands is exemplified by its widespread use in highway and construction work for stabilizing sandy area. However, this pioneer species declines in vigor once the sand surface is stabilized.

Under certain substrate conditions, cottonwood and dune-building shrubs such as sand cherry are able to initiate dune formation or to be present in mixtures with the grasses. Locally sand-dune willow and sand bar willow may be important in accumulating sand in their extensive thickets.

Some combination of the above species first build up and then stabilize the dune. Shade intolerant shrubs such as bearberry, prostrate juniper, prickly-pear cactus and northern red cedar readily invade as dune establishment occurs. Poison-ivy, bittersweet, grape and greenbriar form impressive mats and tangles on the dunes and frequently persist for considerable periods after forests invade the area. These changes prepare the way for the jack or white pine; thereafter, black oak subsequently replaces the pines as the dominant species. Lowbush blueberry and huckleberry dominate the characteristic shrub stratum on older black oak and pine dunes. Evergreen ground cover such as wintergreen, partridge berry, trailing arbutus and shinleaf are also characteristic of better-developed forest communities.

As the dune becomes more completely stabilized by forest vegetation, community changes occur more slowly. Mesic conditioning of the soil normally occurs within about 1,000 years.[33] The rich, deep mesophytic climax forests develop only on these better soils, whereas oak communities become an edaphic climax over most of the dune landscape. Fire has played an important role in retaining the fire-resistant black oaks.

One of the most outstanding features of the dunes area is the "forest graveyard communities" that have been uncovered by shifting sand (See Frontispiece) and the efforts of man. These skeletal trunks sometimes number in the thousands and are of huge dimensions, indicating that the dunes were previously stabilized by a mature forest. Most of the dead trees are white pines, northern white cedars and intermixed hardwoods, giving further evidence that past climates were sufficiently different to support a forest community dominated by more typically northern species.[34]

## Aquatic Communities

In 1908 the United States Department of Agriculture estimated that the amount of marsh, swamp and overflow land still remaining in Indiana was about 1,000 square miles. Of this amount, 15,000 acres were classified as permanently ponded land.[48]

Throughout northern Indiana kettle-kame topography typifies a much glaciated landscape. The physiographic area designated as the Northern Lake and Moraine Region, which covers about one-quarter of the state contains numerous kettle-hole lakes that represent the greatest area of aquatic habitat in the state.

In addition to fresh water lakes many bogs, swamps, marshes, wet prairie, and temporarily flooded areas occurred in Indiana. The marsh bordering the sluggish Kankakee River in Northwestern Indiana was one of the greatest waterfowl and furbearer areas in the world. Efforts to drain this marsh began before the turn of the century and accelerated during the teens and twenties, until today only scattered portions remain. At Jasper-Pulaski and Willow Slough one can get some notion of what settlers called "the lost land."

Bogs, marshes and swamps differ basically in substrate and physiography and in the plant communities which they support. Bog and marsh communities are dominated largely by herbaceous plants or shrubs that fill depressions with their organic remains. Poor aeration and acid conditions retard the decay of organic materials. Sphagnum moss is one of the main contributions to this filling process. Most extensive bog deposits that are being mined today are primarily Sphagnum peat. Swamps, on the other hand, are depressions usually occupied by tall woody vegetation. The resulting soil is high in organic matter and quite fertile, but is not considered a true organic soil by agronomists.

Baxter's Bog in Salt Creek Township in Monroe County is a most unusual area in that it developed in reverse sequence to the normal one of depression filling.[39] In less than a man's lifetime, the gradual expansion of wet soil eliminated the lowland forest along Salt Creek and a shrub dominance of hazel-

nut, alder and winterberry was initiated. Since the initiation
of bog formation, peat has accumulated to several feet in
depth. Small green wood orchid, yellow Bartonia and
Sphagnum moss in Baxter's Bog are about 150 miles from
their natural range.

Another very interesting bog is Cabin Creek Raised Bog
near Farmland in Randolph County. It is called a raised bog
because the peat moss forms a convex elevation, contoured
somewhat like a giant watch crystal, about ten feet above the
floodplain of Cabin Creek. The plant community has been
gradually lifted by weak hydrostatic pressure of the underlying artesian spring and the accumulation of organic plant
remains.[22] The abundance of spring water which is high in calcium and other nutrients favors growth of a very luxuriant
community of Sphagnum moss, sedges, true mosses, prairie
grasses and bog herbs and shrubs. Showy ladyslippers are
found abundantly in the bog. The rich shrub flora includes red-
osier dogwood, nannyberry, ninebark, hazelnut and sumac.

Of the several swamps originally present in Indiana, perhaps Little Cypress Swamp, Knox County; Bacon Swamp,
Marion County; Leesburg Swamp, Kosciusco County; and several tamarack swamps of the Dunes area are representative
of the range of variation within the swamp communities of
the state.

Little Cypress Swamp is discussed in some detail in the
succeeding section on Floodplains since it occurs in a back
water area of the Wabash Valley. The forest vegetation is
dominated by water-tolerant trees some of which have southern affinities such as bald cypress (53% of stand), green ash,
silver maple and swamp cottonwood. Shrubs such as buttonbush, spicebush, vines and such herbs as lizard tail and
clearwood are dominant in their respective strata.

An early scientific study of the lowland area known as
Bacon's Swamp noted that it was really a bog dominated by
reedgrass in the lower areas. Surrounding the bog were several stages of lowland vegetation beginning with cattails, then
a buttonbush shrub zone, followed by a black willow forest
and terminating in a lowland forest containing principally
red maple, cottonwood, pumpkin ash and black gum.[8] This
pattern of successional zonation is more typical of a swamp
than of a bog because of the partially-drained character of

the lowland. There was a gradual increase in the number of species and complexity of communities through each succeeding stage of the swamp vegetation.[38] Generalizing broadly, the successional communities originally represented at Bacon's Swamp could be considered to be rather typical of lowland areas in Indiana.

In the Leesburg Swamp[54] in northeastern Indiana and in tamarack swamps in the dunes,[34] several interesting northern species add to community diversity. Tamarack, northern white cedar, poison sumac, dwarf birch, huckleberry, pitcher plant, sundew, wintergreen and lady's slippers are important components.

Indiana has a few treacherous quaking bogs which are so named because the plant community is actually floating on the high water table. Walking or jumping in these areas will cause the shrubs and even trees to move and "quake." Should a person break through the vegetation mass, a most perilous situation ensues.

Margins of northern Indiana lakes have an interesting sequence of communities. All successful stages of deposition and filling of the lakes occur, including stands of mesophytic climax forest on former lake sites. Moving landward from Indiana lakes, some seven community zones are typically encountered: (1) submerged aquatic plants, (2) floating-leaved aquatics, (3) emergent aquatics, (4) sedge meadow, (5) marginal shrubs, (6) lowland forest and (7) mesic climax forest. At any given location, one to several of these stages may be missing due to physiographic or ecological differences.

Aquatic plant communities are the most sensitive of all to environmental changes. They are usually the first to be modified or lost as civilization develops. Most lake margin communities have been greatly altered today by demands for cottage sites and other recreational facilities.

### Floodplain Communities

Rivers were the frontier highways that brought the first Europeans to Indiana in 1679. They accelerated settlement of such Indiana cities as Madison, Vincennes, Fort Wayne, Terre Haute, Lafayette and Logansport. Indiana streams, which nourished the finest hardwood forests of Eastern North America by virtue of their periodic flooding and deposit of fertile alluvium, also provided the reason and means for decimating those forests. Growing towns and cities needed vast quantities of wood for everything from cradles to coffins. The streams provided easy transportation of logs to the mills and frequently powered the sawmills. Settlers soon learned that soils supporting the finest trees would also grow the best corn; thereafter, the floodplains were rapidly cleared. It is small wonder that few remnants of the magnificent virgin floodplain forests remain today.

Streams provide relatively uniform ecological conditions over considerable geographic distance, thus providing natural plant migration corridors. The distributive power of streams with regard to invasion of weedy species is obvious to the floodplain farmer. The prevalence of such southern trees as bald cypress, pecan, sweet gum, pin oak, Shumard's oak, southern red oak, persimmon and sugarberry in the lowland forests of southwestern Indiana resulted from movement up the Mississippi and Ohio Rivers in the wake of the glacial retreat.

Streams continually mature and change course within the wide valleys they have carved from the surrounding upland. As a result of continual denuding and depositing, a series of plant habitat types is created. Included are the stream itself, the water margin, insular and point bars, cutbanks, backwater pockets, the floodplain proper. floodplain depressions and one to several stream terraces. Each of these areas differs physiographically and ecologically, resulting in distinct plant community development. Susceptibility to flooding, soil texture and watershed fertility are major controlling environmental factors.

Alluvial features are among the most unstable and frequently ephemeral of all landscapes. Occasionally a new island is formed by a single flood or an existing one is swept away. Stream islands actually "drift" downstream as erosion occurs on the upstream end and deposition occurs on the downstreams end. This provides a changing habitat of varying ages, increasing in age upstream. Increasing development of plant communities also progresses upstream, but before really stabilized vegetation develops, the upper end of the island is eroded away.

Man has greatly changed the nature of Indiana streams by

cutting the forests, draining, damming, building levees, dredging, polluting, cultivating and increasing erosion and siltation rates. These effects of civilization are severely limiting to floodplain plants. In the absence of man's influence, floodplain conditions result in a sequence of plant communities similar to those noted for lake margins. At higher floodplain levels there is a natural transition to the slope and upland communities typical of that region.

Comparatively few ecologists have given the attention to streambank and floodplain vegetation that these interesting communities deserve. However, detailed studies have been done on the floodplain vegetation of the White[26], Tippecanoe and Wabash Rivers.[29] In 20 stands on both the East and West forks of the White River[26], 71 species of woody plants play a role in the vegetation cover. Ten tree species listed in order of decreasing importance make up 86.2% of all 20 stands taken collectively: silver maple, sycamore, American elm, cottonwood, hackberry, cork elm, box-elder, black willow, white ash and red elm. Important understory trees in order of decreasing importance were hawthorn, redbud, wild plum, hop hornbeam and flowering dogwood. Similarly, the important shrubs were elderberry, spicebush, wahoo, swamp-privet, wafer-ash and pawpaw; vines included poison-ivy, grapes, green briar, trumpet creeper and Virginia creeper.

The large number of tree species sharing dominance is noteworthy. All floodplain species are relatively intolerant to shade, but produce abundant seeds which germinate well and become established in soils with high moisture levels. The more equable environment along the mature White River permits a more mixed forest and greater similarity of numerous stands throughout the river system than would be found over a similar distance in upland forests.

A recent study of 56 lowland forest stands along the Wabash and Tippecanoe Rivers[29] indicated more variability in forest composition. This is understandable since the latter study covered 230 miles latitude and 430 miles of river distance. However, from near Vincennes to Logansport the latitude factor was of little importance in affecting composition of forest stands on first bottoms. The chief species were black willow, silver maple, American elm, and cottonwood. Species proportions were determined largely by age or successional development of the stand.

On less frequently flooded second bottoms there is a shift toward species which are less water tolerant, but more shade tolerant. As better drained sites are reached, a forest is encountered which greatly resembles the climax forests of the upland. A stand of this type near Logansport has hard maple (black-sugar) and beech as co-dominants, comprising 63% of the stand. Sub-dominants, in decreasing importance, include American elm, hackberry, cork elm, Ohio buckeye and slippery elm.

Perhaps the most interesting Indiana floodplain forest is found in the lower Wabash Valley. At Hovey Lake in Posey County, bald cypress represents 60% of the stand, while important subordinate species are silver maple, river birch, pecan, ash and sugarberry. Bald Cypress, whose durable wood is used for shingles, decking, flooring and other outdoor uses, was once abundant in several counties in southwestern Indiana. Originally they reached enormous size in the fertile bottomlands. In the 1870's, Ridgway[51] measured several stumps 9 and 10 feet across indicating that the finer trees had previously been cut. One of the largest known trees measured in Indiana in recent years is an 81.5" diameter bald cypress in Little Cypress Swamp in Knox County.[29] Bald cypress extended naturally as far north as northern Knox County, but it is hardy when planted to within 85 miles of Chicago.[61] The cypress forests probably escaped complete destruction only because the swamps where they grow are generally unsuited for agriculture.

Beech, though important in floodplain forests in presettlement times, is practically absent in floodplain forests today.[28] Perhaps more widely fluctuating stream levels in recent years than in presettlement days exceed the flood-tolerance of the beech.[28]

Another tree expressing great importance in the alluvial forests in presettlement times was our "state tree," the tulip poplar. However, in the recent study, tulip tree was recorded only twice along the Tippecanoe and it was not found along the Wabash. What became of those splendid trees that Ridgway photographed which towered 180-200 feet in height and reached 11 feet in diameter?[14] Tulip poplar is not adapted to the first bottoms which are often still forested, but originally occupied the higher, better drained floodplains. These areas have been almost completely cleared for agriculture or have been severely cut over.

Even today a number of very large trees remain in floodplain forests.[27] Along Sugar Creek in Turkey Run State Park, black walnut, ash, sycamore and hackberry trees reach enormous proportions.[56] Some walnut trees are four feet in diameter with clear lengths of 30-40 feet. Another fine aggregation of huge floodplain trees is located along the Wabash below Perrysville. At least three trees over 70″ diameter and others over 60″ were recorded during the Wabash floodplain study.[29] Numerous trees over 3½ feet diameter were noted along the Wabash River at that time. Even though the forest monarchs described by Ridgway are largely gone today, perhaps Hoosiers will have the foresight to save what is left.

### Upland Climax Forests

It is a feeling of confinement which begins to damp the spirits, from this complete exclusion of distant objects. To travel day after day among trees of a hundred feet high, without a glimpse of the surrounding country, is oppressive to a degree which those cannot conceive who have not experienced it; and it must depress the spirits of the solitary settler to pass years in this state. His visible horizon extends no farther than the tops of the trees which bound his plantation—perhaps, five hundred yards. Upwards he sees the sun, and sky, and stars; but around him an eternal forest from which he can never hope to emerge . . . . .
—Morris Birkbeck, 1818[5]

So reads the impression which Indiana's landscape made on one English farmer on his way to the prairie country ("that noble expanse was like the opening of bright day upon the gloom of night"). Having known only pastoral landscape, his immersion into the eastern deciduous forest of 1818 was psychologically akin (if the reverse) to what many Indiana farmers felt a generation later while crossing the treeless plains on their way to Oregon. The forest which so depressed Mr. Birkbeck, however, has not proven to be eternal. For the most part, we have emerged and while most Hoosiers are just as happy to have missed those exhausting settlement years and the attendant miseries, something in us occasionally wonders what it must have been like to travel day after day among trees of a hundred feet in height. What kinds of trees? What kinds of forests?

When Indiana was originally platted by the General Land Office Surveyors circa 1799 to 1834, two bearing or "witness" trees were used to mark each section and quarter section corners. The species name, diameter and distance from the corner point were recorded for each bearing tree. Allowing for trees common to two or more sections, data were recorded for an average of six trees per section. These survey records furnish much of the same type of information concerning a forest which an ecologist might obtain from an existing stand for vegetational description.[11] Computer analysis of these records provided the basis for the generalized map of pre-settlement vegetation shown (Fig. 58).

The map depicts the broad areas of poorly drained soil as *wetlands* (approximately 10%) and the areas of excessively drained soil on which surveyors encountered no forest growth as *dry prairie* (approximately 3%). Much of the wetlands area was occupied by lowland prairie communities and marshes. The wetlands of northwestern Indiana were chiefly wet prairie, while those of the northeastern section were more often swamps or bogs, dominated by woody vegetation.

Of the many forest community types which ecologists have recognized as having been segregated from the mixed Tertiary forest[6] three are in evidence in Indiana (Figure 58). These are: (1) Western Mesophytic which comprised approximately 8% of the original vegetation of the state, (2) Beech-maple which occupied 50%, and (3) Oak-hickory which dominated the remaining 29% of the landscape.

## Western Mesophytic Association

With the onset of Pleistocene glaciation, the mixed Tertiary forest migrated southward and was subjected to the evolutionary forces of extinction, addition and change of species. These changes were evidently conservative because the present-day forests of the southern Appalachians have a composition very similar to the Tertiary forests. The magnificent cove forests in the Great Smoky Mountains National Park are examples of the "mother type" from which modern forests radiated outward in the wake of the Pleistocene.[6]

A segregate of this rich, mixed forest currently occupies

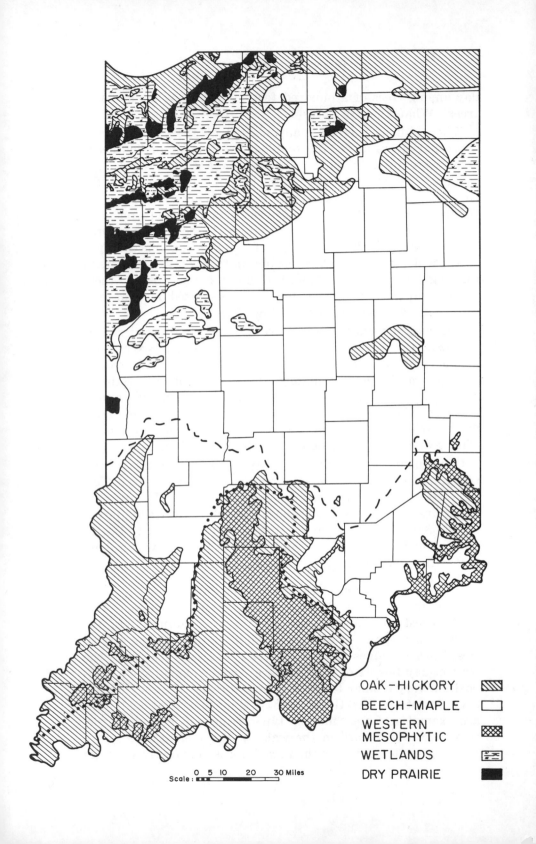

OAK–HICKORY

BEECH–MAPLE

WESTERN
MESOPHYTIC

WETLANDS

DRY PRAIRIE

Scale: 0  5  10    20    30 Miles

the limestone-derived soils on the karst topography of the Mitchell Plain in south-central Indiana and on the steeper slopes of the Ohio River and Laughery Creek drainages of the Dearborn Upland in southeastern Indiana.[28]

Although this mixed forest is not extensive in Indiana, it is one of the most interesting plant communities of the state because of the great number of species sharing dominance. Frequently 10 to 20 species share in the crown cover and exert their controlling influence on the forest community.

In the dissected area of Illinoian age glacial till in southeastern Indiana, yellow buckeye and white basswood are important (Table 6). These two species are considered to be the most typical of the true mixed mesophytic forests of the Cumberland Mountains, indicating an affinity of the western mixed mesophytic forests of Indiana to the parent forest type farther south.[6]

TABLE 6. Percentage composition* of principal species in representative stands of the Western Mesophytic Association.

| Species | Illinoian Drift | | Unglaciated |
|---|---|---|---|
| | (Dearborn Co.)[a] | (Jefferson Co.)[b] | (Lawrence Co.)[c] |
| Beech | 26 | 28 | 23 |
| Sugar Maple | 22 | 20 | 23 |
| White Oak | 12 | — | 21 |
| Red Oak | 6 | 10 | 4 |
| White Ash | 5 | 9 | 3 |
| Tulip Poplar | 2 | 9 | 2 |
| Pignut Hickory | 8 | — | 3 |
| White Basswood | — | 15 | — |
| Yellow Buckeye | — | 9 | — |
| Black Gum | 3 | — | 4 |
| Shagbark Hickory | 2 | — | 5 |
| Red Maple | 4 | — | 4 |

* Based on relative density
[a] Lubbe's Woods[41]
[b] Clifty Falls State Park[6]
[c] Donaldson's Woods[30]

Fig. 58. Generalized map of the natural vegetation of Indiana *circa* 1816, based on original land-survey records and modern soil maps of counties. Wetlands included mostly wet prairie, but also marshes, swamps and bogs. Except for wetland, the type shown is that of gently to moderately sloping terrain within the vegetation type boundaries. The *broken line* marks the approximate southern limit of Wisconsin glaciation in Indiana; the *dotted line,* that of Illinoian glaciation. Map from Lindsey, Crankshaw and Qadir, 1965[28] by permission University of Chicago Press.

Most southeastern Indiana mixed forests have beech as the dominant species along with sugar maple, tulip poplar, white ash, basswood, walnut, white and red oak, red elm and black gum.

The unglaciated Hill Section of south-central Indiana is variously called the "Knobs" or the "chestnut oak upland"[12] (Fig. 59). In this area, the mixed forests usually occur in ravines and on the cooler slopes, whereas oak or oak-hickory forests clothe the drier slopes and ridges. These mixed forests generally have a greater abundance of beech and maple instead of buckeye and basswood of the southeastern mixed forest.[6]

Probably the best remaining virgin stand in the south-central area is Donaldson's Woods in Spring Mill State Park. Dominating this forest is white oak, sugar maple and beech (Table 6). Donaldson's Woods is undergoing a transition toward an increase in beech and maple so it is probably not a climax forest.[30]

American chestnut was present in the southern Indiana mixed forests, but it has been totally removed as a mature tree by the Asian chestnut blight. The successional patterns involved in the replacement of chestnut have not been completely resolved, but chestnut oak and tulip poplar seem to be invading the open communities most rapidly.

Well-developed strata exist in the mixed forest with flowering dogwood, redbud and blue beech frequently occupying the understory tree layer. Shrubs such as pawpaw, spicebush, greenbriar and leatherwood are common in this type. The herb layer is very pronounced, particularly in the spring when the floral display is at its peak. Wake robin, slender toothwort, rock larkspur and twinleaf are typical herbs. Nodding trillium is locally abundant.

The steep slopes and heavily dissected topography have discouraged the extensive clearing of this type for agriculture. although selective logging has altered the composition of most stands. A significant portion of the Hoosier National Forest is represented by this association.

### Beech-Maple Association

The beech-maple association developed from the mixed mesophytic forest as northward postglacial migration occurred. There was a natural shift of dominant species toward those able to rapidly advance onto the youthful glaciated topography.[6] The beech-maple communities were still undergoing compositional changes and boundary adjustments at the time of Indiana settlement. The Xerothermic period, in which oaks advanced, evidently delayed the migration of beech and maple into Indiana, as is indicated by their late appearance in most pollen records.

Forests classified as beech-maple usually have beech as the most abundant canopy tree, while sugar maple is co-dominant in the canopy and frequently dominates the understory. This forest association occurs most commonly within the area covered by Wisconsin age glacial till, but it continues southward into Illinoian age till in both southeastern and southwestern Indiana.[28] Its northwestern extension stops near the prairie border.[47]

Beech has never been a valuable timber tree; consequently, it has been favored by selective logging practices which quickly removed higher grade species such as walnut, white oak, tulip poplar and ash. This cutting practice has shifted most remaining woodlots toward a more pronounced domination by beech, especially in the larger size classes. Both sugar maple and beech are very tolerant to shade, and with seedlings readily established, they rapidly begin to fill in the sapling size classes when forests are disturbed by cutting or natural causes.

Usually these dominant species are distributed widely and relatively evenly throughout the stand. Trees of such species as sassafras, black cherry, tulip poplar and walnut are more often encountered in groups. The seedlings of these species do not tolerate shade well; however, their efficient means of seed dispersal and rapid growth rates allow them continuing development where and when gaps occur in the canopy (as from death and windthrow).

The prevalence of these species in any particular stand is considered an indication of disturbance. Another indication of disturbance is the presence in a stand of many stems having the same age or similar diameters. Such stands are referred to as "even-aged" and are usually the result of some widespread disturbance in the past, such as lumbering or a tornado. Virgin stands or less-disturbed stands, on the other

Floral Areas of Indiana

hand, tend to be "all-aged", with new individuals continually entering as periodic crown openings occur.

As shown in Table 7, beech and maple commonly comprise 50% or more of the Indiana forests stands in this association. In fact, the stand dominance of these species in the association as a whole is frequently 80%.[6] In the lowland phase of the beech-maple community, elm often comprises one-fourth of the total crown cover (Table 7). Since its introduction into Indiana in 1937, the Dutch Elm disease fungus has destroyed extensive elm timber. Together with the virus disease, phloem necrosis, it has essentially eliminated American elm as a canopy tree in many of the remnant stands. The question of which species will occupy this forest vacancy is as yet uncertain.

Small tree understory in the woods of the beech-maple association is generally either redbud-dogwood-blue beech or dogwood-hop hornbeam. Shrub layers usually include one or a combination of the following: pawpaw, spicebush, greenbriar, elderberry, leatherwood, wahoo and maple-leaf viburnum. Exceptionally fine spring floral displays are typical in undisturbed beech-maple forests. Common species include rue anemone, jack-in-the-pulpit, spring beauty, cutleaf toothwort, pretty bedstraw, mayapple, false Solomon's seal and wild ginger.

Today the beech-maple forest is mostly farmland. Because it is a community type which occupies the better soils, it has suffered most with agricultural clearing. Drainage has lowered the water table of the depressional soils so that they too are now farmed. As one drives across the gently rolling Tipton Till Plain of central Indiana, only a few scattered, well cutover beech-maple forests break the horizon of the vast crop lands.

## Oak-Hickory Association

The oak-hickory association has its best development in the northern Ozarks where it dominates the entire landscape. In Indiana, however, oak-hickory dominated communities are

Fig. 59. Map of the natural floral areas of Indiana based not on the conspicuous and important vegetational dominants (See Figure 58), but on the distribution of the many species (irrespective of commonness or rarity) of the floristic list of the state. From Deam 1940[12].

in sensitive balance with both beech-maple and western meso-phytic types and are found across the landscape today in many areas of Indiana as a mosaic pattern with these other two types.[6]

The distribution in Indiana of oak-hickory and beech-maple forests is closely tied to physiography. Indiana's general climate has been interpreted as favoring the beech-maple type[44]; however, various topographic and edaphic controls supersede climate in controlling community vegetation.[40] Where slopes are pronounced, beech-maple communities are best developed on north-facing and east-facing slopes, while oak-hickory forests are usually found occupying south-facing and west-facing slopes.[21] In general, moisture content of the soil is consistently lower in the oak-hickory type.

TABLE 7. Percentage composition* of principal species in representative stands of the Beech-Maple Association.

| Species | Northern Moraine and Lakes Region | Tipton Till Plain | | Illinoian Drift | | Unglaci-ated |
| | (Kosciusko Co.)[a] | (Montgomery Co.)[b] | (Wayne Co.)[c] | (Owen Co.)[d] | (Franklin Co.)[e] | (Orange Co.)[f] |
|---|---|---|---|---|---|---|
| Beech | 16 | 35 | 30 | 44 | 11 | 41 |
| Sugar Maple | 27 | 34 | 18 | 32 | 39 | 14 |
| Tulip Poplar | 14 | 9 | — | 10 | 5 | 15 |
| White Ash | 6 | 1 | 9 | 3 | 4 | 2 |
| American Elm | 1 | 1 | 23 | 1 | 1 | — |
| Slippery Elm | 1 | 4 | 9 | 2 | 1 | 1 |
| Cork Elm | 23 | — | — | — | — | — |
| White Oak | — | — | — | 1 | — | 7 |
| Bur Oak | 4 | 2 | — | — | — | — |
| Red Oak | 2 | 3 | — | 1 | 2 | 4 |
| Basswood | 4 | 4 | 2 | — | — | — |
| Black Gum | — | — | — | 1 | 16 | — |
| Black Walnut | 1 | 1 | 1 | 1 | — | 10 |
| Black Cherry | 1 | 2 | 1 | 1 | 7 | — |
| Mockernut Hickory | — | — | — | — | 8 | |

\* Based on relative basal area
a  Berkey Woods[45]
b  Rush Woods[35]
c  Jones[25]
d  Hoot Woods[36]
e  McCoy[32]
f  Cox Woods[46]

It seems evident that the oak-hickory forests at the time of European immigration were generally undergoing a gradual replacement by more mesic species. Early lumbering records indicate that white oak was much more important in the original forest of Indiana than it is today.[13] The oak-hickory association which became widespread during the Xerothermic Period was being invaded by beech and maple.

Recent analyses of certain old-growth forest stands depict this with oak abundant only in the larger size classes and beech and maple predominant below 30″ diameter.[30, 36] It is common today to find mature oak-hickory stands with maple and beech reproduction in the understory. The reverse does not occur. Selective cutting of the oak timber from settlement to the present has simply augmented the natural replacement process.[13]

Segregates of the oak-hickory association which are frequently described as oak-maple or white oak-beech are more accurately viewed as successional stages in this oak forest replacement. However, they are often of long duration. The oak-hickory type expresses more variation in species composition throughout its Indiana range than occurs throughout the entire beech-maple association.[6] Examples of species composition reported for oak-hickory stands located in the various floral areas of the state are listed in Table 8. It can be seen that maple and beech are frequently important species in these communities, indicating their successional condition.

In the lowland phase of the oak-hickory association in Indiana, species such as bur oak, pin oak, swamp white oak, Shumard's oak shellbark hickory and bitternut hickory increase in importance. In the Lower Wabash Valley, pecan, swamp chestnut oak and overcup oak are locally important. On the dry ridges of the unglaciated portion of Indiana, chestnut oak, scarlet oak, post oak and mockernut hickory are more frequently found.

The fungal disease, oak wilt, has caused extensive disturbance in the composition of oak-hickory communities in recent years. Red and black oaks are particularly susceptible, although the infection is also reported for white and bur oak.[53]

Oak-hickory forests frequently have a less well developed understory stratum than is found in the other two forest types of Indiana. Frequently only one or two species such as hop hornbeam, blue beech, service berry or dogwood dominate this layer along with the maple reproduction. Shrubs common in the dry sandy ridge forests of Northern Indiana include blueberry, huckleberry, snowberry and nannyberry. Jersey-tea, ninebark, witch-hazel, wild gooseberry, Virginia creeper are locally important.

In addition to differences in the composition of woody species, forest community types often differ markedly in their herbaceous components.[19, 43] The most prominent herbaceous representation in the beech-maple forest occurs in the spring, while in the oak-hickory type herbaceous flowers are more prominent in late summer and autumn. Also, oak-hickory forests have from 45 to 50% more herbaceous species than beech-maple. Among the most common herbs present in the oak-hickory type are pussy-toes, common cinquefoil, wild licorice, tickclover, blue phlox, waterleaf, bloodroot, Joe-pye-weed, woodland asters and goldenrods, wild geranium and bellwort.

The oak-hickory association grades into the prairie of Northwestern Indiana, where forests generally are limited to slopes of ravines or on morainic ridges. The alternation of prairie and oak-hickory woods is easily seen in the mosaic pattern of the dark prairie and light-colored forested soils. Today heavily grazed oak-hickory stands occupy the rougher topography in this excellent farming area.

### Prairie

It is perhaps appropriate that the best assemblages of prairie species are often found today in cemeteries which date from settlement. These remnants and a few small communities of prairie grasses and forbs occurring on small knolls, along highway easements and railroad rights-of-way are all that is left of that part of the prairie peninsula that once extended eastward into Warren, Benton, Newton, White and other counties of northwestern Indiana (just south of Fowler on U.S. 52, an excellent remnant of tall grass prairie exists at the time of this writing.) This prairie, which occupied approximately 13% of the Indiana landscape of 1816 (Fig. 58), is known to us only through such remnants and from imperfectly recorded memories.

To biologists the prairie is something more than land covered with grass. It is a highly complex formation of plant and

animal species in equilibrium with environmental conditions.[57]
A reasonable semblance of original prairie vegetation may be
developed within half a century, even on soils derived originally under forest vegetation.[5] However, the dark and fertile
soil of the *true* prairie was the product of centuries.

It is of ecologic significance that the prairie formation included both northern and southern segregates. Species such
as Canada wild rye, western wheat grass, Kentucky blue grass,
needle grass and Pennsylvania sedge originated in cooler
northern climates. These species initiate new growth early in
the spring, maturing by early summer. Species which evolved
in warmer southern climates, such as big and little bluestem
grasses, Indian grass, switch grass and prairie dropseed, have
a season of growth which begins later but extends through late
smmer and early fall. Together these cool-season and warm-
season species produced a continuous and prolonged cover and
forage which made the American prairie one of the most productive range lands in the world. The enormous herds of buffalo were once a quantitative expression of this productivity.

TABLE 8. Percentage composition* of principal species in
representative stands of the Oak-Hickory Association.

| Species | Northern Moraine and Lakes Region[a] | Tipton Till Plain | | Illinoian Drift | Unglaciated |
| | | (Parke Co.)[b] | (Clinton Co.)[c] | Owen Co.)[d] | (Dubois Co.)[e] |
| --- | --- | --- | --- | --- | --- |
| White Oak | 44 | 50 | 23 | 28 | 47 |
| Black Oak | 14 | 5 | — | 12 | 23 |
| Red Oak | 3 | 10 | 27 | 10 | — |
| Pignut Hickory | — | 1 | — | 22 | 6 |
| Shagbark Hickory | 9 | 1 | 6 | 9 | 6 |
| Sugar Maple | 3 | 14 | 5 | 13 | — |
| American Beech | 6 | — | 8 | 1 | — |
| White Ash | 3 | 3 | 2 | — | 3 |
| Swamp White Oak | — | — | 12 | — | — |
| Chinquapin Oak | 4 | — | 1 | — | 6 |
| Bur Oak | 4 | 1 | — | — | — |
| Mockernut Hickory | — | — | — | 4 | 3 |
| American Elm | 2 | 2 | 8 | 1 | — |
| Slippery Elm | — | — | 5 | — | — |
| Black Gum | — | — | — | 1 | 1 |

   * Based on relative basal area
   [a] From original land survey records[28]
   [b] Allee Woods[37]
   [c] Smith Woods[25]
   [d] Green's Bluff[37]
   [e] Mauntel's Woods[42]

Most settlers, however, were suspicious of land that did not grow trees, assuming the soil to be infertile. Those who did venture cultivation of adequately-drained prairie sites found the task of breaking the sod an enormous one. It required six or eight yoke of oxen to pull an iron-plated breaking plow through virgin prairie sod. In fact, cast iron plows were frequently broken in the attempt, making extensive cultivation of the prairie impossible until John Deere developed the steel plow circa 1840.

The original prairie was of three general types: wetland prairie, upland dry prairie and the areas where grassland and forest met. This latter type was not a well-defined border in most places, but rather a mosaic of prairie and oak timber, termed 'oak openings'.[16] The "edge effect" of the two habitats allowed increased diversity of plant and animal life. This was encouraged by natural fires and by Indian tribes which periodically fired the prairie to drive game and maintain grassland which continued to attract and support herds of buffalo.

In addition to the Indiana prairie which was contiguous with and a part of the so-called "Grand Prairie" of Illinois, island "prairies" along stream-terraces and within the forest proper were frequently encountered by western migrants— small meadowlands of a few to several hundred acres which had prairie-type vegetation. Indian crop fields were occasionally found in such openings.

The oaks most frequently associated in the island forests of the prairie borders were white oak, black oak, yellow oak, bur oak and jack oak, given here in the order of their abundance as revealed by analysis of the original land survey records. (It is probable that "black oak" and "yellow oak" were references to the same species, *Quercus velutina.*)

These more dry land oaks accounted for 85 to 100% of the forest composition in the western oak openings. The remainder was usually one or more species of hickory; however, scattered recordings of sugar maple and beech are present in land survey records for each of the prairie counties (except Jasper), indicating that at least a few local mesic sites existed in prairie landscape.[52]

These island forest stands generally occurred on sandy knolls and were more prevalent along the higher ground of terminal moraines. They were frequently surrounded by wetland prairies.[60] In many areas, the oaks did not form a closed canopy but were scattered within the grassland producing a savanna-type landscape.

Five prairie community types have been recently described in Indiana.[5] These are (1) big bluestem, (2) little bluestem, (3) prairie dropseed, (4) poverty grass-bluegrass and (5) slough grass. (The compositions of the dominant species within these types are given in Table 9.)

The distribution of these communities is controlled principally by the nature of soil drainage. Of the communities mentioned, big and little bluestem were of greatest importance and widest extent. Big bluestem communities dominated lower moist slopes and the better aerated parts of lowlands. Forbs were noticeably more abundant in this prairie type than in any other, although they rarely amounted to more than 5% of the total ground cover. Where big bluestem incurred frequent disturbance, such as burning or flooding, Indian grass often became an important component of the community. Heavy grazing would likewise favor Kentucky and Canadian bluegrass.

TABLE 9. Order of relative importance (combined frequency and density values) of principal species in five prairie community types.[5]

| Species | Big Bluestem | Little Bluestem | Prairie Dropseed | Poverty-Bluegrass | Slough Grass |
|---|---|---|---|---|---|
| Big Bluestem | 1 | 10 | 9 | 14 | — |
| Aster | 2 | 2 | 3 | 7 | — |
| Goldenrod | 3 | 3 | 1 | 6 | — |
| Swamp Saxifrage | 4 | 12 | 12 | 8 | — |
| Entire-leaved Rosinweed | 5 | — | — | — | — |
| Canadian Bluegrass | 6 | 11 | 13 | 2 | — |
| Rosinweed | 7 | 7 | 6 | 10 | — |
| Slough Grass | 8 | — | — | — | 1 |
| Ragweed | 9 | 6 | 15 | 11 | — |
| Sawtoothed Sunflower | 10 | — | — | — | 2 |
| Panic Grass | 11 | 9 | 5 | 4 | — |
| Canadian Cinquefoil | 12 | 14 | 11 | 3 | 3 |
| Arrowleaved Violet | 13 | 4 | 2 | 5 | — |
| Prairie Cat's Foot | 14 | 8 | 7 | 9 | — |
| Little Bluestem | 15 | 1 | 8 | 13 | — |
| Partridge Pea | 16 | 5 | 10 | 12 | — |
| Prairie Dropseed | 17 | 13 | 4 | — | — |
| Poverty Grass | 18 | 15 | 14 | 1 | — |

*Based on combined frequency and density values.

Little bluestem grass was found in all other community types except those which were very wet. As a community dominant it was best expressed on well-drained upper slopes and ridges. The densely-tufted prairie dropseed was usually found restricted to mid and lower slopes. Soils which supported this prairie community were found to have less available moisture than in the previous two types. It has been reported that only more dry-ground upland forbs occur in this community.[59]

Poverty grass-bluegrass communities were restricted to erosional sites on steeper slopes of soils low in organic matter and available moisture. This type, which is found throughout Indiana, is not considered to have been important in the original prairie vegetation. It has been enhanced by disturbance on both the original prairie and on previously timbered soils.

The slough grass (also called cordgrass) type is typical of poorly drained soils and bottomlands. It often shares dominance with sawtoothed sunflower. Both the Indian and early settlers used this coarse grass for thatching roofs. In Figure 58, the area mapped as wetlands includes the lowland big bluestem prairie type along with reed grass and the wet prairie slough grass community. Also included were the bogs and swamps, sedge meadow and marshlands.

The prairie had not always been distributed as the settlers found it. It became established over several thousand years. It invaded deglaciated landscapes, covered knolls and lowlands and previously timbered soils. It followed the fires.[59] In certain areas, prairie-type vegetation advanced or retreated considerably within one man's lifetime. It continues to do so today. The aggregation of prairie species in pastures and fallow land, along the highways and railroads, in the vacant lots and alleys of cities, reminds us of the mobility and invasion potential of these as well as other species.

### Weed Communities

Plant communities continually respond to the prominent factors of their environment. Human activity is one of these factors. Man's impact upon vegetation has come historically in two phases wherever his population has increased significantly. The first of these comes with the pioneer culture and involves the gradual dismemberment of plant communities, increasing the periphery of individual stands and isolating them genetically. Eventually the only persisting natural vegetation is composed of remnants left primarily on topography too rigorous or otherwise unsuitable for agriculture. The second phase and the one we are a part of, is that of intensive use or continual disturbance. This involves the further obliteration or deterioration of these remaining natural communities through such practices as sustained selective lumbering, pasturing of wooded tracts, heavy grazing of grassland and a general urban and industrial expansion. Even trampling by humans bent on outdoor activity is a substantial modifying factor in areas considered relatively natural otherwise.

In response to these effects, there has evolved a type of community uniquely ours—the weed community. Taking the place of the specifically adapted, highly integrated plant groups which characterized the climax vegetation are the less integrated, less stable communities of vigorous, cosmopolitan weed species. Many of our common weeds have been introduced from Europe. Many of these were originally introduced into Europe from Asia during Neolithic human immigrations. One of these non-native or exotic species which has become dominant in the weed communities of Indiana following deterioration of natural vegetation is Kentucky bluegrass. For man and his overgrazing livestock this was a fortunate occurrence. Other components such as dandelion, crabgrass and Canadian thistle are surveyed with less enthusiasm.

There are very few reported studies of weed communities, though this is the most prevalent of all our plant community types. Ecologists in the past have focused primarily on cultivated crops or undisturbed natural communities while the weed vegetation surrounded and invaded both. Weeds have been studied primarily as a target for herbicides, yet within these recently derived communities some botanists have recognized evolution in process—new plants and new plant communities developing in the "hybridized habitats" which man has made.[1]

## The Future of Natural Communities

Addressing the Indiana Academy of Science in 1902, a young forester, Samuel Record, lamented the loss of nearly all the good forest stands in Indiana.[50] What young ecologist starting his career today would not count it a windfall of fortune to see some of the forest and prairie remnants which have been lost since 1902?

Ninety-five percent of the remaining natural vegetation of Indiana (approximately 6% of the original) is privately owned.[58] The woodlots of small farms account for nearly three-fourths of this.[7] The remaining privately owned areas which are relatively undisturbed (and there are more than is generally realized) exist today because in the past successive owners chose to "let it stand". The reasons for preserving such areas have been many, but it is perhaps inappropriate to elaborate on them here. At the time of this writing there is no state-directed or authorized effort toward assuring the preservation of representative examples of our original vegetation. Other states, less richly endowed, are far ahead of us in this respect. These nature museums and outdoor laboratories are a cultural luxury to some Hoosiers, but a necessity to others for the quality they add to human life. Some people believe that remnants of our natural landscape and the history which they represent may not be worth preserving. Our generation will necessarily make that value judgment, both for ourselves and for those who will inherit the Indiana landscape.

## LITERATURE

1. ANDERSON, EDGAR. 1956. Man as a maker of new plants and plant communities. Man's role in changing the face of the earth. Univ. of Chicago Press, pp. 763-777.
2. BENNINGHOFF, W. S. 1964. The prairie peninsula as filter barrier to post glacial plant migration. Indiana Acad. Sci. Proc. **73**:116-124.
3. BERRY, E. W. 1923. Tree ancestors. Williams and Wilkins Co., Baltimore, pp. 270.
4. BIRKBECK, MORRIS. 1818. Notes on a journey in America from the coast of Virginia to the Territory of Illinois. Dublin, p. 117.
5. BLISS, L. C. and S. W. COX. 1964. Plant community and soil variation within a Northern Indiana Prairie. Amer. Midland Nat. **72**:115-128.
6. BRAUN, E. LUCY. 1950. Deciduous forests of Eastern North America. The Blakiston Company, Philadelpha, Pa. 596 pp.
7. BRUNDAGE, R. C. 1955. Forests of Indiana and their importance. Dept. of Forestry and Conservation, Purdue University, Division of Forestry, Indiana Dept. of Conservation, pp. 5-7, 20.
8. CAIN, S. A. 1928. Plant succession and ecological history of a Central Indiana swamp. Bot. Gaz. **86**:384-401.
9. COWLES, H. C. 1899. The ecological relations of the vegetation on the sand dunes of Lake Michigan. Bot. Gaz. **27**:95-117, 167-202, 281-308, 361-391.
10. _____ 1901. The physiographic ecology of Chicago and vicinity. Bot. Gaz. **31**:73-108, 145-182.
11. CRANKSHAW, W. B., S. A. QADIR and A. A. LINDSEY. 1965. Edaphic controls of tree species in presettlement Indiana. Ecology **46**:688-698.

12. DEAM, C. C. 1940. Flora of Indiana. Dept. of Conservation, Indianapolis, Indiana. 1236 pp.
13. DENUYL, DANIEL. 1954. Indiana's old growth forests. Ind. Acad. Sci. Proc. 63:73-79.
14. _____ 1958. Forests of the Lower Wabash Bottomlands during the period 1870-1890. Indiana Acad. Sci. Proc. 68:244-248.
15. ENGLEHARDT, D. W. 1960. A comparative pollen study of two early Wisconsin bogs in Indiana. Indiana Acad. Sci. Proc. 96:110-118.
16. FINLEY, D. and J. E. POTZGER. 1952. Characteristics of the original vegetation in some prairie counties of Indiana. Butler Univ. Bot. Stud. 10:114-118.
17. FREY, D. G. 1959. The two creeks interval in Indiana pollen diagrams. Invest. Ind. Lakes and Streams 5:131-139.
18. FRIESNER, R. C. 1937. Indiana as a critical botanical area. Indiana Acad. Sci. Proc. 46:28-45.
19. _____ and C. M. EK. 1944. Correlation of microclimatic factors with species distribution in Shenk's Woods, Howard County, Indiana. Butler Univ. Bot. Stud. 6:9-14.
20. _____ and J. E. POTZGER. 1934. Climax conditions and the ecological status of *Pinus strobus*, *Taxus canadensis* and *Tsuga canadensis* in the Pine Hills Region of Indiana. Butler Univ. Bot. Stud. 3:65-84.
21. _____ and J. E. POTZGER. 1937. Contrasts in certain physical factors in Fagus-Acer and Quercus-Carya communities in Brown and Bartholomew Counties, Indiana. Butler Univ. Bot. Stud. 4:1-12.
22. _____ and J. E. POTZGER. 1946. The Cabin Creek Raised Bog, Randolph County, Indiana. Butler Univ. Bot. Stud. 8:24-43.
23. GLEASON, H. A. 1939. The individualistic concept of the plant association. Amer. Midland Nat. 22:92-110.
24. HANSON, H. C. and E. D. CHURCHILL. The Plant Community. Rinehold Press. 218 pp.
25. JONES, J. J. 1952. A survey of fifteen forest stands in the early Wisconsin drift plain of Indiana. Butler Univ. Bot. Stud. 10:182-204.
26. LEE, M. B. 1945. An ecological study of the floodplain forest along the White River system of Indiana. Butler Univ. Bot. Stud. 7:1-21.
27. LINDSEY, A. A. 1962. Analysis of an original forest of the lower Wabash floodplain and upland. Indiana Acad. Sci. Proc. 72:282-287.
28. _____, W. B. CRANKSHAW and S. A. QADIR. 1965. Soil relations and distribution map of the vegetation of presettlement Indiana. Bot. Gaz. 126:155-163.
29. _____, R. O. PETTY, D. K. STERLING and W. V. ASDALL. 1961. Vegetation and environment along the Wabash and Tippecanoe Rivers. Ecol. Monogr. 31:105-156.
30. _____ and D. C. SCHMELZ. 1964. Comparison of Donaldson's Woods in 1964 with its 1954 forest map of 20 acres. Indiana Acad. Sci. Proc. 74:169-177.
31. LINDSEY, A. J. 1932. The trees of Indiana in their local and general distribution according to physiographic divisions. Butler Univ. Bot. Stud. 2:93-124.
32. McCOY, SCOTT. 1939. A phytosociological study of the woody plants constituting twenty-five type forests of the Illinoian till plain of Indiana. Indiana Acad. Sci. Proc. 48:50-66.
33. OLSON, J. S. 1958. Rates of succession and soil changes on Southern Lake Michigan sand dunes. Bot. Gaz. 119:125-170.
34. PEPOON, H. S. 1927. An annotated flora of the Chicago area. Lakeside Press, Chicago, Illinois. 554 pp.
35. PETTY, R. O. and D. HARWOOD. 1963. Rush Woods, a lowland extension of the beech-maple climax, Montgomery County, Indiana. Indiana Acad. Sci. Proc. 72:220-226.
36. _____ and A. A. LINDSEY. 1961. Hoot Woods, a remnant of virgin timber, Owen County, Indiana. Ind. Acad. Sci. Proc. 71:320-326.
37. PETTY, R. O., E. C. WILLIAMS, JR. and R. A. LAUBENGAYER. 1961. Ecological studies of a ridge forest and adjacent floodplain. Annual Progress Report, AEC. Wabash College, Crawfordsville, Ind. 197 pp.
38. PHILLIPS, ALICE. 1929. Life-forms and biological spectra of the flora of Bacon's Swamp, Indiana. Butler U. Bot. Stud. 1:41-53.
39. POTZGER, J. E. 1934. A notable case of bog formation. Amer. Midland Nat. 15:567-580.
40. _____. 1935. Topography and forest types in a central Indiana region. Amer. Midland Nat. 16:212-229.
41. _____. and L. CHANDLER. 1952. Oak forests in the Laughery Creek Valley, Indiana. Ind. Acad. Sci. Proc. 62:129.
42. _____. and R. C. FRIESNER. 1934. Some comparisons between virgin forest and adjacent areas of secondary succession. Butler Univ. Bot. Stud. 3:85-98.

43. _____ and R. C. FRIESNER. 1940. A phytosociological study of the herbaceous plants in two types of forests in Central Indiana. Butler Univ. Bot. Stud. 4:163-180.

44. _____ and R. C. FRIESNER. 1940. What is climax in central Indiana. A five mile quadrat study. Butler Univ. Bot. Stud. 4:181-195.

45. _____ and R. C. FRIESNER. 1943. An ecological survey of Berkey Woods: A remnant of forest primeval in Kosciusko County, Indiana. Butler Univ. Bot. Stud. 6:10-14.

46. _____, R. C. FRIESNER and C. O. KELLER. 1942. Phytosociology of the Cox Woods: A remnant of forest primeval in Orange County, Indiana. Butler Univ. Bot. Stud. 5:190-221.

47. _____ and C. O. KELLER. 1951. The beech line in Northwestern Indiana. Butler Univ. Bot. Stud. 10:108-113.

48. _____, M. E. POTZGER and JACK MCCORMICK. 1956. The forest primeval of Indiana as recorded in the original U. S. land surveys and an evaluation of previous interpretations of Indiana vegetation. Butler Univ. Bot. Stud. 13:95-111.

49. _____ and I. T. WILSON. 1941. Post-Pleistocene forest migration as indicated by sediments from three deep inland lakes. Amer. Midland Nat. 25:270-289.

50. RECORD, S. T. 1902. Forest conditions in Montgomery County, Indiana. Acad. Sci. Proc. p. 84.

51. RIDGWAY, ROBERT. 1872. Notes on the vegetation of the Lower Wabash Valley. Amer. Naturalist 6:658-665.

52. ROHR, F. W. and J. E. POTZGER. 1951. Forest and prairie in three Northwestern Indiana counties. Butler Univ. Bot. Stud. 10:61-70.

53. SCHUDER. D. L. 1954. Distribution of three important insect transmitted tree diseases. Indiana Acad. Sci. Proc. 64:116-120.

54. SCOTT, WILL. 1905. The Leesburg Swamp. Ind. Acad. Sci. Proc. 209-226.

55. SMITH, W. M. 1937. Pollen spectrum of Lake Cicott Bog, Cass County, Indiana. Butler Univ. Bot. Stud. 4:43-54.

56. SWANSON, CAROLINE H. 1928. The ecology of Turkey Run State Park. Part I — The floodplain, Ind. Acad. Sci. Proc. 38:165-170.

57. TRANSEAU, E. N. 1935. The prairie peninsula. Ecology 16:423-437.

58. U. S. CENSUS OF AGRICULTURE. 1950. U. S. Department of Commerce, Bureau of Census for Indiana.

59. WEAVER, J. E. 1954. North american prairie. Johnson Pub. Co., Lincoln, Nebraska. 348 pp.

60. WELCH, WINONA H. 1929. Forest and prairie, Benton County, Indiana. Indiana Acad. Sci. Proc. 39:67-72.

61. _____ 1932. An ecological study of the bald cypress in Indiana. Indiana Acad. Sci. Proc. 41:207-213.

62. WHITTAKER, R. H. 1953. A consideration of climax theory: The climax as a population and pattern. Ecological Monogr. 23:41-78.

# 17

# *Limnology*

DAVID G. FREY
Indiana University

Limnology is the study of all inland waters—flowing or stationary, fresh or salt, clean or polluted, past, present, and future. It is concerned with the composition and structure of the communities of organisms occurring in these waters and the ways in which they respond to, and in turn modify, the physical and chemical regimes and processes of their environment. In no other field of ecology is the interplay between organisms and environment more readily demonstrable to the average intelligent but untrained person.

Lakes and reservoirs have many uses, but few persons have a broad appreciation of them in their diverse ramifications. Some persons are interested in these water bodies for flood control, power development, maintenance of low stream flow, or as sources of water for industries and communities. Others are interested more in the recreational aspects such as fishing, swimming, boating, water skiing, or the purely esthetic appeal of a lake in its changing moods brought about by weather and the seasons. Frequently the uses of the water bodies are in conflict with one another, and especially when the wastes from industries, communities, and even the dense fringe of cottages around the lakes find their way into the waters. Under such conditions changes in limnology occur that seriously affect the recreational and commercial uses of the waters.

Streams occupy a different regard in our culture. Since their flow is always away from us they have provided from the earliest days of civilization a means of getting rid of all kinds of waste materials and unwanted refuse. Man has tended to absolve himself from further responsibility for his own waste once it gets into a stream. No thought is given to the condition of the river or subsequent use of its water farther downstream. The stream is nobody's problem because it is everybody's, and only by united effort can many of our deplorable situations be remedied. Increasing attention is and must be given to these problems, because our water resources although renewable are not inexhaustible, and, as our population continues to expand, the same water will have to be reused a number of times by different communities and their industries in its passage from the land to the oceans. What one community does to a river very definitely affects the uses that downstream communities can make of the water. Moreover, being subject to great and sudden increases in discharge from rains and snow melt, rivers in flood can cause extensive damage to installations and activities in their flood plains. A major effort of engineers is to harness the rivers by reservoirs and levees or by watershed control in order to reduce such flood damage.

The ordinary person is probably aware only of the fishes in the water, the growths of water weeds that may foul the propellor of his motor boat, the dense scums of algae that may make swimming undesirable or that during their decomposition give off horrible odors, the shells of snails or mussels that children collect along the shores, or the dense swarms of various adult insects that are attracted to cottage windows at night. These are only a few of the many interrelated components of life in waters, and we cannot understand them in their desirable or undesirable aspects without considering the total community.

## LAKES[15, 22]

The natural lakes of Indiana are largely confined to two regions of glacial moraines in the northern part of the State —the Valparaiso Morainal Area to the west and the Steuben Morainal Lake Area to the east.[26] The three northernmost tiers of counties contain approximately 500 lakes greater than 5 acres in area. These are mostly small (average area 85 acres) and shallow (average maximum depth 39 feet), although 13 are larger than 500 acres (Wawasee is the largest at 2618 acres) and 19 are deeper than 80 feet (Tippecanoe is the deepest at 123 feet). The Indiana Department of Natural Resources in cooperation with the U.S. Geological Survey is engaged in a program of mapping these lakes. Maps of more than 200 of the major lakes of the State can be purchased at nominal cost from the Division of Water Resources. Also available is a booklet "Guide to Indiana Lakes," which lists the lakes greater than 10 acres alphabetically and by county and tabulates such information as area, maximum depth, availability of maps, boats for rent, and public access areas.

Other natural water bodies include a series of oxbow cut-offs along the lower Wabash River and a considerable number of small ponds in the karst region of the Mitchell Plain in southern Indiana. Many of these latter are strictly seasonal, or intermittent over longer time intervals, depending on the degree of connection with the underlying channels in the limestone.

Besides these there are a large number of artificial ponds constructed for private fishing or recreation or for stock watering. There were estimated to be 7500 such ponds in Indiana in 1952[19], and the number is certainly greater than 10,000 by now. In the strip-mining area along the southwestern border of the State, ponds develop in the abandoned strip-mine channels. These typically are strongly acid in their early years and then gradually become more alkaline as the production of sulfuric acid in the waste piles declines. A biological succession accompanies the decreasing acidity.

Destined to assume a progressively greater role in the overall water resources of the State are the large reservoirs being constructed on many of the streams of the State. Monroe Reservoir in southern Indiana is now the largest body of water within the State, being several times larger than Lake Wawasee even at conservation pool stage.

Most studies on basin limnology have been carried out on the natural lakes in the north, chiefly in connection with the Indiana University Biological Station, variously located at Lake Wawasee, then at Winona Lake, and now at Crooked Lake in Noble-Whitley Counties.[16] Many of the reports of these studies have been published in the "Investigations of Indiana Lakes and Streams," sponsored variously by Indiana University and the Indiana Department of Natural Resources. Relatively few studies have been conducted on the artificial waters—either farm ponds, reservoirs, or strip-mine pits— and likewise relatively few studies have been conducted on the seasonal or ephemeral waters in the Mitchell Plain or elsewhere.

### Thermal Stratification

A lake (or any other body of water) typically receives most of its heat through the surface by direct absorption of long-wave solar radiation. Since this radiation cannot penetrate very far through water, the heating is confined to a relatively thin layer at the surface. As water is heated above 4° C (39° F) it expands and becomes less dense (lighter) and hence tends to remain at the surface. The only way this surface accumulation of heat can be distributed throughout the rest of the lake is by the action of wind in generating waves and currents. But the differences in density between warm water and colder water creates a "resistance" to mixing, and this resistance increases as the temperature increases. In most lakes there comes a time during the warming phase when the wind no longer can supply enough energy to overcome this resistance, so what it does is the next best thing—it continues to circulate only the upper part of the lake. When this point is reached, summer stratification has begun. Further heat increments are distributed by the wind throughout this upper zone—known as the epilimnion (Fig. 60)—which becomes progressively warmer during the summer, with only relatively small amounts of heat being distributed downward by turbulence into the underlying zone of rapid temperature change, known as the metalimnion or thermocline. Below this is a zone of cold water—the hypolimnion—which remains cold throughout the summer.

In late summer as the daily heat gains by the lake become less than the heat losses, the lake begins to cool. Cooling occurs first in the epilimnion. The winds are now able to circulate a progressively greater thickness of the water, which pushes the metalimnion into greater depths. Finally at some time generally in October or November the last differences in density are overcome· and the lake circulates from top to bottom. This is the period of autumnal overturn.

Overturn continues until the lake freezes, or if it does not freeze overturn continues throughout the winter until summer stratification is established the next year. If the lake does freeze, then a period of winter stratification is established in which, contrary to the condition in summer, the warmest water is at the bottom of the lake and the coldest at the top immediately below the ice. This "inverse" stratification results from the peculiar property of water that its maximum density occurs not at the freezing point as in nearly all other liquids but instead at 4° C.

The greater daily heat receipts in spring permit first the melting of the ice and then the warming of the water until the lake is again uniform in temperature from top to bottom and is being circulated by the wind. This is the period of spring overturn.

Thus, in our region and in the temperate zone in general, lakes that do not freeze experience one period of stratification in summer and a long period of circulation the rest of the year, whereas lakes that do freeze have periods of stratification in summer and winter, separated by periods of circulation in spring and autumn.

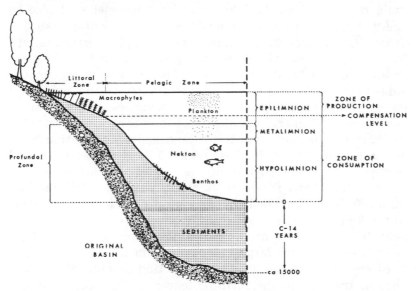

Fig. 60. Diagrammatic cross section of a lake and its basin, showing the zones that become established in summer as a result of thermal stratification and light gradient.

Of course, not all lakes stratify, and even in those that do the depth of the metalimnion can vary greatly from one lake to another. Obviously a lake must exceed a certain depth with respect to its wind exposure in order to stratify. Shallow lakes and ponds generally do not stratify except temporarily during periods of calm weather. Moreover, any factors such as size and shape of the lake, height of surrounding trees, buildings, hills, etc., that reduce the effectiveness of the wind in getting to the surface and in setting up waves and currents tend to restrict the thickness of the epilimnion. Shallow, protected lakes tend to have a much thinner epilimnion (sometimes only 3 or 4 meters) than large, relatively unprotected lakes (epilimnion up to about 10 meters thick). Even the smallest pond or puddle can stratify, at least temporarily, if it is in a location protected from wind action.

### Light Penetration

A second major factor in limnology is light, which is necessary for green plants to carry on photosynthesis. Light is absorbed exponentially as it passes through water. The rate at which it is absorbed is controlled by the amount of brown stain that gets into the lake from its watershed and also by the quantity of particles (turbidity) in the water resulting from clay, silt, organic detritus, microscopic organisms, etc. The more of these, the faster the light is absorbed. At some depth, which varies from lake to lake and even within the same lake from one season or year to another, the amount of energy fixed in the process of photosynthesis just balances the amount of energy needed by the organisms in carrying on their metabolism. This is the so-called compensation level, which is roughly the depth at which 1% of the surface light is still present. The portion of the lake above this level fixes more energy than it needs—it has a positive metabolic balance and hence is called the zone of production. The portion of the lake below the compensation level has a negative metabolic balance and hence is called the zone of consumption. Organisms here are largely dependent on the importation of fixed energy from the zone of production or from the watershed of the lake in the form of leaves, pollen, and other organic detritus.

### Community Structure

Within a lake are a number of more-or-less distinct, although interrelated, communities of organisms. Living free in the open water are a host of microscopic organisms, consisting of algae and bacteria, protozoans, small crustaceans, and rotifiers, collectively known as the plankton. The algae carry on photosynthesis, grow, and reproduce more of their own kind. The animals feed on the live and dead algae, on organic detritus that may originate in the pelagic zone, in the shallow-water zone, or be washed in from the watershed, and on bacteria. The bacteria are constantly involved in breaking down dead organisms, metabolic wastes and feces, and detritus into simpler compounds and eventually to the mineral nutrients (carbon dioxide, phosphates, nitrates, sulfates, etc.) that the algae require in their metabolism. Thus, there is a continual and generally rapid recycling of these substances in the open water, from inorganic substances through living organisms and back to inorganic substances. At the same time these microscopic organisms and their detrital products are continually settling into the hypolimnion as plankton rain. This is the chief mechanism whereby the organisms in the zone of consumption obtain much of their fixed energy and also the means whereby the epilimnion is progressively depleted of essential plant nutrients during a period of stratification.

In shallow water above the compensation level occur beds of macrophytes or "weeds". These also carry on photosynthesis and produce organic matter. Moreover, they provide a substrate within the lighted zone for sessile algae and fungi, some sessile animals such as sponges, bryozoans, and Hydra, and a large variety of microscopic and sub-microscopic animals that crawl through or over the surface of the dense gelatinous coverings that can form on the plant stems. The same type of covering can also occur over rocks, logs, or other materials on the bottom in the littoral zone. The macrophytes have a major period of growth each summer and then generally die back in winter. They tie up essential plant nutrients for a longer period of time than do the algae and other small organisms. Also they produce large quantities of cellulose and other organic compounds relatively resistant to decomposition, compared to proteins for example, that settle to the bottom in the littoral zone or are carried offshore into the pelagic zone. Productivity is high in the littoral zone and recycling of nutrients rapid except those involved in the seasonal growth of the macrophytes.

The plankton rain and the excess production of organic matter in the littoral zone settles to the bottom, where it forms a rich food supply for a variety of larger animals, collectively called the benthos. The benthos of the littoral zone is much more diversified than that of the profundal zone, including snails and mussels, a great variety of insect larvae and adults, and a great diversity of other types of animals. Many of these feed directly on the algae, organic detritus, and bacteria, relatively few feed on the macrophytes, and many feed on other animals. Feeding interrelationships are extremely complex here in the zone that enjoys light and warm temperatures in summer.

The benthos of the profundal zone by comparison is much restricted in composition. It includes mainly those organisms that can spend their entire lives in deep water (such as the segmented worms) or those immature insects that can emerge as adults by swimming to the surface offshore (midges and some mayflies and caddisflies), rather than having to crawl out of the water, as do many of the immature insects in the littoral zone. The profundal species are mainly detritus eaters, although some are predators on them or on the microscopic crustaceans that live in the surface film of the mud or in the adjacent water.

Finally, at the top of the whole community complex are the fishes, sometimes collectively referred to as the nekton. A few, such as the gizzard shad, feed on phytoplankton directly, and some of the coarse fishes may feed on detritus or on the macrophytes, but most depend largely on other animals. Regardless of the food habits of the adults, the young of nearly all fishes feed on the microscopic animals of the plankton or of the littoral zone. As the fishes increase in size, they tend to shift to larger food items such as insects or small fishes. Thus, there is an intricate interrelationship among all the organisms in the lake—primary producers, prey, and predator—varying with species, size or stage of development, season, and location within the lake.

### Oxygen Balance

Excluding the fixed energy that gets into a lake from its watershed as organic detritus, the chief basis of support for the organisms in a lake is the photosynthesis carried on by the algae and higher aquatic plants. In large, deep lakes in which the littoral zone comprises a relatively small percentage of the total area of the lake, the phytoplankton is more important in this regard. In clear, shallow lakes the rooted aquatic plants and their attached algae are more important. But whatever the food base is, it has to support all the animals and bacteria involved in the successive steps of energy transfer and utilization.

Lakes vary in their fertility according to the geological nature of the watershed. Hardwater lakes are generally richer (more productive) than softwater lakes, in part because the calcium and magnesium bicarbonates in the water provide reserve supplies of carbon dioxide needed in photosynthesis and in part because these substances serve as buffers to make a more favorable environment for many organisms. However, extremely hardwater lakes that are depositing marl on the bottom tend to be less productive through interference with certain aspects of the nutrient cycles.[28, 29, 31]

Man has increased the productivity of lakes by his agricultural and domestic wastes. The fertilizers that are applied to crop land stimulate the growth of algae when they are washed into lakes, as do the phospates, nitrates, and other substances present in sewage, sewage plant effluents, and septic tank drainage. The inevitable consequence of man's activities in and around lakes is a progressive increase in the amount of plant nutrients and hence in the total amount of photosynthesis that can be accomplished in the lakes. Such increases usually have undesirable consequences.

Since oxygen is released in photosynthesis and used in respiration, the oxygen content of a body of water reflects the balance of these two processes, after suitable allowance has been made for diffusion between the water and the atmosphere. In the daytime when photosynthesis exceeds respiration, the oxygen content of the trophogenic zone increases, and during the night when only respiration is going on the oxygen content decreases. The amplitude of these daily changes in oxygen content reflects the quantity of life in the water. In highly productive situations the water can become strongly supersaturated during daylight and virtually depleted of oxygen during the night, especially in small water bodies, such as ponds, during calm weather. At such times fish can be killed by asphyxiation. In unpolluted situations, however, except perhaps in dense weed beds, the decline in oxygen is seldom this extreme.

In the hypolimnion only respiration takes place. Moreover, because the metalimnion forms an effective barrier to downward diffusion by turbulence, the oxygen content of the hypolimnion at the time stratification begins is a non-renewable, finite quantity that must suffice for all organisms in the hypolimnion until autumnal overturn commences. The extent to which the oxygen content of the hypolimnon declines during stratification depends on the balance between oxygen supply and oxygen demand. The supply is determined mainly by the volume of the deep water: the greater this is and the colder the temperatures, the more oxygen there is available for use. Hence, deep lakes typically experience a lesser degree of oxygen depletion than shallow lakes. The demand for oxygen is determined by the amount of utilizable organic matter that gets into the hypolimnion by plankton rain, littoral detritus, and watershed detritus. This material furnishes the nutritional substrate for bacteria, segmented worms, insect larvae, microscopic animals, etc. The more organic material, the more organisms can be supported, and hence the more oxygen is utilized.

In many lakes in Indiana the hypolimnion becomes completely exhausted of oxygen during summer stratification.[11] Long before such extreme condtions are reached, nearly all higher organisms will have been eliminated from the deep water. Under these conditions, aerobic processes give way to anaerobic. Various gases such as hydrogen sulfide, methane, carbon monoxide, and hydrogen are produced, and substances such as iron and manganese, which are insoluble in the oxidized state at an alkaline pH, begin to appear in the water. Communities that process such sources of water for their domestic needs are bound to run into problems.

Through the gradual accumulation of sediments in a lake, the volume of the hypolimnion becomes progressively smaller with time, thereby reducing the oxygen supply available for heterotrophic metabolism during periods of stratification. Even without any increase in the rate of production in the trophogenic zone and hence in the plankton rain, this would result in a progressive reduction in the summer oxygen content of the hypolimnion. The original deepwater animals that require high levels of dissolved oxygen (or associated conditions) are displaced by other species that tolerate somewhat lower levels, they in turn by species that tolerate even lower levels, etc., to the eventual complete elimination of higher organisms in response to the anaerobic conditions that develop.

Detailed studies have revealed, for example, that 44% of the original volume of Winona Lake and 32% of Tippecanoe have been eliminated by the accumulation of sediments.[30] Numerous smaller lakes have been completely snuffed out since they first formed in Cary Time, perhaps 15,000 years ago, and many other lakes of the same age have become so shallow that they are completely choked with aquatic weeds in summer. Their life expectancy is very short, indeed.

### Paleolimnology

The accumulated sediments in a lake provide a chronological record of the lake and of its watershed. From the remains of plants and animals in the sediments and from the chemical composition and physical makeup of the sediments, much information is available concerning past conditions, which is the province of paleolimnology.[12]

The chronological framework for the paleolimnologist was originally, and to a considerable extent still is, the pollen diagram. The pollen and spores, chiefly of terrestrial plants, are abundant and well preserved in lake and bog sediments. Their changing abundance from one level to another reflects the changing climate and other conditions in the time interval represented, most generally the late-glacial-postglacial period. The many pollen diagrams from specific localities in Indiana and adjacent regions give clear indications what the forests and general vegetations were like in earlier times.[5] The predominantly spruce forest of late-glacial time was replaced successively by a short maximum of pine and this in turn by a mixed hardwood forest with oak dominant and with lesser percentages of elm, ash, hickory, maple, beech, etc. The immigration of western agricultural man into the region is clearly marked by the appearance and rapid buildup to relatively high percentages of such agricultural weeds as ragweed (Ambrosia), etc. These constitute useful time markers for assessing the effects of man in accelerating the rate of lake development.

Within the past two decades techniques have been devised for determining the absolute age of materials by the disintegration rates of various natural radioisotopes they contain and the accumulation of their breakdown products. For the period encompassing the last 30,000 years, and back as far as 60,000 years or so with less precision, radiocarbon is a very effective means of dating. The carbon-14 formed in the upper atmosphere by cosmic-ray bombardment of nitrogen becomes incorporated into plant tissues through photosynthesis and eventually becomes distributed through the entire biota in the same proportion. On death of the organisms, the contained C-14 undergoes a very slow decay with a half life of 5730 years, giving off weak beta radiation in the process. From the ratio of C-14 to C-12 in the sample being dated as compared with that in fresh organic matter (prior to 1950), the radiocarbon age of the sample can be calculated. Sequential radiocarbon dates in the same sedimentary cross section enable the rates of change of limnological variables to be assessed, as well as the absolute rates of accumulation of sediments and their components, such as pollen grains, diatom frustules, Cladocera, etc. Such studies are in their infancy, although they hold great promise.

Among the profundal benthos, midge larvae respond with greatest clarity to changes in hypolimnetic conditions. In fact, many years ago a typology of lake succession was proposed for northern Europe, which has since been shown to be more or less valid for the rest of the world as well, based on the species of midges that are dominant in deep water—from those that require high levels of oxygen to those that can tolerate very small quantities or can even exist as facultative anaerobes. The fact that lakes do change progressively with time is demonstrated by the succession of midge types that can be recovered from sediments.[25] Remains of algae, especially the diatoms and desmids, and of certain microscopic animals such as the Cladocera also help in the interpretation of past conditions in lakes.[7, 21]

The declining levels of oxygen in the hypolimnion also affect the presence and abundance of fishes that require both cold water and rather high levels of oxygen for their survival. Such species include the lake trout, ciscoes, whitefishes, burbot, and a few others. Except for the cisco, these species have long since disappeared from Indiana lakes. A number of lakes in the State have water sufficiently clear in summer that light can penetrate into the metalimnion permitting photosynthesis.[9, 10] The oxygen resulting from excess photosynthesis accumulates here because of the hydrostatic pressure and re-

duced vertical turbulence, often resulting in supersaturation
with reference to atmospheric pressure. The cisco, although
driven out of the hypolimnion by low levels of oxygen, is able
to survive in the somewhat warmer, although still cool, water
of the metalimnion with its favorable levels of oxygen. This
seems to have been a major factor in the maintenance of the
cisco in these marginal waters.[11] Rainbow, brook, or brown
trout introduced into these lakes can frequently survive because of the close similarity of their oxygen-temperature requirements to those of cisco.

Another factor that can drastically alter the composition
of a fish population in a lake is winter kill. Dissolved oxygen
is removed from the water under the ice by heterotrophic
activity in the same way as it is from the hypolimnion of a
lake in summer. Clear ice permits sufficient light to enter the
water for photosynthesis, but generally the zone of production although intense is quite thin compared with the summer.
Snow is much less transparent to light, so that if there is an
appreciable snow cover, if the ice cover lasts for a long time,
and if the lake contains large amounts of organic matter and
organisms, then all or nearly all the oxygen can be used up
under the ice, resulting in the asphyxiation of large numbers
of fishes. Obviously, anything that increases the productivity
of a lake, such as pollution or agricultural drainage, by supplying plant nutrients or organic matter will accentuate the
condition. Water level at the time of freezeup can also be important. A low water level means reduced water volume and
hence a lesser total quantity of oxygen available for the winter period.

## Productivity

During periods of stratification the plankton rain carries
nutrients into the deep water where they are regenerated
(mineralized) by bacterial action. Because of the diffusional
barrier imposed by the metalimnion, however, these nutrients
cannot be transported upward into the epilimnion, but this
must wait until the next period of overturn in spring or
autumn. These big surges of plant nutrients coupled with the
external light climate produce big surges or blooms in the phytoplankton populations. Typically the spring bloom, normally
consisting mostly of diatoms, is bigger than the autumn bloom.

The standing crop of plankton in unpolluted situations is usually less in summer and least of all in winter when temperatures are low and the total daily light input is small.

The magnitude of the standing crops can be determined by direct counts or approximated by measuring chlorophyll content, but these data pose problems in productivity studies because they give no indication of rates of turnover of nutrients. Rates of photosynthesis that are sufficiently high can be calculated from oxygen changes in light bottles (where both photosynthesis and respiration go on) and dark bottles (where only respiration can take place), when these bottles have been resuspended at the depths from which the water samples were removed. More recently, photosynthesis has been calculated from the rate at which the phytoplankton in bottles utilizes labelled carbon dioxide (carbon-14), taking into account the total amount of C-14 added in relation to the total amount of natural C-12 available in the water. Such studies in Indiana lakes[27] have shown, for example, that in Sylvan Lake, which is quite highly polluted, the mean daily photosynthesis over the entire year is about 1.5 g carbon per square meter, with a maximum of almost 5 g. This makes Sylvan Lake one of the most productive natural lakes of the world for which data are available. Nearby Goose Lake is also highly productive compared with many other natural lakes, with a mean daily productivity of about 0.7 $g/m^2$. The marl lakes of this region are much less productive, Crooked Lake for example having a mean daily productivity of 0.4 $g/m^2$. Through the use of organic compounds labelled with C-14, such as glucose and acetate, it is now possible to measure the rate of heterotrophic uptake of these compounds from the water.[32] Natural waters can also be bioassayed for nutrient deficiencies by measuring the increase in C-14 uptake through photosynthesis resulting from the addition of one or another chemical to the water in the experimental bottles.[28]

Other techniques for estimating primary productivity are based on the daily cycles of oxygen and pH in the water itself. Attempts have also been made to get some idea of the metabolism of an entire lake from the rate at which oxygen is depleted from the hypolimnion or the rate at which carbon dioxide accumulates there.

The measurement of productivity at higher levels of energy

utilization is much more complicated because of the intricacies of the food webs, with their changing major pathways according to species, stage of development, and seasons. Such measurements are probably most difficult of all at the level of the fishes, and yet for the bluegill sunfish a very significant study has been made.[14] From laboratory studies on the feeding efficiency (conversion of food to fish protein) of bluegills of various sizes it was possible to calculate the amount of food that a natural population of fish in Wyland Lake must have consumed in a year to account for the observed growth of the entire population. The quantity of food eaten was considerably larger than the standing crop of food organisms in the lake, indicating that the fishes are continually cropping off a certain portion of the food supply, which has the problem of maintaining itself as well as supporting the fish and other predators. This is another example of the difficulty in using data on standing crops by themselves for assessing productivity. As a general approximation, only 10% of the fixed energy ingested by a given species is converted into flesh of that species. The rest is lost as metabolic heat or through other means.

## Effects of Pollution

Through man's unintentional intervention, the natural process of aging of our lakes—called eutrophication—is being accelerated. Increased quantities of nutrients bring about greater and more frequent blooms of algae in summer, particularly of the objectionable bluegreens.[6] These, being lighter than water, rise to the surface in calm weather, where they can form solid unbroken mats over many acres of the lake's surface. Along shore as these mats become crusty and decompose, they give off horrible odors that at times are scarcely tolerable. Through wave action this material paints the rocks, trees, piers, etc., for some distance above the water level. Recreation all but ceases, and property values become depressed. At times hydrogen cyanide is produced by such decomposition, which can kill cattle that drink the water.

The blooms of algae have other consequences in addition. By cutting down the penetration of light in the water they restrict the downward distribution of the rooted aquatic plants and eventually may cause their complete disappearance. Since the weed beds are important producers of small animal life that can serve as fish food and also are important nursery areas for the small fishes, their curtailment or elimination has severe repercussions on the fish populations.

Moreover, the increased production of organic matter in the epilimnion accelerates the rain of organic matter into the hypolimnion, which brings about an increased rate of oxygen depletion during summer stratification. Cold-water fishes are eliminated if this has not happened already, and the composition of the invertebrate benthos is drastically changed.[2] Moreover, the lake is much more subject to winter kills because of the high oxygen demand of its sediments.

Such extreme conditions do not come about overnight, but require years or even decades of gradual deterioration. Finally the situation becomes so bad that the population affected demands action—immediately. What has taken years to accomplish cannot be undone in one week or a month. Even if all further addition of nutrients is stopped, recovery will probably be slow because of the large reserves of nutrients in the sediments. A recent detailed study on Lake Sebasticook in Maine estimated that even if all the proposed recommendations were activated' at least 10 years would be required for major improvement to be realized.[20] And, regretfully, we do not have any guidelines based on past experience for directing the recovery of such lakes. Control of algae with copper sulfate or other chemicals is merely palliative—it does not get to the root of the trouble. Since lakes are much more conservative than streams in rates of change, the best course of action is to realize what will happen inevitably if nothing is done and then to take the necessary steps to prevent the development of these undesirable conditions.

## STREAMS[17]

Water at any effective elevation will flow to a lower level if unrestrained. Such flow generates kinetic energy, which can do work. The work normally done by flowing water on the land surface results in a channelization of the surface flow into a drainage pattern, with small headwater brooks and rills uniting into progressively larger streams and finally into the master stream of the drainage area. This brings about an unidirectional flow and a constantly changing identity of the

water at any particular location, two of the chief characteristics that distinguish streams from lakes.

Water in a stream channel has two chief origins—surface
runoff and groundwater. Surface runoff, which occurs chiefly
during and immediately after periods of excess precipitation
or snow melt, washes in debris and other loose material from
the land, which is responsible for much of the turbidity of
streams. Groundwater, because of its intimate contact with
the soil and subsurface matrix, contributes much of the chemical load of a stream. Stream discharge increases rapidly,
often precipitously, during rains or snow melt and declines
gradually during dry periods, the phase of decline reflecting
the gradual depletion of the groundwater reserves and of the
water stored in the channel system itself. The chemistry and
turbidity of a stream in a humid region are controlled largely
by the relative amounts of surface runoff and groundwater
being contributed at any time.

There are really two streams in each channel, a stream of
water that is moving continually and a stream of materials
on the bottom—the bed load—that is moved intermittently
and selectively. Since the size or weight of particles that can
be moved by a current varies as the sixth power of the current velocity, materials on the bottom remain in place for a
longer or shorter period of time depending on their size in
relation to the current velocity. At severe flood stage the entire bottom of a stream can be set in motion, even the largest
boulders. At somewhat lesser discharges the largest rocks
and boulders may remain in place, but their exposed surfaces
become scoured clean by the sand, gravel, and rubble that
are being moved downstream along the bottom like a giant
rasp. Such conditions tax the survival limits of stream organisms. At lesser stages only the fine particles are actively transported downstream. At still lesser stages the groundwater
reserves may be insufficient to maintain surface flow, and as
a result the stream bed is reduced to a series of isolated pools
or even becomes completely dry. Subsurface flow or seepage,
however, may be adequate to maintain aquatic organisms in
the interstices of the channel fill until surface flow becomes
reestablished.[4]

Typically the gradient of a stream is steepest toward the
headwaters and progressively less toward the mouth. This re-

sults in a gradation of bottom materials, from boulders and rubble in the steeper portions to sands, silts, and clays in the more quiet portions. Similar variations in bottom composition occur in the pool-riffle sequence in the headwater reaches and even in the dead-water spaces downstream from boulders and other obstructions in rapids. Thus, especially in the high-gradient sections, a stream bottom tends to be a mosaic of various bottom types according to the local current patterns.

Other longitudinal gradients of environmental variables besides current velocity, bottom composition, chemistry, and turbidity occur in streams, two of the most important of which are temperature and light. Because the headwater portions of a stream are in close contact with the groundwater system, they tend to have cooler mean temperatures and lesser seasonal and daily fluctuations than farther downstream.[3] Moreover, the upstream portions by being shallower and less turbid have adequate light for photosynthesis to penetrate to the bottom, whereas downstream in the deeper and more turbid region the trophogenic zone is thinner and encompasses the substrate only in shallow marginal locations. In many respects the headwater portions of streams correspond to the zone of production in lakes and the downstream portions to the zone of consumption.

As a result of these gradients a stream although continuous in a physical sense is in reality a linear succession of environmental types and consequently of communities of organisms adapted to these types. European limnologists have long divided their streams into four major regions on the basis of the dominant fishes present—an uppermost trout zone, followed downstream by a grayling zone, then a barbel (a cyprinid minnow) zone, and finally a bream (another cyprinid) zone. The fishes are merely a conspicuous index of the changing composition of the entire communities of their respective reaches.

## Biota

The food base of a stream, as of a lake, consists of the photosynthetic aquatic plants and of the organic matter imported from the watershed. Because of intimate contact with its watershed through numerous small tributaries, a river system is much more dependent on imported organic matter

in its total metabolism than is a lake and in fact is coming
to be regarded as being mainly dependent on this source of
fixed energy.[18] At times, however, the natural addition of
organic matter can be too great for the stream to assimilate,
as during leaf fall in autumn when the water is pooled.[23]

Whenever light penetrates to the bottom, solid surfaces
tend to become covered with dense films of sessile algae, chiefly
diatoms. Since these are being continually broken loose
(cropped) by the current and washed downstream, the organisms that are free in the water are largely the same as those
on the bottom. Plankton entering from a lake is often rapidly
removed by biological and physical means in a stream, but
where the current is slow and the retention time in the stream
channel sufficiently long relative to the life cycle of the respective forms, populations of true planktonic algae consisting
of the same species as in lakes can develop and can attain
bloom proportions under suitable conditions.

The effect of current on the stream biota is most readily
apparent in the benthos. In quiet reaches with a muddy bottom, the benthos is scarcely distinguishable from that of
lakes, but as the current velocity increases, species with particular adaptations to current come to dominate the benthos,
giving it a completely different aspect from lake benthos.
Such adaptations include streamlining and various methods
of attachment, straining food particles from the flowing water
by specially modified appendages or by the construction of
nets, etc. Current itself increases productivity by facilitat-
ing those metabolic processes that are limited by the rate of
diffusional exchange with the water, and hence riffles typically have a greater biomass of organisms than the adjacent
pools. Immature insects of various kinds are the most characteristic component of current-adapted benthos.

Organisms of the benthos also tend to be swept downstream. This is in part a depletion phenomenon, which is coun-
teracted by a tendency of many organisms to move direc-
tionally against the current and by the tendency of adult
insects to fly upstream before depositing their eggs. It is also
a mechanism that helps bring about optimum utilization of
food resources and provides for recolonization of stretches
depleted by flash floods or other means.

The diversity of organisms in a stream is related to the

complexity and continually changing character of its environment. In a healthy stream the diversity is great because of the large variety of microhabitats available for colonization. The components of the biota are in good balance with one another, and the stream is able to assimilate or incorporate into its community structure without detriment the normal amounts of organic matter and nutrients deriving from the watershed. Pollution changes this diversity.

## Effects of Pollution

Pollution of surface, and even subsurface, waters is one of the major problems facing man. The large variety and tremendous quantities of waste materials produced by man and his technology must be got rid of in some way, and the time-honored means of doing this, contrary to anti-pollution laws in all the states, has been to dump the wastes into a stream and forget about them. Undesirable conditions result that severely restrict the subsequent reuse of this water for domestic or industrial purposes. Many of our waterways are little more than unsightly and malodorous sewers, and where the wastes get into lakes the undesirable conditions already described develop. Much effort is being devoted by engineers and biologists to find ways of reducing and controlling pollution. The Industrial Waste Conference held annually at Purdue University represents one means of summarizing progress toward these objectives. The reports presented at each conference are published in a proceedings volume.

The purpose of the following section is not to consider the public health aspects of pollution—the danger of pathogenic organisms or of direct toxic substances and the nusiance of undesirable tastes and odors—or the industrial aspects of altered water quality, but rather the effect of waste materials on the limnology of the receiving stream.

Pollution is a relative condition, governed largely by local culture and the use made of the water. There is no hard and fast definition. What is tolerated in one part of the world might be completely unacceptable in another, but regardless of acceptability of the resulting conditions by man the addition of wastes has quite predictable consequences on the biota.

Such substances as silts and clays from gravel washings or construction projects, coal dust from collieries, and limestone

dust from finishing mills are largely inert materials that affect
the biota chiefly by reducing light penetration and by smoth-
ering the bottom with a blanket of fine material that eliminates many of the microhabitats otherwise present.[24] As a
result, the diversity of the biota is reduced.

Many industrial and agricultural wastes are directly toxic
to organisms, including man. They are removed from a stream
in part by direct chemical action, such as precipitation of
heavy metals, but mostly by biological activity. The detoxifica-
tion of a stream is an exponential function with the rate of
decline controlled largely by progressive dilution of the water
and the relative ease that the substances are acted on by biological systems. Some substances, such as chlorinated hydrocarbons, are extremely resistant and retain their toxicity for
long periods. The duration of the potential harmfulness of ra-
dionuclides varies according to their half lives.

Even heat from generating stations or other sources can
have appreciable effects on streams by increasing water temperatures above the tolerance limits of many of the organisms
or by providing warm temperatures even in winter that make
it possible for cold-sensitive organisms to invade the region
and become established.

The commonest type of pollution, however, is the organic
matter in sewage and sewage-plant effluents from communities and in waste water from such industries as pulp and paper
mills, condenseries, canneries, meat-processing plants, etc.
This material is acted upon by organisms, chiefly bacteria, as
a result of which dissolved oxygen in the water is consumed.
The organic matter has a biochemical oxygen demand (B.O.D.).
The utilization of oxygen produces the oxygen-sag curve of the
sanitary engineers (Fig. 61). If the quality of organic matter
introduced is greater than the assimilation capacity of the
stream—in other words, when the stream is overloaded—undesirable conditions develop. All the oxygen can be used up,
creating an anaerobic zone with the production of such substances as hydrogen sulfide and methane, as in the hypolimnion of a productive lake. All higher organisms, except a few
air breathers that are particularly resistant or specifically
adapted, are eliminated.

The degree of oxygen depletion is dependent on the amount
of organic matter introduced relative to the volume of flow of

the stream—a dilution factor. Hence, at any one place there can be daily fluctuations depending on the discharge regimes of the communities and the industries as well as seasonal variations depending on major variations in stream discharge. Conditions are usually most severe in summer when low stream flows are coupled with high water temperatures.

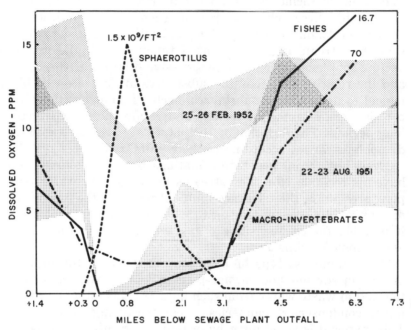

Fig. 61. Longitudinal response of Lytle Creek, Ohio, to a single source of pollution entering at Mile 0. The curve for *Sphaerotilus*, a filamentous bacterium associated with pollution, shows the number of cells per square foot of bottom. The curve for fishes shows the average number of species collected at each station during the study. The curve for macro-invertebrates (chiefly insects) represents the number of species or genera collected at each station in October 1961. Both fishes and macro-invertebrates are sensitive to pollution, and hence their diversity declines as pollution becomes progressively more severe. The two shaded zones show the variation in dissolved oxygen at each station over two 24-hour periods, one during high discharge in winter and the other during low discharge in summer. (Extensively modified from Gaufin and Tarzwell, 1956.)

Downstream there is a gradual recovery. The B.O.D. becomes reduced by the progressive degradation of the complex organic compounds. As plant nutrients are released by this process, algae begin to appear and frequently develop massive blooms. Through their photosynthesis and through diffusion from the atmosphere, oxygen levels are gradually built up, permitting higher organisms to become reestablished. Eventually, if there is no further pollution, which is a rare situation, recovery is complete, and the stream once again has a "healthy" appearance, with a diversity of organisms. [1,8]

Hence, recovery from organic pollution is a two-stage process—the utilization of the organic matter by bacteria with the resulting decrease in oxygen levels, and then the assimilation by algae of the released nutrients into new organic matter. If pollution is relatively mild, both processes proceed simultaneously, and the environmental deterioration is not excessive. If pollution is extreme, the two processes tend to be sequential, although overlapping, because the algae cannot thrive in the septic zone.

Waste treatment concentrates on removing solids and reducing the B.O.D. of the effluent. This is good, but it is not sufficient. Plant nutrients released by biological activity in the treatment process stimulate the development of blooms of algae in streams, the same as nutrients regenerated from untreated or partially-treated effluents in the stream itself and with the same potentially deleterious results. Fish kills most commonly occur in the algal zone, because here although the oxygen content may exceed saturation during daylight as a result of photosynthesis, it may drop to lethal levels during nighttime. In the septic zone there are no fish to be killed. One of the major problems of the sanitary engineers is to remove these plant nutrients chemically or else to concentrate them by some biological means with a usable end product.

Thus, in addition to the normal gradients that exist in a stream there are also those imposed by pollution. In response to any major source of pollution a biological zonation becomes established in which the curtailment of biotal diversity is a direct function of deterioration of habitat.

### LITERATURE

1. BRINLEY, F. J. 1942. The effect of pollution upon the plankton population of the White River, Indiana. Invest. Indiana Lakes & Streams 2(9):137-143.
2. BRITT, N. W. 1955. Stratification in western Lake Erie in summer of 1953; Effects on the *Hexagenia* (Ephemeroptera) population. Ecology 36:239-244.
3. CHANDLER, C. M. 1966. Environmental factors affecting the local distribution and abundance of four species of stream-dwelling triclads. Invest. Indiana Lakes & Streams 7. In press.
4. CLIFFORD, H. F. 1966. The ecology of invertebrates in an intermittent stream. Invest. Indiana Lakes & Streams 7. In press.

5. CUSHING, E. J. 1965. Problems in the Quaternary phytogeography of the Great Lakes Region, pp. 403-416, *in*: The Quaternary of the United States, H. E. Wright, Jr., and D. G. Frey, editors. Princeton Univ. Press. x, 922 p.

6. DEAN, J. M. 1964. The effect of sewage on a chain of lakes in Indiana. Hydrobiologia 24:435-440.

7. DeCOSTA, J. J. 1964. Latitudinal distribution of chydorid Cladocera in the Mississippi Valley, based on their remains in surficial lake sediments. Invest. Indiana Lakes & Streams 6:65-101.

8. DENHAM, S. C. 1938. A limnological investigation of the West Fork and Common Branch of the White River. Invest. Indiana Lakes & Streams 1(5):17-72.

9. EBERLY, W. R. 1959. The metalimnetic oxygen maximum in Myers Lake. Invest. Indiana Lakes & Streams 5:1-46.

10. _____. 1964. Further studies on the metalimnetic oxygen maximum, with reference to its occurrence throughout the world. Invest. Indiana Lakes & Streams 6:103-139.

11. FREY, D. G. 1955. Distributional ecology of the cisco (*Coregonus artedii*) in Indiana. Invest. Indiana Lakes & Streams 4:177-228.

12. _____. 1964. Remains of animals in Quaternary lake and bog sediments and their interpretation. Arch. Hydrobiol., suppl. Ergebnisse der Limnologie 2:1-116.

13. GAUFIN, A. R., and C. M. TARZWELL. 1956. Aquatic macro-invertebrate communities as indicators of organic pollution in Lytle Creek. Sewage and Industrial Wastes 28:906-924.

14. GERKING, S. D. 1962. Production and food utilization in a population of bluegill sunfish. Ecol. Monogr. 32:31-78.

15. _____. 1963. Central states, pp. 239-268, *in*: Limnology in North America, D. G. Frey, editor. Univ. Wisconsin Press. XVIII, 734 p.

16. _____. 1963. The Indiana University Biological Station. Amer. Zool. 3:326-330.

17. HYNES, H. B. N. 1960. The biology of polluted waters. Univ. Liverpool Press. xiv, 202 p.

18. _____. 1963. Imported organic matter and secondary productivity in streams. Proc. XVI Intl. Congress Zool., Washington, D. C. 4:324-329.

19. KRUMHOLZ, L. A. 1952. Management of Indiana ponds for fishing. J. Wildlife Mgt. 16:254-257.

20. (MACKENTHUN, K. M.). 1966. Fertilization and algae in Lake Sebasticook Maine. Federal Water Pollution Control Administration, Tech. Services Program. 124 p.

21. MUELLER, W. P. 1964. The distribution of cladoceran remains in surficial sediments from three northern Indiana Lakes. Invest. Indiana Lake & Streams 6:1-63.

22. RUTTNER, FRANZ. 1963. Fundamentals of limnology. Univ. Toronto Press. xvi, 295 p.

23. SCHNELLER, MYRTLE V. 1955. Oxygen depletion in Salt Creek, Indiana. Invest. Indiana Lakes & Streams 4:163-175.

24. SLACK, K. V. 1955. A study of the factors affecting stream productivity by the comparative method. Invest. Indiana Lakes & Streams 4:3-47.

25. STAHL, J. B. 1959. The developmental history of the chironomid and *Chaoborus* faunas of Myers Lake. Invest. Indiana Lakes & Streams 5:47-102.

26. WAYNE, W. J., and J. H. ZUMBERGE. 1965. Pleistocene geology of Indiana and Michigan, pp. 63-83, *in*: The Quaternary of the United States, H. E. Wright, Jr., and D. G. Frey, editors. Univ. Princeton Press. x, 922 p.

27. WETZEL, R. G. 1966. Variations in productivity of Goose and hypereutrophic Sylvan lakes, Indiana. Invest. Indiana Lakes & Streams 7. In press.

28. _____. 1966. Nutritional aspects of algal productivity in marl lakes with particular reference to enrichment bioassays and their interpretation. Mem. Ist. Ital. Idrobiol., suppl. 18:137-157.

29. _____. 1966. Productivity and nutrient relationships in marl lakes of northern Indiana. Proc. Int. Assoc. Limnol. 16. In press.

30. WILSON, I. T. 1938. The accumulated sediments in Tippecanoe Lake and a comparison with Winona Lake. Proc. Indiana Acad. Sci. 47:234-253.

31. WOHLSCHLAG, D. E. 1950. Vegetation and invertebrate life in a marl lake. Invest. Indiana Lakes & Streams 3:321-372.

32. WRIGHT, R. T., and J. E. HOBBIE. 1965. The uptake of organic solutes in lake water. Limnol. Oceanogr. 10:22-28.

# 18

# The Free Living Invertebrates

FRANK N. YOUNG
Indiana University

The possibilities for discovery in research on the free-living invertebrates of Indiana are so great that they overpower the imagination. Indiana is not blessed with high mountains or rolling oceans, but it has a pleasant assortment of prairies, woodlands, river bottoms, lakes, ponds, bogs, swamps, ravines, caves, slow and swift streams, orchards, farmlands, gardens, and urban areas which offer invertebrates of many kinds suitable living conditions. Even excepting the ubiquitous insects and the parasites, Indiana has enough invertebrates for everyone.

Excluding insects, and parasitic forms, a conservative estimate of the numbers of invertebrate species for Indiana is probably more than 3,000. Estimates for the various phyla are as follows: Protozoa (single-celled animals), about 500; Porifera (sponges), about 12; Coelenterates (jellyfish cordylophorans and hydras), about 12; Platyhelminthes (freshwater flatworms) about 50; Rhynchocoela or Nemertea (freshwater nemerteans) only 1; Aschelminthes (roundworms, rotifers, and gastrotrichs) about 450; Endoprocta (moss animals) possibly 1; Annelida (segmented freshwater and earthworms, polychaete worms, and leeches) about 100; Mollusca (snails, limpets, clams, and mussels) about 200; Tardigrada (bear animalcules) about 50 or more; Ectoprocta or Bryozoa (moss animals) about 7 or more considering varieties of *Plumatella repens* Linnaeus. Arthropoda (segmented animals) are especially numerous. The classes are estimated as follows: Crustacea (fairy shrimp, ostracods, copepods, cladocera, amphipods, isopods, crayfish, and freshwater shrimp) about 400; Arachnida (spiders, phalangids, scorpions, mites, and ticks) possibly as many as 1,500; Symphyla (symphylids) possibly 3; Pauropoda (pauropods) possibly 4; Diplopoda (millipeds), 50 or more; Chilopoda (centipedes) about 30 or more; and the Protura (minute antenna-less arthropods usually disdained by the entomologists) 5 or more.

These figures are, of course, very rough estimates. Some of them are even wildly speculative, and include a projection of the new species which will ultimately be discovered. The mites, for example, are hardly known for Indiana or even for the United States in general. New species, genera, and even families are being described every month. In such groups, Indiana may be found to harbor distinctive species, even genera, in its glacially isolated caves, ravines, and other situations. On the other hand, in the Mollusca which is the best known invertebrate group in the state about 186 species have been definitely recorded and another dozen probably occur. Dr. William J. Wayne of the Indiana Geological Survey, has recorded approximately 100 species of land snails, aquatic snails, fingernail clams, and mussels from Pleistocene deposits. Many of these are identical with living forms, but others extend the ranges of northern and southern species into Indiana.

The total estimate of over 3,000 invertebrates other than insects and parasites is comparable to that for Europe.[2] This may seem excessive in view of the far greater knowledge of the European fauna and the more varied habitats available, but the land and freshwater fauna of the central United States is notably rich and varied. Indiana, for example, certainly has more land and freshwater mollusks than all of Europe west of the Urals. It is probable that other groups will show a similar diversity, blending elements from northern and southern areas within the state.

Two phyla, the Brachiopoda and Echinodermata, missing from the list of present-day animals, are well represented in fossil deposits in Indiana. Many marine groups not now represented are also abundant as fossils. For example corals, marine mollusks, marine coelenterates, trilobites, and others. In fact, the majority of living and many extinct invertebrate types can be demonstrated by the teacher with material obtained within the confines of the state.

### Where and How to Find Free-Living Invertebrates

Finding free-living invertebrates is one of the simplest things possible. In some cases it is not even necessary to hunt them because they hunt you. Many such as the phalangids (grand-daddy longlegs), spiders, and plant-living mites are found running or sitting on tree trunks or other vegetation. Most invertebrates, however, conceal themselves beneath dead logs, stones, or in the leaf mold during the day. Many of the latter can easily be collected at night by the use of a headlight or jack light which can be purchased at sporting goods stores. At night the eyes of spiders and phalangids glow in the beam of the light, and they can be hunted down even in dense grass or other cover. Spiders may also be found near the edge of lighted areas where they prey upon insects attracted to the light.

Turning over logs and stones is usually very productive of invertebrates even in the winter. Here isopods, phalangids, spiders, diplopods, centipedes, symphylids, pauropods, snails, and annelid worms can be found in abundance. Raking up leaf mold or gravel, rolling up sphagnum moss, or breaking up stumps or logs are also good methods of collecting. Collections of leaves and other debris in the beds of small dried-up streams may yield aquatic as well as land types. Piling up leaf mold or debris and sprinkling it liberally with household ammonia will often drive out things whose presence was not even suspected.

For small invertebrates one of the best collecting tools is the Berlese funnel. As originally designed by the Italian entomologist Berlese, this was a large and elaborate device for extracting the small insects and other invertebrates from soil. The principle, however, can be applied with any size funnel. The large galvanized funnels sold in hardware stores are ideal for field use. They can be set in a gallon jar with a few ounces of alcohol or dilute formaldehyde in the bottom and leaf mold or other debris placed on a screen at the top of the funnel. Small organisms will begin to drop through into the liquid almost immediately and if care has been taken little debris will be mixed with them. Better results will usually be obtained by using larger funnels made up of sheet metal or of roofing paper which are kept in the laboratory. There the material can be left for several days and full advantage taken of the tendency for small animals to move downward as the leaf mold or soil dries. A lamp placed over the top of the funnel will speed this process. Sphagnum and other mosses, leaf mold, decaying grass cuttings, decayed wood, bracket or other fungi, soil, or almost any accumulation of debris in which small animals may hide are productive. Small spiders, centipedes, millipeds, proturans, tardigrades, small worms, mites, and even snails are easily caught in this manner with little effort on the part of the collector. If the specimens are wanted alive a dry jar can be substituted for one with liquid. However, this must be checked frequently or the carnivorous types eat all of the others so that only centipedes and spiders may be left.

Aquatic invertebrates can be collected by many methods. An ordinary coffee strainer or tea sieve is ideal for catching isopods, amphipods, crayfish, snails, and other larger types. Long handled nets can be used to reach jellyfish and other forms in deep quarries and lakes. Finer nets made of gauze or bolting silk are required to strain out small copepods, cladocera, ostracods, rotifers, gastrotrichs, and others. Dipping water with a cup or dipper into a cone of silk is a good way to work in a small puddle or pond. If the bottom is roiled up the debris blocks the net and also makes the animals hard to find later.

Protozoa, rotifers, and gastrotrichs can often be collected simply by bringing a gallon or two of water from a pond or stream into the laboratory. Some bottom debris and sediment, and samples of the aquatic vegetation, will include forms which ordinarily do not swim freely. Hydra can often be seen on the bottom in ponds and collected by picking up the debris to which they are attached with forceps. Bryozoa and other forms may also be seen in clear water or be found attached to sticks or stones lifted out of the water.

There are also many specialized methods of collecting specific organisms. Flatworms for example may be baited by putting small pieces of liver on strings in a pond or stream. Special nets and traps can be constructed for catching specific animals Gallon jars baited with meat and with a cone of screen wire inserted in the mouth will trap crayfish and other aquatic forms.

An interesting way of obtaining forms which live in deep water is to examine the stomach of fish or other vertebrates. Fish stomachs can be obtained from ice fishermen during the winter and sometimes yield an astounding number and diversity of small invertebrates.

## Culture Methods

Many protozoa and other small organisms can be raised in the laboratory by simply placing aquatic vegetation, bottom sediments, or debris in jars and allowing nature to take · its course. An interesting experiment is to extract a gallon of water and some mud from the bottom of a small pond in winter by cutting a hole in the ice. The sequence of animal and plant forms appearing from this material in an aquarium in the laboratory makes a fascinating study.

Some organisms are quite delicate, however, and special methods must be used to keep them alive. The methods are so diverse that those interested should consult Galtsoff, et al.[1] This book also gives helpful information on collecting.

## Identification of Invertebrates

The most difficult task faced by the teacher or research worker is the identification of the organisms with which he wants to work. In the free-living invertebrates this is particularly difficult because many groups have not been studied and others are so large and complex that only intensive study allows more than the roughest identification of species.

The following list is not intended to be exhaustive. It includes works which have proven useful to the writer and his colleagues. Where a group does not have a separate heading the best treatment is considered to be in one of the general works. The teacher, who requires only a tentative determination, may find the series of books entitled "How to Know the Protozoa", etc., from Wm. C. Brown, Dubuque, Iowa, more useful than more technical treatments.

### General Works

Eddy, S. and A. C. Hodson, 1961. Taxonomic keys to the common animals of the North Central States, exclusive of the parasitic worms, insects, and birds. Burgess, Minneapolis.

Grasse, P. P. (editor). 1952-1955. Traite de Zoologie, 17 vols. Masson & Cie, Paris.

Hyman, L. 1940-1959. The invertebrates, 5 vols. McGraw-Hill, New York.

Pennak, R. W. 1953. Fresh-water invertebrates of the United States. Ronald Press, New York.

Pratt, H. S. 1948. A manual of the common invertebrate animals (exclusive of insects). Blakiston, Philadelphia. (revised edition)

Ward, H. B. and G. C. Whipple. 1959. Fresh-water biology. Wiley, New York. (revised edition)

### General Soil and Leaf Mold Fauna

Kevan, D. K. McE. 1962. Soil animals. Philosophical Library, London.

Lawrence, R. F., 1953. The biology of the cryptic fauna of forests. A. A. Balkema, Cape Town and Amsterdam.

## Groups of Invertebrates
### Protozoa
Hall, R. P. 1953. Protozoology. Prentice-Hall, New York.
Kudo, R. R. 1960. Protozoology. Thomas, Springfield, Illinois. (revised edition)

### Porifera
Old, Marcus. 1932. Taxonomy and distribution of the fresh-water sponges (Spongillidae) of Michigan. Pap. Mich. Acad. Sci., Arts, and Let. 15:439-447.
Smith, Frank, 1921. Distribution of fresh water sponges of North America. Bull. Ill. State Lab. Nat. Hist. 14:11-22.

### Coelenterates
Hyman, L. H. 1931. Taxonomic studies on the hydras of North America. IV. Description of three new species with a key to the known species. Trans. Amer. Micros. Soc. 50:302-315.
Lytle, C. F. 1960. A note on distribution patterns in *Craspedacusta*. Trans. Amer. Micros. Soc. 79:461-469.
—————. 1961. Patterns of budding in the freshwater hydroid *Craspedacusta*. *in* The Biology of Hydra, Univ. of Miami Press, Miami, Florida.
Payne, F. 1924. A study of the fresh-water medusa, *Craspedacusta ryderi*. Jour. Morph. 38:387-430.

### Platyhelminthes
Hyman, L. H. 1951. Synopsis of the known species of fresh-water planarians of North America. Trans. Amer. Micros. Soc. 70:154-167.

### Aschelminthes
Goodey, J. B. 1963. Soil and freshwater nematodes. Metheun, London.

### Ectoprocta or Bryozoa
Davenport, C. B. 1904. Report on freshwater bryozoa of the U. S. Proc. U. S. Nat. Mus. 27:211-221.

### Annelida
Galloway, T. W. 1911. The common fresh-water Oligochaeta of the U. S. Trans. Amer. Micros. Soc. 30:285-317.
Mann, K. H. 1962. Leeches (Hirudinea). Their structure, physiology, ecology, and embryology. Pergamon Press, New York and London.
Miller, J. A. 1929. The leeches of Ohio. Franz. Theodore Stone Lab., Contrib. 2:1-38.
Moore, J. P. 1901. Hirudinea of Illinois. Bull. Ill. State Lab. Nat. Hist. 5:479.
Olson, H. W. 1928. The earthworms of Ohio. Ohio Biol. Surv. Bull. 17:45-90.
Stephenson, J. 1930. The Oligochaeta. Clarendon Press, Oxford, England.
Welch, P. S. 1914. Studies on the Enchytraeidae of North America. Bull. Ill. State Lab. Nat. Hist. 10:123-212.
—————. 1920. The genera of the Enchytraeidae. Trans. Amer. Micros. Soc. 39:25-50.

### Mollusca
Baker, F. C. 1945. The molluscan family Planorbidae. Univ. Illinois Press, Champaign-Urbana, Illinois.
—————. 1939. Field book of Illinois land snails. Ill. Nat. Hist. Survey, Urbana, Illinois.
Blatchley, W. S. and L. E. Daniels. 1903. On the molluscs of Indiana. 27th Ann. Rept. Ind. Dept. Geol. and Nat. Res., pp. 571-652.
Call, R. E. 1900. A descriptive catalogue of the Mollusca of Indiana. 24th Ann. Rept. Ind. Dept. Geol. and Nat. Res., pp. 335-535.
Goodrich, Calvin. 1932. The Mollusca of Michigan. Pub. Univ. Mich. Mus., Mich. Handb. Ser. 5.
Goodrich, Calvin and H. van der Schalie. 1944. A revision of the Mollusca of Indiana. Amer. Midl. Nat. 32:257-326.

*Arthropoda-General*

Brues, C. T., A. L. Melander, and F. M. Carpenter. 1954. Classification of insects: Keys to the living and extinct families of insects, and to the living families of other terrestrial arthropods. Bull. Mus. Comp. Zoology 108:1-917. (revised edition)

*Phyllopoda*

Creaser, C. W. 1930. Phyllopods of Michigan. Pap. Mich. Acad. Sci. 11:381-388.

Dexter, R. W. and C. H. Kuehnle. 1951. Further studies on the fairy shrimp populations of northeastern Ohio. Ohio Jour. Sci. 51:73-86.

Mackin, J. G. 1939. Key to the species of Phyllopoda of Oklahoma and neighbouring states. Proc. Okla. Acad. Sci. 19:45-47.

*Ostracoda*

Furtos, N. C. 1933. The Ostracoda of Ohio. Bull. Ohio Biol. Surv. 29:413-524.

Hoff, C. C. 1942. The ostracods of Illinois. Univ. Ill. Biol. Monogr. 19:1-196.

Tressler, W. L. 1947. A check list of the known species of North American freshwater Ostracoda. Amer. Midl. Nat. 38:698-707.

*Isopoda*

Eberly, W. R., 1953. The terrestial isopods (Oniscoidea) of Indiana. Proc. Indiana Acad. Sci. 63:272-277.

Hubricht, L. and J. G. Mackin. 1949. The freshwater isopods of the genus Lirceus (Asellota, Asellidae). Amer. Midl. Nat. 42:334-339.

Mackin, J. G. and L. Hubricht. 1940. Descriptions of seven new species of Caecidotea (Isopoda, Asellidae) from central United States. Trans. Amer. Micros. Soc. 59:383-397.

Richardson, Harriet. 1905. A monograph of the isopods of North America. Bull, U. S. Nat. Mus. 54:1-727.

Van Name, W. G. 1936. The American land and freshwater isopod Crustacea. Bull. Amer. Mus. Nat. Hist. 71:1-535.

——————————. 1940. A supplement to the American land and freshwater Isopoda. Bull. Amer. Mus. Nat. Hist. 77:109-142.

——————————. 1942. A second supplement to the American land and fresh-water isopod Crustacea. Bull. Amer. Mus. Nat. Hist. 80:299-329.

*Tardigrada*

Ramazzoti, G. 1962. Il Phylum Tardigrada. Mem. Dell'istituto Ital. di Idrobiologia 14:1-595.

*Cladocera*

Brooks, J. L. 1957. The systematics of North American Daphnia. Mem. Conn. Acad. Arts and Sci. 13:1-180.

Hoff, C. C. 1943. The Cladocera and Ostracoda of Reelfoot Lake. Jour. Tenn. Acad. Sci. 18:49-107.

Scourfield, D. J. and J. P. Harding. 1941. A key to the British species of freshwater Cladocera with notes on their ecology. Freshwater Biol. Assoc. British Empire, Sci. Publ. (ed. 2) 5:1-55.

*Copepoda*

Gurney, R. 1931-33. The British fresh-water Copepoda 2 vols. Ray Soc., London.

Marsh, C. D., 1907. A revision of the North American species of Diaptomus. Trans. Wis. Acad. Sci., Arts and Let. 15:381-516.

——————————. 1909. A revision of the North American species of Cyclops. Trans. Wis. Acad. Sci., Arts and Let. 16.

——————————. 1933. Synopsis of the calanoid crustaceans, exclusive of the Diaptomidae, found in fresh and brackish-waters, chiefly of North America. Pros. U. S. Nat. Mus., 82:1-58.

Wilson, C. B. 1932. The copepods of the Woods Hole Region, Massachusetts. U. S. Nat. Mus. Bull. 158:1-635.

Yeatman, H. C. 1944. American cyclopoid copepods of the viridis-vernalis group (including a description of Cyclops carolinianus, n. sp.) Amer. Midl. Nat. 32:1-90.

*Amphipoda*

Gaylor, D. 1922. A study of the life history and productivity of Hyalella knickerbockeri Bate. Proc. Indiana Acad. Sci. (1921) :239-250.

Hubricht,, L. 1943. Studies on the Nearctic freshwater Amphipoda. III. Notes on the freshwater Amphipoda of Eastern United States with descriptions of ten new species. Amer. Midl. Nat. 29:683-712.

Hubricht, L. and J. G. Mackin. 1940. Descriptions of nine new species of fresh-water amphipod crustaceans with notes and new localities for other species. Amer. Midl. Nat. 23:187-218.

Weckel, A. L. 1907. The freshwater Amphipoda of North America. Proc. U. S. Nat. Mus. 32:25-58.

*Decapoda*

Hobbs, H. H., Jr. 1942. A generic revision of the crayfishes of the Subfamily Cambarinae (Decapodae, Astacidae) with the description of a new genus and species. Amer. Midl. Nat. 28:334-357.

Turner, C. L. 1926. The crayfishes of Ohio. Bull. Ohio Biol. Surv. 13: 145-195.

*Acarina*

Baker, E. W. and G. W. Wharton. 1952. An introduction to acarology. Macmillan, New York.

Baker, E. W., et al. 1958. Guide to the families of mites. Institute of Acarology, Contrib. No. 3:1-242.

Banks, Nathan. 1908. A revision of the Ixodoidea, or ticks, of the United States. U. S. Dept. Agric., Tech. Ser. 15:1-61.

*Araneida*

Comstock, J. H. and W. J. Gertsch. 1948. The Spider book. Comstock, Ithaca, New York (revised edition).

Kaston, B. J. 1948. Spiders of Connecticut. Bull. Conn. State Geol. and Nat. Hist. Survey No. 70:1-874.

*Phalangida*

Bishop, S. C. 1949. The Phalangida (Opiliones) of New York. Proc. Rochester Acad. Sci. 9:159-235.

Walker, M. E. 1928. A revision of the order of Phalangida of Ohio. Bull. Ohio Biol. Surv. 19:153-175.

*Scorpionida*

Ewing, H. E. 1928. Scorpions of the western United States. Proc. U. S. Nat. Mus. 73:1-24.

Hoffman, C. C. 1932. Los Scorpiones de Mexico. An Inst. Biol. Mexico 3:243-282.

*Chelonethida* or *Pseudoscorpionida*

Chamberlin, J. C. 1938. The arachnid order Chelonethida. Stanford Univ. Pub. Biol. Ser. 7:1-284.

*Pauropoda*

Bagnall, R. S. 1935. Classification of Pauropoda. Ann. Mag. Nat. Hist. 16:619-629.

Starling, J. H. 1943. Pauropoda from the Duke Forest, with list of known species. Proc. Ent. Soc. Wash. 45:183-200.

*Diplopoda*

Chamberlin, R. V. and R. L. Hoffman. 1958. Checklist of the millipeds of North America. Bull. U. S. Nat. Mus. 212:1-236. (Contains complete bibliographic references and localities known.)

*Chilopoda*

Bailey, J. W. 1928. Chilopoda of New York state. Bull. New York State Mus. No. 276:1-50.

*Symphyla*

Hilton, W. A. 1931. Symphyla from North America. Ann. Ent. Soc. Amer. 24:537-552.

Michelbacher, A. E. 1939. Notes on Symphyla. Ann. Ent. Soc. Amer. 32:747-757.
——————. 1941. Two new genera of Symphyla. Ann. Ent. Soc. Amer. 34:139-150.
——————. 1942. Synopsis of Scutigerella. Ann. Ent. Soc. Amer. 35:267-288.
——————. 1943. Genera of Symphyla new to the United States. Ann. Ent. Soc. Amer. 36:139.150.

For exact determination of an organism, it is suggested that Pennak, Pratt, or Brues, Melander and Carpenter be consulted first. From there one should go on to the research papers in journals, monographs, and books. Few groups have been exhaustively studied for any area in the United States, but the larger and more conspicuous an organism is the more likely it is to have an extensive bibliography. Abstracting and indexing journals such as Biological Abstracts and Zoological Record should be consulted for recent work.

## 101 Things to Do With Invertebrates

The number of demonstration and research projects which can be undertaken with profit on Indiana invertebrates is almost infinite. They are limited only by the imagination and ingenuity of the teacher or investigator. The following suggestions attempt to point out areas in which information is deficient or types of experiments which can be undertaken in the school laboratory to demonstrate biological principles. There is no real distinction between these two types of activity. Research may aid in teaching, and laboratory demonstrations may be extended into research projects.

*Surveys:* Those who find the diversity of organisms interesting will think immediately of making surveys of the kinds of organisms in different habitats. In planning a survey be careful to limit it so that it can be finished in a finite time. An attempt to survey all the invertebrates in a pond, lake, stream, bog swamp, or woodland is doomed at the beginning because the investigator is simply overcome and discouraged by the mass of organisms accumulated. Some surveys of limited scope are: 1) protozoa of pitcher plants of Indiana bogs (2) comparison of micro-invertebrates of water filled treeholes in virgin and second growth forests (3) invertebrates associated with skunk cabbage flowers *(Symplocarpus foetidus* (L.) Nutt.) 4) invertebrates found in sand along streams (the psammon habitat) (5) mites associated with birds' nests 6) a quantitive comparison (by families) of the invertebrates of various types of forest leaf mold (7) comparison of Crustacea found in intermittent and small permanent streams (8) distribution of land snails in a small forest tract (9) micro-invertebrates of mosses and lichens growing on trees (10) protozoa (and algae) found by filtering city drinking water (11) invertebrates found in sidewalk cracks in urban and suburban areas.

Surveys have the advantage of requiring little equipment. Most of the types suggested above can be carried out using Berlese funnels, home-made nets, or simple culture methods. Surveys have the distinct disadvantage that to be scientifically worthwhile the determination of specimens must be complete and accurate. As demonstrations of principles, however, they may be carried on with no identification at all. Specimens may simply be sorted into groups of like individuals and numbered. Even elementary classes, however, can learn to recognize major groups and separate them.

*Population Studies:* A number of kinds of invertebrates lend themselves to population studies using the marking-releasing-recollecting technique. For example, (12) snails in a woodland area can be marked with colored fingernail polish and released. The next day or later a second collection should contain a number of marked individuals. It is then easy to calculate the local population on the basis of the equation $N = \dfrac{MC}{R}$ where N is total population, M is number of individuals marked, C is number caught during recapture period, and R is number of marked individuals recaptured. This method may be applied with varying success to other invertebrates such as, (13) snails in a small pond, (14) isopods in a small stream, or (15) crayfish in a stream, pond, or cave. This sort of study can also yield information on home ranges, preferred habitats, migration, and other phenomena.

Population growth, competition, and predation can be studied using *Paramecium* and other protozoa. Several species of *Paramecium* can usually be found by taking dead vegetation from a small pond or puddle in the fall. Pure cultures can be established by using baked lettuce-boiled water or boiled hay infusions into which individual protozoans are transferred with a micropipette made by drawing out an ordinary eye-dropper in a flame. (16) A simple growth curve for a single kind of *Paramecium* can be determined by daily (or preferably more frequent) counting under a binocular dissecting microscope when they are grown in small depression slides. Larger cultures require sampling with measured pipettes and use of a haemocytometer or other counting grid. (17) Comparison of different species makes an interesting study while (18) the same species can be studied under different temperatures, amounts of salts in the medium, or conditioned media (those in which protozoa have already been grown) compared with newly made media. (19) Comparisons may also be made between different species grown alone and in the same culture as a measure of competition. (20) The ciliate *Dydinium* which is often found with *Paramecium* can be injected into cultures to demonstrate the effect of predation.

*Genetic and Evolutionary Studies:* Genetic studies with Protozoa and other invertebrates can be made with considerable ease except that pure lines and considerable time is required. (21) One of the simplest demonstrations is that of the inheritance of mating types for which material of *Paramecium* can be obtained from supply houses. (22) Demonstration of the inheritance of Kappa particles in *Paramecium* is possible, but it is difficult to obtain the necessary strains.

Almost any invertebrate which can be reared in pure culture will show variation and genetic experiments can be made by segregating and interbreeding variants. This, however, may take a considerable amount of time, and simple Mendelian ratios are not to be expected from crossing specimens taken directly from the wild or with characters which are inherited on a quantitative basis. Invertebrates which are easily cultured and for which there is little genetic information on most species include (23) *Daphnia*, (24) *Cyclops*, (25) aquatic isopods, (26) ostracods, (27) various species of *Planaria*, (28) rotifers, (29) some plant feeding mites (Acarina), and (30) aquatic snails.

*Physiological and Behavioral Studies:* A number of types of experiments and demonstrations of physiological and behavioral adjustments can be undertaken with invertebrates with relatively simple equipment. (31) Aquatic isopods exposed to the air show distinctive reactions to moisture gradients as do (32) terrestrial isopods. Gradients can be maintained by using various solutions of sulphuric acid or other substances as given in tables in handbooks of chemistry. Physiological adjustments to various concentrations of salts can be studied in (33) *Daphnia,* (34) *Paramecium,* and (35) *Hydra.* Light reactions are also beautifully shown by (36) *Daphnia.* (36) The reaction of *Paramecium* and other ciliates to a weak electric current can be demonstrated with a six volt lantern battery and copper wire. (37) The reaction of *Planaria* and other animals to such stimuli can also be studied. Other taxes and kineses of small animals can be studied with simple devices such as (38) thigmotaxis in amphipods, (39) geotaxis in leaf mold invertebrates and (40) phototaxis in many kinds of small invertebrates. In such experiments, however, one must be careful to control the other factors which may affect the behavior.

*Descriptive Behavior:* Observations on the behavior of almost any invertebrate can be of interest and scientific value. The difficulty is to reproduce in the laboratory conditions under which the organisms behave normally, or to continue observations in the field over any prolonged period. Some invertebrates on which observations on mating behavior can be made are (41) spiders, any species, (42) millipeds, (43) centipedes, (44) mites, many species, and (44) land snails. (44-50) Many other activities of intevertebrates are worth observation such as burrowing, nest or web building, oviposition, attitude toward or care of young, and predator-prey relationships.

In the school laboratory many observations are excellent for demonstrating principles. For example, *Hydra* can be observed in regard to (51) engulfing prey, (52) reactions in contact with different kinds of prey, (53) size of prey which can be engulfed, (54) effect of salt or other chemicals on acceptance of prey, and (55) relation of time to feeding.

*Regeneration Experiments:* A number of Indiana animals are suitable for regeneration experiments. (56) The planarian *Dugesia* is ideal for showing the effect of cephalization. It can be cut up into quite small pieces and still regenerate. (57) Various earthworms show regeneration, although some experimentation is necessary to find suitable local species. With those that show regeneration, pieces can be cut off from the body, sections removed and the ends sewed back, and many other experiments performed. (58) *Hydra* is also good material on which to study regeneration. With suitable instruments very interesting experiments can be performed besides simply clipping off the stalk. For example, with care pieces can be transplanted from one *Hydra* to another and by using those containing commensal algae and others without the algae the effects of the transplants can easily be studied. Regeneration experiments with Protozoa are also possible. (59) Dr. Vance Tartar was able to obtain different portions of the cells of *Euglena* by whirling a stick beset with numerous razor blades in a thick culture. The pieces desired were then picked out and placed in separate cultures and the results observed. (60) With some of the larger amoebae, the cell can be divided by cutting with a razor blade by hand. (61) Some of the more refined techniques such as removing the nucleus from an amoeba and inserting it into another cell are possible with proper equipment.

*Life History Studies:* Ecological life histories in which the stages of organisms are correlated with the conditions under which they live are needed in every group of invertebrates. Some of the organisms which have not been extensively studied under Indiana conditions include (62) sponges, (63) numerous rotifers, (64) gastrotrichs, (65) numerous soil inhabiting nematodes, (66) millipedes, (67) many mites, (68) Symphyla, (69) Pauropoda, (70) moss animals, (71) the fresh-water Nemertean, (72) some *Planaria* and many other flat-worms, (73) numerous spiders, (74) amphipods, (75) isopods, and many others.

Various aspects of the life histories of invertebrates may be made the subjects of comparative studies. For example, (76) diapause and factors relating to it in eggs of fairy shrimp (Phyllopoda), (77) overwintering habits of land snails, (78) reactions to drought and its relation to overwintering in soil organisms, (79) conditions of hatching of spider eggs, and (80) relation of temperature to growth and reproduction in aquatic invertebrates.

*Cytology and Embryology:* Cytology and embryology are subjects which can be investigated readily in many invertebrates. Usually, however, they require a considerably greater background and preparation than other types of research.

(81) Determination of the chromosome numbers of different species may be relatively easy using aceto-carmine and aceto-orcein stains. Oil emersion optics are required, and one must be prepared to spend a considerable amount of time in looking at preparations. Some groups in which worthwhile results might be expected are (82) various species of snails, (83) flatworms, (84) leeches, and (85) the myriapod groups.

Embryological studies require special techniques for fixing, embedding, sectioning and staining materials, but once these are perfected very gratifying results may be obtained. Gross observations can be made in some forms, however, where the eggs are exposed as in (86) the leeches and (87) aquatic and (88) terrestrial isopods. Little experimental embryology has been done with invertebrates and (89) transplant, (90) excision, and (91) vital staining experiments might prove exciting. Detailed studies of classical embryology are needed in some groups such as (92) the Myrientomata or Protura, (93) the tardigrades, and (94) gastrotrichs. (95) Comparative embryology of genera and species should also prove profitable.

*Bioassay, Medical, and Control Experiments*: The possibilities for using invertebrates in these areas are unlimited. (96) Spiders are now being studied as indicators of the effects of various psychotherapeutic drugs. The effects of the drugs can be assayed by their effect on web spinning activities. (97) The effects on mammals of the venom of such common Indiana pests as the fiddle-back spider *(Loxosceles)* have not been thoroughly investigated. The use of mice for such work would also allow (98) experiments on effectiveness of treatments. Much more work is needed on insecticides to be used against such human pests as (99) chigger mites and (100) ticks.

Finally, (101) the whole area of the influence of invertebrates on human culture is a grossly neglected field. We say that the wasp potters may have been an inspiration to early man to create pottery. Did the crayfish chimney have any effect? What about the nets of spiders? Did they inspire early man to think of weaving seines and nets for fishes and birds? Or, more basically, what were the roles of edible invertebrates such as crayfish, mussels, and snails in the life of the Indians or even the early white settlers in Indiana?

## LITERATURE

1. GALTSOFF, P. S., F. E. LUTZ, P. S. WELCH, and J. G. NEEDHAM. 1937. Culture methods for invertebrate animals. Dover Publishing Co., New York (reprint).
2. GISLEN, T. 1940. The number of animal species in Sweden with remarks on some rules of distribution especially of the microfauna. Lunds Univ. Arsskrift, N. F. Avd. 2, Bd. 36:1-23

# 19

# *Animal Parasites*

R. M. CABLE

Purdue University

In the zoological sense, parasitism is a form of symbiosis, a relationship in which a smaller animal is obliged to live on or in the body of a larger one. Fortunately, the guest is often a commensal or messmate which does its host no apparent harm, and sometimes the relationship is even mutualistic with each dependent on the other. Less happy is the more frequent situation in which the guest is truly parasitic and causes the host injury. Unlike predators, parasites are insidious in their approach but the host-parasite relationship often is so well adjusted that the host can tolerate an unbelievable burden of parasites and yet forfeit its life slowly, if at all.

Because there are far more parasitic animals than hosts and almost every animal species large enough to support parasites has them, a survey of the natural features of Indiana, or of any political or geographic unit for that matter, would be decidedly incomplete were the indigenous parasites not taken into consideration. Yet there is no reason why the parasite fauna of Indiana should differ from that of any other state with comparable physiography and population densities of potential host species with similar habits. Certainly parasites in the northern lake region are more like those of southern Michigan than the ones in the more heavily forested southern part of the State with its rocky streams. Even with prolonged isolation, parasites may change more slowly than do their hosts. For example, an intestinal worm that is common in the shovel-nosed sturgeon of the Wabash River is so similar to one in a different sturgeon in Russia that the two parasites can scarcely be told apart.[2] Moreover, neither has been reported elsewhere in any fish.

In exploiting new territories, man alters the parasitological picture as well as the landscape. A case in point is malaria that made parts of Indiana notoriously unhealthful for early settlers. But well before the role of mosquitoes in transmitting the malarial parasite was known, the clearing and drainage of

land for agriculture reduced the swampy breeding places of
the important vector mosquito to the extent that with the later
screening of houses, malaria has practically disappeared from
the State. That mosquito is still with us but not in sufficient
numbers and with the opportunity to bite enough people to
sustain an epidemic. Now and then, small outbreaks occur as
happened in Vigo County in 1938. That outbreak may have
been seeded by the then common practice of treating syphilitic
patients by deliberately infecting them with malaria.[8] Also,
rainy weather and highway construction at the time caused
prolonged standing water containing perhaps none of the minnows which are the natural enemies of mosquito larvae and
keep them in check in permanent bodies of standing water.
At present, a greater threat than malaria in Indiana is enceph-
alitis, a virus disease transmitted by mosquitoes other than
the species which serves the malarial parasite.[10]

Nearly every phylum of animals contains parasitic species
but the majority are in three large categories: (1) the protozoa or monocellular animals; (2) the helminths or worms
which are mostly in three phyla; and (3) the arthropods
which include the crustaceans, insects, ticks and mites.

## Protozoa

In the protozoa, the Class Sporozoa contains only parasitic
species. Among them are the gregarines which are common in
our invertebrates, especially annelids and arthropods; the coc-
cidians some of which cause destructive diseases of birds and
mammals; the malarial parasites of birds as well as man; and
the cnidosporidians of which some infect invertebrates and
others are responsible for tumors that can be found at will in
our fishes.

Parasites of several types occur in the large group of protozoa known as flagellates. Among them are the trypanosomes
which live in blood of vertebrates of all classes and are transmitted by blood-sucking invertebrates. Fortunately those indigenous to Indiana include only such non-pathogenic trypanosomes as a species in rats, transmitted by fleas, and another
common in sheep and spread by the so-called sheep "tick."
More abundant are the intestinal flagellates and related species
which are common in both vertebrates and invertebrates of
the State. Most are harmless, but a species of *Giardia* causes

diarrhea in man and has been found in 2% of the patients in one of the state mental hospitals.[7] A similar flagellate has been accused of causing an acute enteritis which destroyed entire flocks of turkeys in Dearborn County some years ago and has since appeared sporadically elsewhere. The outbreaks in Dearborn County were followed by one of blackhead, a less destructive but still important disease associated with another flagellate which gets from bird to bird while enclosed in the egg of a common worm parasite of poultry.[4]

Three species of flagellates known as trichomonads parasitize man. The intestinal species has been found in Indiana but much more common is another type which lives in the male prostate and female vagina, and causes a troublesome vaginitis. Abortion in cattle has been attributed to a similar trichomonad in the reproductive organs of bulls and cows. A trichomonad is associated with atrophic rhinitis leading to deformed nasal structure in swine, and another species causes a severe canker of the mouth, throat and crop of birds, especially doves, and is contacted by hawks from infected prey.

A more homogeneous group of protozoan parasites includes the amebae. All six of the species that infect man have been found in Indiana, and no doubt those parasitizing other vertebrates are abundant here. The only species pathogenic in man causes amebic dysentery when it invades and ulcerates the large intestine, or amebic abscesses by migrating from that site to others, especially the liver and lungs. Most people harboring the infection show no symptoms, and it was demonstrated by research in the State that the ameba must be accompanied by at least one other type of microorganism for dysentery to occur.[12]

Much less important than other protozoa are the ciliates. The rumen and large intestine of herbivores teem with species that are the most complex of all protozoa; some of them may be mutualistic. Potentially dangerous to man is a ciliate that is a harmless parasite of our pigs. But in the human intestine, it can cause a severe disease resembling amebic dysentery. Human infections are rare in the U.S. but more common in countries where people live more intimately with their pigs than is to our liking. A ciliate that we encounter often is one that invades the skin of fish to cause a disease known as "ick" and especially destructive of fishes confined to aquaria.

## Helminths

Parasitic worms are of four major types: the trematodes or flukes, the cestodes or tapeworms, the acanthocephala or thorny-headed worms, and the nematodes. All are abundantly represented in the State, especially as parasites of wild and domesticated animals. Most trematodes are of the digenetic type with complex life cycles that require a mollusk as an intermediate host, a vertebrate final host, and usually a second intermediate host as well. Animals serving each of these capacities are abundant and varied in Indiana whose especially rich molluscan fauna probably is not exceeded in any other state, and is reflected in a comparably rich trematode fauna. Among the species whose life cycles have been demonstrated here are such unusual trematodes as the turtle lung fluke which has a family all to itself,[3] and a species that occurs in Tippecanoe River catfish and is the only member of its large family that is known to mature in a fish.[13] The same is true of another fluke in our catfish, and it has the added distinction of living in the ovaries, and of being the only trematode of any kind reported to be an intracellular parasite at *any* stage of the life cycle. After reaching the catfish, young worms have been observed inside the eggs and mature ones are commonly seen through the wall of the ovary as dark spots which actually are only the uteri of the worms filled with thousands of eggs.[11]

Despite their abundance, trematodes are of little importance in human or veterinary medicine in the State. A species common in the oviduct of our red-winged blackbirds has been accused of causing reduced egg production and the laying of malformed eggs in poultry. A lung fluke that we see occasionally in dogs and cats is so much like one parasitizing man in the Orient that it would be decidedly risky to eat raw crayfish, the second intermediate host. The same is true also of certain other trematodes, notably mammalian liver flukes that are obtained by eating uncooked fish. Trematodes known as blood flukes parasitize fish, turtles, birds and mammals of the State but require no fondness for raw food because their larvae leave the snail host and bore directly into the final host to grow to adults in the blood stream. Fortunately, none that menace human life is established in the U.S. but the larvae of species common in certain of our birds and mammals can enter the human skin but they die there and cause a severe rash and discomfort known as swimmer's itch. This unpleasantness is most likely to be encountered in our northern lakes which favor pulmonate snails and attract the natural vertebrate hosts as well as vacationists.

Monogenetic trematodes have direct life cycles requiring only a vertebrate host. They are commonly found anchored to the gills and skin of our fishes and certain amphibians, and to the lining of the mouth or bladder of frogs and turtles. Unlike most digenetic trematodes, these parasites are highly specific for their vertebrate hosts.

Adult tapeworms occur in all classes of vertebrates in the State and require intermediate hosts except for the dwarf tapeworm of man and rodents. It can be obtained by eating either an insect intermediate host or the eggs passed by the vertebrate host. They contain larvae which hatch in the intestine of the vertebrate, enter villi to undergo the same development that otherwise occurs in intermediate hosts, and then re-enter the intestine to grow to adult worms.

Tapeworms are adept at taking advantage of predator-prey situations, and feeding habits of the host. Thus few dogs except the most sheltered pets escape a kind of tapeworm obtained by eating fleas, and dogs that are permitted much freedom obtain another species by eating rabbits. A similar species profits by cats' fondness for rat and mouse liver, and herbivores obtain certain tapeworms from the arthropods they eat along with grass. From these and other examples that could be cited, it is not surprising that the commonest large tapeworm of man in Indiana lurks in rare steaks. Another obtained from pork is decidedly rare here, as also is a species imported in Scandinavian immigrants with a fondness for uncooked fish, and well established in states farther north. Five cases have been reported in Indiana; three were in Jewish people including two housewives who admitted to seasoning *Gefülltefisch* to taste before cooking it.[6, 9]

The thorny-headed worms are intestinal parasites of all classes of vertebrates and have arthropod intermediate hosts. Best known is the giant species that pigs get by eating beetle grubs. For some unkown reason, only turtles of the Western Hemisphere harbor acanthocephala. Three and probably four of the five known species occur in our turtles, sometimes in fantastic numbers.[5]

From the economic standpoint, nematodes are by far the most important worm parasites in the State. Besides those parasitizing plants, many more species infect a variety of animals, vertebrate and invertebrate. Most of them do not utilize intermediate hosts but notable exceptions are swine lung-worms and fowl gapeworms which along with the spiruroids are obtained by eating intermediate hosts. Also, the filarioids as a group are transmitted by blood-sucking intermediate hosts, and include such parasites as the dog heartworm which is transmitted by mosquitoes and a species that we commonly find in the body cavity of crows.

Nematodes of the type known as pinworms occur in various mammals. The human pinworm probably infects more people in Indiana than do all other worms combined, probably because contact with food or soil is not required to obtain the infection. Instead, the female migrates from the rectum to lay her eggs which are picked up on the fingers and clothing to become widely scattered in households. Understandably, pinworms are especially prevalent in children.

Trichinosis, a common disease of carnivorous and omnivorous mammals, is due to one of the smallest parasitic nematodes, and man becomes infected by eating improperly cooked pork containing the young worms in cysts. Liberated in the intestine, the worms grow to sexual maturity and the females deposit larvae which migrate to striated muscles, penetrate their fibers, and become encysted after a time. Severity of the disease varies with the number of cysts eaten because each female produces a limited number of larvae, and symptoms are due to their entering the muscle fibers. To judge from surveys in other states by examinations following death from all causes, probably at least 20% of the people in Indiana contract the infection sometime during their lives. Related nematodes include the whipworms in the large intestine of mammals and species that localize in other parts of various birds and mammals. One sometimes causes losses in quail by invading the crop in such numbers that its wall literally becomes a feltwork of worms.

Another large group of nematodes includes the hookworms and their allies. Although human infections are rare in the

State, domesticated and wild animals harbor many species. Included are such well known parasites as hookworms, stomach worms, nodule worms and lungworms of mammals and gapeworms of birds. Also common in our birds and mammals are the ascarid nematodes. Opinions differ as to whether those of man and pigs are distinct species, and it is often said that man is resistant to the pig strain. However, several instances of human infection in the Lafayette region seem attributable only to a swine source. Most of them occurred in a large housing development constructed where pig lots had been. After it was occupied, children living there passed adult ascarids from time to time for about five years. Eggs of the worms are notoriously long-lived and resistant to environmental factors; we have had them live as long as eight years in feces preserved in formalin.

### Arthropods

From the economic standpoint, least important of the parasitic arthropods in Indiana are the crustaceans which include mostly parasites of fishes but some of them are of much zoological interest because of their extreme modification in adaptation to parasitism. More important is the class of arthropods containing the ticks which are so well known as to require no further comment, and the mites most familiar of which is the common chigger. Other parasitic ones include the blood-sucking mites of birds and mammals, hair-clasping mites, species that invade the lungs and other body passages, and those that enter the skin to cause the various manges of birds and mammals.

The largest of all arthropod classes, the Insecta, is well represented by parasitic species in Indiana. In that class, species of the Order Diptera illustrate the full range of the duration and intimacy of the host-parasite relationship from the "hit and run" tactics of mosquitoes, blackflies, stable flies and horseflies to the louseflies that rarely leave their hosts. The sheep lousefly or ked has become so modified that it is sometimes mistaken for a tick. A parallel situation exists among fly larvae or maggots. Some, ordinarily scavengers, are facultatively parasitic in the intestine or may invade necrotic tissue, and one, the screwworm, invades the flesh of sheep and cattle, causing heavy losses in the South and occasionally working its

way into Indiana by late summer. The other extreme is seen
in such well known parasites as the ox warble, sheep nose bot,
horse stomach bot and the large black warble commonly seen
in rodents and occasionally in pets. These are larvae of flies
whose adults are unable to feed and are sustained by nourishment obtained parasitically during their larval period.

The fleas which comprise another order of insects are well
represented in the State. Relatively a newcomer is the tropical
rat or plague flea, found in Indianapolis some 41 years ago as
the first inland record in the U.S. Since then, it has been collected elsewhere in the State, once by the hundreds from rats
in Lafayette.[1] This species is of concern because it is the most
important transmitter of bubonic plague from rodent reservoirs to man and that disease is widespread in rodents from
the West Coast to the plains states.

Among the true bugs, we of course have the common bedbug
which needs no further comment, and the so-called kissing
bugs that inflict painful bites occur in the southernmost part
of the State. Thus far, none has been found infected with the
trypanosome of Chaga's disease in Indiana. That situation will
bear watching because infected animal reservoirs potentially
dangerous to man have been found as far north as Maryland.

Unlike fleas and bugs, the lice are highly host specific,
whether of the chewing type predominantly parasites of birds,
or the blood-sucking lice which are even more partial to mammals. The human body louse or cootie prefers the clothing to
body hair and therefore has suffered from modern laundry
and dry cleaning practices, but has a friend in migrant labor.
More widespread is the crab or pubic louse but commonest of
all is the head louse even though we do not regard it as Tibet-
ans do in their expression of felicity, "May your hat always be
inhabited!"

Some parasitic insects of other orders, especially the Hymenoptera, are beneficial in that they aid in the control of
other insects. A familiar example is a species whose larvae
destroy caterpillars and then spin cocoons attached to the surface of their victims as commonly seen in the large tomato or
tobacco worm.

\*　　　\*　　　\*

Parasites play a major part in the balance of Nature by
keeping host populations in check, and are beneficial from the

human standpoint when such host populations compete with man for his food and fiber. However, the conquest of disease has played an important part in the human population explosion, and to survive, man finds it necessary to crowd more and more of his domestic plants and animals to the acre and then use every conceivable means to protect them from epidemics of their own diseases that intensive agriculture invites. It is safe to predict that the second sesquicentennial year of Indiana's history will find that problem still with us. The prospect for parasites of wildlife is less certain and will depend on the fate of their hosts.

## LITERATURE

1. CABLE, R. M. 1943. The Indian rat flea, *Xenopsylla cheopis*, in Indiana. Proc. Ind. Acad. Sci. **52**:201-202.
2. _____ 1955. Taxonomy of some digenetic trematodes from sturgeons. J. Parasit. **41**:441.
3. CRANDALL, R. B. 1960. The life history and affinities of the turtle lung fluke, *Heronimus chelydrae* MacCallum, 1902. J. Parasit. **46**:289-307.
4. DOYLE, L. P., R. M. CABLE, and H. E. MOSES. 1947. A destructive turkey disease. J. Am. Vet. Med. Assn. **111**:57-60.
5. FISHER, F. M. 1960. On acanthocephala of turtles with the description of *Neoechinorhynchus emyditoides* n. sp. J. Parasit. **46**:257-266.
6. HEADLEE, W. H., J. M. KMECZA, and R. M. CABLE. 1939. Report of a native case of infection by the fish tapeworm, *Diphyllobothrium latum*. J. Ind. State Med. Assn. **32**:188-189.
7. HOPP, W. B. 1944. On the epidemiology of human intestinal parasite infections in a state hospital of Indiana. Am. J. Hyg. **39**:138-144.
8. JACKSON, J. W. 1939. Malaria in Indiana. J. Ind. State Med. Assn. **32**:305-308.
9. LYON, M. W. 1930. The fish tapeworm and its occurrence in Indiana. J. Ind. State Med. Assn. **23**:72-75.
10. MARSHALL, A. L. 1957. Beware of that mosquito. Monthly Bull. Indiana. State Bd. Health **59**:10-11.
11. PERKINS, K. W. 1956. Studies on the morphology and biology of *Acetodextra amiuri* (Stafford) (Trematoda:Heterophyidae). Am. Midl. Nat. **55**:139-161.
12. PHILLIPS, B. P., P. A. WOLFE, and I. L. BARTGIS. 1958. Studies on the ameba-bacteria relationship in amebiasis II. Some concepts on the etiology of the disease. Am. J. Trop. Med. Hyg. **7**:392-399.
13. STANG, J. C., and R. M. CABLE. 1966. The life history of *Holostephanus ictaluri* Vernberg, 1952 (Trematoda:Digenea), and immature stages of other North American freshwater cyathocotylids. Am. Midl. Nat. **75**:

# 20

# The Origin and Composition
# of the Insect Fauna

LELAND CHANDLER

Purdue University

It would be desirable to begin our study of the insect fauna of Indiana at that point in geological time when the area became emergent and a terrestrial biota became established. Unfortunately, the fossil record required for such an undertaking is hopelessly fragmentary. We do know that it was during the Carboniferous period when the marine waters began to recede; and, during the latter part of this period, the Pennsylvanian, that Indiana became a terrestrial area.

Most of our information regarding the conditions of this time has come from fossil deposits located in adjacent states, such as Mazon Creek, Illinois, and similar sites. We may expect some additional evidences from the strip mine excavations in the vicinity of Terre Haute. The land was apparently quickly covered by a luxuriant forest growth with many kinds of insects present. Two species of insects, *Paolia gurleyi* Scudder and *P. vetusta* Smith, have been described from fossils taken near Paoli in Orange County. These insects belonged to the extinct order Paleodictyoptera. Although this assemblage of insects became extinct during the more rigorous Permian Period which followed, it is interesting to note the striking similarity between the cockroaches of the Pennsylvanian and the native woodroaches which occur in Indiana today.[13]

From the Pennsylvanian until recent historical time we have only "landmark" fossil evidences from widespread localities. While these data are relatively adequate for gross explanations, they contribute little to our understanding of the Indiana fauna. Therefore, we must utilize other analytical methods to bring this picture into focus. In our discussion we have used four primary approaches as applied to selected insect groups: 1) the biogeographic data of distribution; 2) the phylogenetic (evolutionary) relationships; 3) the ecological amplitudes of species cited; and 4) the historical records indicating changes in ranges.

It is a paradox that the period of Pleistocene glaciation both complicated and simplified various aspects of distributional analysis. The insect fauna now present in the glaciated area had to move into this area after the ice sheet had receded. The influence of glaciation on the biota of the adjacent unglaciated region is a controversial subject.

Recognizing that there are about 20,000 different kinds of insects in Indiana, most of these poorly-known, we have selected groups to illustrate patterns and principles. By both our inclusions and omissions, we hope to provide the stimulus for continued studies of faunal dynamics. It must also be pointed out that distributional patterns of organisms are not stable, that ranges expand and contract, there are invasions and recessions, there is origin and extinction.

## Faunistic Areas

### Distribution of Orthoptera

Four years after Merriam[8] published his famous life zone paper, Blatchley[1] modified the Merriam concept as it applied to Indiana. Utilizing the evidences from the distribution of Orthoptera, Blatchley defined and characterized the life zones of the state. Accordingly, he recognized the Upper Austral Zone as covering the entire state with 93 of 148 species of Orthoptera belonging to the Carolinian fauna; the Transition Zone (Alleghanian Fauna) overlapping the three northern tiers of counties with 23 representative species; and, the Lower Austral Zone, with 32 species characteristic of the Austroriparian fauna, occurring south of a line from Vigo County to Switzerland County.

Concerning the Lower Austral Zone, Blatchley commented that the northern boundary was remarkably coincident with the southern boundary of glaciation. He also postulated that the ancestors of many of these southern forms existed in Indiana in preglacial times. On this second point both Webster[19] and Thomas[17] concur, the latter giving a number of examples which not only support a preglacial existence but existence during glaciation in areas adjacent to the glacial edge.

Orthopteran species cited by Blatchley as being characteristic of the Lower Austral Zone were (selected by us from his list) : the dark woodroach, *Ischnoptera deropeltiformis* (Brunner) ; the lesser two-lined walking stick, *Anisomorpha ferruginea* (P.d.B.) ; the Carolina leafroller, *Camptonotus caroliniensis* (Gers.) ; and, the handsome tree cricket, *Phyllopalpus pulchellus* (Uhler). Excluded from this list are the grizzled mantid, *Gonatista grisea* (Fab.), an obvious introduction; the Carolina mantid, *Stagmomantis carolina* (L.), and the ant-loving cricket, *Myrmecophila pergandei* Brun., both of which now occur throughout much or all of the state. To his list, however, may be added: the social cockroach, *Cryptocercus punctulatus* Scudder (Clark Co., 14:VI:1938; 20:-VII:1932) ; and the cypress katydid, *Inscudderia taxodii* Caudell (Hovey Lake, Posey Co., 12:X:1958, on cypress).

The clear-winged locust, *Camnula pellucida* Scudder, and the maritime locust, *Trimerotropis maritima* (Harris), are two species (of 23) characteristic of the Transition Zone.

### Distribution of Coleoptera

Blatchley[2] defined more specifically the life zones of Indiana by incorporating distributional data of the beetles. The Transition Zone was delimited by an arc which was drawn from the western edge of Indiana to include the northern third of Lake County to central Fulton County to the southeastern corner of DeKalb County at the eastern edge of the state. The Lower Austral Zone was limited southward of a line drawn from northwestern Vigo County southeastward to northern Clark County, thence northeastward to include portions or all of the counties bordering the Ohio River (terminating about midway along the eastern boundary of Dearborn County).

Faunistically, the characteristic species of Orthoptera were unchanged from his previous list. The Lower Austral Zone beetle fauna included: the large tiger beetle, *Tetracha virginica* L. (he did not have *T. carolina* L.) ; the giant stag beetle, *Lucanus elaphus* F.; the rhinoceros beetle, *Dynastes tityrus* L.; the unicorn beetle, *Xyloryctes satyrus* F. (which is more widely distributed than would be typical for the Lower Austral) ; the scarab, *Phileurus valgus* L.; and the green June beetle, *Cotinis nitida* L. Since 1950, however, the latter species has extended its range northward and is locally abunðant in the vicinity of Lafayette. To this list could be added *Polyphylla hammondi* Lec. and *Cicindela celeripes* Lec., both from Posey County.

It is obvious from his distributional studies that Blatchley always associated the elements of the Alleghanian fauna with the northern part of the state. Although our supporting data are presently inadequate, preliminary work indicates that Alleghanian faunal elements are present in the unglaciated central region of Indiana. In fact, it would appear that remnants of a pre-Pleistocene fauna have existed there as a continuum to the present day. Since this region has been the least studied of any in the state, further discussion of it would be purely speculative.

### Distribution of Odonata*

The Odonata fauna of Indiana consists of 147 nominal species, of which four *(Enallagma piscinarium* Williamson, *Gomphus williamsoni* Muttkowski, *Macromia wabashensis* Williamson, and *Somatochlora hineana* Williamson) are endemic to northern Indiana and adjacent counties of Ohio.

The 147 forms of Odonata divide easily into three groups: 83 found throughout the state (generally of very wide distribution—the entire eastern United States, throughout most of North America, or, even cosmopolitan) ; 49 found only in the northern part of the state; and 15 known from the southern half only. The division of the state is a line approximately from Parke to Franklin counties.

It may be expected that with the increase of lakes, ponds and reservoirs in southern Indiana the number of species found there will increase. As a matter of fact, seven of the 15 species found only in the southern half have spread into the state during the past 35 years, probably during the hot, dry cycle of years in the 1930's. These include: *Archilestes prandis* Rambur, *Teleallagma daeckii* Calvert, *Ladona deplanata* Rambur, *Erythrodiplax minuscula* Rambur, *E. umbrata* Linnaeus, *Celithemis fasciata* Kirby, and *C. verna* Pritchard. Rather extensive collecting from about 1897 to 1950 (by the late E. B. Williamson and B. E. Montgomery) make it possible to indicate that these species were not here previously.

Some factor, or factors, seem to have encouraged the spread

*Prepared by B. Elwood Montgomery, Department of Entomology, Purdue University of Odonata about 1930-1940, and some newly created bodies of water in southern Indiana provided places for establishment. All of these species were established for a few years as breeding populations where newly emerged imagoes or naiads were taken. *T. daeckii* and the two species of *Erythrodiplax* were present for several years, then disappeared, but the others have continued to increase, and to some extent, spread farther into the state.

*Enallagma basidens* Calvert entered the state at the same time but continued to spread throughout the state and eastward to the Atlantic coast. Both *E. basidens* and *A. grandis* were southwestern species, unknown north or east of Texas and Oklahoma before 1930. *E. basidens* came into the state more or less directly from the southwest but *A. grandis* appears to have entered from the southeast (Ohio and Kentucky) and is still found only in the southeastern quarter of Indiana. This route of migration may have been due to the habitat of the species which breeds in streams flowing over rock ledges. The other six "migrant" species were southern or southeastern in general distribution.

A numerical study of the relationships of the distribution patterns of the different groups of Odonata indicates that, in general, the northern portion of the state has strong affinities with the northern faunae, and that the southern half is a transitional zone. Excluding exclusively western genera, only three northern North American genera do not reach as far north as southern Indiana. Tabulations of the indices of similarity of the faunae of the two halves of the state and other selected areas indicate that the two halves of the state have an index generally near or below the level (0.73) indicating the same faunal zone, and that the similarity of northern Indiana and southern Michigan is greater than that of northern and southern Indiana and, generally, above the level of the two areas of the same zone.

The indices of similarity of different groups of Odonata of each portion of the state with the other areas are shown in Table 10.

## Distribution of Hymenoptera

The distribution of bees and wasps in Indiana, particularly the former, yields some interesting patterns. In general, these

Table 10. Indices of similarity for different groups of Odonata occurring in selected geographic locations.

| | Northern Indiana | Southern Michigan | Northern Michigan | Maine | Maritime Provinces | Newfoundland | Louisiana |
|---|---|---|---|---|---|---|---|
| | | | Zygoptera | | | | |
| Northern Indiana | — | 0.88 | 0.72 | 0.77 | 0.60 | 0.31 | 0.54 |
| Southern Indiana | 0.77 | 0.67 | 0.45 | 0.53 | 0.45 | 0.20 | 0.55 |
| | | | Gomphidae | | | | |
| Northern Indiana | — | 0.72 | 0.56 | 0.20 | | | 0.38 |
| Southern Indiana | 0.64 | 0.49 | 0.26 | 0.14 | | | 0.52 |
| | | | Aeshnidae | | | | |
| Northern Indiana | — | 0.80 | 0.59 | 0.66 | | | 0.43 |
| Southern Indiana | 0.80 | 0.62 | 0.41 | 0.52 | | | 0.53 |
| | | | Corduliidae | | | | |
| Northern Indiana | — | 0.30 | 0.18 | 0.34 | | | 0.32 |
| Southern Indiana | 0.47 | 0.22 | 0.21 | 0.41 | | | 0.52 |
| | | | Libellulidae | | | | |
| Northern Indiana | — | 0.84 | 0.67 | 0.58 | | | 0.53 |
| Southern Indiana | 0.73 | 0.59 | 0.45 | 0.36 | | | 0.59 |

patterns would support Blatchley's ideas of life zones with only moderate alterations of his boundaries. However, it would appear that other kinds of divisions can be made and these may be more meaningful.

There is a striking parallel between general distributional patterns of bees and the patterns of the Illinois-Indiana herpetofauna.[16] Additionally, while recognizing that botanists are not unanimous in their support of the floral areas of Deam[30] (Fig. 59), the ranges of many bee species are remarkably coincident.

Examples of northern species occurring in the Transition Zone of Blatchley are: *Andrena hirticincta* Prov., *Megachile gemula* Cr., *Bombus borealis* Kirby, *Vespula vulgaris* (L.) (with a possible relict population recorded from the Shades State Park), *V. arenaria* (F), *V. vidua* (Sauss.) (also from Tippecanoe Co.), and *Aphilanthops frigidus* (F. Smith). Three northern species, *Bombus affinis* Cr., *B. fervidus* (F.)

and *Andrena wilkella* (Kirby), occur north of the Wisconsin maximum glacial line.

Southern Indiana, south of the Wisconsin glacial maximum and excluding the extreme southwestern corner of the state, is characterized more by the absence of northern forms than by the presence of different species. The recently established European hornet, *Vespa crabro germana* Christ, and the polistine wasp, *Polistes rubiginosus* Lep. are restricted to the southern portion. Our only record of *Bicyrtes fodiens* (Handl.) is from Jackson Co.

The incidence of stylopized wasps, especially *Polistes* spp., increases significantly in this southern region.

The entire western edge of Indiana is the area of the greatest admixture of species. By and large, the species that occur in the eastern half are found at comparable latitudes in the west. Here they intermingle with a fauna composed of prairie elements; and, in the southwest corner, with western, southwestern and coastal plains species.

Representative species which occur exclusively, or nearly so, in the lower Wabash Valley (southern Knox Co. to Posey Co.) and the lower Ohio Valley (Posey and Vanderburg counties) are the bees: *Nomia nortoni* Cr., *Exomalopsis asteris* Mitchell, *Svastra atripes atrimitra* (LaBerge), *Tetralonia rosae* (Robt.), *Emphoropsis laboriosa* (Fabr.), *Nomada seneciophila* Mitchell; and, the wasps: *Polistes exclamans* Viereck, *Bembecinus neglectus* Cresson, *Cerceris frontata raui* Rohwer, and *Trypoxylon texense* Sauss. Notably absent from this area are *Ptilothrix bombiformis* (Cr.), *Bombus vagans* F. Sm. and *Psithyrus citrinus* Sm.

Moving eastward along the Ohio River, the ranges of these species terminate abruptly, none occurring east of the region where the broad, annually flooded bottomlands give way to the rougher river bluffs. Moving northward along the Wabash, however, the ranges are not so abruptly terminated. Additionally, some associated and characteristic species of the area are found as far north as Tippecanoe and Marion counties (e.g., *Bombus fraternus* (F. Sm.), *Perdita 8-maculata terminata* (Ckll.)), while others range full-length of the state, (e.g., *Nomia heteropoda* (Say)).

Other prairie and/or sand-dwelling species which have been taken north of this southwestern region and, with two exceptions are confined to the west, are other *Perdita* spp., *Pseudopanurgus* spp., *Psaenythia bancrofti* (Dunning) and *P. mexicanorum cockerelli* (Dunning), *Eucerceris zonata* (Say), *Stizoides unicinctus* (Say), and *Stizus brevipennis* Walsh. The two exceptions are within the genera *Perdita* and *Pseudopanurgus*, species of both having been taken in LaGrange Co.

## Summation of Faunistic Areas

Investigators involved in regional analyses have a great tendency to recognize boundary lines of larger biotic areas (e.g., life zones, biomes) as occurring within their region, especially if such lines have not been considered there previously. In Indiana, the overwhelming number of Upper Austral (Carolinian) species which occur throughout the state fairly well dictates the conclusion that this area falls completely within this faunal zone.

The ranges of many species are limital in Indiana and, when a number of these are plotted, a series of unit patterns can be defined. Asking the questions: where in Indiana are the major areas in which a number of ranges are coincidentally limital?; and, why is this so?, the following areas may be considered as biotic units (Fig. 62):

I. NORTHERN REGION. This region includes all of the area north of the Tipton Till Plain. It is characterized by the faunal elements of the Transition (Alleghanian) fauna as discussed earlier under Orthoptera and Hymenoptera. Within this region are recognized three biotic units:

1. *The Dunes.* This unique area has an equally unique assemblage of insect species. Many of the species which occur here are not restricted to this unit but occur more abundantly here than elsewhere. The white tiger beetle, *Cicindela lepida* Dej., and the seaside locust, *Trimerotropis maritima* (Harris), which are so characteristic of The Dunes are not restricted to it. There are, however, a number of species which are not found outside of this unit (in Indiana). These would include the dunes termite, *Reticulitermes arenincola,* and certain species of plant-feeding insects confined to plant species peculiar to the unit (e.g., the bearberry aphid, *Tamalia coweni,* and the bearberry leafhopper, *Texananus cumulatus*).[13]

2. *The Kankakee Sand Ridge Unit.* South and east of The Dunes is an area characterized by sparsely vegetated sand

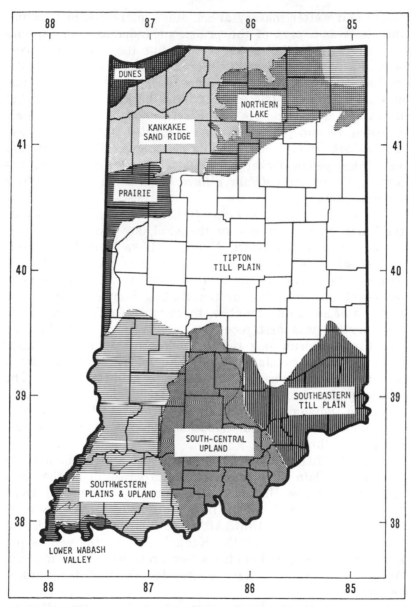

Fig. 62. The biotic units of Indiana based upon insect distribution patterns. Relict, disjunct, or specialized areas within units are not denoted. Certain lines delimiting areas are purposely coincident with those proposed or defined by Deam[30] and/or Wayne and Zumberge.[18]

ridges and wetter marshy areas. Most references to this unit include it as a part of the prairie of Indiana. Many species of western (prairie) species occur but they are intermixed with the northern elements. Several species of plants categorized as coastal[3] are found here. It is possible that no species of insect is restricted in its distribution to this unit but the faunal composition is distinct. The nocturnal bee, *Sphecodogastra texana* (Cr.), the white-banded anthophorid bee, *Anthophora walshii* Cr., the horse guard, *Stictia carolina* (F.), the yellow-jacket, *Vespula vidua* (Sauss.), and the hornet, *V. arenaria* (Fabr.) have been taken here in their greatest abundance.

3. *The Northern Lake Unit.* The remaining area of the Northern Region, east of the Kankakee Sand Ridge Unit has been designated as The Northern Lake Unit. Few "western" species are found here; in fact, it is the lack of these elements that tend to characterize the unit. In the extreme northeast corner of this unit, including Steuben County and portions of adjoining counties, there is a weakly defined area. This portion was first recognized by Wilson[21] who reported that the American dog tick, *Dermacentor variabilis* (Say), had only recently (since World War II) become established here and that it was still unknown to many residents. The wingless grasshopper, *Melanoplus islandicus* Blatchley, is known in Indiana only from Steuben County. Other evidences from plant and animal distributions tend to support the recognition of this area.

II. CENTRAL REGION. The central region of Indiana is the Tipton Till Plain Unit; however, the area south of the Kankakee Sand Ridge Unit, composed largely of the level areas west of the Wabash River into Vigo County, has been retained as the Prairie Unit. Although this Prairie Unit is but a southern extension of the Kankakee Unit, the soil is not sandy, not rolling and contains few areas which are marshy. Agricultural practices have obliterated most of the natural vegetation.

Few northern species are present in the Central Region, those that do occur extending to its southern boundary, the Wisconsin glacial maximum. Western species of the Prairie Unit do not generally occur farther eastward than Lafayette.

The Wabash River Valley is a corridor by which several

southern species extend northward to the Lafayette area. Additionally, the West Fork of the White River evidently offers a similar passageway into Marion County.

III. SOUTHERN REGION. This region extends southward from the Wisconsin glacial maximum to the Ohio River including both the Illinoian Till Plain and the unglaciated area. Four biotic units are recognized within this region.

1. *The Lower Wabash Valley or Pocket Unit.* This unit is most typically expressed at Hovey Lake, Posey County. It is confined to the Wabash River Valley, becoming more weakly defined northward and, for identification purposes, terminating about west-central Knox County. Eastward it is confined to the Ohio River Valley as far as Warrick County.

2. *The Southwestern Plains and Upland Unit.* This is a rather ill-defined unit including both Illinoian Till Plain and unglaciated portions. It abuts the Pocket Unit on the west and the South-Central Upland on the east. It is characterized by the overlap of faunal elements of each reflecting the influence of the Wabash, White and Ohio River Valleys.

3. *The South-Central Upland Unit.* As defined, this unit coincides with the chestnut-oak upland of Deam[3]. It is within this unit that remnants of an Alleghanian fauna persist. Two species of ticks, the lone-star, *Amblyomma americanum* (L.), and the wood-rat tick, *Ixodes woodi* Bishopp, have not been taken outside of this unit except for two questionable source records.[21]

A number of economically important species have entered the state through this unit (e.g., Mexican bean beetle, alfalfa weevil, giant hornet) or have made secondary entrances here (spotted alfalfa aphid).

4. *The Southeastern Till Plain Unit.* The unit occurs eastward of the South-Central Upland and is the eastern counterpart of the Southwestern Plains and Upland. The unit is entirely Illinoian Till Plain. Western and southwestern species are almost entirely absent (see Odonata) but are replaced by some Alleghanian elements.

### Origins

The brief treatment of faunal composition hopefully left the impression that life zones, or areas, or other biotic designations are but temporal, geographic assemblages. Each is composed of a multitude of species of diverse lineages and of different ages. To understand better the development of these assemblages, to indicate dispersal routes and the times favorable for these dispersals, it is necessary to understand the origin of the groups involved.

Biogeographical studies may be of three types: descriptive, ecological or evolutionary. Origins dictate the latter approach. Evolutionary biogeography depends upon phylogeny for its data and, in turn, yields its own information of time, trends or directions, physical and ecological potentials. Biogeography serves as a check and balance for phylogenetic interpretation.

In a series of papers, Ross[12, 14, 15] has treated many aspects of dispersal dynamics. We believe that it is also fitting on this occasion to recognize the pioneering work of the late Alfred Kinsey [6, 7] whose elucidation of the "new systematics" incorporated the approaches here.

We have drawn from the literature a few examples of species groups that are better known to illustrate the complexities which exist.

Data from Rehn [11] concerning various groups of Orthoptera are particularly enlightening. The Carolina mantid, *Stagmomantis carolina*, belongs to a genus Neotropical in origin. The larger Chinese mantid, *Tenodera aridifolia sinensis* Sauss., was introduced near Philadelphia years ago and is now generally distributed throughout the state. The walkingstick, *Diapheromera femorata* (Say), is considered to belong to a genus Sonoran in origin but with a secondary center of development in the southeastern and central United States.

The cockroaches provide a series of examples of diversity of origins. The pest species belonging to the genera *Blatta*, *Blattella*, *Periplaneta* and *Supella* are believed to have originated in Africa and to have been transported in commerce. The woodsroach genus, *Parcoblatta*, is endemic to North America. This group must have had an early origin from a Neotropical ancestor with the center of differentiation in the eastern and central United States. The genus *Cryptocercus*, containing the single North American species, *C. punctulatus*, has a disjunct distribution. It occurs in the eastern Appalachians and the Appalachian Plateau from New York to Georgia, through Kentucky and into Indiana. Another segment of this population occurs in western Washington, the Cascades of Oregon, and possibly in the Sierra of California. Such a range separation probably came about during the Pleistocene and was maintained by the development of the central prairie region of the United States. Interestingly, several species of *Cryptocercus* occur in eastern Asia. Thus, the importance of Eurasian-North American land connections are emphasized.

Hurd[4] reported a similar phenomenon for two species of carpenter bees, the eastern *Xylocopa virginica* (L.) and the western *X. californica* Cr. According to Hurd, the ancestral population of these species entered North America from Eurasia. These bees were associated with the transcontinental Arcto-Tertiary Forest of North America. When the geographic continuity of this forest was broken, the eastern and western populations became isolated. Each population continued to differentiate until it became specifically distinct.

Natural spread of insects from western Eurasia is more difficult to document. This is because connections between North America and Europe occurred and were broken in a more remote past. (There are some who argue that no such connections ever existed). In addition, the severe glaciation in eastern North America has caused subsequent readjustments which obscure our evidences. Perhaps our best evidence of European relationships has been provided by Mills[9] in his studies of Collembola. He concluded that the strongest relationships were with Europe, not Asia. Preliminary studies on the Collembola of Indiana by Wilkey[20] and Pedigo[10] would confirm this evidence.

The role that man has played in the introduction of pest species is well-documented. Lindroth has recorded many non-economic species that have been transported to North America from Europe. Aside from the usual importations via infested stock and like materials, the dumping of soil ballast from the holds of incoming ships has yielded a variety of immigrants. Among the non-destructive species introduced via commerce are the aphid wasp, *Pemphredon lethifer* (Shuckard), its chrysidid parasite, *Omalus auratus* L., and the alfalfa leaf-cutter bee, *Megachile rotundata* (Fab.).

Thus, the fauna of Indiana has been derived from many geographic areas; but all species have not come from the out-

side. Many species and species groups have evolved within
the region of which Indiana is a part. Much of the evidence
has been obliterated by glaciation, but glaciation itself was
a phenomenon which initiated speciation processes.

### Dispersal Routes Into Indiana

Having indicated something of the composition of the insect
fauna and the diversity of origins (allbeit briefly), it is necessary to consider the major pathways or corridors by which
insects entered the state, especially following glaciation. Also,
having avoided it to date, it becomes necessary to take a
stand on the influence of glaciation on the fauna of the unglaciated portion.

From evidences of biotic response to present day glaciers,
and from evidences from unglaciated areas which occurred
within the glacial sheet, we would have to conclude that several things occurred. Undoubtedly, some forms of life became
extinct, both from a changing physical environment as well
as from biotic factors. Most organisms evidently survived
by moving ahead, in an orderly fashion, of the glacier and
occupying areas of reduced size including refugia. There is
every reason to believe that certain groups survived in places
near the edge of the glacier. These latter groups have been
identified in two ways: either as those which reinvaded the
area of glaciation almost as it retreated; or, those which
remain with ranges coincident with the glacial maximum. In
the second instance, it is usually inferred that suitable habitat
areas were not available for further spread, thus an ecological restriction.

The sequence of climatic events which have occurred since
the Pleistocene has had a tremendous impact upon Indiana.
The north-south, east-west climatic tension zones are clearly
reflected in the present biotic patterns.

Thomas[17] presented a list of faunal elements which he felt
would include the majority of forms. With brief modifications these are used by us: (1) Alleghany Plateau species;
(2) boreal relicts; (3) Coastal species; (4) immigrants from
the south and southwest; (5) western species of the Xerothermic Period; and, (6) species which have altered their
range as a result of European settlement.

Thomas reported three species of Orthoptera of the genus

*Orchelimum* which he believed to represent Alleghanian Plateau species which had moved into the glaciated area as it became available. It seems likely that many of the species characteristic of Blatchley's Transition Zone belong to this category. As was inferred previously, it is likely that the unglaciated region of the state will yield others.

Indiana lacks much of the topography necessary to ensure the survival of boreal relicts. Ross[15] cited the caddisfly, *Rhyacophila parantra* from Bloomington, with a related species in the White Mountains of New Hampshire. The Shades-Turkey Run-Pine Hills region of Montgomery and Parke counties provides a suitable but limited area for boreal relicts. The occurrence of *Vespula vulgaris* at The Shades and records of winter stoneflies and of certain caddisflies from these places is somewhat indicative of their relict nature. The reports by Siverly of certain mosquito species in Indiana bogs depicts a relict situation.

Coastal species enter Indiana primarily from the southwest corner. The Wabash River Valley appears to be a corridor for extensive northward expansion. A number of species have ranges extending disproportionately northward within this valley and it is by this pathway that several species enter the state annually although they are unable to survive the winter. Included are species of *Drosophila, Aedes* and *Culex*. A secondary route for coastal species is apparently through the Great Lakes Region although such a passageway is not well documented.

Immigrants from the south and southwest enter by at least three different pathways. Many southern species enter the state at the southwest corner. More commonly, however, these enter at some point along the unglaciated portion with most of our records from Harrison, Floyd and Clark counties. We have used this evidence in support of Deam's southcentral floral area which roughly divides his Illinoian Till Plain. On the other hand, many southwestern species enter along the western border as well as the southwestern corner. The damselfly, *Archilestes grandis*, however, considered to be a southwestern species, has entered the state from the southeast. Many southwestern and western species whose habitat area is sand deposits form a peculiar and unique, disjunct "sand fauna" with hard-to-define interarea movements.

Species that entered the area presumably during the Xerothermic Period are characteristic of the Kankakee Sand Ridge Unit and disjunct sand and prairie remnants scattered to the east. Typically however, agricultural practices have so reduced these areas that faunal elements are difficult to identify. In addition, many agricultural practices counterfeit prairie conditions thus it is difficult to discern the time of entry.

The last category, altered ranges as a result of European settlement, is two-pronged. We ordinarily consider these as range extensions, but extermination from portions of ranges is probably as common. Range extensions among insects are best-documented for economically important species. This is more adequately treated by others (Osmun and Giese, this volume). An example of a North American species which has extended its range into the state as a direct result of human activities is the squash bee, *Peponapis pruinosa* (Say). According to Hurd and Linsley[5] the natural range of this species is coincident with that of *Cucurbita foetidissima* HBK. It exceeds the range of the wild squash only through the utilization of domestic *Cucurbita* spp.

Range extermination in Indiana is less-well documented. In the case of monophagous insect species whose plant or animal host has been eliminated we would logically assume that the insect suffered the fate of its host. Similarly, if certain species were restricted to an unique ecological area that the destruction of the area would eliminate the insect.

The encroachment on certain unique natural areas by human activities has profoundly influenced insect ranges and/or population densities. The disappearance of northern bogs through drainage, timbering and peat-digging is probably the most widespread example. Aquatic areas are also changed by dams, silting, and factors which alter water quality.

### The Indiana Insect Fauna of the Future
Indiana is a small state, lacking in extreme topographic features and located within a rather similar climatic environment. Yet with all of its commonness, it represents a vast laboratory for biogeographic analysis. Containing a heterogeneous assemblage of insects, the distributional patterns are not hopelessly confusing.

The first 150 years finds us sadly lacking in data, and the next 10 threatens to eliminate some of the unique natural areas required for obtaining these. We rather confidently predict that Bicentennial times will find an insect fauna containing a majority of present day species, a variety of new and newly-discovered ones, with a different pattern of distribution. The challenge of our time is to establish a baseline from which change can be measured.

## LITERATURE

1. BLATCHLEY, W. S. 1902. The Orthoptera of Indiana. 27th Ann. Rpt., Dept. Geol. Nat. Res. of Indiana: 123-471.
2. _____ 1909. The life zones of Indiana as illustrated by the distribution of Orthoptera and Coleoptera within the State. Proc. Indiana Acad. Sci. (for 1908): 185-191.
3. DEAM, C. C. 1940. Flora of Indiana. Dept. of Conservation, Division of Forestry, Indianapolis. 1-1236 (esp. 15-19, 1164).
4. HURD, P. D., Jr. 1956. Notes on the subgenera of the New World carpenter bees of the genus *Xylocopa* (Hymenoptera, Apoidea). American Mus. Novitates No. 1776: 1-7.
5. _____ and E. G. LINSLEY. 1964. The squash and gourd bees — genera *Peponapis* Robertson and *Xenoglossa* Smith — inhabiting America north of Mexico. Hilgardia 35(15): 375-477.
6. KINSEY, A. C. 1930. The gall wasp genus *Cynips*, a study of the origin of species. Indiana Univ. Studies 16 (Studies No. 84, 85, 86): 1-577.
7. _____ 1936. The origin of higher categories in *Cynips*. Indiana Univ. Publ. Science Series No. 4:1-334.
8. MERRIAM, C. H. 1898. Life zones and crop zones of the United States. U. S. Dept. Agric., Div. Biol. Surv., Bull. No. 10:1-79.
9. MILLS, H. B. 1939. Remarks on the geographical distribution of North American Collembola. Bull. Brooklyn Entomol. Soc. 34:158-161.
10. PEDIGO, LARRY. 1965. The bionomy of Collembola in a heterogeneous woodland. Unpublished Master's Thesis, Purdue University Library.
11. REHN, J. A. G. 1958. The origin and affinities of the Dermaptera and Orthoptera of western North America. in Zoogeography, American Assoc. Advance. Sci. Publ. No. 51:253-298.
12. ROSS, H. H. 1953. On the origin and composition of the Nearctic insect fauna. Evolution 7(2): 145-158.
13. _____ 1963. The dunesland heritage of Illinois. Illinois Nat. Hist. Survey Circ. 49: 1-28.
14. _____ 1964. The colonization of temperate North America by mosquittoes and man. Mosquito News 24(2): 103-118.
15. _____ 1965. Pleistocene events and insects. in The Quaternary of the United States. Princeton Univ. Press. 583-596.
16. SMITH, P. W. and S. A. MINTON. 1957. A distribution summary of the herpetofauna of Indiana and Illinois. American Midl. Nat. 58(2): 341-351.
17. THOMAS, E. S. 1951. Distribution of Ohio animals. Ohio Jour. Sci. 51(4): 153-167.
18. WAYNE, W. J. and J. H. ZUMBERGE. 1965. Pleistocene geology in Indiana and Michigan. in The Quaternary of the United States. Princeton Univ. Press. 63-84.
19. WEBSTER, F. M. 1903. The diffusion of insects in North America. Psyche 10: 47-58.
20. WILKEY, R. F. 1950. A preliminary study of the Collembola of Tippecanoe County, Indiana. Unpublished Bachelor's Thesis, Department of Entomology Library, Purdue University.
21. WILSON, N. A. 1961. The ectoparasites of Indiana mammals. Unpublished Doctoral Dissertation, Purdue University Library.

# 21

# Insect Pests of Forest, Farm and Home

JOHN V. OSMUN AND RONALD L. GIESE
Department of Entomology
Purdue University

The natural features of Indiana portray an image of plant and animal communities existing in a reasonably balanced state. To impose insect pests into it may seem to be an incongruity. Insects assume a very real and vital part in the natural history of our time, and because of the effect of man on the changing face of Indiana, many of them must be designated as pests. An understanding of their temporal advance into our forests, farms and homes establishes insects as forces to be reckoned with in all environments.

The species discussed in this paper are representative of the kinds of insects involved, the variety of environments in which they live, and the factors which contribute to their behavior, density and damage.

## Insects of the Forest

The great number of tree species in Indiana which grow in very diverse plant communities give rise to an immense complex of forest insects. However, in communities which we call natural climax stands, insects rarely cause biotic catastrophes. Historically, outbreaks of this nature have not occurred in Indiana forests. Usually, the greater the variety of vegetational forest composition, the more resistant it is to damaging insects.[3]

Our forests are not always this complex. When they comprise only one or a very few species, we speak of them as being at the other extreme of a species gradient. A pure pine plantation would be an example. Such a plantation provides an optimal environment for a pine insect pest, an environment which provides little resistance. The balance of nature is broken and an insect epiphytotic may develop. Consequently, it is in pure stand situations where the greatest number of economic insect problems are found.

Forest insects are even more diverse than the species of trees within a forest. To illustrate this we will examine eight different kinds of forest pests. The status of these insects during the last four decades has been dynamic. Some were indigenous to certain areas of Indiana but expanded their geographic ranges. Others were newly introduced into the state. Two species moved north and two other species moved south in the state. A fluctuating climate, the influence of managing forest land, interstate commerce and natural dispersal all contribute to an ever changing condition of the distribution and abundance of forest insects.

## Columbian Timber Beetle

Perhaps the most important insect affecting forest trees is the Columbian timber beetle, *Corthylus columbianus* Hopkins[2]. In Indiana this pest is also known as the "boatworm" or "flagworm" and the staining associated with it "greasespots". Although an ambrosia beetle, the Columbian timber beetle differs from all other representatives of the group in the state because it attacks only living hardwood hosts and causes no mortality of the infested trees. This pest is well distributed south of Highway 40 in Indiana. One particular habitat is characteristic for this beetle — flat, low lying and poorly drained forest areas. Floodplain stands are prominent in terms of severe outbreaks of the timber beetle. Hence, tree hosts are limited to bottomland species. Three kinds are now known in Indiana — silver maple, red maple and sycamore.

Spring activity begins in April and May with adults boring into the sapwood. Two signs which often accompany new invasions are cream-colored boring dust and wet spots on the bark. Mating occurs within the gallery system. Eggs are deposited in small chambers excavated by the adult. Most egg chambers are directed upwards. By the time the eggs hatch, the surrounding wood is lined with a mat of yeast. Larvae feed on the yeast only and cannot use the woody tissue. The remaining development takes place in the same gallery complex and finally adults emerge from the tree. Two such generations occur during the growing season. A symbiotic relationship exists among three dissimilar organisms where the *tree* provides a substrate on which *fungi* grow and in which *beetles* bore and live (Fig. 63, p. 381).

Ten microorganisms have been isolated from occupied galleries and artifacts, but because of their abundance and usual presence, two are especially important. *Ceratocystis* sp. is found consistently in galleries and also in egg chambers following emergence of the adults. While eggs and larvae inhabit the small chambers, a yeast *(Pichia* n. sp.) completely covers the walls of each chamber and it is this microsymbiote that provides the entire food mass for the developing larvae. Adult males possess a thoracic organ, the *mycetangium*, which stores and transmits the yeast. The association between the yeast and beetle is a mutualistic one where the beetle serves as the overwintering site and vector for the yeast and provides a substrate (holes in the host tree) on which it grows. The yeast, in turn, supplies the only food for the ambrosia beetle larvae.

Although the distribution of beetle attacks around the circumference of the tree is random, such is not the case when considering the vertical position of attacks throughout the height of the tree. There is a decided preference for the lower portion of the trunk; in fact, the lowest one-quarter of this main stem harbors about 90% of the population.

An attribute which makes the timber beetle a unique organism for basic ecological studies is the fact that even large densities of invading beetles cause no host mortality so that, through dissections, frequencies and densities of individual colonies can be derived and the animals can be studied historically in time and space. Such investigations have revealed excellent information on population fluctuations. It is now known that this insect has been present in Indiana from the beginning of the twentieth century but in very small numbers. In 1949, following a buildup period of several years, a population explosion occurred. Two more outbreaks were discovered in 1956 and 1959.

These three population explosions were primarily the result of *climatic release*. Climatic release is a situation which develops when climatic factors, normally holding an insect population down, relax. It is a situation where a small insect population exists in a refuge area (a *refugium)*, so protected that even when biotic factors favor population growth, it does not occur until controlling climatic factors are withdrawn for a period of several years. The exact mode of action of climatic release is not clear. However, in the case of the Columbian timber beetle, precipitation is the responsible climatic factor. Outbreaks follow periods of drought.

The climatic barrier, a limited habitat distribution, and a small host range indicate that in Indiana, the Columbian timber beetle represents a *fringe population*, that is the periphery of the species range where biotic and physical stresses normally impose severe controls on a population. The outbreaks, relatively new phenomena in this area, represent *swells*, peak population densities following the breakdown of a barrier. In southwestern Indiana the three indicated outbreaks are well represented, but in the southeastern region of the state, only the 1956 and 1959 outbreaks were present. The swell then, has moved in a northeasterly direction up the Ohio River watershed. As Indiana populations become better established we can predict expansion of the range, increased habitat types and the invasion of new kinds of host trees.

The tunneling by the beetles, dark color of the tunnels imparted by the associated fungi and a green and brown stain penetrating the sapwood up and down from the tunnels constitute the damage from the standpoint of wood utilization. The vertical stain lengths average 10 and 18 inches in red and silver maple and are equally long above and below the galleries. Although generally assumed to be caused by staining fungi, the large sapwood stains always found as a typical part of the artifact result from a chemical response to the mechanical damage of boring by the ambrosia beetles. No good control program has been devised, due primarily to the internal features of the insects' biology, the short time of adult exposure outside of the tree and the expense of conventional methods on long-term "crops". Since the late 1940's, this pest has been responsible for 30-50% reduction in timber values of soft maple.

The Columbian timber beetle has become well established in Indiana and will continue to play an important economic role in the State's timber using industry.

*The Locust Borer*

A typical and important wood boring insect is the locust borer, *Megacyllene robiniae* (Forster). It is a round-headed wood borer whose adults (long-horned) are black bodied with yellow cross bands on the wings and about ¾" in length. Eggs are deposited in bark crevices in the fall; they hatch and the larvae bore into the bark where the winter is spent. In spring of the following year, the larvae bore into the wood. Wet spots of flowing sap on the bark indicate larval activity. Early in the development of these immatures, white wood dust is expelled from the holes but later in the season when the tunneling larvae excavate heartwood, the dust becomes yellow. By early August, locust borers have completed larval feeding and development and then transform to adults (Fig. 64).

Several factors influence the abundance of borer populations. Dry and warm seasons favor survival of the critical larval stage. Even during favorable weather, dense stands with closing canopies inhibit borer establishment because of temperature modifications. Trees in a poor growing condition appear to be especially susceptible. Finally, texture and thickness of the bark are important determiners of susceptibility. It is this point which demonstrates differential susceptibility due to age. Young saplings do not generally provide rough enough bark for egg deposition and larger trees have bark which is too thick for the young larvae to penetrate. Trees between one and six inches in diameter are most likely to be attacked.

Because of the durability of the wood, the rapid growth habit, and the ability to grow on poor sites, black locust is an excellent candidate for erosion control and soil bank planting as well as the production of posts and poles. However the locust borer, the most serious pest of black locust, has discouraged the planting of this tree. Extensive mining through the heartwood results in "honeycombing", and trees become severely damaged, susceptible to wind breakage and sometimes die. Borer attack usually prevents commercial utilization of trees and entire stands are often destroyed.

### The Tulip Tree Borer[13]

Newly discovered in Indiana in 1961, the tulip-tree borer, *Euzophera ostricolorella* Hulst, is a lepidopterous insect which could become one of the most important forest pests in the state. In the spring adult moths deposit eggs in the root collar area of tulip poplar trees. Larvae bore beneath the bark throughout the summer. The principal concentration of burrows in the lowest one foot of the tree suggests a preference for a habitat of high moisture. The system of burrows in the soft phloem tissue is black in color. The outer bark is also darkly colored (having the appearance of having been burned), and is easily dislodged. The dark coloration is probably imparted by the presence of fungi. This insect is recorded from the North-South extremities and several counties in central Indiana. Further surveys will probably reveal its presence throughout the state.

Although a primary invader, the damage caused directly by the insect's activity is not severe. Rather, it predisposes the host to a succession of secondary invaders that can result in mortality. Following the generalized mining activity in the cork and outer phloem regions, the invasion of secondary fungi and insects becomes obvious. Observations indicate that several years of insect and disease activity predisposed by the tulip poplar borer causes a deterioration of the basal portion of the tree and less vigorous trees succumb and others become susceptible to windthrow.

### The Zimmerman Pine Moth

Ten years ago a new state record was established when the Zimmerman pine moth, *Dioryctria zimmermani* (Grotel), was discovered in northern Indiana.[12]

Infestations of this insect are noticeable because of white resin masses and sawdust-like droppings near branch whorls. Larvae may be found tunneling in the terminal portion of the tree, later invading the whorl region where side branches join the main stem. This insect overwinters in the larval stage under the bark. In spring and summer the larvae continue their development and most adults emerge in mid-August. Two factors that enhance population development are open type stands and wounds. Plantation situations provide open habitats favorable for the pine moth, and diseases, sapsucker feeding and mechanical damage enhance infestations. Once a tree has been damaged, it becomes even more susceptible to further attack.

Thirteen counties in northern Indiana comprise the known

distribution. Although most pine species can be attacked, Scotch and red pine serve as the primary important hosts in Indiana. The continual establishment of pine stands in the state under synthetic conditions will furnish expanded habitats for the pest and its importance is likely to increase.

Dead tops, girdling and stem deformities constitute the damage of the Zimmerman pine moth. Partially girdled trees elaborate a characteristic bulging growth above the level of damage.

### The Northern Walkingstick

Of all the walkingsticks in North America, the northern walkingstick, *Diapheromera femorata* (Say) is the most common and widely distributed. The adult insect is 3″ long, resembles a twig and is green, brown or grey in color.

Eggs are dropped by females from wherever they happen to be, and lie in the litter over the winter. Hatching occurs in early summer; the young nymphs feed on hazel, basswood or cherry and finally move during later nymphal stages to the preferred oak trees. Characterized by gradual metamorphosis, all immature stages have the appearance of miniature adults and become successively larger at each stage. This insect prefers relatively xeric (dry) conditions as evidenced by the preponderance of outbreak loci in open, dry, second growth stands of pioneer oak. Red and black oak are common hosts. Indiana populations demonstrate a remarkable difference compared to those slightly north in that they complete a generation each year whereas neighboring populations have a two year obligatory diapause in the egg stage which gives rise to alternate year influxes of walkingsticks.

The distribution in the state is quite general and one area in Starke County has supported a dramatic outbreak for twenty years. Large population densities in Indiana are the exception however; due to the wingless feature of this pest, dispersal is a slow process. Growth loss results from leaf destruction and is caused by both nymphs and adults. Repeated defoliation results in an increased mortality rate compared to natural mortality and accelerates stand deterioration.

### European Pine Sawfly[5]

Many kinds of sawflies infest Indiana trees but the European pine sawfly, *Neodiprion sertifer* (Geoffroy), has become established as one of the most significant of these defoliating insects. Introduced into North America over 40 years ago, it invaded northern Indiana about 1950 and has steadily increased its range to the point where the current distribution is nearly statewide.

In late summer and fall, adult females deposit eggs in boot-shaped holes in the needles of pines. Hatching occurs in spring of the following year. New larvae feed, in groups, on the outer tissues only, but in later stages consume the entire needle. About 50% of all foliage consumed by a given colony is eaten during the final larval stage. Cocoon formation and pupation generally occur in litter beneath infested trees; adults emerge from August to November.

The two-needled pines serve as the most common hosts and in Indiana, Scotch, red, Virginia and jack pines are sporadically invaded. Damage to the tree is the removal of the mature needles proceeding from the top to the bottom of the tree. Since larvae feed on foliage produced in the previous year, mortality is unusual; however, a loss of potential growth results from the defoliation. No host age preference has been observed.

The European pine sawfly presents an excellent example of the utility of biological control agents. A specific polyhedral virus disease kills the majority of sawflies when disseminated during early larval development. The value of natural agents is great and this technique is often used in Indiana. The virus is easily applied with no hazard and causes mortality of the sawflies in 4 to 10 days. The few survivors can transmit the disease to succeeding generations effecting a somewhat permanent residual quality, and there is no affect to other kinds of organisms. In addition, diseased larvae can be collected, stored and new suspensions made for introduction into new infestations. As a rule one dead larva contains enough polyhedral bodies to infect colonies on an acre of pine forest. The use of a pathogen to manipulate insect populations in Indiana is a progressive and biologically sound practice.

### The Bagworm

The bagworm, *Thyridopteryx ephemeraeformis* (Haworth), is primarily a shade tree and hedge pest and has been responsible, for over thirty years, for more inquiries than all other Indiana tree insects.

Caterpillars arise from eggs in the spring, crawl to foliage and construct silken bags to which fragments of foliage are attached. Larvae carry the bag with them as feeding occurs, and as development progresses, the bags are made larger to accommodate the growing caterpillars. In late summer the bagworms pupate, transform to the adult stage and the female moths lay eggs in the case. Females are wingless and spend their entire life in the bag.

This insect was common in southern Indiana and limited to that area during the 1920's. By 1934, it had spread as far north as Lafayette. Northward extension of the geographic range continued through the 1940's such that now the distribution is statewide. The most severe widespread outbreak on record was in 1956.

The damage imposed by the bagworm is the removal of foliage. The bagworm has an extremely wide host range including most coniferous and hardwood trees; this attribute makes it an unusual and interesting pest. The results of defoliation on different hosts are noteworthy in that major and complete needle removal from conifers eventually causes tree mortality whereas deciduous hosts can withstand more severe and frequent defoliation with generally a loss only in growth potential.

### The European Pine Shoot Moth[10]

Like the European pine sawfly, the shoot moth, *Rhyacionia buoliana* (Schiffermüller), was introduced into North America during the current century and similarly this pest is a northern insect.

The larval stages have an alternating feeding habit where young larvae mine out the needles and older larvae bore into and destroy the buds. Adult moth flight occurs within rather narrow limits of light and temperature during the early evening hours. Most species of pine serve as hosts for the shoot moth but red pine is especially susceptible to attack.

The moths are rather strong fliers and this is the major factor contributing to the natural dispersal of populations. Early infestations began in northern Indiana. The pest has moved south to the extent that it is now known from all counties north of Highway 40 and several counties in the southern half of the state.

Because of bud destruction, severe infestations prevent normal height growth and cause serious deformities. Compact, bushy growth and crooks in the main stem are typical symptoms of shoot moth presence. Outbreaks of this insect create considerable problems for Christmas tree growers and repeated attacks render trees useless for timber use.

* * *

These species are representative of the types of insects and damage occurring in natural and planted Indiana forest stands. Other damage types would include pests which attack virtually every portion of a tree for there are insects which invade roots, destroy cones and seeds, girdle twigs, cause excessive growths called galls, mine leaves and transmit disease organisms to trees.[1] Even though most species have been present since lumbering began, they now attain greater importance as the demand increases for a decreasing resource.

### Insects of the Farm

Although the appearance of agricultural land differs dramatically from that of the forest and is certainly a more frequently fluid environment, a considerable range of conditions exist which support insect development. In fact, more often opportunities are present on the farm which favor biotic catastrophes. Man in his highly successful tillage of the soil has improved the potential for development of many species of insects. He has concentrated crops in well delineated areas; he grows them to a peak of nutritional value; he frequently provides a better environment for the pest than for the latter's natural biotic enemies. The introduction of new crops and the development of vast acreages have resulted in conditions that are havens for the many introduced pests which flourish in the absence of parasites and predators not simultaneously introduced. Most conducive to the success of many insects has been the agricultural trend away from crop rotation and the increasing practice of continuous planting of the same crop on the same land. Great diversity and adaptive abilities occur among the insect pests making it all the more difficult to regulate their populations below an economic threshold. At least 500 species of insects can be considered pests of the farm in Indiana. Those discussed here are representative of crops, insect groups, patterns of distribution, and a variety of ecological situations.

## European Corn Borer

It is generally believed that one of our most important agricultural pest insects, the European corn borer, *Ostrinia nubilalis* (Hübner), was introduced into Massachusetts from Europe in broomcorn about 1908. After its initial identification in 1916, only 10 years were necessary for it to enter Indiana. By 1940 its distribution within the state was rather complete. Originally this western population of the insect possessed but one generation per year but since the late thirties it has had a second generation, and there is strong evidence that in the southern portions of the state a partial third exists. Overwintering in the corn stalk is in the larval stage with spring pupation followed by adult emergence in late May. Eggs are deposited on the underside of the leaves and the hatched larvae migrate to the whorl where they feed on the leaves; by the fourth instar they have entered the stalk. Second generation larvae are also found frequently in the ear.

Although the injury is less severe than two decades ago, the European corn borer is still one of the most destructive corn insects (1965 loss approximately $5,500,000). First generation borers decrease yield by reducing ear size and weight; second generation forms predispose the stalk to breakage and may reduce yield when larval feeding occurs in the ear shank. Other hosts, such as potatoes and gladiolas, contribute to continuing reservoirs of this insect. Although chemical controls are still practiced against early stages, the European corn borer is a good example of the impact of an insect being mitigated by improved corn varieties, late planting, and gradual establishment of a biotic balance (Fig. 65).

## Hessian Fly

Supposedly at the time of the Revolutionary War, the Hessian troops brought with them from Europe in their bed straw the Hessian Fly, *Mayetiola distructor* (Say). Since 1844, it has been present in all wheat producing areas of Indiana. The minute fly deposits its eggs in leaf grooves in late August and early September. The fall brood passes the winter as larvae protected in puparia ("flaxseeds") on stubble, volunteer wheat, and early seeded winter wheat. Spring emerged flies are short-lived and the new generation is started immediately. Files are again present in September.

Wheat, infested before jointing, assumes a characteristic stunted appearance and the leaves are shorter and broader; individual tillers or the entire plant may be killed. In some cases, larval attack blocks transfer of nutrients to the wheat head. Heavily infested fields yield 25-30% less wheat. Two especially successful approaches are used for control: one is sowing sufficiently late in the fall to avoid egg laying; another is the use of plant varieties resistant to larval development. Research at Purdue is especially involved with the latter. Progress has been complicated by the development of five different populations of the Hessian fly, each with individual capacities for survival on different wheats.

## Corn Rootworm

One of our important economic insects, *Diabrotica undecimpunctata howardi* Barber, is known commonly by two names, spotted cucumber beetle and southern corn rootworm. It is native to North America and is found throughout the year in the southern states. Migration northward occurs annually and through this mechanism adults are present early in the year in southern Indiana. It may overwinter in small numbers in our southern counties but these individuals are of less importance than the migrants. The yellowish, black spotted beetle lays eggs in the spring in the ground around the base of corn plants, and developing larvae burrow in the roots, crown, and stems. There are two generations in the southern part of the state and at least a partial second in the north.

Larval damage to corn roots by this insect and the related northern corn rootworm is severe. The adults feed extensively on the leaves, shoots, blossoms, and fruit of a wide range of cucurbits. In addition, they are well adapted to feed on beans, potatoes, beets, asparagus, tomatoes, and many other flowering garden plants. This species, along with the striped cucumber beetle, is a vector of cucumber bacterial wilt and is implicated in the spread of mosaic virus. The active beetles are positively phototropic and their attraction to lights with wave lengths of 3500-5300 angstroms may prove to be an effective control.

## Cereal Leaf Beetle

Seldom have insects been first introduced into this country through the interior states. This happened with the cereal leaf beetle, *Oulema melanopus* (L.), a few miles east of Lake Michigan in 1962 in the states of Michigan and Indiana. It had apparently been introduced about four years previously from the western Eurasian continent; its mode of entry was possibly the St. Lawrence Seaway.

This insect overwinters as an adult beetle which is small in size and a metallic blue in color. Its host plants are found only in the grass family (Gramineae). In spring it lays its eggs first on various species of wild grasses followed by winter wheat, from which it moves to spring oats as new seedlings emerge. Larvae hatch, feed on these plants, and exude black fecal matter over their bodies thus apparently providing some protection from adverse environmental factors. These larvae pupate in the ground and emerge as adults in July. These adults feed for only a short time and then enter an inactive period of aestivation until winter hibernation. One generation occurs per year.

The spread of the cereal leaf beetle is principally by the adults which are active flyers and easily carried many miles by the wind. Here is an example of the considerable influence prevailing winds may have on the dispersion of insects. From a small geographical locus, this species has moved 350 to 400 miles eastward, 100 miles south, but only 65 miles to the west. The economic impact of the cereal leaf beetle is to spring seeded small grains, the leaves of which both adults and larvae consume.

## Japanese Beetle

Long a devastating pest in the East, the Japanese beetle, *Popillia japonica* Newman, is now a thoroughly established insect in Indiana. It was originally introduced into the United States in 1916. The spectacular metallic green and red adults emerge from the soil in June and feed on leaf surfaces. Their eggs are deposited in the soil where developing larvae feed on plant roots both in the fall and spring.

Its presence in Indiana is especially interesting. First its mode and routes of entry can be clearly plotted along railroad right-of-ways where it has dropped from west bound freight trains over a progression of years. Secondly, its behavior and choice of host plants is in one case at least unique. The traditional damage by the adult is that of skeletonizing the leaves of fruit trees, roses, and other plants, and severely damaging deciduous fruits; the larvae are devastating to the roots of grass. In the Kentland area of our state, the adults are heavy feeders on soybean leaves and the silks of corn; larvae feed on the roots of corn and related plants. Chemical controls are directed against both larvae and adults, but especially significant is the success experienced in maintaining non-economic levels by the use of the bacteria causing milky disease in the larvae.

### Corn Leaf Aphid

Many aphids occur in Indiana but the impact of this group is perhaps best illustrated by the corn leaf aphid, *Rhopalosiphum maidis* (Fitch). Although not reported in this country until 1870 when Fitch described it in New York, it appears to have been perennially present in Indiana where it has survived on grasses. Although it has very recently been observed by R. T. Everly on barley near Evansville in February, it is not thought to overwinter farther north in the state. Winged forms move from the southern states north with the warming seasons, and colonies are found on Johnson grass in southern Indiana by early May. By midsummer, all areas of Indiana are infested and quite curiously (possibly due to exhaustion or a cold front fallout of migrating populations), the heaviest populations are in the most northern counties.

All reproduction is ovoviviparous and parthenogenic; no males have been found here in nature. Eleven or more generations may occur during a summer. The corn leaf aphid moves from grasses to corn, feeding and developing first in the whorl and then heavily infesting the tassel area. The effect on the corn plant is dramatic and a degree of sterility ranging from slight to complete may occur. Yield is affected, and nubbin ears with incomplete kernel development are common. Presently this aphid is considered in some areas to be the principal pest of corn. Loss in Indiana in 1965 was estimated at $38,500,000. The corn leaf aphid is also a vector of the dwarf maize mosaic and yellow dwarf virus of barley. Of its 67 host plants, corn, barley, sorghum, and Johnson grass are especially important. At present, the need to control this insect is difficult to determine since few clues are available to suggest whether or not heavy populations are developing in a particular field.

## Cattle Grubs

In Indiana there are two species of cattle grubs, the bomb fly, *Hypoderma bovis* (L.) and the heel fly, *H. lineatum* (de Villers). They are frequently known as ox warbles or bot flies. Eggs of the bomb fly are laid singly and those of the heel fly in a row on hair of cattle. The hatched larvae immediately crawl down the hair and bore through the skin to connective tissue. Initial migration of the heel fly larvae is to the esophagus where they remain for 1 to 2 months; the bomb fly larvae display a more random migration. Still as first instar larvae, both species resume migration to a subdermal position in the back where tumerous swellings are produced. Holes are then produced in the hide to obtain air.

Distribution in Indiana reflects the broad, continental distribution of these two species. The heel fly or southern species is the only one present in the southern half of the state; it shares in rather equal numbers the northern cattle areas with the bomb fly or northern cattle grub. The cattle grub can be important in two ways. Both species found in animals can have their origin in Indiana. At the same time both can be brought into the state in transported cattle and it is this latter type of infestation which may prove economically serious. The impact of these insects is in the exhaustive running of cattle caused especially by the bomb fly, the ruined hides, and the less valuable carcasses. Some success has been realized recently in reducing the problem by the use of systemic chemicals circulating in the bodies of the animals.

## Alfalfa Weevil

The newest insect pest of consequence in Indiana is the alfalfa weevil, *Hypera postica* (Gyllenhal). An old world species wherever alfalfa is grown, it was first noted in this country at Salt Lake City in 1904. For nearly fifty years the alfalfa weevil was confined to the West, but in 1952 it was discovered in Maryland and Virginia. By 1964 it had traversed the Appalachians and crossed the Ohio River into Indiana. Once in Indiana's lush alfalfa fields, this beetle spread northward nearly to Indianapolis in only one year. Very shortly it is expected to enter northeastern Indiana from populations in Ohio.

The alfalfa weevil has a tremendous capacity for adapting to a wide range of climatic environments. Wherever it occurs, it has developed habits for that region. In southern Indiana it overwinters in both the egg and adult stages. There is one generation per year developing from egg to adult in about six weeks. Fall laid eggs have been found to hatch as early as March 4 in Harrison County. Meanwhile the adults continue to oviposit in alfalfa stems throughout the spring. With an egg production of nearly 1000 per female the economic impact of this insect could be catastrophic if all survived. Consequently, the alfalfa weevil must be considered potentially as our most devastating pest.

Alfalfa is consumed, frequently to the ground, by both the adults and larvae. An infestation of 200 larvae per square foot is not uncommon. Since all stages are present during the spring, timing of controls is difficult. At this writing, controls are largely cultural and chemical, expensive to the grower, and not always reliable.

### Two-spotted Mite

An arthropod normally considered along with pest insects is the two-spotted mite, *Tetranychus telarius* (L.). The adult is 8-legged, tiny in size, and varies in color from pale yellow to green to reddish-brown depending in part upon feeding activity. Each female lays about 100 eggs which hatch into 6-legged larvae; progressively the stages are then: protonymph, deutonymph, and adult. Brief, quiescent periods occur before each molt. In dry, hot weather, survival is high and all stages are very numerous on plants ranging from apple trees, to arborvitae, roses, clematis, cucumbers, tomatoes, chrysanthemums, and melons.

Leaves of infested plants present a peculiar appearance. Light infestations have pale blotches; in heavy infestations, the entire leaf appears light-colored, dries up, and often turns brown on the edges. The plants themselves lose vigor and frequently die. These mites spin silken threads on the undersurfaces of leaves and large populations frequently web over an entire plant. Mite problems may have been aggravated in recent years by the use of certain insecticides which decrease the natural biotic agents. Certainly problems have increased and chemical control is often difficult.

## Codling Moth

The most persistent and destructive pest of apples throughout the world is the larva of the codling moth, *Carpocapsa pomonella* (L.). It is the traditional worm of a wormy apple. The codling moth was introduced into the colonies before the Revolutionary War and spread westward as the settlers planted apples. It doubtless reached Indiana in the late 1700's or early 1800's.

This insect spends the winter as diapausing larvae in cocoons under such places as the bark of apple trees. By late spring, pupation is complete and the moths emerge in May. Eggs are laid near a cluster of apples and the young larvae enter the fruit rather soon after hatching. Their penetration to the seeds suggests a need for protein supplement in their diet. Development of the codling moth is closely related to temperature; below 50°F. it is inactive and above 86°F its development is retarded. One to three generations occur each year.

The economic impact of this insect is considerable. It attacks not only apple, but pear, quince, crab apple, haws, and English walnuts. Unless controlled by the application of a series of sprays, it often renders a crop entirely worthless.

## Tomato Fruit Worm

The confusion sometimes surrounding common names of insects is particularly evident with one of our most common and important pests, *Heliothis zea (Boddie)*. Its accepted names of tomato fruitworm, corn earworm, cotton bollworm, and vetchworm simply reflect four of its hosts. This is a New World insect and its occurrence in corn in Indiana is presumably as old as the presence of corn itself. Each summer it is found throughout the state.

The overwintering stage of this moth is the pupa but in Indiana north of 40° latitude, this link in its life history is seldom successful. Actually, light trap catches have provided convincing evidence that the substantial early moth flights are actually migrations from the southern states. This moth feeds on the nectar of many flowers and deposits eggs singly on such locations as the silks of corn ears and the leaves of tomatoes. Larval development in corn involves the migration down the silks to the distal kernels where feeding is completed. In the case of the tomato, the larvae move rapidly from the leaves to fruit which they enter and rather thoroughly consume. In all cases, pupation is in the soil and the adults emerge some 30 days after their eggs were laid.

The larvae are very general feeders attacking many cultivated crops and weeds, but being most important on those hosts providing the insects their names. In Indiana, corn is the preferred host and frequently it is the tomato fields near corn that are especially heavily infested. The familiar light, grayish-brown moths are readily attracted to lights, and especially to those producing ultraviolet wavelengths. One of the promising controls incorporates these lights in a trap placed in fields to intercept the females before they lay eggs.

## Insects of the Home

The insects which are of concern in our homes are also associated with diverse environmental conditions.[14] Although there may be profound differences among the environments, all of them, to some degree at least, possess the similarity of an interdependence with the daily activities of man.[6] A dwelling offers several conducive conditions: temporal succession which may support successively several species of insects; a changing variety of foods, furniture and appliances, wall voids and other enclosures, and a wide range of temperature and humidity.[9] Of about 150 species of insects sometimes encountered in structures in our state, only a few are discussed as representative.

### Indian Meal Moth

An important insect pest of both farm and home is the Indian meal moth, *Plodia interpunctella* (Hübner). It is a small, attractive moth with front wings tannish on the basal third and coppery on the distal two thirds. European in origin, this insect was introduced by early immigrants and spread rapidly across the country as settlers moved westward. In unheated storage buildings, this insect overwinters as larvae, but in warm and protected environments breeding and feeding are continuous. The entire life cycle from egg to adult seldom exceeds six weeks. Very important to the economics of this pest is the fact that the mature, creamy white larvae migrate extensively before spinning their cocoons.

The immature stages feed on all kinds of grain and flour, corn meal, dried fruits, and particularly any dried foodstuff about the home. In grain elevators and farm storage bins, these insects are surface feeders and often the top layers of grain are heavily webbed by active larvae. In food processing plants, infestations occur in machinery and storage containers. In the home, bags of flour and mixes are sometimes found riddled by exiting larvae. As the latter crawl about homes, they are frequently mistaken for the larvae of the webbing clothes moth. In a similar manner, the adult Indian meal moth is confused with clothes moths, and when this occurs people are hard put to determine the source of infestation.

### Subterranean Termite

Homeowners throughout the state fear the attack of termites. Our principal species is a subterranean termite, *Reticulitermes flavipes* (Kollar), which is generally an inconspicuous and integral part of the natural environment. It is because these insects are well adapted to share man's dwellings and many of his possessions that termites have become economically important. They were here long before man.

The subterranean termite is a social insect and is characterized by a rather complete caste system. A normal colony will contain "workers," soldiers, primary reproductives, and replacement reproductives. Although new colonies may be started by the primary forms, the growth and continuance of large

Fig. 63. The Columbian timber beetle. A—Soft maple logs from southern Indiana heavily stained due to timber beetle attacks. B—Magnified cross sectional view of two Columbian timber beetle artifacts, one cut slightly above the gallery system to show 14 egg cradles. C—A stylized artifact in tangential aspect (left) with associated elliptical stain and typical three galleries and a radial view (right) showing zoned stain, a central gallery and eight egg cradles projecting up and down from the horizontal gallery. D—General population curves and river stages indicating the relationship of preoutbreak periods to drought conditions (Refined intensive techniques have now demonstrated three outbreaks.) E—Male Columbian timber beetle with the prothorax partially cut away to reveal the position and relative size of the *mycetangium*. F—The fungus, *Ceratocystis* sp., associated with timber beetle galleries. G—*Pichia* n.s.p., the yeast which provides the larval nutrient mass.

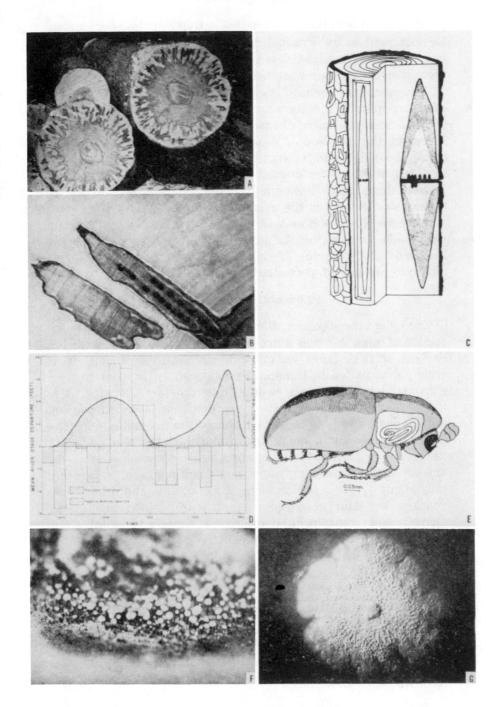

colonies are due to the reproductive activity of the secondaries. Development is by gradual metamorphosis and it takes 1-2 years from egg to alate. It is the dark-bodied wing form, often seen in swarms, which attracts people's attention.

This species of termite is closely dependent upon a complex of environmental factors which normally restrict the colony to the soil. Soil is a source of essential moisture and harbors food including the cellulose of dead roots, fallen timbers, and discarded boards. Termites are unable to digest the ingested cellulose, but it is broken down into usable carbohydrates by intestinal flagellates. Economic damage occurs when the white-bodied workers enter the wooden members of buildings, consuming the inner portions and leaving the shell intact. In our state such damage, or the prevention of it, costs the people hundreds of thousands of dollars per year. Control is principally by means of persistent insecticides.

### Oriental Cockroach

The oriental cockroach, *Blatta orientalis* (L.), is a close associate of man and was introduced into this country with the earliest settlers from Europe and the Mediterranean. It is widely distributed in Indiana. People frequently refer to it as a "water-bug" or "black beetle" but, the fact remains, it is a cockroach. Metamorphosis is gradual and each succeeding stage appears to be a larger edition of the preceding one. The adults are brown to black and dimorphic, the females (1¼ inches long) having small, rudimentary wing pads, and the smaller males possessing short, non-functional wings covering only about ¾ of their abdomens. Eggs of this and other cockroaches are laid in capsules (oothecae) which are purse-shaped cases containing two rows of eggs and crimped together along one edge. Development from egg to adult is influ-

Fig. 64. A—cross section of a 5 inch diameter black locust with heartwood excavation and an adult locust borer. B—Tulip tree borer larva with a darkly stained gallery in the root collar area. C—damaged whorl region with greatly elaborated growth above area infested with Zimmerman pine moth. D—male adult northern walkingstick feeding on hazel. E—Colony of European pine sawfly larvae (right) and a defoliated branch (left). F—Bagworm cases on cedar foliage. G—Map showing western and eastern populations of alfalfa weevil (1965, Note route of introduction into southern Indiana). H—Larvae of cereal leaf beetle feeding on wheat.

enced by temperature but usually requires one year for completion.

Unlike the other house infesting species of cockroaches, the oriental species demonstrates seasonal periodicity in its development. The peak number of adults appears in late spring or early summer, but due to natural mortality the numbers decrease in the early fall. It is common for these cockroaches to spend considerable time outdoors during warm weather. They react to dry weather, however, and frequently move to the more humid environments of drains and basements. As cold weather approaches, migration to the indoors is normal, and within structures, movement toward warm areas of a building is common. It is their obnoxious presence in our homes and food establishments which is the principal factor that classifies it as a pest. This cockroach is a scavenger and exhibits a wide choice of food ranging from starches, to sweets, to meat products, to book bindings.

### Black Carpet Beetle

A survey made at Purdue a number of years ago revealed that the black carpet beetle, *Attagenus piceus* (Olivier), is our most important fabric pest. It is the larval stage that is destructive. The tiny larvae which hatch from the eggs are characteristic in possessing a distinctive, elongated carrot shape with a long brush of tail bristles. Development is slow, being related to temperature and nutrition; it involves a variable number of molts and can take from nine months to three years to reach maturity. The adults are small and shiny black. They fly readily and are found outdoors in flowers in spring and early summer.

Development can take place under a wide range of temperature and humidity conditions and the larvae are much less susceptible to climatic change than are those of the clothes moth. Larvae tend to avoid light and are found in accumulations of lint, in air ducts, beneath baseboards, in woolen rugs and furniture, and in the lower part of clothes closets. Other

Fig. 65. A—corn stalk cut open to show larval damage and a corn borer pupa. B—Tomato fruit worm. C—Japanese beetle and typical leaf feeding by adults. D—Indian meal moths on grain. E—Back of steer with hair clipped to show a number of cattle grubs. F—Photo of inside surface of a hide with implanted cattle grubs. G—Female oriental cockroach. H—Subterranean termites showing small nymphs, workers, and nearly developed reproductives.

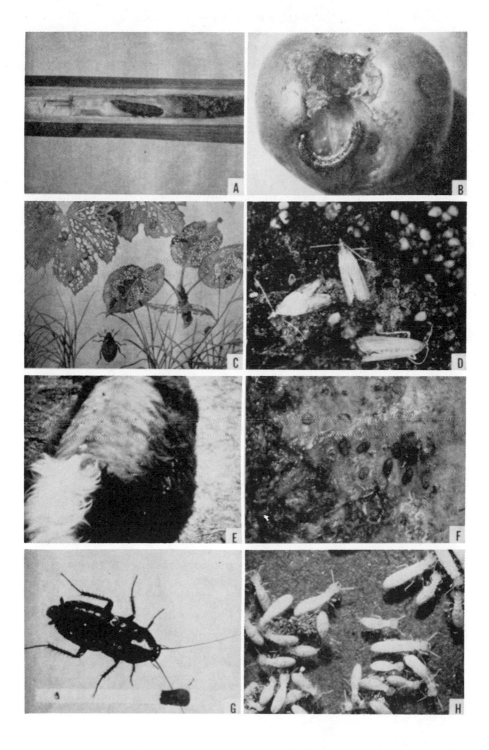

foods include hair, hides, fur and cereals. Their ability to handle the digestion of keratin, an important constituent of wool, hair, and feathers, greatly enhances the destructive potential of this insect. The larvae wander frequently and are found in most unlikely places. It is because they can eat large, irregular holes in wool and devour many other materials that they have great economic importance.

## Floodwater Mosquito

Of the many species of mosquitoes occurring in Indiana, none is more generally troublesome than a floodwater mosquito, *Aedes vexans* (Meigen). Eggs are laid on the ground surface and hatch when flooding occurs. Depending on the temperature, the larval and pupal stages may require from 7 to 30 days. Larvae of this species actively seek organic material in the bottom region of pools.

Adult floodwater mosquitoes are active fliers which frequently migrate 5-10 miles from their place of emergence. This ability complicates control due frequently to the difficulty of locating the sources. The females (male mosquitoes do not bite) are vicious biters even in protected areas in the daytime; at dusk, they are perhaps the worst. They are positively phototropic at night. This species of mosquito is not presently implicated in disease transmission. Control is most effectively accomplished by eliminating water sources, but with this species, the variety of water bodies renders this difficult.

## House Fly

The house fly, *Musca domestica* L., continues to be our most noticeable, undesirable, and hazardous fly. As compared with other common flies, it is less numerous than it was two decades ago but is still widespread in distribution during the warm months. Each female lays 5 to 6 batches of 100 eggs each, these hatching into larvae or white maggots within a day. The developing larvae tunnel through food and pupate in the contracted fourth instar larval skin. Less than two weeks is usually necessary for development and the many generations per year result in peak numbers in the fall. There is little

Fig. 66. Known distribution of selected insect pests as of April, 1966. A—Alfalfa weevil. C—Cereal leaf beetle. PS—European pine sawfly. SM—European pine shoot moth. T—Tulip tree borer. TB—Columbian timber beetle. W—Northern walkingstick. Z—Zimmerman pine moth.

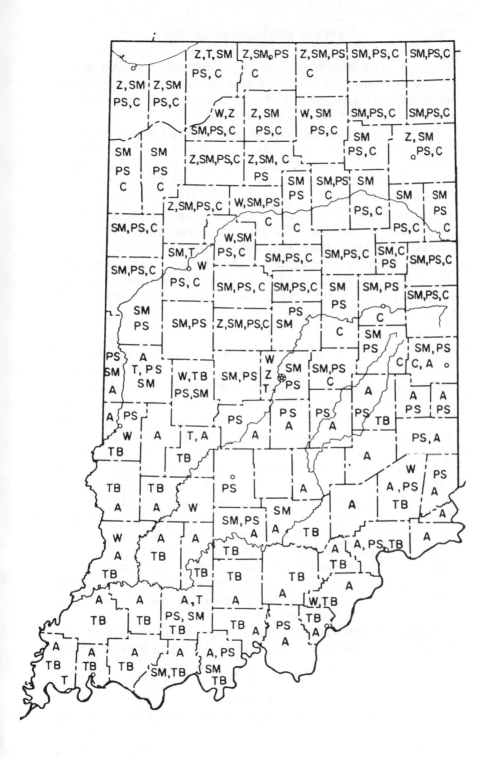

overwintering in Indiana and spring populations have moved in from the south. Larval development occurs in animal manure, human excrement, garbage, decaying vegetable matter, and other suitable organic material.

House flies are a nuisance because they are attracted to most types of food odors. Their sponging mouth parts permit the flies to ingest only liquid materials. By the facility of regurgitated saliva, however, solids are liquified for consumption. House flies are active flies and when they do alight, their choices are usually corners, edges, and thin objects such as wires and strings. Besides their nuisance factor, they are carriers of a large variety of disease organisms such as those of typhoid fever, paratyphoid, cholera, and some types of dysentary. Control is based on improved sanitation and chemicals. This species of fly has demonstrated a remarkable ability to develop populations resistant to many insecticides.

*     *     *

We have selected only a small sample of the thousands of insect species that attack man, animals and flora in Indiana. Although some pests are remarkable because of their universal presence, most species vary in their importance from year to year. Favorable weather conditions for one group of insects may inhibit the development of others. Natural biotic agents, the parasites, predators and diseases which regulate pest populations to variable degrees, respond to independent sets of factors. The continual bombardment by insect populations originating in remote areas and brought to Indiana by frontal systems compound the existing pest situation. The introduction of new pests which become permanently established has given us some of our most important insects and such occurrences continually add to an already rich insect pest fauna.[11] The role of these factors in insect pest dynamics creates a fluctuating mosaic of problems that is never the same for two successive years.[4, 8]

Ecological attributes, damage, representative stages and distribution of selected species are presented in Figures 63-66.

## LITERATURE

1. CRAIGHEAD, F. C. 1950. Insect enemies of eastern forests. U.S.D.A. Misc. Pub. 657. 679 p.

2. GIESE, R. L. 1966. The bioecology of *Corthylus columbianus* Hopkins. Material and Organisms (In press).
3. GRAHAM, S. A., and F. B. KNIGHT. 1965. Principles of forest entomology, 4th ed. McGraw-Hill, New York, 417 p.
4. HUBER, R. T., and J. V. OSMUN. 1966. Insects and other arthropods of economic importance in Indiana during 1965. Proc. Ind. Acad. Sci. **75**. In press.
5. LYONS, L. A. 1964. The European pine sawfly, *Neodiprion sertifer* (Geoff.) (Hymenoptera:Diprionidae). A review with emphasis on studies in Ontario. Proc. Entomol. Soc. Ont. **94**: 5-37.
6. MALLIS, A. 1964. Handbook of pest control, 4th ed. MacNair-Dorland, New York. 1148 p.
7. METCALF, C. L., W. P. FLINT, and R. L. METCALF. 1962. Destructive and useful insects, 4th ed. McGraw-Hill, New York. 1087 p.
8. OSMUN, J. V., and R. A. BRAM. 1965. Insects and other arthropods of economic importance in Indiana in 1964. Proc. Ind. Acad. Sci. **74**: 207-218.
9. OSMUN, J. V., and W. L. BUTTS. 1966. Pest Control. Ann. Rev. Entomol. **11**: 515-548.
10. POINTING, P. J., and G. W. GREEN. 1962. A review of the history and biology of the European pine shoot moth, *Rhyacionia buoliana* (Schiff.) (Lepidoptera: Olethreutidae) in Ontario.
11. ROSS, H. H. 1965. A textbook of entomology, 3rd ed. John Wiley and Sons, New York. 539 p.
12. SCHUDER, D. L. 1960. The Zimmerman pine moth *Dioryctria zimmermani* (Grote). Purdue Univ. Agr. Exp. Sta. Res. Bull. **698**. 8 p.
13. SCHUDER, D. L., and R. L. GIESE. 1962. *Euzophera ostricolorella* Hulst (Lepidoptera: Phycitidae), a root collar borer of tulip tree. Proc. N. Cent. Br. Entomol. Soc. Amer. **17**: 137-138.
14. TRUMAN, L. C., and W. L. BUTTS. 1962. Scientific guide to pest control operations. Pest Control Mag., Cleveland. 181 p.

# 22
# *Cave Fauna*

CARL H. KREKELER and ELIOT C. WILLIAMS, JR.
Valparaiso University and Wabash College

The most significant feature of caves is the absence of light. This means, of course, that photosynthetic plants so conspicuous in terrestrial communities cannot survive in caves. Thus the cave organisms in which biologists are usually interested, and the subject of this paper, are animals.

The earliest American paper dealing with a true cave animal, a blind fish from Mammoth Cave, appeared in 1842, twenty-six years after Indiana became a state.[3] Since that time there has been considerable interest in animals capable of living in the cave environment. In the decades following the publication of *The Origin of Species* biologists the world over sought evidences pro and con on the controversial questions raised by Darwin. In this connection the special modifications seen in cave animals attracted the attention of a number of eminent biologists. Indiana cave animals were included in many of their studies. A classic report by Packard[13] included reference to animals from at least a dozen Indiana caves, notably the large and well known Wyandotte Cave. In the summer of 1896 Indiana's outstanding naturalist W. S. Blatchley undertook a five week exploration trip of Indiana caves and later gave a detailed report on these caves and their fauna.[4] Other classic studies relating particularly to Indiana cave fauna were Eigenmann's work, much of it conducted at Donaldson's Cave at Spring Mill, with the blind cave fish[6] and Banta's intensive study at Mayfield's Cave over a period of several years.[1]

### The Cave Environment and Adaptations to It

What makes cave animals of special interest to biologists is their adaptations to an unusual environment. The most significant feature of caves, as mentioned, is the absence of light in the true cave. Other habitats, such as great ocean depths, are similarly not reached by light rays from the sun. Interestingly, however, many abyssal organisms are luminous, so that light is present and utilized in many deep sea environments.

In contrast, there are few records of light-producing cave animals. The best known is a "glow-worm" found in New Zealand caves, the larva of a particular species of fly.

Caves in addition are usually considered to be quite constant with respect to temperature and relative humidity and to lack significant air movement. As compared to the situation above ground this is certainly true. Nevertheless there is considerable variation in these conditions, depending upon factors such as the size and type of cave, the topography and climate of the region in which it is located, and the number and types of entrances. The temperature deep in Indiana caves is usually between 50° and 55° F, near the mean average temperature of the region. Near the entrance summer temperatures are higher and winter temperatures lower than this. Even deep within the cave there may be temperature variations of three degrees or so. Most Indiana caves have water seeping in from above, and many of them have water flowing at least through some part or in some season, and relative humidity is in most cases between 95 and 100%. There are some dry caves, however, in which relative humidity may be as low as 80%, and there is some variation in relative humidity in moist caves from season to season or area to area. The fact that streams and standing bodies of water are often found in caves means also, of course, that there are regularly habitats available for aquatic as well as terrestrial animals. Indiana does not have caves, such as known elsewhere, in which there is conspicuous "breathing" in and out of air. In many small passages connecting larger portions of caves, however, conspicuous air currents are noticed, and at times air movement can be detected in the large chambers.

The constancy of the cave environment provides an advantageous situation for many forms of life. The environmental fluctuations characteristic of most habitats (i.e., winter and summer, night and day, or wet and dry seasons) present important problems to living organisms. The distribution of most organisms is limited by one or more environmental conditions which are periodic in their appearance. For example, many tropical or sub-tropical forms could easily adjust to the summer climate of Indiana, but the winter conditions keep them out. Moreover the conditions of temperature, relative humidity, and air movement are such that water loss by evap-

oration is low. Thus animals requiring non-drying environments may find the cave a suitable habitat. For example,
springtails outside caves are found in litter, under rocks, or
under bark of rotting logs, but roam about freely on the surface within caves.

On the other hand, the cave environment presents some
distinct problems to animals. Living in an environment without light they must be able to carry out such functions as food
getting and mating without the use of eyes. These functions
are achieved rather with the use of tactile, auditory, or chemical senses, and in many cases there is a distinct compensatory
hypertrophy of organs of these non-visual senses. Moreover,
as is well known, the visual structures of cave animals are
often degenerate or lacking. Also cave animals are regularly
depigmented. In lighted environments pigments serve to protect the living tissue from harmful light rays and in many
cases to provide a coloration which affords protection from
predators. Well developed eyes and pigmentation are lost in
the unlighted cave environment, the reasoning runs quite logically, because of the absence of selection for their maintenance.

Animals living in caves, in general called cavernicoles, show
various degrees of adaptation to cave life, and various schemes
for recognizing this have been proposed. Possibly the best is
this, though the boundaries are not always sharp and it must
be recognized that not enough may be known of a given form
to place it with certainty in a particular category. True cave
animals, those which live only in caves and which are so highly
modified that they cannot live outside caves, are called troglobites; the best known Indiana troglobite is the modern cavefish, *Amblyopsis spelaea*. Animals which regularly live in caves
and complete their life cycle there, but which may also be
found outside caves and/or which lack the rudimentary features which would restrict them to caves, are called troglophiles; the earthworms commonly found in cave mud are
troglophiles. Animals which regularly occupy caves but which
must leave the true cave for some function such as food getting
are called trogloxenes; an example is the cave cricket, *Ceu-
thophilus stygius*. Some animals, such as the common pickerel
frog, *Rana palustris*, get into caves from time to time and find
this a suitable habitat for a while; these are best called acci-

dentals even though they may move into the cave voluntarily.

## Indiana Troglobites

Our primary concern in this paper is with the Indiana troglobites which are listed in Table 11. Cave animals are both terrestrial and aquatic. They belong to many groups. Among the invertebrates there are flatworms and snails; but the largest assemblage belong to the phylum Arthropoda—the aquatic crustaceans and the terrestrial insects, spiders, millipedes and their relatives. Vertebrates are represented by fishes and salamanders. Other groups, as far as is known, have not developed true cave forms. Bats which are commonly found in caves do not qualify as troglobites since they make periodic forays into the outer world.

In the study of cave organisms there are certain aspects of their biology which are of special interest. Each of these topics is considered below in connection with the cave fish and beetles. But other organisms, which contribute especially to our understanding of some of these problems, are mentioned as we list these topics. 1) RELATIONSHIPS. How are the cave forms related to epigaean (above ground) forms and to one another? Troglobitic isopods, commonly considered in the past as comprising a distinct genus *Caecidotea,* are clearly derived from the epigaean genus *Asellus.* It now appears that several different cave adapted lines are involved, each derived from different *Asellus* stocks, hence many modern authors consider them all *Asellus.* 2) PREADAPTATION. Cave forms are typically derived from epigaean forms which are preadapted, that is have adaptations which tend to suit them for life in cave environments. Epigaean springtails living in litter do not depend to any extent on sight for their various activities and in many cases have degenerate or no eyes. Therefore it is not surprising that a great variety of springtails is found living in caves. 3) ADAPTATIONS AND REGRESSION. True cave organisms have a variety of special adaptations to the cave environment, physiological and behavioral as well as morphological. In addition their visual organs and pigmentation are regularly lost. Recent studies on springtails, for example, have disclosed that peculiarities in their foot morphology, long used in classification, are significant for their locomotor behavior on substrates characteristic of caves.[5] 4) ISOLATION AND DISPERSAL. True

Table 11. True cave animals known for Indiana (adapted from Nicholas[12] with assistance of William R. Eberly).

PHYLUM PLATYHELMINTHES
  Class Turbellaria
    Order Tricladida
      *Phagocota subterranea*
        Hyman
PHYLUM ARTHROPODA
  Class Crustacea
    Order Amphipoda
      *Bactrurus mucronatus*
        (Forbes)
      *Crangonyx gracilis packardi*
        Smith
      *C. obliquus* (Hubricht and
        Mackin)
      *Stygobromus vitreus* Cope
    Order Isopoda
      *Asellus stygius* (Packard)
    Order Decapoda
      *Orconectes inermis* Cope
      *O. pellucidus pellucidus*
        (Tellkampf)
      *Cambarus bartoni laevis*
        Faxon
    Order Ostracoda
      *Donnaldsoncythere
        donnaldsonensis* Klie
    Order Copepoda
      *Cyclops jeanneli* Chappuis
      *Attheyella pilosa* Chappuis
  Class Diplopoda
    *Pseudotremia indianae*
      Chamberlin and Hoffman
    *Conotyla bollmani* (McNeil)
    *Scytonotus cavernarum*
      Bollman
  Class Insecta
    Order Collembola
      *Parasinella cavernarum*
        (Packard)
      *Hypogastrura lucifugus*
        (Packard)

Order Coleoptera
  *Pseudanophthalmus emer-
    soni* Krekeler
  *P. eremita* (Horn)
  *P. leonae* Barr
  *P. shilohensis shilohensis*
    Krekeler
  *P. shilohensis boonensis*
    Krekeler
  *P. shilohensis mayfieldensis*
    Krekeler
  *P. tenuis tenuis* (Horn)
  *P. tenuis blatchleyi* Barr
  *P. tenuis jeanneli* Krekeler
  *P. tenuis morrisoni* Jeannel
  *P. tenuis stricticollis* Jeannel
  *P. youngi youngi* Krekeler
  *P. youngi donaldsoni*
    Krekeler
  *Batrisodes* (?*Babnor-
    modes*) *krekeleri* Park
Class Arachnida
  Order Pseudoscorpionida
    *Kleptochthonius packardi*
      (Hagen)
  Order Araneae
    *Phanetta subterranea*
      (Emerton)
    *Willbaldi cavernicola*
      Keyserling
  Order Acarina
    *Rhagida cavicola* Banks
PHYLUM CHORDATA
  Class Osteichthyes
    Order Teleostei
      *Amblyopsis spelaea* Dekay
      *Typhlichthys subterraneus*
        Girard

cave animals are usually unable to cope with the above-ground environment and thus are often isolated within a single cave or cave system. This plays an important role in speciation and the evolutionary history of cave forms. Terrestrial forms are often more effectively isolated than aquatic species since the latter may move some distance by underground streams and never really leave a cave environment. Of 98 described species and subspecies of troglobitic carabid beetles, 54 are known only from a single cave. On the other hand, some of the linyphiid cave spiders have extensive distribution. A species found in Indiana caves ranges east to Pennsylvania and south to Virginia, Tennessee and Alabama.

## Fish

Undoubtedly the best known Indiana cave animal is the northern cavefish, *Amblyopsis spelaea*. Thousands of people have seen these blind unpigmented fish at Twin and Donaldson's Caves in Spring Mill, and they have often been exhibited at the state fairs in Indianapolis. They are found in many Indiana caves south of Bedford. Eigenmann's work early in this century (remains of his rearing pools are still visible at the entrance to Donaldson's Cave) disclosed much of its biology, but recent work has added greatly to our knowledge.[14, 15] The northern cavefish together with the troglobitic Ozark cavefish (*Amblyopsis rosae*) and southern cavefish (*Typhlichthys subterraneus*), the troglophilic spring cavefish (*Chologaster agassizi*), and the epigaean swampfish (*Chologaster cornutus*) constitute a distinctive family, the Amblyopsidae. Morphological peculiarities indicate that either the three genera arose independently from an ancestral stock or that *Amblyopsis* represents one branch from an ancestral stock while *Chologaster* and a derivative *Typhlichthys* represent another branch. Whatever their exact relationships, the fact is that the members of this family show increasing adaptation to life in caves. The epigaean swampfish, though eyed and pigmented, avoids light and is more nocturnal and inactive than other fish in its swamp habitat in the southeastern states. Moreover its chemoreceptors and tactile receptors are highly developed. These characteristics indicate that the swampfish regularly obtains food without dependence on light and is preadapted to life in caves. The early morphological studies of reduction of eyes and pigment in members of the family revealed an increasing regression in the sequence: *C. cornutus*, *C. agassizi*, *T. subterraneus*, *A. spelaea*, *A. rosae*. Recent studies disclose increasing adaptation to cave life in the same sequence in the following respects: hypertrophy of non-visual sensory structures and their brain centers; decrease of absolute growth rate; production of larger and fewer eggs; decrease in metabolic rates; and decrease in reaction to disturbing stimuli.

*A. spelaea* feeds on virtually all its common associates, especially copepods, amphipods, and isopods. It swims slowly and almost continually along the margins of the water and substrate, sometimes in midwater, foraging for food; it orients to food an inch or more away. Reproduction occurs only once every several years, and only a few females reproduce then. The eggs are few in number, are relatively large and rich in yolk, and the eggs and yolk-sac fry are carried by the females in the gill chambers. Such branchial gestation obviously affords considerable protection in the cave environment. Still, mortality of the young occurs as a result of cannibalism. The adults have no predators and indications are that mortality by disease or parasitism is low. It is postulated that dispersal between caves and cave regions occurs via subterranean channels below the water table. Although first described from Mammoth Cave in Kentucky, *A. spelaea* has not been taken there recently. Possibly its habitat in this area has been restricted by competition with the southern cavefish commonly found there.

## Beetles

The most numerous North American (and Indianan) troglobites in species are the carabid cave beetles. Because they average only ⅕″ in length, however, they are not well known to most cave visitors. Most of the American species, and all those known for Indiana, are of the genus *Pseudanophthalmus*, though other genera are also found. In most cases their eyes are completely lacking and dissections show no optic ganglia. Pigment is reduced, so that the beetles range from straw to reddish brown in color. Functional wings are also absent. The appendages and antennae are unusually long. The former and the extremely long bristles scattered over the body presumably enhance tactile sense reception and possibly other non-visual senses.

Other members of the subfamily in which *Pseudanophthalmus* is placed are found in temperate areas of North America, the genus *Trechus* even rarely in Indiana. But the genus to which *Pseudanophthalmus* seems most closely related is *Trechoblemus* whose distribution is temperate Europe and Asia. Probably *Trechoblemus* or a stock from which it and *Pseudanophthalmus* were derived was at one time distributed also through temperate North America. The epigaean forms have subsequently disappeared, as they were probably unable to adjust to climatic vagaries during the Pleistocene, while a number of derivative forms living in the protective cave environment have survived. *Trechoblemus* and a number of other genera in a given portion of the subfamily typically live in deep litter and crevices in the soil and do not depend to any great extent on vision. Eyes, wings, and pigmentation are often reduced. But in addition many of these forms, obviously preadapted to cave life, invade caves. In some cases in Europe a series of forms has been found transitional between eyed, winged, and deeply pigmented epigaean beetles and eyeless, wingless, and depigmented cavernicolous beetles.[7]

The described species of Indiana *Pseudanopthalmus* fall into five distinct groups and at least another three await description. Forms within groups isolated in different cave systems are distinctive enough in most cases that they are recognized as species or subspecies.[2, 8, 9] One species of the *tenuis* group from a cave in Indiana is closely related to a species living in Kentucky caves; these forms have apparently been isolated since the formation of the modern Ohio River in mid-Pleistocene. Another form of the same group, differing about the same extent from its nearest relative, is found in caves that were probably not formed until late in the Pliocene. Thus divergence to this extent in isolation appears to require on the order of a million years. Forms in two of the Indiana groups *(tenuis* and *youngi)* are found in caves of the Blue River, Lost River, and the East Fork of the White River drainages. In many cases forms of both groups are found in the same cave. These facts present some interesting problems. 1) How are two closely related forms able to coexist? According to theoretical analysis of competition and studies of other kinds of animals this is possible only if the two species have somewhat different ecological niches. In caves of nearby states different species in the same cave are observed to have distinct microhabitat preferences—as sandy banks, mud flats, or under wet cobbles—but such preferences have not been recognized for our Indiana forms. 2) How did these true cave animals get to the caves in which they are found and how do they move between caves? Underground movement via inter-cave channels seems to be the most common type of movement, and whether or not such movement is possible appears to play a distinct role in determining species distribution. In areas where caves are in rocks lying nearly horizontally and are likely to be connected by small channels, species have relatively broad distributions, while in areas where there is much folding of rocks and limited possibility of inter-cave channels species are strikingly limited in their distribution. There is evidence, however, that movement may occur in other than underground passages, for certain closely related forms are known to be separated by rock strata in which extensive underground passages are not found.[10]

## Cave Ecology

Caves and their flora and fauna are an example of a simple ecosystem. They are isolated communities of highly specialized forms adapted for existence in an environment which would be extremely hostile for most other organisms. The complete absence of light in the true cave rules out all photosynthetic activity which is the basic source of food in aboveground communities. Although there is evidence that autotrophic organisms such as iron and sulphur bacteria may play some part in the food cycle within a cave, it is certainly true that most troglobites are dependent in the final analysis upon materials from the upper world.[11] Because of the tenuous food supply and the difficulties of the habitat in general, animal populations in caves are often extremely small and subject to extermination. These animals should not be collected, except with care by research specialists, for fear of endangering many species.

There are really two distinct aspects of the cave ecosystem, the terrestrial and the aquatic. The aquatic organisms are more likely than their terrestrial companions to have a constant, although meager, supply of organic materials continually arriving via the stream in which they live. Upon such material bacteria will thrive and become a source of food for protozoans. Both in turn, as well as the organic detritus, may serve as food for small crustaceans such as copepods, ostracods, isopods, and amphipods. Cave planarians may also feed upon such microorganisms as well as upon the small crustaceans. The crustacea as well as the planaria are in turn a source of food for cave crayfish and cave fish. The cave fish may occasionally feed upon their own young or upon the cave crayfish. Wastes from all of these animals as well as their remains return to the system through the action of the bacteria.

The terrestrial troglobites face an even more scanty fare than their aquatic counterparts. An important portion of their food supply consists of plant and other organic debris brought in by underground streams at flood stage or falling in at sloping entries to the cave. On this material, as well as on the remains of dead animals and bat guano, a variety of molds may be found. Anyone who has visited a cave will recall that almost every scrap of wood, dead animal, or discarded cigarette stub is covered by a hoary plant growth of some kind. Chance visitors losing their way may die or at least leave droppings which serve as a base for growth of heterotrophic plant life. Such visitors include rats, foxes, raccoons, and other small mammals as well as various bat species which are more than chance visitors. Upon these imported organic materials and the molds growing on them a variety of troglobites subsist. Included in this group are mites, springtails, millipedes, snails, phalangids, and pselaphid beetles. Dependent upon the preceding forms and upon each other are the troglobitic predators. In this category we find carabid beetles, spiders, and pseudoscorpions.

In most caves there are organisms commonly present, at least in the twilight zones, which also occur above ground. Consideration of the cave as an ecosystem would be incomplete without mention of such species. The cave salamander of Indiana *(Eurycea lucifuga)*, earthworms, and assorted beetles and flies, to mention only a few examples, fall into this category. Since they may die or succumb to predation while within the cave, they form significant additions to the food web of the cave ecosystem.

## LITERATURE

1. BANTA, A. M. 1907. The fauna of Mayfield's Cave. Carnegie Inst. Washington, Publ. **67**, 114 pp.
2. BARR, T. C., JR. 1960. A synopsis of the cave beetles of the genus *Pseudanophthalmus* of the Mitchell Plain in southern Indiana (Coleoptera, Carabidae). Amer. Midland Naturalist **63**: 307-320.
3. ————————. 1966. Evolution of cave biology in the United States, 1822-1965. Bull. Nat. Speleological Soc. **28**: 15-21.
4. BLATCHLEY, W. S. 1896. Indiana caves and their fauna. Indiana Dept. of Geol. and Nat. Res., 21st Ann. Report, pp 121-212.
5. CHRISTIANSEN, KENNETH. 1965. Behavior and form in the evolution of cave Collembola. Evolution **19**: 529-537.
6. EIGENMANN, C. H. 1909. Cave vertebrates of America: a study in degenerative evolution. Carnegie Inst. Washington, Publ. **104**, 241 pp.
7. JEANNEL, RENE. 1928. Monographie des Trechinae, III. L'Abeille: Journal d'Entomologie **35**: 1-808.

8. _____. 1949. Les Coleopteres cavernicols de la region des Appalaches. III. Etude systematique. Notes Biospeologiques, Publ. du Mus. d'Hist. Naturelle, Fasc. **IV**, No. **12**: 37-104.

9. KREKELER, C. H. 1958. Speciation in cave beetles of the genus *Pseudanophthalmus* (Coleoptera, Carabidae). Amer. Midland Naturalist **59**: 167-189.

10. _____. 1959. Dispersal of cavernicolous beetles. Systematic Zoology **8**: 119-130.

11. MOORE, G. W. and BROTHER G. NICHOLAS. 1964. Speleology: The Study of Caves. D. C. Heath and Co.

12. NICHOLAS, BROTHER G. 1960. Checklist of macroscopic troglobitic organisms of the United States. Amer. Midland Naturalist **64**: 123-160.

13. PACKARD, A. S. 1888. The cave fauna of North America, with remarks on the anatomy of the brain and origin of the blind species. Nat. Acad. Sci., First Memoir, Vol. **4**, 156 pp.

14. POULSON, T. L. 1963. Cave adaptation in amblyopsid fishes. Amer. Midland Naturalist **70**: 257-290.

15. WOODS, L. P. and R. F. INGER. 1957. The cave, spring, and swamp fishes of the family Amblyopsidae of central and eastern United States. Amer. Midland Naturalist **58**: 232-256.

# 23
# *The Fishes*

JAMES R. GAMMON and SHELBY D. GERKING
Department of Zoology, DePauw University
and
Department of Zoology, Indiana University

## Introduction

The fishes of Indiana have fascinated scientists and non-scientists for a long time. Samuel Rafinesque collected and identified fish from the Ohio River near Jeffersonville shortly after Indiana became a state.[10] Early work at Indiana University concentrated mainly upon taxonomy, anatomy, distribution, and natural history. The kinds of fishes and their distribution are now fairly well known and the questions being asked about them have changed.[6, 9] For example, why is it that some species are represented by many individuals while others have only a few? What causes fish populations to fluctuate from year to year? What determines the amount of fish that can be produced during a period of time. Can productivity be increased by altering these factors? What is the best way to increase the density of sport fishes and reduce "rough" fishes?

Considerable time and research has been devoted to these and other questions during the past several decades. Some have been answered, at least in part. Basic research is yielding growth rates, survival rates, mortality factors, food conversion efficiency, species interrelationships, etc., in order to furnish information upon which to solve present and future problems.

Every Indiana resident lives within a few miles of some aquatic habitat. Growing numbers take advantage of the opportunity to go fishing. The fish caught provide a welcome and nutritious addition to their diet, but of even greater value is the relaxation and recreation that is so uniquely a part of fishing. Knowledge about the fish not only deepens the satisfaction that comes with fishing, but also increases the size of the catch. The variety of shapes, sizes, and coloration in our fishes, as well as their unusual, mysterious habits imparts a fascination of fishes to even the casually interested person.

## Fish Fauna

Our fish fauna has undoubtedly changed during the past several thousand years. When the Wisconsin glacier covered the northern two-thirds of Indiana, coldwater species such as trout, grayling, whitefish, and cisco probably swam in the frigid waters of the southern part of the state. As the climate warmed and the ice disappeared, these species moved northward, and warmwater fish gradually migrated from the south into the area and established themselves in favorable aquatic habitats. Large, shallow, short-lived lakes were formed and the basic drainage pattern was established at this time. Many of our most widely distributed species of fish entered through the Ohio and Wabash Rivers and their larger tributaries. Some species entered the Kankakee and Iroquois drainages through a waterway connecting with the upper Tippecanoe. The St. Joseph River flowed into the Kankakee providing another pathway. Other species undoubtedly entered Northern Indiana from the west through the Illinois and Kankakee Rivers.

A total of 177 species of fish have been described from Indiana waters. Some of these are depicted in the accompanying illustrations (Figs. 67-69). Ten have not been collected since 1900 and may no longer live here. Twenty species are rare, some because of specific habitat requirements, but many more because of extensive man-induced changes in the environment. Siltation and the draining of chemical, industrial, mining, and municipal wastes into our streams and rivers have adversely affected many species of fish and continue to be major problems today. Species which are declining in abundance are lake sturgeon *(Acipenser fulvescens)*, shovelnose sturgeon *(Scaphirhynchus platorynchus)*, paddlefish *(Polyodon spathula)*, blue catfish *(Ictalurus furcatus)*, walleye *(Stizostedion vitreum)*, yellow bullhead *(Ictalurus natalis)*, muskellunge *(Esox masquinongy)*, smallmouth bass *(Micropterus dolomieui)*, and many smaller species. Those which are increasing include gizzard shad *(Dorosoma cepedianum)*, carp, goldeye *(Hiodon alosoides)*, and orange-spot sunfish *(Lepomis humilis)*. Numerous fish kills occur each year from intentional or accidental discharge of certain industrial and untreated municipal wastes into rivers. Chemical wastes on occasion have led to the severe impairment of the flavor of food fishes. It has been shown that detergents destroy the taste buds of catfish and may thus interfere with normal feeding.[1] Unless preventive measures are employed these and other forms of pollution may become more prevalent in the future as our population and industrial growth increase.

Several species have been introduced by man. The European carp *(Cyprinus carpio)* was introduced about 1880 and is now found throughout the state. Goldfish *(Carassius auratus)* occasionally escape from ponds or careless bait fishermen. Three species of trout (brook trout, *Salvelinus fontinalis;* brown trout, *Salmo trutta;* and rainbow trout, *Salmo gaird-*

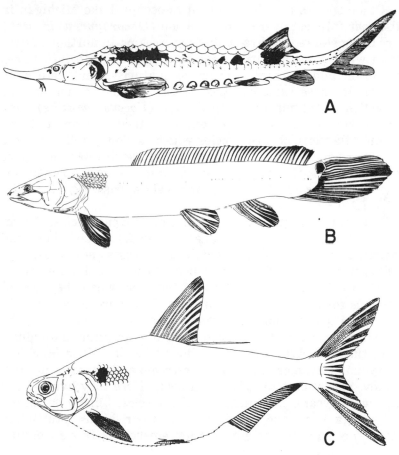

Fig. 67. A—Lake or rock sturgeon. B—Bowfin. C—Gizzard shad. (Drawn by D. Tibbitts, courtesy University of Wisconsin Laboratory of Limnology.)

*nerii)* are stocked annually in a few coldwater streams in northern Indiana.[21] In the 1920's smelt *(Osmerus mordax)* were stocked in a tributary of Lake Michigan and rapidly spread throughout the Great Lakes.

Other species have entered of their own accord within recent times. The sea lamprey *(Petromyzon marinus)* invaded Lake Erie via the Welland Canal about 1921. The alewife *(Alosa pseudoharengus)* followed the same route and in 1963 comprised more than 25% of the total commercial catch in Lake Michigan. The threadfin shad *(Dorosoma petenense)* has entered the Ohio River within the past fifteen years.

Other species may be expected to occupy Lake Michigan in the near future. Silver or coho salmon *(Oncorhynchus kisutch)* are being stocked in three tributary streams in northern Michigan with the expectation that they will migrate into Lakes Superior and Michigan, grow to maturity, and return to spawn in these same streams. If the salmon do not become established, the marine striped bass *(Roccus saxatilis)* may be stocked. Both species are excellent food and sport fishes.

An Atlantic seaboard species which is slowly following the westward route of the sea lamprey and alewife into the upper Great Lakes is the white perch *(R. americanus)*, a relative of the white bass *(R. chrysops)* and yellow bass *(R. mississippiensis)*.

The most primitive of our fishes are seven species of lampreys (Family Petromyzontidae). These forms lack jaws and paired fins, have a single nostril, and possess seven pairs of gill openings which form a row behind each eye. Lampreys are most in evidence in the spring of the year when they ascend streams for the purpose of spawning. Nests are constructed in sand and gravel riffles by removing stones by means of the sucking disc, which is also used to anchor spawning individuals over the nest. After spawning, the adults die. Upon hatching, the young larvae are carried downstream and burrow into soft, sandy, mucky bottoms of stream pools. Here they live for one to several years, depending on the species, blindly straining microorganisms and detritus with their heads protruding from the mud. In the spring they emerge as free-swimming

Fig. 68. A Cisco. B—Black bullhead. C—Northern pike. D—Yellow perch. (Drawn by D. Tibbitts, courtesy University of Wisconsin Laboratory of Limnology.

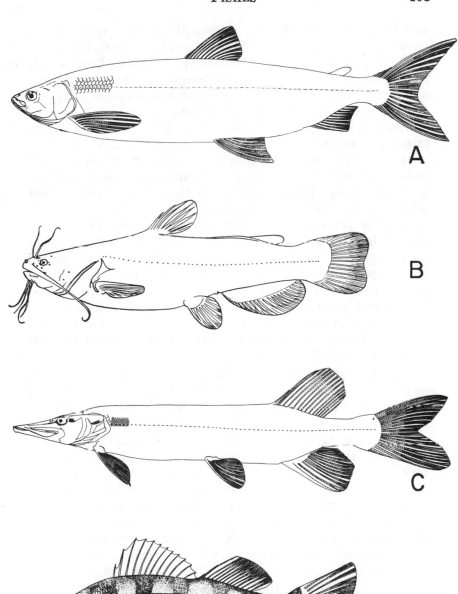

A

B

C

D

mature adults. The three non-parasitic species subsequently spawn and die, but four other species live a parasitic existence for one or more years before they spawn. They attach themselves to large fish, rasp through the skin and scales, and extract the blood. Native species of the parasitic lampreys are not abundant and have never been a problem. The sea lamprey, however, spread throughout the Great Lakes and tributary streams including some in Indiana and by 1946 caused the first decline in the lake trout fishing industry of Lake Michigan. Many millions of dollars have been spent by both the United States and Canada in efforts to reduce and ultimately rid the Great Lakes of this lamprey.

Another primitive and most unusual species, the paddlefish *(Polyodon spathula)*, is scaleless and has a long, broad, paddleshaped snout whose function is unknown. The paddlefish or spoonbill migrate into tributary streams in the spring to spawn over gravel bars in swift water.[22] It obtains food by swimming with its cavernous mouth open and straining microscopic organisms from the water with sieve-like gill rakers.[14] Individuals may live thirty or more years and exceed 100 pounds in weight.

The gar family (Lepisoteidae) is exclusively North American and is distinguished by thick, rhomboidal scales and long, tooth-studded jaws. Gars are frequently maligned because they eat other fish and are themselves neither sport fish nor good to eat. While gars may sometimes become too numerous, they usually perform a useful function, preying upon forage fishes which might otherwise become overabundant. They have the conspicuous habit of basking near the surface on warm days and nights. Four species are found in Indiana. A few enormous alligator gar *(Lepisosteus spatula)* still occur in the lower Ohio and Wabash Rivers. Shortnose gar *(L. platostomus)* are less rare but are restricted to larger rivers including the lower White River. In contrast to shortnose gar, spotted gar *(L. oculatus)* are rather common in the northern glacial lakes and oxbow lakes along the lower Wabash River. The abundant longnose gar *(L. osseus)* inhabits lakes, rivers, and streams throughout Indiana.

Another "living fossil" confined to North America solely is the bowfin *(Amia calva)*, also called dogfish or grindle, which inhabits weedy lakes and river backwaters feeding on fish and crayfish. It may be distinguished from all other fish in this area by the long dorsal fin which extends over most of the length of the back. This species is of considerable scientific interest but is regarded as an undesirable fish by most anglers because it, like gar, eats game and pan fish. Bowfin

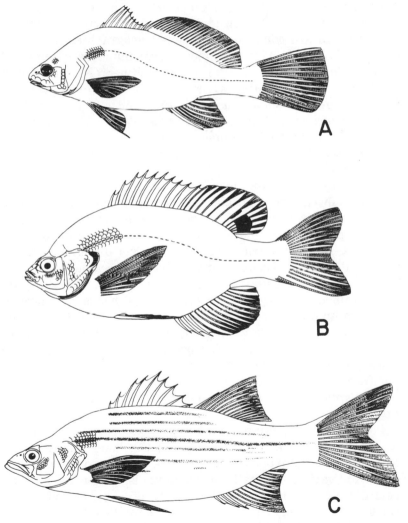

Fig. 69. A—Freshwater drum or "white perch". B—Bluegill. C—White bass. (Drawn by D. Tibbitts, courtesy University of Wisconsin Laboratory of Limnology.)

may be readily caught on live or artificial bait and are game fighters.

To most people a minnow is any small fish. Actually there is a distinct minnow family (Cyprinidae) which is the largest of all fish families and is represented by over 300 species in North America alone. Many of Indiana's 48 species of minnows are small, silvery, similar, and hard to identify. The most common species is the bluntnose minnow *(Pimephales notatus)* which is found in abundance in all types of waters. Most species are somewhat restricted geographically and/or ecologically. Large rivers support large numbers of emerald shiner *(Notropis atherinoides)*, mimic shiner *(N. volucellus)*, sand shiner *(N. stramineus)*, river shiner *(N. blennius)*, silvery minnow *(Hybognathus nuchalis,)* and silver chub *(Hybopsis storeriana)*. Blacknose *(N. heterolepis)* blackchin *(N. heterodon,)* pugnose *(N. anogenus)*, and ironcolor shiners *(N. chalybaeus)* are restricted to quiet weedy waters in the north.

Many species of minnows are best adapted for living in streams. Twenty-two species are common and widely distributed. Stonerollers *(Campostoma anomalum)* frequent riffles and scrape algae from rocks with a specially-adapted, hard lower lip. Another riffle species which has increased greatly in abundance in recent years is the suckermouth minnow *(Phenacobius mirabilis)*. Rosyface shiners *(N. rubellus)* are found immediately below riffles in the pool heads. Our largest native minnows, the striped shiner *(N. chrysocephalus)* and the creek chub *(Semotilus atromaculatus)*, reach 8 to 10 inches in length. inhabit stream pools, and are often caught on worms or artificial flies. They are frequently accompanied by bluntnose minnow, redfin shiner *(N. umbratilis)*, spotfin shiner *(N. spilopterus)*, and silverjaw minnow *(Ericymba buccata)*.

For all their apparent similarity in appearance, minnows occupy a broad spectrum of roles in the lakes and streams. A few are vegetarian, but most are carnivorous and feed on a wide variety of small aquatic animals. As such they compete directly for food with the young of larger sport fishes. On the other hand, they serve as food for sport fishes, crayfish, and fish-eating birds.

Another group of small fishes which is unknown to many

persons is the darters. They are too small for food, not very useful as bait, and are most secretive in their habits. These relatives of the yellow perch *(Perca flavescens)*, sauger *(Stizostedion canadense)*, and walleye *(Stizostedion vitreum)* seldom exceed three to four inches in length, and some become brilliantly colored with green, blue, and orange during the spring breeding season. Twenty-seven species of darters have been found in Indiana. All but the Iowa darter *(Etheostoma exile)* and the least darter *(E. microperca)*, which prefer quiet weedy water, are true stream fish. Many are highly adapted for life on swift gravelly riffles or raceways by virtue of having no air bladder and relatively enormous pectoral fins. Some bury their eggs in the gravel and desert them, while others carefully attach their eggs to the undersurfaces of large rocks and diligently guard them. All are carnivorous and feed on a variety of aquatic invertebrates.

The geographic location of Indiana with respect to the distributional ranges of the northern coldwater species on the one hand and the southern warmwater species on the other is partly responsible for our rich fish fauna. Northern Indiana has 24 species which are not found in southern Indiana. Most of these have ranges which extend only as far south as the upper Wabash River. Eight species characteristic of the southern United States are limited to the southern third of Indiana. Nineteen more species characteristically live in larger rivers and, therefore, do not find suitable habitats in the north. The great variety of aquatic habitats available in Indiana also contributes towards our rich fish fauna. It is not possible to explore all of the many interesting characteristics of our fishes. Therefore, the remainder of this paper will focus attention on a few species of fish typical of several important aquatic habitats: lakes, ponds, reservoirs, brooks, streams, and rivers.

### Lakes

Approximately 1000 lakes are scattered across northern Indiana, formed from the melting of huge ice blocks which were left embedded in the ground when the glaciers receded northward. These lakes have changed greatly in the several thousands of years elapsing since their birth. A thick coat of sediment and organic debris covers the original rocky, sandy bottom of existing lakes. Sheltered bays have become populated with rooted aquatic vegetation. The water itself has grown more fertile as nutrients from the surrounding drainage have been added over the centuries.

Most of our glacial lakes are rich, eutrophic lakes which support large fish populations. Typical species of fish found in the glacial lakes include largemouth bass *(Micropterus salmoides)*, bluegill *(Lepomis macrochirus)*, redear sunfish *(L. microlophus)*, pumpkinseed sunfish *(L. gibbosus)*, warmouth *(Chaenobryttus gulosus)*, black crappie *(Pomoxis nigromaculatus)*, rock bass *(Ambloplites rupestris)*, yellow perch *(Perca flavescens)*, yellow bullhead *(Ictalurus natalis)*, brown bullhead *(I. nebulosus)*, lake chubsucker *(Erimyzon sucetta)*, bowfin, spotted and longnose gar, northern pike, *(Esox lucius)*, grass pickerel *(E. americanus)*, brook silversides *(Labidesthes sicculus,)* golden shiner *(Notemigonous crysoleucas)*, and smaller minnows and darters which have already been mentioned. A few Indiana lakes also provide marginal conditions for the cold-water cisco *(Coregonus artedii)*.[5] (see Frey, this volume.)

The bluegill, which regularly comprises 80% of the fisherman's catch, is a typical lake species. Bluegills can be found in or near beds of rooted vegetation and are one of the species best known with regard to its life history and vital statistics. Most of the sunfishes build nests and spawn at discrete intervals over a protracted period of time and the bluegill is no exception. The males move onto sand or gravel areas from 1 to 3 feet deep near shore, and create hollow depressions 2 to 6 inches deep and about 12 inches across. A particularly favorable area may become pitted with miniature craters, each vigorously defended by a darkly colorful male. Spawning may occur from May to early August but is most active in June.

Once the nest is completed, the lighter colored females are courted and induced to deposit their eggs among the pebbles and debris in the nest. The eggs are immediately fertilized by the male. A female may spawn in several nests and several females may contribute a part of their eggs to one nest. Once spawning is completed the females move out of the nesting areas and the males aerate and clean the eggs by gently fanning them with their large pectoral fins.

The small eggs develop at a rate dependent on the water temperature and hatch into fry in two to five days. An average of 18,000 fry per nest were found during one study although one nest contained 60,000. The male guards the fry for a few days after hatching then leaves the nesting area. Since the fry have only a small amount of yolk to provide them with energy, they must locate suitable food within about two days of hatching or starve. This period is also critical because once the male has withdrawn his care, the fry are easy prey to many fishes including other bluegills and predaceous aquatic insects.

According to one Indiana study, bluegill fry move into open water and feed on zooplankton. Several weeks later they move back to the shoreline adding small insect larvae to their diet. Bluegills older than one or two years feed mostly on zooplankton and insect larvae that live on and in the bottom sediment.

The rate of growth in any particular lake is strongly influenced by the quantity of food available and the density of the population in relation to food abundance. Two-inch fish from one lake and six-inch fish from another may both actually be the same age. Bluegills in hypereutrophic Sylvan Lake average 1.7 inches in length at the end of their first year of life, 3.7 inches in the second, 5.6 inches in the third, 6.9 inches in the fourth, 7.3 inches in the fifth. In Pretty Lake, bluegills average 1.2 inches when one-year-old, 2.2 inches when two, 3.5 inches when three, 5.3 inches when four, 6.6 inches when five, and 8.0 inches when six.

Although bluegills feed somewhat on zooplankton in the winter, their greatest feeding activity and their entire annual growth occurs during a 150-day period from May through September. Young bluegills gain an ounce in weight for every three or four ounces of food eaten and hence grow quite rapidly where food is plentiful. With increasing age they become less and less efficient in converting invertebrates into bluegill and may eventually almost stop growing, although they continue to eat.[12]

Research on Indiana bluegill populations, particularly with regard to mortality rates, has revealed some surprising facts which have had far-reaching effects on fishing regulations. The total mortality rate of adults includes deaths from fishing and from natural causes such as predation, parasitism, disease, and senility, and may be estimated in several ways. The total population of bluegills is estimated by "mark and recapture" methods. This involves capturing the fish, usually with nets or some other apparatus, marking them by clipping off a fin or attaching a tag, returning them to the lake, and then recapturing as many as possible by a combination of methods which might include angling. In the process, the fish are weighed and measured and a few scales are removed for later use in determining the age of the individual and for estimating the average growth rate. In this manner estimates are obtained of the numbers of fish in distinct age groups as well as for the entire population. Marking experiments carried out for two or more years often form the basis for estimating total mortality.

Creel censuses during the experiments contribute data used for the estimates and also provide estimates of angling mortality or, as it is called, the rate of exploitation. Investigation of bluegill populations in several Indiana lakes has revealed the surprising fact that 50% of the bluegills die annually from natural causes, if the population is not being exploited by angling.[10] The causes for this are obscure, but senescence is believed to be important since the mortality rate increases with age in some lakes. Mortality due to exploitation by angling may be as high as 35 per cent[8] but is usually somewhat less. Since angling mortality rarely, if ever, is as great as mortality from other causes, there is little likelihood that fishing could seriously deplete a population. This realization led to a liberalization of bag limits and a year-round fishing season for bluegills and most other panfish. This policy has proved to be a sound one for panfish because they mature at an early age — as early as the second year of life in fast-growing bluegills — and are very prolific. The fact that most of the sunfishes spawn at intervals over a fairly long period of time no doubt favors their successful existence even when the total mortality rate exceeds 80% annually.

Bluegills are the most abundant game fish in many of Indiana's lakes. The size of the populations varies from lake to lake primarily because of different physical and chemical conditions. Rich lakes containing large population densities of 50 to 150 pounds per acre yield 25 to 50 pounds of bluegills per acre annually to anglers.

## Reservoirs

The construction of a large dam does more than merely change the stream into a lake. Many resident stream fishes are unable to live and/or reproduce in the newly-formed lake because their particular requirements for life have disappeared. Riffle-inhabiting darters and minnows, sculpins, rock bass, and smallmouth bass are all adversely affected by impoundment. Most of the suckers and longear sunfish will persist in small numbers. Species which normally occur in small numbers only in streams and find the new environment much more favorable include largemouth bass, bluegill, drum or white perch, white crappie, bullheads, catfish, gizzard shad, buffalo, and carp.

Reservoirs frequently cover fertile bottom lands and normally begin their lives with a high productivity. Plankton populations quickly develop and within three months bottom-dwelling invertebrates become well established. Fish populations, normally supplemented by heavy stockings of desirable sport fishes such as largemouth bass, bluegill, redear sunfish, and channel catfish, expand almost as dramatically and reach maximum standing crops in about five years.

The most numerous large predators of our reservoirs, as well as of our lakes and ponds, are largemouth bass (*Micropterus salmoides*). When the spring water temperature reaches 60° F. in suitable shallow areas one or two feet deep, males will begin fanning out shallow depressions one to two feet wide.[17] Nests may be hollowed out among the roots of aquatic plants, in sand or marl, or they may be nothing more than a mat of fibrous debris. Rarely eggs may be deposited on aquatic vegetation. Bass are highly territorial, but unlike bluegills they never nest close together. If the water temperature continues to rise, spawning takes place one or two days later.

Spawning details and embryological development do not differ significantly from the bluegill, except that fewer eggs are deposited per nest (200 to 35,000, with an average of from 3000 to 5000). After spawning has been completed, the females are driven from the nesting area and the male assumes the duties of caring for the eggs and young. Important mortality factors during this period which may reduce the number of bass produced include the following:

1. Sudden temperature changes to below 50° F.
2. Destruction of nest, eggs, or embryos, by waves and wind
3. Predation by various species of fish
4. Severe turbidity and siltation
5. Scarcity of appropriate food after resorption of the yolk sac.

Should one nest fail, the male bass may renest within one or two weeks. As many as four distinct nesting sessions may occur during the five-week to six-week-long spawning period from April through May, each triggered by a sudden warming trend following a temperature dip.

The young swim-up fry form tight schools at first. They drift slowly about the shoreline feeding on zooplankton as they go and are closely tended by the male bass. As the fry grow larger the schools become looser and the male eventually leaves. Insect larvae and small fish fry are eaten by bass as small as one inch and form the principal food of bass over two inches. Larger fish and invertebrates such as crayfish are added with further growth, but the basic diet of all bass larger than two inches is approximately half fish and half invertebrates. Insect larvae, crayfish, tadpoles, frogs, and various species of fish are all acceptable foods, but bass are selective and do not ordinarily feed indiscriminately if there is a choice. For example, "fish-shaped" fish like minnows, suckers, perch, or even bullheads are eaten in preference to flat panfish like bluegills or crappie.[15] Approximately four ounces of food must be consumed for each ounce of weight gained.[24]

Work by the Indiana Department of Natural Resources, Division of Fish and Game, indicates that largemouth bass reach a length of 5.5 inches at the end of the first year, 8.0 inches the second, 10.0 inches the third, 12.5 inches the fourth, 15.0 inches the fifth, 16.4 inches the sixth, and 17.5 inches the seventh. Maturation is reached the second or third year at lengths of 9 to 10 inches.

Teams of scientists are now at work unravelling some of the mysteries of reservoir fishes using a variety of skills and modern techniques, including a two-man submarine. Hopefully, our inadequate knowledge of this subject will soon be remedied. One of the major problems of reservoirs is their tendency to become gradually less productive with age. Bass populations decrease and white crappie become numerous and stunted. Rough fish, like carp, carpsuckers, and buffalo, may become so numerous that they muddy the water in certain areas. The fish populations of Cataract Lake (Cagles Mill Reservoir) reached this stage 10 years after its creation.

Fortunately, the fish manager has recourse to several methods which singly or collectively can restore balanced populations. The basic aims are not unlike those employed in managing fish populations of ponds, to be discussed next, but the labor and expense is considerably greater. The populations of rough fish must be reduced. At the present time, two methods are commonly practiced: (1) Areas of the lake which contain concentrations of rough fish are poisoned. Sometimes a bait like sour corn is effective as an attractant. (2) Various types of traps and nets are used to capture as many rough fish as possible.

Both methods were used on Cataract Lake in 1963. An estimated 50 tons of fish were killed when the upper shallow part of the lake was treated with a toxicant; 80% were rough fish and most of the remainder stunted crappie. Over 30 tons, mostly buffalo, were removed by a commercial fisherman working under a special permit. Rough fish and sport fish alike feed heavily on bottom invertebrates. Reducing the rough fish population relieves the sport fishes of competition for this food and usually improves their growth rate. Crappie which moved into upper Cataract Lake after the toxicant had disappeared grew 1.3 inches during the next year, while those at the lower end grew only 0.6 inches.

The Divison of Fish and Game is eradicating stream fish populations before impoundment wherever possible and stocking the reservoir only with desirable sport fishes. This excellent policy should serve to prolong the period of high productivity of sport fishes.

Other developments which may change the fishing habits of Hoosiers include the possibility that many of our reservoirs could support populations of what are now rather uncommon sport fishes such as white bass, walleye pike, and sauger.

### Farm Ponds

An estimated 38,000 to 40,000 tiny impoundments now dot

our landscape. These small farm ponds, averaging one acre in size, are growing in numbers at a rate of over 1000 each year and will become even more important in the future than they are now. Some ponds are constructed to provide water for household and barn use, livestock, irrigation, etc., while others are constructed exclusively for recreational purposes. All may be used for production of fish, although the management practices employed will be influenced by the main purpose of the pond.

Careful advanced planning of ponds is absolutely essential for successful establishment and maintenance of balanced fish populations. First the site must be satisfactory in several respects: (1) The subsoil must contain enough clay to hold water. (2) Since ponds depend on surface runoff to replace evaporative and other losses, they should have 6-10 acres of drainage basin for each acre of water surface area. (3) The drainage basin must have a permanent covering of vegetation, preferably pasture and/or woodland, to assure that the pond will not quickly fill in with sediment. (4) Ponds built in the northern snow belt should have a considerable volume of water deeper than fifteen feet in order to minimize the dangers of winter-kill.

Secondly, certain details incorporated into the pond at the time of its construction will greatly increase the possibilities for controlling fish production.

1. If the pond also serves as a source of water for stock, fence off all but one small area of shoreline or, better yet, install a self-regulating system for piping water to a stock tank located at the base of the dam. Many good ponds have been ruined by cattle. Their activities in shallow water usually create a high turbidity which, in turn, causes low-standing crops of fish.

2. The installation of a device for draining the pond will be well worth the additional cost.

Research on fish populations in ponds has concentrated on (1) the numbers, sizes, and kinds of fish to be stocked, (2) the establishment and maintenance of balanced populations of predator and forage fishes, and (3) means of increasing the yields.[4]

What species to stock depends, in part, on the desires of the owner. Good production has been obtained using largemouth and/or smallmouth bass either alone or in combination with golden shiners and crayfish as a food source. Both species of bass grow well in ponds, but smallmouth must have gravel areas if they are to reproduce.

The largemouth bass—bluegill combination has received wide acceptance throughout the country as the result of extensive research in Alabama ponds. In northern ponds this combination has not been completely satisfactory because the bluegills become overpopulated and stunted and cause unsuccessful bass reproduction through predation on the fry and eggs.[2] Bass and redear sunfish alone or with bluegill has been a successful combination for Indiana ponds.[18] Redear sunfish grow to a large size and rarely over-reproduce. Unlike the bluegill, the redear seldom takes a surface lure and may not receive the esteem of the "popping" enthusiast. White or black crappie are sometimes stocked with the other species to add variety, but their value has not yet been accurately determined. Other suitable pond fishes include brown, black, or yellow bullhead, yellow bass, warmouth bass, pumpkinseed, and pickerel.

Indiana ponds will probably respond well to an initial stocking of 100-200 bass fry or fingerlings and 10-30 adult or 500-1000 fry sunfish per acre. Those pond owners interested primarily in bass should stock the sunfish a year later than the bass. These ratios most often lead to the establishment of balanced fish populations which demonstrate good growth and a high sustained yield. Balanced populations develop when bluegills produce enough young annually to serve as food for bass and replace losses through natural mortality and angling, and bass produce enough young to keep the bluegill population under control and replace their losses.

Many ponds are inadequately and/or improperly harvested by removing too many bass and too few bluegills. This usually leads to overabundant, stunted bluegill populations, which feed so heavily on bass eggs and fry that few young bass are produced. Unbalanced ponds usually contain many small bluegills 3-5 inches long and a few large bass. The simplest and best corrective treatment is to simply drain the pond and restock it with the correct numbers again. If no drain has been built into the pond, it may be necessary to poison the pond and restock it. If this is not practical or desirable several other management practices, requiring more time and effort, may be tried. Stocking more carnivorous fish such as bass or pike will help if they are not soon removed by angling. Removing heavy weed beds makes young bluegills more vulnerable to predators and is a surprisingly effective technique providing there are enough predators. As many 3-4- and 5-inch bluegills as possible should be removed by angling, trapping, seining, etc. One of the hardest lessons taught by fishery research is that it is not always ecologically desirable to throw back the small ones. These collective measures may lead to the reestablishment of balanced populations if intensely applied over a long enough period of time.

## Brooks

One of the effects of settling Indiana and clearing land for agriculture has been to accelerate the run-off from rainfall and thereby convert small, permanent headwaters into intermittently flowing brooks. Blacknose dace *(Rhinichthys atratulus)*, red-bellied dace *(Chrosomus erythrogaster)*, and sculpin *(Cottus bairdii)*, probably were once common throughout the state, but are now scarce because of this transformation.

Other species from downstream stretches often mingle with these residents of permanent brooks or inhabit intermittent brooks by themselves. These include creek chub, striped shiner, bluntnose minnow, silverjaw minnow, stoneroller, rainbow darter *(Etheostoma caeruleum)*, orangethroat darter *(E. spectabile)*, and occasionally green sunfish *(Lepomis cyanellus)* and small hog suckers.

The sculpin is a small, rather ugly fish with a broad head, bulging eyes, huge pectoral fins, and a tapering brown body. It is particularly abundant in brooks with limestone rubble or coarse gravel riffles. Stomach contents include aquatic insets and larvae, some algae, and fish eggs when available.

The month of May is the spawning season for the unbelievably beautiful red-bellied dace. At this time the males develop brilliant scarlet stripes on each side of the abdomen. Vivid slashes of red also mark the chin and the base of the dorsal fin. The lower fins turn a lemon yellow and a double black lateral stripe contrasts sharply with the silvery sides. Tiny tubercles cover the males, a breeding characteristic of many minnows and suckers. The coloration of the larger females is muted except for striped sides and an occasional patch of red behind the head.

Schools of dace spawn in shallow water over gravel, the males often outnumbering females seven to one.[23] Several males may fertilize the eggs which settle into protective crevices between rocks. Spawning as they do in shallow water and having such a restricted habitat, this species depends on a stable flow of clear water for its continued existence.

### Streams

Small brooks flow together to produce streams which are more typical of Indiana than any other aquatic feature. It is difficult, if not impossible, to describe an average stream in view of the variety of stream habitats found in different parts of Indiana. Many streams on the Wabash lowland of southwestern Indiana are sluggish, turbid, and debris-choked. Their bottoms are thickly layered with silt and they often stagnate or dry up completely in the summer. Streams of central and southeastern Indiana are turbid to clear with long pools and short riffles. The composition of the bottoms ranges from mud and clay to sand and gravel or even solid limestone. The pools are not usually vegetated, but the emergent water willow *(Dianthera)* commonly grows in or near riffles. The clear streams of the northern third of the state have a greater stability of flow and often contain luxuriant beds of submerged and emergent vegetation. Some are cool enough to support trout, although natural reproduction alone will not sustain the populations.

Not only do streams vary in character from place to place, but within each may be found a wide variety of small habitats differing in bottom type, velocity of water flow, depth, and cover. It is not surprising that more species of fish are found in our streams than in any other major aquatic habitat. Not all species are found everywhere, of course, but it is not at all uncommon to find thirty-five or more species of fish in one short section of a stream. As a general rule the larger the stream, the more species of fish it will contain. Tiny brooks seldom have more than half a dozen species. Larger streams offer deeper water for larger species and a large variety of microhabitats to satisfy the needs of numerous species of fish. Streams support large standing crops of fish, even when compared to productive ponds and lakes. The total standing crop is correlated with the depth of stream pools, a finding which will not surprise many fishermen. Pools having a significant amount of water deeper than two feet may contain 1000 or more pounds per acre. Shallow pools may contain less than 50 pounds per acre. The composition of populations of fish in streams vary as much as the standing crops. In many streams minnows make up more than half the total weight.[7]

In other streams the various members of the sucker family (Catostomidae) are often the most obvious residents. Identification of many members is difficult. The relatively scarce silver redhorse (*Moxostoma anisurum*) and black redhorse (*M. duquesnei*) closely resemble the abundant golden redhorse (*M. erythrurum*), known to most fishermen as the "white" sucker. The common white sucker (*Catostomus commersoni*) becomes darkly colored during the spring breeding season and is known as the "black" sucker to anglers who fish for it only at this time. Three species of carpsuckers or "sicklebacks" (*Carpiodes sp.*) may occur together in streams of the southern half of Indiana and are almost indistinguishable from each other. Somewhat less confusing stream suckers are the spotted sucker (*Minytrema melanops*), creek chubsucker (*Erimyzon oblongus*), and the unique hog sucker (*Hypentelium nigricans*), which inhabits stream riffles and has a huge head and pectoral fins, concave forehead, and a tapering mottled-brown body.

Other species which contribute to the richness of stream fish fauna are carp, brook lamprey *(Lampetra lamottei)*, black bullhead (*Ictalurus melas*), yellow bullhead, log perch (*Percina caprodes),* and other darters, blackstripe topminnow (*Fundulus notatus*), brook silversides, and various species of madtom (*Noturus sp.*). None of the favorite stream gamefish such as channel catfish *(Ictalurus punctatus),* smallmouth bass, rock bass, white crappie, and longear sunfish *(Lepomis megalotis)* are as abundant or taken as frequently by anglers as golden redhorse and/or white suckers.

Golden redhorse or mullet, as it is sometimes called, is a sedentary species that tends to remain within two or three adjacent stream pools throughout the summer months.[11] In November this species, together with many other members of the sucker family, tends to aggregate in the deepest pools where they remain for the winter. Activity increases in the spring when the water temperatures rise and culminates in the spring sucker run. It is commonly supposed that suckers travel long distances in the spring run, but this is not believed to be the case. Most of the yield to anglers occurs during April, but only a very small percentage of the total population is harvested. Golden redhorse flesh is sweet and palatable, especially when the numerous Y-bones are softened by thorough cooking. The eggs or roe is also regarded as a delicacy by many. In addition to their use as food, this species provides considerable sport when light tackle is used.

When the water temperature approaches 60° F. mature male redhorse begin to congregate on gravelly riffles. Some ascend small tributaries near their home range, but most of them remain in the main stream for this purpose. Little is known about the spawning behavior, egg development, or the early life of the young. Nests as such are not constructed, but the large eggs are fertilized, deposited in gravel depressions on the riffles, and receive no subsequent care. No doubt eggs and fry are eaten in large numbers by many fishes and die from a variety of other causes.

Like the other suckers and redhorse, the golden redhorse has a large ventral mouth and broad lips liberally sprinkled with taste buds which enable it to locate and feed upon organic materials, algae, and insect larvae in the bottom sediments.

Golden redhorse in Big Walnut Creek, Putnam County, are 4 inches long at the end of the first year of growth, 6¼ inches at Age II, 8½ inches at Age III, 10 inches at Age IV, 11½ inches at Age V, 13½ inches at Age VI, and 15 inches at Age VII. Males first spawn as three-year-olds and females as four-year-olds.

## Rivers

Species of fish characteristic of streams usually become less abundant in larger rivers downstream. Conversely, fish which are rather scarce or absent in medium-sized streams increase in abundance in larger streams and rivers. Channel, blue, and flathead catfish (*Ictalurus punctatus, I. furcatus,* and *Pylodictus olivaris*); smallmouth, bigmouth, and black buffalo (*Ictiobus bulalus, I. cyprinella,* and *I. niger*) ; drum or "white perch" *(Aplodinotus grunniens)* ; spotted bass *(Micropterus punctulatus);* as well as white crappie, sauger, white bass, gizzard shad, and several species of minnows which have already been mentioned are primarily river residents. Some of our largest, rarest and most interesting species reside in the Ohio and lower Wabash Rivers: paddlefish, shovelnose and lake or rock sturgeon, alligator gar, Ohio muskellunge, and blue sucker *(Cycleptus elongatus).*

Our knowledge about large river habitats and their fishes is inadequate at the present time. A recent study of Ohio River fishes suggests that standing crops of fish average approximately 300 pounds per acre with gizzard shad making up about 50% of this weight, drum and channel catfish 10% each, and carp 5%.[19] Angling pressure is fairly light considering the size of the waters and channel catfish and drum are equally important and together comprise 70% of the catch.[3] Largemouth bass, spotted bass, longear sunfish, bluegill, white crappie, white bass, and carp are also taken in small numbers.

Commercial fishing is not highly developed in Indiana. Most commercial fishermen in Northern Indiana are licensed to operate in Michigan waters of Lake Michigan, since Indiana waters are generally unproductive of commercially important species. Only 14 of the 49 tons of fish taken commercially from the Wabash River in 1963 were harvested by Indiana.[16] The total annual catch, valued at only $10,300, consisted primarily of carp, channel catfish, buffalo, sheepshead and sturgeon, arranged in order of their relative abundance. In surprising contrast, the harvest of mussel shells in the Wabash River was valued at $144,000 for 1963 and is estimated at $650,000 for 1965. Mussel shells are exported to Japan where particles of ground shell are inserted into oysters to serve as nuclei in the culturing of pearls. Investigations are now under way to determine the population density of mussels, to evaluate the effect of present harvesting methods on these mussels, and to establish harvest levels which would ensure maximum yield without depleting the resource.

The Ohio River yielded 13,700 pounds of fish worth $2,400 to Indiana commercial fishermen in 1963. No mussels were harvested, probably because the series of low dams has had a deleterious effect on them and has also rendered them less easily cropped than in the Wabash River.

It appears that river fishes could be utilized to a greater extent by both commercial and sporting interests than they are at the present time. The gizzard shad which comprised about half the standing crop in the Ohio River has no commercial value at the present time.

The channel catfish is the most important species to both sport and commercial fishermen. Although it is most abundant in large rivers, this species is also widely distributed in our lakes, streams, and reservoirs. It apparently eats little when water temperatures are below 40° F., but when the temperature exceeds 40° F. it feeds on a wide variety of plant and animal material. Crayfish, snails, small clams, insect larvae and adults, dead and live fish, abattoir wastes, fruit, seeds, algae, and other odd items are all used for food at one time or another. Most fish have an acute sense of smell, but bullhead and catfish have, in addition, a well-developed sense of taste. Taste buds literally cover the entire skin and are particularly abundant on the barbels. Consequently, they are able to feed successfully in the dark or in muddy water. When streams are clear channel catfish actively feed at night, often entering shallow water in their travels. When light rains cause an increase in the water level and turbidity catfish may be active day and night, feeding on food items that have been washed into the rivers. Angling success is often good at such times.

Age and growth of channel catfish in Indiana streams is being studied at the present time by the Fish and Wildlife Division of the Department of Natural Resources. No scales are present, but thin sections of the pectoral spines have alternating light and dark rings which are formed, respectively, in the summer and winter. The age of the fish can be determined by counting the number of dark rings. Average growth of Iowa channel catfish at the end of each year of life is: 5.5 inches at Age I; 9.5 inches at Age II; 11.7 inches at Age III; 13.3 inches at Age IV; 15.6 inches at Age V; 17.8 inches at Age VI; 21.0 inches at Age VII; 22.0 inches at Age VIII; 24.8 inches at Age IX; 26.0 inches at Age X.[13] Faster growth might be expected in Indiana since the growing season is a bit longer.

Channel catfish reach sexual maturity when they are four or five years old. Spawning takes place after the water temperature reaches about 75° F. The eggs are glued as a gelatinous mass to surfaces of rocks, hollow logs, or other solid objects including tin cans, and are protected by the male catfish who chases the female away as soon as the eggs are deposited. While engaged in parental duties the males do not feed, consequently angling success decreases during the spawning season in late June and July. The fry hatch within 6 to 10 days and travel for a week or two in dark schools feeding in shallow, quiet water. Eventually the schools disperse and the young catfish seek traditional catfish habitat like brush piles, submerged boulders, logs, pilings, and drift piles.

The foregoing discussions have attempted to summarize some of the more interesting aspects of our fishes and their lives. The life histories and population dynamics of most fishes are poorly known at best and even the best-known are being profitably investigated at the present time. Research is actively progressing on streams, lakes, and reservoirs and the inadequately-studied problems of the fishes of strip pits, oxbow lakes, river backwaters, and the rivers themselves will gradually come into focus.

## LITERATURE

1. BARDACH, J. E., M. FUJIYA, and A. HOLL. 1965. Detergents: effects on the chemical senses of the fish *Ictalurus natalis* (LeSueur). Science **148** (3677): 1605-1607
2. BENNETT, G. W. 1962. Management of artificial lakes and ponds. Reinhold Publishing Corp., N. Y.
3. CHARLES, J. R. 1962. Creel census data for Kentucky waters of the Ohio River. Section IV *in* Aquatic-life resources of the Ohio River. Ohio River Valley Water Sanitation Comm.: 91-102.
4. DENDY, J. S. 1963. Farm Ponds, p. 595-620. *In* Limnology in North America. D. G. Frey, ed. Univ. of Wisconsin Press.
5. FREY, D. G. 1955. Distributional ecology of the cisco (*Coregonus artedii*) in Indiana. Invest. Indiana Lakes & Streams IV:177-228.
6. GERKING, S. D. 1945. Distribution of the fishes of Indiana. Invest. Indiana Lakes & Streams III (1): 1-137.
7. _____. 1949. Characteristics of stream fish populations. Invest. Indiana Lakes & Streams **3**(7): 283-309.
8. _____. 1952. Vital statistics of the fish population of Gordy Lake, Indiana. Trans. Am. Fish. Soc. **82**:48-67.
9. _____. 1955. Key to the fishes of Indiana. Invest. Indiana Lakes & Streams IV:49-86.
10. _____. 1957. A history of the study of fishes in Indiana. Proc. Indiana Acad. Sci. **66**:275-285.
11. _____. 1959. The restricted movements of fish populations. Biol. Rev., **34**:221-242.
12. _____. 1962. Production and food utilization in a population of

bluegill sunfish. Ecol. Mono. **32**:31-78.
13. HARLAN, J. R. and E. B. SPEAKER. 1956. Iowa fish and fishing. 3rd edition. State of Iowa, Des Moines. 377 pp.
14. HUBBS, C. L. and K. F. LAGLER. 1958. Fishes of the Great Lakes region. The University of Michigan Press, Ann Arbor, Mich. 213 pp.
15. LEWIS, W. M. and D. R. HELMS. 1964. Vulnerability of forage organisms to largemouth bass. Trans. Am. Fish. Soc. **93**:315-318.
16. LYLES, C. H. 1965. Fishing statistics of the United States 1963. Fish and Wildlife Service Statistical Digest No. 57, U. S. Government Printing Office, Washington, D. C.
17. KRAMER, R. H. and L. L. SMITH, Jr. 1962. Formation of year classes in largemouth bass. Trans. Am. Fish. Soc. **91**:29-41.
18. KRUMHOLZ, L. A. 1952. Management of Indiana ponds for fishing, p. 254-257. *In* Symposium on farm fish ponds and management. J. Wildl. Mgmt. **16**:233-288.
19. KRUMHOLZ, L. A., J. R. CHARLES, and W. L. MINCKLEY. 1962. The fish population of the Ohio River. Section III *in* Aquatic-life resources of the Ohio River. Ohio River Valley Water Sanitation Comm.:49-89.
20. RICKER, W. E. 1945. Natural mortality among Indiana bluegill sunfish. Ecol. **26**:111-121.
21. RICKER, W. E., H. F. MOSBAUGH, and M. LUNG. 1945. Utilization and survival of trout in Indiana. Invest. Indiana Lakes & Streams III:271-281.
22. PURKETT, C. A., Jr. 1961. Reproduction and early development of the paddlefish. Trans. Am. Fish Soc. **90**:125-129.
23. SMITH, B. G. 1908. The spawning habits of *Chrosomus erythrogaster* Rafinesque. Biol. Bull. XV(1):9-18.
24. WILLIAMS, W. E. 1959. Food conversion and growth rates for largemouth and smallmouth bass in laboratory aquaria. Trans. Am. Fish. Soc. **88**:125-127.

# 24
# Amphibians and Reptiles

SHERMAN A. MINTON
Indiana University Medical School

## Introduction

There is no way of knowing how many species of amphibians and reptiles inhabited Indiana in 1816, but 82 species were recorded from the state between 1947 and 1957. Seven species listed by earlier workers[2] were not found during this period; however, five of these were probably recorded from Indiana in error. A fauna of about eighty species is fairly large for a small state well within the temperate zone and lacking marked variation in topography. The composition and distribution of the Indiana herpetofauna is best explained by changes that have occurred since the retreat of the last (Wisconsin) ice sheet about 13,000 years ago.[6,7] As conditions became suitable for amphibians and reptiles, a group of species adapted to a cool moist climate moved in. The next 10,000 years were characterized by gradual warming until the climate was probably somewhat warmer than it is today. The latter part of this period, which ended about 3000 years ago, was characterized by drier conditions that allowed prairie vegetation to spread across much of the state. During this stage, southern amphibians and reptiles spread northward mostly along the river valleys, while grassland species spread eastward. The final climatic change has featured a cooler and wetter climate with westward spread of the northern hardwood forest and an influx of amphibian and reptile species adapted to this environment. With each ecological shift, the immigrant species have tended to replace the old residents as dominant forms; but the latter have usually remained in appropriate refugia. The latest changes have been those wrought by man. Human agency has accounted for no introductions of reptile or amphibian species, and only one species, the large semiaquatic snake, *Farancia abacura,* seems to have been exterminated in the state within historic times. The distributions of most species[1] have been significantly altered, however, and several are seriously endangered in their Indiana ranges.

## Salamanders

Largest of Indiana's 19 salamanders and perhaps the most primitive amphibian in America is the Hellbender (*Cryptobranchus alleganiensis*). It is a clumsy, flabby looking creature with a broad flat head and tiny eyes. On each side of the body is a wrinkled fold of skin, and at the base of the head is a slit like opening. Most adult specimens are 12 to 18 inches long. Hellbenders are completely aquatic and once were common in the Ohio and its larger rocky tributaries and in the lower Wabash. Their numbers have decreased greatly during the last 50 years. Hellbenders feed largely upon crayfish and fish. Although nonpoisonous, they can inflict a painful bite.

The Mudpuppy or Spotted Waterdog (*Necturus maculosus*) is found in large streams and lakes throughout Indiana. Presence of four rather than five toes on the hind feet and tufts of bushy gills at the base of the head identify it. Mudpuppies eat almost any type of aquatic creature slow enough to be captured and small enough to be swallowed. They are among the very few northern amphibians or reptiles that feed heavily during the winter.

The Lesser Siren (*Siren intermedia*) is unlike any aquatic animal native to Indiana. Resembling an eel in general shape, it has gill tufts at the base of the head and just behind them a pair of short stumpy legs. There are no hind limbs. Large specimens are slightly over a foot long. Sirens inhabits shallow quiet water with dense aquatic vegetation. If the water dries they can burrow into mud and remain dormant for weeks. The Indiana range includes swampy parts of the Wabash, Kankakee, and lower White River valleys and several localities in the northern lake country.

The Mole Salamanders (*Ambystoma*) are seldom seen even in localities where they are plentiful, for they spend most of their time in shallow burrows or under large stones or logs. Most of them are forest animals.

The Tiger Salamander (*A. tigrinum*) and Spotted Salamander (A. *maculatum*) (Fig. 70) are relatively large (usually 6 to 8 inches) dark salamanders with bold yellow spots. The small chunky Marbled Salamander (*A. opacum*) is black with white or silvery crossbands. The Jefferson's (*A. jeffersonianum*), Bluespotted (*A. laterale*), and Small-mouthed (*A. texanum*) are medium sized grey to dark brown salamanders often speckled or frosted with pale grey or blue. The latter part of winter, late January to mid-March in central and southern Indiana, is the breeding season for most of these salamanders. On nights when temperatures in the high 40's or 50's are accompanied by rain or melting snow, these hardy amphibians migrate to ponds or ditches where they mate and deposit their jelly-like masses of eggs. Under field conditions these require two weeks or more to hatch. The larval salamanders resemble small Mudpuppies. During early summer their gills disappear, and they take up life on land. The Marbled Salamander has a different breeding cycle. Its eggs are laid in the fall in a low moist spot that will be flooded by late autumn or winter rain.

Fig. 70. The Spotted Salamander is a handsome species characteristic of hardwood forest. Spots on the body are lemon yellow; those on the head are often orange in Indiana specimens. Photo, John H. Daily.

The female stays with the eggs protecting them from drying and the attacks of insects and other small creatures. When water floods the nest the female leaves, and the eggs soon hatch. An exceedingly curious situation exists with Jefferson's Salamander and some of its relatives. Certain populations in central and northern Indiana are composed entirely of females with a triploid number of chromosomes.[3,8] Details of their breeding cycle are still unknown, but it seems probable that sperm of some other species of *Ambystoma* are necessary to initiate egg development, although they contribute nothing genetically.

Newts (*Notophthalmus viridescens*) are found throughout the forested sections of Indiana. They often breed in the same ponds with *Ambystoma*. Adult newts are about 4 inches long.

The compressed tail, slightly rough skin and lack of costal grooves distinguish them from other salamanders. They are brown or greenish with a row of small red spots on each side. The aquatic larval stage is followed by the characteristic eft or land stage which resembles a small stocky lizard with dry finely granular skin. After a year or so as an eft, the newt becomes a sexually mature semi-aquatic adult.

Almost half of Indiana's salamanders belong to the Family Plethodontidae. The outstanding characteristic of this family is the absence of lungs. Respiration takes place through the skin and the mucous membranes of the mouth.

The Slimy Salamander (*Plethodon glutinosus*) is the largest Indiana representative of its genus reaching a length of about 7 inches. It is rather stocky and has often been confused with salamanders of the *Ambystoma jeffersonianum* group. It is shiny black, heavily speckled with white. Glands on the tail exude a copious gummy secretion when the salamander is disturbed.

The small species are the Redbacked Salamander (*P. cinereus*) found in forests throughout the state; the Zigzag Salamander (*P. dorsalis*) in hilly country north to Turkey Run and Shades; and the Ravine Salamander ( *P. richmondi*) in the extreme southeastern part of the state. These three are slender, short-legged salamanders rarely more than 4 inches long. They occur as two color phases, one dark grey with light flecks or frosting and the other with a wide red, orange or yellow midline stripe. The striped phase is extremely rare in *P. richmondi*. Salamanders of this genus are among the few amphibians that have dispensed with a free-living larval stage. They lay a few comparatively large eggs in a moisture-saturated cavity deep underground or within a hollow log. The hatchling salamanders have gills, but these disappear in a few days.

The Dusky Salamander (*Desmognathus fuscus*) is a small stocky species best identified by the narrow light line from the eye to the angle of the jaw. It is abundant in small rocky brooks in southeastern Indiana. The female salamander lays a cluster of eggs under a stone during late June or July. She remains curled about them until hatching occurs in late August or September.

The Four-toed Salamander (*Hemidactylium scutatum*) is a small slender species rarely more than 3 inches long. It is rare in Indiana, and its distribution in widely separated colonies over the state suggests that it was an early post-glacial immigrant.

The Two-lined Salamander (*Eurycea bislineata*) is another small, slim yellowish to bronzy species found throughout most of the state in small brooks. Its disc-shaped egg mass is often attached to the underside of a submerged stone. The active larva has small gills and lives among stones and debris for about a year after hatching. After transforming to an adult, it may spend considerable time on land.

Two related species, the Longtailed Salamander (*E. longicauda*) and Cave Salamander (*E. lucifuga*) are associated with a cave and spring habitat. Both are long-tailed, long-legged and yellow, orange or reddish with dark marking. The Cave Salamander is widely known in southern Indiana as "Red Lizard". Both species may live in caves, but where they occur together, the Cave Salamander is more likely to be found in a cavern while the Longtailed lives in nearby rocky streams. Both are excellent climbers and may be found in cracks in the roofs of caves or seen on wet nights crawling on vertical rock faces or trunks of trees.

### Frogs and Toads

Toads generally can be identified by their dry warty skins and prominent parotoid glands on the shoulder region. Secretion of these glands is highly toxic by mouth for many animals. Predators that take frogs freely often completely avoid toads. The two toad species of Indiana are the American Toad (*Bufo americanus*) and Fowler's Toad (*Bufo woodhousei fowleri*). Both are almost statewide in distribution and very similar in appearance. In Indiana, Fowler's Toad seems to have been originally associated with sandy or rocky soils and the drier oak-hickory type of forest while the American Toad frequented areas of prairie or beech-maple forest with loam or muck soil with higher water-holding capacity. Both species, however, have adjusted well to human modifications of their habitat and may be common in orchards and gardens. The two species hybridize freely in the laboratory but tend to maintain their identity in nature because the call of the American Toad male does not attract the Fowler's Toad female and vice versa. Also the American Toad has an earlier breeding season, late March through mid-May in most of Indiana, in contrast to the late April through June season of Fowler's Toad. These mechanisms do break down, however, and hybrid toads may be common in some places or during certain years of abnormal spring weather. Toad eggs are deposited in long jelly-like strings. They may be laid in very small collections of water such as wheel ruts or very exposed ones such as plastic wading pools. The eggs hatch quickly into small black tadpoles. The tadpole stage likewise is short, and the newly transformed toads may be no larger than houseflies. The cycle from egg to toadlet takes about 30 to 40 days with Fowler's Toad in southern Indiana. Toads feed entirely upon insects and similar creatures and may play an important part in the natural control of economically undesirable species.

The Eastern Spadefoot (*Scaphiopus holbrooki*) (Fig. 71) is a toad-like creature readily identified by its strongly protruding eyes with vertically elliptical pupils and the dark-edged horny "spade" on the hind foot. It is known from a few widely separated localities in the southern third of the state. Spadefoots are extremely secretive creatures spending the greater part of their lives buried in the soil. Their breeding cycle is triggered primarily by violent rainstorms. Eggs are laid in temporaily flooded places, and the tadpole stage is short.

Nearly every adult in Indiana has heard the voice of the Chorus Frog (*Pseudacris triseriata*), (Fig. 72), although not many have seen this inch-long amphibian. I believe that 20 years ago it would have been possible on a warm, rainy April night to drive from the Ohio River to the Michigan line and not be beyond the sound of the call of this little frog at any time. It does not seem to be quite so abundant today. Although egg laying seems to be confined to a month or so in early spring, the "crreek-crreek" call of the male may be given any time in mild rainy weather. I have heard them at New Albany on Christmas day as well as during mid-summer. The frog itself is brown or greyish with a creamy line on the upper lip. Over most of the state the dorsal pattern consists of three wide stripes, but in some southern Indiana populations these are broken up into small spots. When not aggregated in shallow grassy pools for breeding, Chorus Frogs are terrestrial and very secretive, living in clumps of vegetation and under litter.

The Cricket Frog (*Acris crepitans*) is the most frequently

observed of Indiana's small frogs being plentiful along the grassy sunny banks of almost any permanent body of water. When alarmed it makes a series of surprisingly long erratic jumps. If it lands in water, it often returns to the bank almost immediately. It is the most warty-skinned of the small frogs and often shows a wide stripe of bright green or reddish brown on the back. The call is a series of rapid clicks heard throughout the breeding season which extends from late April through most of July in Indiana.

Fig. 71. A grotesque little gnome of the night, the Eastern Spade-foot sometimes appears in large numbers after rainstorms. Photo by author.

The third small frog of Indiana is the Spring Peeper (*Hyla crucifer*). A dark X-mark on the back and small adhesive discs on the toes are usually enough to identify this tan, grey or reddish-brown frog. Although plentiful in many places, it is more of a woodland species than the Cricket and Chorus Frogs and not likely to be found in heavily farmed land or suburbs. Its call is a series of high piping whistles. A large chorus heard in the distance sounds like sleigh bells; at close range it is almost deafening. Peepers breed in shallow woodland ponds during the early spring. During the rest of the year they are terrestrial and very difficult to find.

The Grey Treefrog (*Hyla versicolor*) is Indiana's only arboreal amphibian. It is of medium size (body length 1¼ to 1¾ inches) and capable of marked and rapid color change from almost white with pale green markings to dark grey or brown with lichen-like mottling. The concealed surface of the thigh is bright chrome yellow to orange. These frogs inhabit trees, shrubs, and old buildings or walls where they hide by day in damp cracks or holes. Breeding takes place in warm, shallow, quiet water from late April through July. The call is a short trill.

Fig. 72. Often heard but seldom seen, the little Chorus Frog begins to sing with the first thaws of March. Photo, Isabelle Hunt Conant.

The Leopard Frog (*Rana pipiens*) may well be America's best known amphibian, for it is very extensively used in comparative anatomy and experimental biology. Two subspecies occur in Indiana, *pipiens* with large pale-edged dark dorsal spots and blunt snout inhabits the northern and most of the eastern part of the state, while *sphenocephala* with small spots lacking light edges and a more pointed snout inhabits the southwestern third. Both types frequent shallow ponds, marshes, ditches and warm sluggish streams. They are most aquatic during the early spring breeding season and often become more or less terrestrial during the summer. The egg cluster containing 3000 to 5000 blackish eggs is laid in shallow water and hatches after a week or two. The tadpole stage lasts two to three months under field conditions in Indiana.

The Pickerel Frog (*Rana palustris*) resembles the Northern Leopard Frog but has more distinctly rectangular spots arranged in a double row. The concealed surfaces of the hind legs are bright yellow to orange. In Indiana it is a rather uncommon frog frequenting cool rocky gorges, springs, caves and sphagnum bogs.

The Crawfish Frog (*Rana areolata circulosa*) (Fig 73) is a large chunky frog with bold spotted pattern. In Indiana it is restricted to prairie in the southwestern and west central section where it typically lives in holes of the large chimney-building crayfish, although other kinds of burrows are doubtless utilized occasionally. There is a brief breeding season in late March and early April. The call is a loud resonant snore or grunt.

Largest of Indiana frogs is the Bullfrog (*Rana catesbeiana*) which occasionally reaches a body length of slightly more than 6 inches and weight of 18 ounces. It is the only Indiana

Fig. 73. The Crawfish Frog is a large but little known species that finds moisture and concealment in crayfish burrows. Photo, John H. Daily.

frog of the genus *Rana* that has no dorsolateral folds. Bullfrogs frequent permanent water, either still or flowing. The breeding season is in the late spring and summer; the tadpole stage lasts at least a year. While most of Indiana's frogs feed upon insects and other invertebrates, Bullfrogs eat many small vertebrates such as other frogs, fish, snakes, birds and young turtles.

The Green Frog (*Rana clamitans melanota*) is similar to the Bullfrog but smaller, not exceeding a body length of 4 inches. It is largely aquatic, preferring relatively clear permanent water in wooded country.

The Wood Frog (*Rana sylvatica*) (Fig. 74) rarely exceeds 2 inches body length and is pinkish brown to dark bronze with a mask-like black band through the eye. It is one of a group of cold weather adapted frogs and ranges far north into Alaska. A primarily terrestrial species, it occurs in moist woods and swamps. Wood frogs breed from late February to early April in Indiana, although the season in any given place is usually short. They are often found breeding in the same ponds with Spotted Salamanders, Newts and Spring Peepers.

Fig. 74. A black mask through the eye identifies the trim and handsome Wood Frog. It has close relatives in northern Europe and Asia. Photo, John H. Daily.

## Turtles

Four of Indiana's 14 species of turtles were first described by scientists from specimens collected at New Harmony during the early 19th century. Two of these were the Spiny Softshell (*Trionyx s. spinifer*) and the Smooth Softshell (*T. m. muticus*). The softshells are extraordinarily flat turtles and unique among reptiles in being almost without scales or scutes. The shell is leathery and flexible. The nostrils are at the tip of a tubular snout. These turtles are adapted to life in water with silt or fine sand bottom. Although speedy swimmers and rapid (for turtles) on land, they spend much time buried in sand or mud. They can carry out pharyngeal respiration and remain submerged almost indefinitely in well aerated waters. The Spiny Softshell (Fig. 75) is found throughout the state in lakes as well as streams. The Smooth Softshell is strictly a river turtle and is restricted to the Wabash, Ohio, and their larger tributaries. As with other aquatic turtles, the softshells bury their eggs in sand or loose soil near water. Softshell eggs are hard shelled, spherical and about an inch in diameter. Large females of the Spiny Softshell may reach a shell length of 13-15 inches and weigh almost 20 pounds. The Smooth Softshell is smaller. Softshells have sharp-edged jaws and can strike with almost snake-like agility. The Spiny is much the worse tempered of the two, but both should be handled with caution.

The Snapping Turtle (*Chelydra serpentina*) (Fig. 76) is easily recognized by its long tail, massive head and small plastron. The only turtle that might be confused with it is the Alligator Snapping Turtle (*Macroclemys temmincki*) which has been reported from Hovey's Lake and New Harmony. The Alligator Snapper has an enormous head with strongly hooked beak and three heavy ridges on the shell. It is doubtful if this species breeds in Indiana; the records are probably based on strays. On the other hand, almost any body of water in Indiana may harbor the Common Snapper. Indeed it is not unusual to see one of these ungainly creatures wandering about at a considerable distance from any stream or pond. Except for the very rare Alligator Snapper, this is Indiana's largest reptile. A Noble County specimen with a shell length of 15½ inches and weight of 46 pounds is the largest of which I have a record. Snappers are voracious and omnivorous, but

Fig. 75. Strongly mottled forelimbs help distinguish the Spiny Soft-shell from its relative the Smooth Softshell. Both have long snouts and flipper-like limbs. Photo, John H. Daily.

Fig. 76. With open mouth, a big old Snapping Turtle turns to fight. One eye is gone, probably the result of a past battle. The jaws of a large Snapper can do serious damage to fingers or toes, but the turtles bite only in self defense. Photo by author.

contention that they destroy significant numbers of game fish, ducklings or young muskrats is not based on very convincing evidence.

The Musk Turtle (*Sternotherus odoratus*) is a small species with high arched shell and a small plastron with wide cartilagenous areas. It is found throughout Indiana in many kinds of permanent water situations. It is a bottom dweller often abundant but seldom observed. The Eastern Mud Turtle (*Kinosternon s. subrubrum*) is similar but has a larger plastron without the wide cartilagenous areas and with two readily discernible hinges. It is rare in the state being recorded only from the lower Wabash valley and the northwestern sand prairie.

Box Turtles are familiar midwestern reptiles recognized by the well developed plastral hinge that permits tight closing of the front of the shell. The Eastern Box Turtle (*Terrapene carolina*) occurs throughout most of the state, although it is more plentiful in the southern third. The Ornate Box Turtle (*T. ornata*) is a prairie relict in the northwestern and southwestern sections. Both species spend most of their lives on land, although Eastern Box Turtles congregate in small ponds and creeks during hot dry weather. Both species are omnivorous, but the young tend to eat a higher percentage of animal food, a condition common among turtles in general. Berries and melons are favorite foods. A half dozen or so large box turtles in a small patch of tomatoes or strawberries can be something of a nuisance. In southern Indiana, Eastern Box Turtles mate during the spring and rarely in the fall. The female buries her 2 to 7 oval leathery eggs in soft soil during the latter half of June, and hatching occurs in late August or September. The baby turtles are extremely secretive. There are well documented accounts of individual adult box turtles observed over periods of 65 to 70 years, and the maximum life span is probably between 100 and 120 years.

Blanding's Turtle (*Emydoidea blandingi*) also has a hinged plastron but is larger than the box turtles and has a more oblong shell. The yellow throat is a good field mark. This turtle is characteristic of prairie ponds and marshes but is also found in ditches, sluggish streams and shallow inlets of lakes. It often crawls about on land.

The Spotted Turtle (*Clemmys guttata*) is a small attractive species with yellow or orange dots on the black shell and orange or yellow head markings. It once occurred in peat bogs, marshes and shallow lakes south to Indianapolis but has suffered severely from human modification of its habitat. Like Blanding's Turtle, it is basically semi-aquatic but not a strong swimmer.

The Midland Painted Turtle (*Chrysemys picta*) is an abundant and familiar turtle easily identified by the red stripes on the limbs and at the base of the neck and tail. It is found throughout Indiana. Quiet, warm, shallow water with much water weed is its favorite home. It is an inveterate sun bather and is active from early March well into November in southern Indiana. It feeds on aquatic plants, insects and snails.

One of the turtles discovered at New Harmony, the Red-eared Turtle (*Pseudemys sciripta elegans*), has become so popular in the pet trade that it now has been introduced into several localities outside its normal range. The original Indiana range included the Wabash, Tippecanoe, Kankakee and lower White Rivers. Quiet waters, plentiful aquatic vegetation and logs or other objects for basking are important requirements for this turtle. Males of this genus have unusually long nails that are used to stroke the face of the female during courtship.

The Slider (*Pseudemys concinna*) is a large aquatic turtle that may reach a shell length of 12 inches. The carapace has an intricate pattern of convoluted light lines, and the head is small with narrow pale stripes. Very rare in Indiana, this turtle has been collected at a few sites in Gibson and Posey Counties in large shallow lakes communicating with the Wabash during high water.

The Map Turtle (*Graptemys geographica*) and False Map Turtle or Sawback (*G. pseudogeographica*) are strongly aquatic species. As with the softshells, there is a widely distributed form (*geographica*) in both lakes and rivers and a riverine form (*pseudogeographica*) largely restricted to the lower Wabash drainage. Females of both these species reach a much greater size than males. The largest males of the Map Turtle have shell lengths of a little over 5 inches while females may slightly exceed 10 inches and have proportionally very large heads. The Sawback is a smaller species. Both are fond of basking in social groups of as many as 30 individuals. Map turtles feed largely upon snails, mussels and crayfish while

Sawbacks tend more toward a plant diet, at least as adults.

## Lizards

A faunal peculiarity of the northeastern and north central United States is the scarcity of lizards, the most familiar of reptiles in most parts of the world. The Fence Lizard (*Sceloporus undulatus*) (Fig. 77), found throughout southern Indiana, is russet to greyish brown with somewhat spiny overlapping scales. Males show bright patches of blue on the sides of the belly. The rail fences now vanishing from the rural scene were once favorite basking places for these lizards, but they still are common in open sunny spots near rock ledges, fallen trees, wood piles and old buildings. Active from late March to November and occasionally on mild winter days as well, they are probably the most frequently seen Indiana lizards. Like most of our other species, they feed on insects. The female lays 5 to 10 eggs under a stone or in a crevice during early summer; they usually hatch during August.

The only lizard with a virtually state-wide range is the Five-lined Skink (*Eumeces fasciatus*). Although basically a woodland species, it is quick to utilize favorable niches created by man such as slab piles of saw mills and foundations of old buildings. It is a shyer, more secretive animal than the Fence Lizard. Starting life as a coal black lizard with yellow stripes and a bright blue tail, it undergoes an involved color change

Fig. 77. The Fence Lizard is a familiar reptile of southern Indiana. The specimen pictured here is a large female. Photo, John H. Daily.

that leaves adult males uniformly brown with touches of red about the jaws. This color suffuses the entire head during the spring breeding season. Females become brownish but retain their stripes; the blue tail becomes greyish. These skinks usually lay their eggs under bark or in rotting wood. Females keep their nests clean, turn the eggs, and often defend them staunchly against animals several times their size. They also protect and groom the newborn young.

The Broad-headed Skink (*E. laticeps*) is a larger version of the Five-lined and undergoes an identical color change. Males may be almost a foot long and quite stout. With their wide reddish heads, they are impressive lizards and are generally believed to be poisonous. This is untrue, although they can give a painful bite. This species is confined to the southern half of the state and is not common. It is quite arboreal and often makes its home in a decayed or hollow tree. Although feeding mostly upon insects, these skinks will eat other lizards, nestling mice and eggs of small birds.

The Ground Skink (*Scincella laterale*) is a tiny slender brown lizard more likely to be confused with a small salamander than with any of the larger Indiana lizards. It is found in rather dry open woods in the unglaciated southern part of the state.

In the dunes and sandy prairie of northwestern Indiana and in a few isolated spots in southern Indiana occurs a representative of a lizard genus very abundant in the arid Southwest, the Six-lined Racerunner (*Cnemidophorus sexlineatus*). The minute granular dorsal scales and larger quadrangular ventrals distinguish it from all other local lizards. It is very active and wholly terrestrial.

The rarest and most distinctive of Indiana lizards is the Slender Glass Lizard or Ophisaur (*Ophisaurus attenuatus*). (Fig. 78). About two feet long and limbless, it resembles a snake but lacks the large ventral scutes seen in all Indiana snakes. It also has movable eyelids, ear openings, and a deep lateral fold; features not seen in any snake. If complete, the tail makes up about two thirds of the Ophisaur's length. Like the tails of many lizards, it is extremely fragile and breaks with the slightest injury. It regenerates but is always shorter than the original. The Ophisaur is found only in the north-

western part of the state in rather dry and open country. A
Pulaski County specimen laid 4 eggs early in July.

Fig. 78. A lizard despite its serpentine appearance, the Ophisaur
frequents sandy prairie in Indiana. Although quite active, it is stiffer
in its movements than a snake. Photo, John H. Daily.

### Snakes

The snake fauna of Indiana includes about 30 species of
which 13 belong to the natricine group. Although herpetolo-
gists are divided on how to define this subfamily and precisely
which species to include, there is general agreement that in the
non-arid parts of the North Temperate Zone the majority of
common and familiar snakes are natricines. As a group they
have a high reproductive potential and rapid growth rate. All
American species are live bearing, and females average considerably larger than males. The group includes the garter
snakes (*Thamnophis*), water snakes (*Natrix*), and some genera of small secretive species.

Probably the most plentiful snake of Indiana is the Eastern
Garter Snake (*Thamnophis sirtalis*). It is highly variable in
color and pattern, although most specimens have the three
yellow, greenish, orange or buff stripes that characterize garter snakes as a group. The lateral stripes in this species are
on the second and third scale rows; there are dark spots and
light flecks between the stripes, and the middle stripe may
be indistinct. This snake is most plentiful in damp, open, grassy places but may be found in nearly all ecological situations
in the state including city parks and vacant lots.

The Plains Garter Snake (*T. radix*) is the dominant garter

snake of most of northeastern Illinois but just enters Indiana in the northwest, particularly in the muck prairie. The lateral stripes are on the third and fourth scale rows. Butler's Garter Snake (*T. butleri*), described from a specimen collected at Richmond and named in honor of Amos Butler, is a small species with an unusually small head. It is known from a few widely isolated colonies from Indianapolis northward. The Eastern Ribbon Snake (*T. sauritus*) and Western Ribbon Snake (*T. proximus*)[5] are slender, long-tailed garter snakes with vivid stripes on a black or dark brown background. Both are snakes of marshes and lake margins; they are the most aquatic of Indiana garter snakes. The Eastern Garter Snake is the least selective species in its feeding. Although showing a preference for frogs and earthworms, it also takes other amphibians, small mammals, fish, birds, mollusks and crustaceans. The Plains Garter Snake restricts its diet much more to earthworms and amphibians, while Butler's Garter Snake feeds almost wholly upon earthworms and leeches, rarely taking small amphibians. The Ribbon Snakes feed almost exclusively upon frogs and fish.

Another very abundant Indiana snake is the Banded Watersnake (*Natrix sipedon*) (Fig. 79). The southern Indiana variety of this snake (*N.s. pleuralis*) is yellowish or buffy grey with reddish brown crossbands that break up into blotches toward the tail. The northern Indiana form (*N. s. sipedon*) is darker, and many of the older snakes become almost uniformly dull brown. This snake reaches an extreme length of about 4 feet but most specimens are smaller. Two larger watersnakes, the Copperbelly (*Natrix erythrogaster*) and the Diamond-backed Watersnake (*N. rhombifera*) are found in the lower Wabash and White River bottoms. The Copperbelly also occurs in small relict populations in northeastern Indiana. These snakes feed almost entirely upon fish and amphibians, but there is no good evidence that they are important predators on game fish. Large examples of all three of these snakes can easily be confused with the poisonous Cottonmouth which has never been recorded from Indiana.

The Queen Snake (*Natrix septemvittata*) is a slender brown water snake with light lateral stripes. It is abundant in rocky streams in southeastern and central Indiana. It feeds almost entirely upon crayfish.

Fig. 79. The Banded Watersnake inhabits nearly every stream and pond in Indiana. Although it bites fiercely if restrained or cornered, it is not poisonous. Photo, John H. Daily.

Kirtland's Watersnake (*N. kirtlandi*) is a small species rarely more than 18 inches long. Although it lives in damp places, it is not at all aquatic and is best known from vacant lots in or near large cities. It eats earthworms.

The Brown Snake (*Storeria dekayi*) is a small reptile averaging about a foot in length. It is fairly plentiful throughout the state but is secretive and not well known. When found, it is usually thought to be the young of some large snake. This snake is another city dweller being quite content in a weed-grown vacant lot where there is cardboard or other rubbish under which it can hide and slugs and earthworms for food. During 1948-50 I marked almost 500 snakes within a mile of Indiana University Medical Center. About a quarter of them were Brown Snakes; the others were Eastern Garter and Kirtland's Snakes.

The Red-bellied Snake (*Storeria occipitomaculata*) is closely related to the Brown Snake but more of a forest reptile. It is curiouly rare in Indiana, almost unknown from the northern half of the state, yet very abundant in much of the northeast and northern midwest of the United States. Of the three red-bellied snakes in Indiana, this is the smallest. The Copperbelly is a larger and heavier reptile at birth than an adult of this species, while Kirtland's Snake has the red area of the belly bordered by a row of black dots.

The Earth Snake (*Virginia valeriae*) is a small greyish brown natricine snake with a yellow belly. The few Indiana records are for the southern and west central parts of the state in rocky wooded terrain.

Most frequently encountered of Indiana's large snakes are the racers (*Coluber constrictor*). The Black Racer (*C.c. pria-*

*pus*) inhabits the southern third of the state and the Blue Racer (*C.c. foxi*) the northern half. The two intergrade over a wide zone in central Indiana. Racers are diurnal and inhabit many types of terrain. They eat a variety of small creatures from large insects to birds and chipmunks. Racers mate in the spring and lay upwards to 32 eggs during June. The eggs are ovoid to almost spherical and their leathery shells appear to be studded with coarse salt grains. Nests have been found under stones and in old rodent burrows. The eggs hatch in August or early September. The young are light grey with dark brown blotches.

The Black Rat Snake (*Elaphe obsoleta*) (Fig. 80), usually called Cow Snake or Chicken Snake in southern Indiana, is dark brown or black, usually blotched or speckled with yellow, dull orange or white. The darkest specimens are from northern Indiana, while those from southwestern Indiana are most strongly blotched. This is one of the largest North American snakes with specimens in excess of 8 feet on record. The largest Indiana specimens I have examined, however, have been just under 6 feet. Males average larger than females as is the rule in American rat snakes and king snakes. The Black Rat Snake is a forest reptile and often climbs trees. It may hibernate in company with Racers, Copperheads and Timber Rattlesnakes. The eggs usually are laid during the last half of July in a well rotted log or stump and hatch after about 8 weeks. The young of this species are distinctly blotched with dark grey on a whitish background. The adult snakes feed largely upon small mammals, birds and their eggs. Prey is killed by constriction.

The Fox Snake (*Elaphe vulpina*) is a blotched snake often with a coppery orange tint to the head. The average length is 3½ to 4 feet. In Indiana it is a northern grassland species that does well in farm land if given a minimum of encouragement. It feeds on meadow mice and other small rodents and is of considerable economic value.

Rivalling the Black Rat Snake in size is the Bull Snake (*Pituophis melanoleucus sayi*) which also reaches a length of 8 feet or more. It is a rather stocky blotched snake with a pointed snout. Its range in Indiana is confined to sandy prairie in the northwestern part of the state with a dubious record for Knox county. A pronounced burrowing tendency helps it to survive in agricultural districts where it renders good service by feeding upon pocket gophers, meadow mice and other destructive rodents. It hisses violently when angered.

The king snake genus (*Lampropeltis*) contains several economically valuable species. The Eastern Milk Snake (*L. doliata triangulum*) is a slender smooth-looking snake usually dove-grey with reddish or greyish brown saddles margined with

Fig. 80. A Rat Snake swallows a blue jay. Strongly blotched snakes such as this one are intermediate between the Black Rat Snake and Gray Rat Snake. Although they take birds readily, these snakes also eat many harmful rodents. Photo by author.

black. On top of the head is a light V or Y-shaped mark. It occurs in northern and eastern Indiana. In the southwestern fourth of the state is found the Red Milk Snake (*L. d. syspila*) which has red, orange or tan saddles that extend far down the sides giving the snake a ringed appearance. The light head mark is absent or reduced to an irregular spot. Milk snakes are night prowling reptiles and not often seen. They are forest snakes but often frequent farm yards and suburban areas.

The Prairie Kingsnake (*L. c. calligaster*) resembles a large dull-colored milk snake. On top of the head is a dark arrowhead mark. It inhabits grassland of western Indiana.

A third large dark snake of southern Indiana is the Black Kingsnake (*L. getulus niger*). It may be distinguished from the Black Racer and Black Ratsnake by its highly polished glassy scales, checkered belly and white bars on the upper lip plates. It frequents sparse dry woods, old fields and clearings. All three of Indiana's kingsnakes feed on lizards and small snakes when young, but the Prairie Kingsnake and Eastern Milk Snake shift largely to a rodent diet as adults. The Black Kingsnake keeps it snake-eating habits into adult life. Kingsnakes are constrictors and immune to pit viper venoms. Since the Black Kingsnake inhabits the same sort of country as Copperheads and Timber Rattlesnakes, it may be important as a natural enemy of these poisonous snakes. In confirmation of this, the remains of a small Copperhead were found in the stomach of a Black Kingsnake only 16 inches long.

A bright yellow collar at the base of the head and dark bluish or brownish grey body identify the handsome little Ring-neck Snake (*Diadophis punctatus edwardsi*). It reaches a maximum length of about 18 inches in Indiana. Salamanders are its chief food, but it will eat almost any creature small enough to be overpowered. It is a woodland snake frequently found under rocks and the bark of fallen trees throughout the southern half of the state.

The Worm Snake (*Carphophis amoena*) is a very small but rather stocky snake rarely exceeding a length of 10 inches. It is brown with a pink belly and highly polished scales. A burrowing snake rarely seen in the open, it is found in timbered rocky sections of southern Indiana and may be locally plentiful.

The smallest Indiana snake if both length and bulk are considered is the Crowned Snake (*Tantilla coronata*) which is about as long as the Worm Snake but more slender. It is pale brown with a dark head and blackish collar. It has been collected within the state only on some of the knobs near New Albany.

Confined to this same area in Indiana is the small but colorful Scarlet Snake (*Cemophora coccinea*) (Fig. 81). The pointed red snout and immaculate white belly are distinguishing characters. Reptile eggs are a favorite food of the Scarlet Snake. If the eggs are too large to be swallowed, the snake slits the shell with its knife-like teeth, inserts its head and swallows the contents of the egg.[4]

Unique among Indiana's reptiles are two slender green snakes of the predominantly Asian genus *Opheodrys*. The Rough Green Snake (*O. aestivus*) is a tree-dwelling, insect-eating species that reaches a length of 25 to 35 inches. It is found throughout the forested sections of southern Indiana. The smaller less arboreal Smooth Green Snake (*O. vernalis*) is a rare inhabitant of northwestern Indiana.

Fig. 81. Beautifully marked with red, white and black, the Scarlet Snake is one of Indiana's rarest reptiles, known in the state only from hills near New Albany. Photo, H. B. Bechtel.

When I was a boy in southern Indiana, one of the most feared snakes was the Spreading Viper or Spreadhead, more properly known as the Eastern Hognose Snake (*Heterodon platyrhinos*). This stubby snake with an up-turned, pig-like snout is one of the most accomplished bluffers of the animal kingdom. Its habit of spreading its head and neck, flattening its body, and hissing loudly, often with the mouth open, usually identifies it in the field. In spite of this behavior, the snake is completely harmless, and it is almost impossible to induce it to bite. If threatening does not frighten away the enemy, the snake begins to writhe about with its mouth open as though it were seriously injured. Its movements become weaker and less coordinated until it rolls onto its back, limp and helpless. It may remain this way for hours if disturbed, but if left alone it soon resumes its normal activity. Color and pattern are highly variable. Some specimens are uniformly black or dark grey; others show yellowish, orange, red or pale brown blotches on a dark background. Hognose Snakes are found throughout Indiana and are partial to regions of loose or sandy soil. They feed almost entirely upon toads and frogs.

Indiana's three poisonous snakes are all pit vipers and therefore characterized by the heat-sensing pit between the eye and nostril. Commonest of the three is the Copperhead (*Agkistrodon contortrix*) (Fig. 82) which takes its name from one of its better recognition features, the essentially unmarked coppery head. The body pattern consists of brown crossbands, narrow in the middle of the back and wider on the sides, on a background of pale brown or pinkish brown. The tail tip is blackish in adult snakes, yellow in the young. The average adult length is 2 to 3 feet. Copperheads are found in rocky wooded sections of southern Indiana north to Fountain County in the west and Franklin County in the east. Like many other local snakes, Copperheads are frequently found in log piles and under stones. They are active by night in hot weather. Mice, frogs and large insects are their favorite foods, but lizards, birds, shrews and small snakes are also eaten. Like

Fig. 82. The Copperhead is the commonest poisonous snake of Indiana. Its bite can cause severe pain and illness lasting several days but is almost never fatal. Photo by author.

other North American pit vipers, Copperheads are live bearing. Up to a dozen young are born during late August or September.

The Timber Rattlesnake (*Crotalus h. horridus*) is one of Indiana's largest snakes reaching a length of close to 6 feet, although the largest Indiana specimen I examined measured 57 inches. As is true of the Copperhead and most rattlesnakes, males of the Timber Rattler are larger than females. Timber Rattlers are greyish to yellow with black crossbands and a black tail when adult. They inhabit rocky wooded hills and once were widely distributed in southern Indiana. They now survive mostly on the comparatively undisturbed State and National forests. Six to 13 young (Fig. 83) are born, usually during September. They are about a foot long at birth and well able to swallow a half grown mouse. Chipmunks, squirrels and rabbits are favorite prey of adult snakes. Most Timber Rattlers do a good deal of preliminary coiling and rattling before they strike and usually can be avoided easily. They are dangerous if sufficiently provoked, and the bite of a large rattler can be fatal within a few hours.

Fig. 83. A Timber Rattlesnake with her brood of new-born young. This is one of the largest rattlesnakes and is comparatively mild tempered but its bite is very dangerous. Photo, John H. Daily.

The Massasauga (*Sistrurus c. catenatus*) is a small rattlesnake reaching a maximum length of 3 feet. It usually is blotched or spotted with a ringed tail, but uniformly black specimens are found in some localities. Typically a snake of tall grass prairie and marsh, it was once found throughout the northern half of Indiana but is now almost exterminated. Most of the remaining colonies are near lakes and marshes in the two northern tiers of counties. Small mammals, especially meadow mice, are the chief food of adult snakes, but frogs, birds and small snakes are also eaten.

## LITERATURE

1. CONANT, ROGER. 1958. A field guide to reptiles and amphibians of the United States and Canada cast of the 100th Meridian. Houghton Mifflin, Boston, 366 pp., 40 pls., 62 figs., 248 maps.
2. HAY, OLIVER P. 1892. The batrachians and reptiles of the state of Indiana. Ann. Rept. Indiana Dept. Geol. Nat. Resources. **17**: 412-602, 3 pls.
3. MINTON, SHERMAN A. 1954. Salamanders of the *Ambystoma jeffersonianum* complex in Indiana. Herpetologica. **10**: 173-179, 2 figs.
4. _____ and H. B. BECHTEL. 1958. Another Indiana record of *Cemophora coccinea* and a note on egg-eating. Copeia. No. 1, p. 47.
5. ROSSMAN, DOUGLAS A. 1962. *Thamnophis proximus* (Say), a valid species of garter snake. Copeia, No. 4, pp. 741-748. 2 figs.
6. SMITH, PHILIP W. 1957. An analysis of post-Wisconsin biogeography of the prairie peninsula region based on distributional phenomena among terrestrial vertebrate populations. Ecology. **38**: 205-218, 46 figs.
7. _____ and SHERMAN A. MINTON. 1957. A distributional summary of the herpetofauna of Illinois and Indiana. Amer. Midland Nat. **58**: 341-351, 12 figs.
8. UZZELL, THOMAS M. 1964. Relations of the diploid and triploid species of the *Ambystoma jeffersonianum* complex. Copeia. No. 2, pp. 257-300, 6 figs.

# 25
# The Birds

J. DAN WEBSTER
Hanover College

Of all the natural features of this state, probably none has given more pure enjoyment to its people than the birds. The flowers are beautiful—but they don't sing. The frogs and toads sing delightfully—but they aren't brightly colored. The fish are exciting to catch—but they don't fly. Only one group of animals is warm-blooded, active, flies, and has feathers. Amongst the more popular recreations in Indiana are hunting (quail and ducks) and bird-watching. And how many small children are entranced by the sparrows on the street? How many housewives feed sunflower seeds to the chickadees?

The early settlers depended on Wild Pigeons, Wild Turkeys, ducks, and Prairie Chickens for a big share of their diet. Today we cannot count table meat as an important economic product of wild birds, but we benefit from the insect-eating of meadowlarks, the weed-seed eating of sparrows, and the carrion-eating of vultures, to mention only a few examples. Of course, crows are troublesome thieves where corn is being drilled, and House Sparrows clutter mess and dirt about eaves and vines.

A scientific assessment of the position of wild birds in Indiana, economic and otherwise, is beyond my knowledge. However, some tentative approximations may be of interest.

## Ecological Position

As regards their food habits, our birds are extremely varied; one can only generalize that all species actively seek out their food and run, fly or swim to catch it, whatever the kind. Many species are herbivores, eating mostly seeds—examples Tree Sparrow and Cardinal—or fruits and buds—example Cedar Waxwing. The majority of species are carnivores of the second trophic level. That is, they eat herbivores—mostly insects, but in other cases fish and rodents.

Insect eaters include the warblers and woodpeckers; fish eaters include the Belted Kingfisher and the mergansers; ro-

dent eaters include most of the hawks and owls. A few birds
are carnivores of the third and fourth trophic levels—they eat
carnivores. Examples of this category would be the Great Blue
Heron, which eats mostly insectivorous frogs and fish, and the
Cooper's Hawk, which eats mostly insectivorous birds. Of
course, a good many bird species are omnivorous, especially
over the calendar year. Thus, many of the sparrows, as for instance the Song Sparrow, eat a high proportion of insects and
other invertebrates in summer, but almost entirely seeds during other seasons. And the Robin eats not only worms, but a
variety of fruits.

It is important to look at the diet of the most abundant kinds
of birds, for they are the ones which most affect the ecosystem. In other words, the bulk of what birds eat is that which
is eaten by the commonest kinds. Of the five commonest winter
birds, four are strictly seed eaters at this season, and one
(Redwinged Blackbird) is primarily a seed eater. Of the
four commonest summer birds (see below), one is strictly
insectivorous, two are primarily insectivorous in summer, and
one (Field Sparrow) eats a sizable portion of insects. Apparently the biggest thrust of birds in the energy and material
flow of Indiana ecosystems is at the second trophic level in
winter and at the third trophic level in summer.

Physical factors of bird environment include the parts of
our equable climate—some snow in winter, but usually not a
lot; rain and drinking water rather well distributed; moderate
cold; moderate heat. Of these, snow and cold are neatly dodged
by many species which migrate south to warmer climates. But
their places are taken by numerous other species which come
in from Michigan and farther north and join the permanent
residents. Winter birds have a difficult time when the snow is
deep, especially if there is a crust on the snow or if ice on the
trees and bushes keep them from their food. Winter bird population studies show an irregular drop in the census of each
small bird species as the winter months go by on each census
plot. Summer heat probably has little direct effect on adult
birds, though it may affect eggs and young. Spring and summer thundershowers often kill nestlings from exposure and
wet.

Biotic factors of bird environment include especially parasites, predators, cover, nesting sites, and food. Food we have

already discussed. Parasites, especially tapeworms, nematodes, flukes (in water and shore birds), malaria, viruses, biting lice, and mites are very common. But seldom are they an important mortality cause in adults, except as they may slow a bird down a bit, so that he is picked off by a hawk or owl. Nestlings, on the other hand, are frequently killed by bloodsucking larval flies of the family Calliphoridae. Predators include snakes, cats (mostly on eggs and young), hawks, and owls. Hunting pressure by man on game species (and on non-game species, chiefly large birds, by lawless, trigger-happy men and boys) should be listed here. Also, the effects of the Brown-headed Cowbird, a brood parasite, are like predation, for the female cowbird removes an egg from the host's nest and substitutes one of her own. Then the early-hatching, fast-growing young cowbird proceeds to usurp nest, food and attention, and his nest-mates often starve.

Cover supplies shelter from the elements and attacking predators, whether it be grass for the Grasshopper Sparrow, spicebush for the Kentucky Warbler, or sycamore tree for the Yellow-throated Warbler. These same plants usually provide food, or a place to find food, and nest site. For other species, however, feeding area, protective cover, and nest site are disparate. For a Robin, a tree or ledge serves as a nest support, a tree as cover, but a lawn as the feeding area. For a pair of chickadees, a stump, post, or dead limb with a natural cavity is the nesting site, but limbs and twigs of several trees are the feeding and cover area.

In our account of the environment surrounding any bird, we must not neglect his own species. Some species are quite solitary; for example, the Mockingbird never tolerates another member of his own species on his own territory except his mate and young during a brief nesting period. Other species espouse togetherness; Cedar Waxwings are always in a flock except for a few weeks in early summer when they withdraw in pairs.

Finally, we must consider the total community of which birds are only a part. A cattail marsh includes not only Coots, Long-billed Marsh Wrens, Yellow-throats, and Redwinged Blackbirds, but muskrats, insects, protozoans, cattails, algae, bacteria, water, sediments, and sub-surface geology. In fact the cattail marsh is all of these together—or none of them. A beech-maple forest in June is not only Redeyed Vireos, Cerulean Warblers, Wood Thrushes, Barred Owls, and Acadian Flycatchers, but all of these together with white-footed mice, gray squirrels, green snakes, box turtles, insects, beech trees, maple trees, Dutchman's breeches, bacteria, soil, and rock.

## What Kinds of Birds Are There in Indiana?

About 366 species of birds have been recorded within the boundaries of the state of Indiana in the 150 years of statehood. Of these, the evidence for the occurrence of some 30 is scientifically poor, and so it is more accurate to say that 336 species of birds have occurred in Indiana. Two species, common in Indiana in the nineteenth century are now extinct—the Passenger Pigeon and the Carolina Parakeet. Nine more species which occurred regularly in Indiana in the nineteenth century no longer occur here, but still exist elsewhere; the Wood Ibis, Trumpeter Swan, Prairie Chicken, Whooping Crane, Eskimo Curlew, Mississippi Kite, Swallow-tailed Kite, Ivory-billed Woodpecker, and Raven. The Wild Turkey was absent from Indiana from 1904 to 1950, but has been replanted in the south-central part of the state.

The following list (Table 12) includes the 239 species most commonly observed in the state.[5,10] Of these, the 148 marked with an asterisk breed in Indiana regularly whereas 91 are only transients, or winter visitants, or both.[3,5,17]

It is interesting to compare the current list of Indiana bird species (Table 12 plus[17]) with that in Butler's book.[3] Butler listed 305 species, of which at least five were based on rather flimsy scientific evidence; 61 species have been added in the ensuing 67 years, as follows: 40 additional species were casual wanderers or vagrants, recorded only once or a very few times. (Some of these 40 species records are scientifically flimsy). Eleven species are of regular occurrence; Butler and his helpers apparently overlooked them—Common Scoter, King Eider, Purple Sandpiper, White-rumped Sandpiper, Western Sandpiper, Caspian Tern, Parasitic Jaeger, Black-backed Gull, Three-toed Woodpecker, Bell Vireo, Oregon Junco, Harris Sparrow. Six species have naturally invaded Indiana since 1897—Cattle Egret, Rock Dove, Western Kingbird, Starling, Western Meadowlark, Brewer Blackbird—and now occur more or less regularly. Four species of game birds native to Europe or Asia have been introduced by the State Conservation Department, and still exist, or recently have existed, in a feral (wild) condition. None of them have increased their numbers, and clearly none could maintain their numbers against hunting pressure.

## Geographic Distribution

Birds are able to move so freely, with their power of flight, that they can pass minor geographic barriers with ease. Indiana is a small state, with no prominent geographic barriers to delimit the range of a bird species; mountains, oceans, and deserts are lacking. However, because birds are dependent on plants for their food, cover, and homesites, geographic barriers that affect plant distribution indirectly may affect bird distribution. Thus the east-to-west precipitation gradient

TABLE 12. Bird Species of Indiana

| | |
|---|---|
| Common Loon | *Turkey Vulture |
| Red-throated Loon | *Black Vulture |
| Horned Grebe | *Sharp-shinned Hawk |
| *Pied-billed Grebe | *Cooper's Hawk |
| Double-crested Cormorant | *Red-tailed Hawk |
| *Great Blue Heron | *Red-shouldered Hawk |
| Common Egret | *Broad-winged Hawk |
| Snowy Egret | Rough-legged Hawk |
| Little Blue Heron | Golden Eagle |
| *Green Heron | Bald Eagle |
| *Black-crowned Night Heron | *Marsh Hawk |
| *American Bittern | *Osprey |
| *Least Bittern | Peregrine Falcon |
| *Canada Goose | Pigeon Hawk |
| Snow Goose | *Sparrow Hawk |
| Blue Goose | *Bobwhite |
| *Mallard | *Ring-necked Pheasant |
| *Black Duck | Sandhill Crane |
| Gadwall | *King Rail |
| Baldpate | *Virginia Rail |
| Pintail | *Sora Rail |
| Green-winged Teal | *Florida Gallinule |
| *Blue-winged Teal | *Coot |
| Shoveller | *Piping Plover |
| *Wood Duck | Semipalmated Plover |
| Redhead | *Killdeer |
| Ring-necked Duck | Golden Plover |
| Canvas-back | Black-bellied Plover |
| Lesser Scaup | Ruddy Turnstone |
| American Golden-eye | *Woodcock |
| Buffle-head | *Wilson's Snipe |
| Old-squaw | *Upland Plover |
| White-winged Scoter | *Spotted Sandpiper |
| Ruddy Duck | Solitary Sandpiper |
| *Hooded Merganser | Greater Yellowlegs |
| American Merganser | Lesser Yellowlegs |
| Red-breasted Merganser | Pectoral Sandpiper |

Least Sandpiper
Red-backed Sandpiper
Dowitcher
Stilt Sandpiper
Semipalmated Sandpiper
Sanderling
Herring Gull
Ring-billed Gull
Bonaparte's Gull
*Forster's Tern
Common Tern
Caspian Tern
*Black Tern
*Mourning Dove
*Yellow-billed Cuckoo
*Black-billed Cuckoo
*Barn Owl
*Screech Owl
*Great Horned Owl
*Barred Owl
Long-eared Owl
Short-eared Owl
*Saw-whet Owl
*Chuck-will's Widow
*Whip-poor-will
*Nighthawk
*Chimney Swift
*Ruby-throated Hummingbird
*Belted Kingfisher
*Flicker
*Pileated Woodpecker
*Red-bellied Woodpecker
*Red-headed Woodpecker
*Yellow-bellied Sapsucker
*Hairy Woodpecker
*Downy Woodpecker
*Kingbird
*Crested Flycatcher
*Phoebe
*Acadian Flycatcher
*Alder Flycatcher
*Least Flycatcher
*Eastern Wood Pewee
Olive-sided Flycatcher
*Horned Lark
*Tree Swallow
*Bank Swallow
*Rough-winged Swallow
*Barn Swallow
*Cliff Swallow
*Purple Martin
*Blue Jay
*Common Crow
*Black-capped Chickadee
*Carolina Chickadee
*Tufted Titmouse
*White-breasted Nuthatch
Red-breasted Nuthatch
*Brown Creeper
*House Wren

Winter Wren
*Bewick's Wren
*Carolina Wren
*Long-billed Marsh Wren
*Short-billed Marsh Wren
*Mockingbird
*Catbird
*Brown Thrasher
*Robin
*Wood Thrush
Hermit Thrush
Olive-backed Thrush
Gray-cheeked Thrush
*Veery
*Bluebird
*Blue-gray Gnatcatcher
Golden-crowned Kinglet
Ruby-crowned Kinglet
Water Pipit
*Cedar Waxwing
Northern Shrike
*Loggerhead Shrike
*Starling
*White-eyed Vireo
*Bell's Vireo
*Yellow-throated Vireo
Blue-headed Vireo
*Red-eyed Vireo
Philadelphia Vireo
*Warbling Vireo
*Black and White Warbler
*Prothonotary Warbler
*Worm-eating Warbler
*Golden-winged Warbler
*Blue-winged Warbler
Tennessee Warbler
Orange-crowned Warbler
Nashville Warbler
*Parula Warbler
*Yellow Warbler
Magnolia Warbler
Cape May Warbler
Black-throated Blue Warbler
Myrtle Warbler
Black-throated Green Warbler
*Cerulean Warbler
Blackburnian Warbler
*Yellow-throated Warbler
*Chestnut-sided Warbler
Bay-breasted Warbler
Black-poll Warbler
*Pine Warbler
*Prairie Warbler
Palm Warbler
*Oven-bird
*Northern Water Thrush
*Louisiana Water Thrush
*Kentucky Warbler
Connecticut Warbler
Mourning Warbler

*Yellow-throat
*Yellow-breasted Chat
*Hooded Warbler
Wilson's Warbler
Canada Warbler
*American Redstart
*House Sparrow
*Bobolink
*Eastern Meadowlark
*Western Meadowlark
*Redwinged Blackbird
*Orchard Oriole
*Baltimore Oriole
Rusty Blackbird
*Brewer's Blackbird
*Common Grackle
*Brown-headed Cowbird
*Scarlet Tanager
*Summer Tanager
*Cardinal
*Rose-breasted Grosbeak
*Indigo Bunting
*Dickcissel

Purple Finch
Pine Siskin
*American Goldfinch
*Rufous-sided Towhee
*Savannah Sparrow
*Grasshopper Sparrow
*Henslow's Sparrow
*Vesper Sparrow
*Lark Sparrow
*Bachman's Sparrow
Slate-colored Junco
Tree Sparrow
*Chipping Sparrow
*Field Sparrow
White-crowned Sparrow
White-throated Sparrow
Fox Sparrow
Lincoln's Sparrow
*Swamp Sparrow
*Song Sparrow
Lapland Longspur
Snow Bunting

limits some more xerophytic plants to the western part of the state, and we might expect a few birds to be so limited. There is, of course, a north-to-south temperature gradient which limits some southern plants to the southern part of the state, and we would expect a few birds to be so distributed. The last is intensified by the limitation of glacial soils and glaciated topography to the north. Primitively, with prairie in the northwestern sector of the state and deciduous forest almost continuous elsewhere (Fig. 58), a number of prairie species (Prairie Chicken, Horned Lark, Grasshopper Sparrow, etc.) were confined to the prairie sector and the outlying islands of prairie in the north. And numerous forest-dwelling species doubtless never reached the sites of Morocco or Fowler (Acadian Flycatcher, Tufted Titmouse, etc.). But now, with much woodland scattered in the former prairie, and a large proportion of the former forests given over to cornfields and pastures, those adaptable species which remain seem, in this state, to be governed mostly by local ecological factors in their distribution.

It is of interest to analyze the present distribution of Indiana birds, while attempting to minimize the effects of local ecological factors. For this purpose, I will confine myself to breeding ranges, which are better known than winter ranges. The distribution of water, shore, and marsh birds within the state clearly depends upon local drainage and water, and so only land birds need be considered. Most of these are found throughout Indiana, wherever local ecological conditions are right, leaving a fairly short list of species which seem to be delimited by geography or widespread ecological factors in Indiana. These are:

### SOUTHERN PART OF STATE ONLY
*(North to Lafayette and Muncie in some cases.)*
Black Vulture (General)
Chuck Wills Widow (Brush and fields)
Carolina Chickadee (Forest)
Worm-eating Warbler (Forest)
Kentucky Warbler (Forest)
Yellow-throated Warbler (Sycamore forest)
Summer Tanager (Forest)
Bachman Sparrow (Fields with brush)

### NORTHERN PART OF STATE ONLY
Saw Whet Owl (Forest)
Yellow-bellied Sapsucker (Forest)
Least Flycatcher (Brush in prairie)
Tree Swallow (Forest edge)
Black-capped Chickadee (Forest)
Brown Creeper (Northeastern corner only; forest)
Veery (Forest)
Golden-winged Warbler (Brushy woodland edges)
Chestnut-sided Warbler (Forest)
Northern Water-thrush (Creeks in forest)
Rose-breasted Grosbeak (Forest)
Western Meadowlark (Prairie)

### WESTERN PART OF STATE ONLY
Bell's Vireo (Brush)
Brewer Blackbird (Northwestern corner only; prairie)

It would appear that Indiana's part of the east-to-west precipitation gradient is not very limiting to birds, for only two species are bounded here. Despite the lack of a prominent ecological boundary or other barrier, and that woodland or forest is now distributed in a "regularly spotty" fashion throughout the state, 14 species of forest birds find their northern or southern limits in the state. And 6 species characteristic of more open areas are so limited. I suggest two hypotheses for this geographical distribution pattern:

(1) The temperature gradient, doubtless accompanied by subtle differences in flora and insect fauna, influences bird distribution in a distinct, although not major way.

(2) The forest species were limited in spread from north to south and south to north by the Prairie Peninsula.[15, 21] While the map of presettlement vegetation (Fig. 58) does not suggest a complete prairie barrier to forest species in Indiana,

it does suggest a partial or filter barrier of prairie and oak-hickory forest which would hinder the northward spread of species (Kentucky Warbler and Summer Tanager, for example) especially adapted to beech-maple or mixed beech-oak-maple-hickory forests. Conversely, it suggests a partial barrier of prairie and beech-maple forest which would hinder the southward spread of species (Yellow-bellied Sapsucker and Black-capped Chickadee, for example) adapted to northern oak-hickory or the cooler forest types.

One historical point to the distribution pattern described above can be made. At least two of the southern-limited birds have extended their ranges somewhat northward in the last 70 years—Chuck Will's Widow and Bachman Sparrow. Also the Mockingbird, although it has been found throughout the state for at least a century, has become distinctly more common in the north in recent decades. Conversely, there have been no breeding records of the northerly Yellow-bellied Sapsucker, Brown Creeper, or Northern Water Thrush for 60 years. There is, then, a suggestion that brushland species have been moving north, and some of the northern forest species have been retreating northward into Michigan.

### How Many Birds Are There in Indiana?

The science of demography—the study of populations—is in an advanced stage as applied to human beings. The United States Bureau of the Census is able to tell us exactly how many people live in each state and township, and how old they are, and how they earn their living, as well as many other "characteristics of the population." When we try to census the chickadees in our back yard, however, we meet with difficulties. The chickadees won't admit their sex, most of the time, and never answer questions as to their age and number of offspring!

A beginning has been made by ornithologists on the demography of birds. Detailed data on longevity, sex, etc., from one local area on one species have been painstakingly gathered and analyzed in several instances (as mentioned later). Total size of populations, by species, has been recorded on a local basis many thousands of times. Let us examine these counts as applied to Indiana.

Most familiar of bird census methods is the "Audubon Christmas Count." One day, each Christmas season, some 200

Hoosiers, in about 20 groups, count all the birds they can. Within a 15-mile diameter circle for each counting group, they make a dawn-to-dark effort. And the counting of owls means that some shivering census-takers must rise *before* dawn or listen along the country roads *after* dark.

I have tabulated the Christmas counts made in Indiana for the last five years;[11,18] the figures for the most common species are given in Table 13.

TABLE 13. Christmas census for common birds.

| Species | Average per count for average of five years | Average estimate of total population in the state |
|---|---|---|
| Starling | 2,237 | 458,585 |
| House Sparrow | 873 | 178,965 |
| Common Grackle | 503 | 103,115 |
| Crow | 322 | 66,010 |
| Junco (both species) | 304 | 62,320 |
| Tree Sparrow | 268 | 54,940 |
| Mourning Dove | 179 | 36,695 |
| Cardinal | 128 | 26,240 |
| Song Sparrow | 74 | 15,170 |
| Black Duck | 72 | 14,760 |
| Blue Jay | 72 | 14,760 |
| Horned Lark | 68 | 13,940 |
| Total (for all species) | 6,080 | 1,247,000 |

The figure in the right hand column, therein, was obtained by extrapolation. (That is, the total acreage of the state was divided by the acreage in a circle of 15 miles diameter, and the dividend multiplied by the left hand figure.) These summary figures don't show any annual fluctuation, and indeed, some species populations seem to remain rather constant from year to year. For instance, the average number of Downy Woodpeckers seen per count was: in 1961, 34; 1962, 51; 1963, 48; 1964, 45; 1965, 42. On the other hand, the populations of some species in Indiana fluctuate widely. For instance, the average counts for the Robin were in 1961, 5; 1962; 1; 1963, 37; 1964, 1; 1965, 44.

A considerably lesser effort has been made by Indiana bird watchers to count birds by the Christmas Count method during the month of May. The figures for the last three years[12] for the commonest species are in Table 14.

A more accurate, but more time consuming, method is used by bird students, called the "winter bird population study."[8] [20, 24] Essentially, this method involves the careful count of all

TABLE 14. May census of birds for 3 years.

| | Average per count for all three years | Average estimate of total population in state for all three years |
|---|---|---|
| Redwinged Blackbird | 189 | 38,730 |
| House Sparrow | 134 | 27,500 |
| Common Grackle | 123 | 25,200 |
| Starling | 78 | 15,990 |
| American Goldfinch | 46 | 9,430 |
| Total (for all species) | 1,799 | 369,795 |

the birds on a measured area of 15 to 50 acres of uniform habitat on 8 different days of the winter. An average of the 8 counts is assumed to be a true figure. Altogether, 12 of these have been made in Indiana, from 1949 to 1965, and including forests, abandoned fields, and orchards. For my analysis in Table 15, some major habitats had not been censused in Indiana; for these I borrowed density figures from Illinois, taken from the book by Graber and Graber.[6] State figures were calculated by extrapolation. Notice the contrast in total state winter bird population—almost 34 million here—as compared with 1.2 million for the Christmas count! There can be little doubt that the higher figure is *nearer* the truth, but even it is subject to suspicion. It may be either too high or too low. I am inclined to think it may be too low, because a good deal of the "other land" may be brushy, with a higher bird density than I have calculated.

If the most abundant bird species figures are totaled from Table 16, the top ones are:

| Horned Lark | 4.2 million in Indiana |
| Junco | 2.8 million in Indiana |
| Redwinged Blackbird | 2.3 million in Indiana |
| Tree Sparrow | 2.3 million in Indiana |
| Lapland Longspur | 2.3 million in Indiana |

In each case, the total figure would be slightly higher if the species could be calculated for "other land" (miscellaneous habitats) and if minor species components of included habitats were calculated in. Again notice the contrast with Christmas Count figures. The Horned Lark is the twelfth most abundant bird by the Christmas count, but first (by a wide margin) by the winter population study. The Starling is the most abundant species by the Christmas count, but only eighth here. Evidently Christmas counters spend too much time in the suburbs and too little time in the corn stubble.

Probably the most accurate method of counting birds in general use is the "Breeding bird census."[1, 7, 23] Altogether, 26 have been made in Indiana, in several kinds of forests, wet meadow, residential suburb, apple orchard, and pasture. Briefly, this method depends on the fact that nearly all male birds are prominently territorial during the breeding season. They

TABLE 15. Indiana Winter Bird Populations

| Area | Acres in State (8,21) | Density (Birds/ 100 acres) | Authority | Total Birds in State |
|---|---|---|---|---|
| Forest | 4,140,000 | 172 | Webster, 1965 | 7,130,000 |
| Brushland (=shrubland) | 540,000 (estimated) | 1,064 | Graber, 1963 | 5,750,000 |
| Pasture (Not woodland or brushland) | 2,544,000 | 112 | Graber, 1963 | 2,850,000 |
| Hay | 1,399,000 | 108 | Graber, 1963 | 1,511,000 |
| Long-term grass and legume, not pastured or cropped | 397,000 | 161 | Graber, 1963 | 639,000 |
| Orchard | 19,000 | 254 | Gregory, 1956 | 48,000 |
| Corn | 5,103,000 | 132 | Graber, 1963 | 6,730,000 |
| Wheat (Assume all winter wheat) | 1,197,000 | 37 | Graber, 1963 | 443,000 |
| Other small grains | 986,000 | 114 | Graber, 1963 | 1,124,000 |
| Soybeans | 2,269,000 | 159 | Graber, 1963 | 3,610,000 |
| Other crops (Assume plowed and bare) | 604,000 | 66 | Graber, 1963 | 399,000 |
| Other land (Waste, houses, roads, grass; probably some brush; much of it urban and suburban) | 3,960,000 | 88 | Sintz, 1963 (abandoned broomsedge field) | 3,490,000 |
| Totals | 23,158,000 | | | 33,724,000 |

TABLE 16. Winter bird populations by species.

| Area | 1st speciaes in abundance | Density (Birds of this species/100 acres) | Total in State in this habitat |
|------|---------------------------|-------------------------------------------|-------------------------------|
| Forest | Tufted Titmouse | 38 | 1,573,000 |
| | Chickadee (sp.) | 20 | 828,000 |
| | Downy Woodpecker | 16 | 663,000 |
| | Robin | 14 | 580,000 |
| | White-breasted Nuthatch | 13 | 538,000 |
| | Red-bellied Woodpecker | 9 | 373,000 |
| | Cedar Waxwing | 9 | 373,000 |
| | Cardinal | 9 | 373,000 |
| Brushland | Tree Sparrow | 413 | 2,270,000 |
| | Junco (sp.) | 236 | 1,299,000 |
| | House Sparrow | 140 | 756,000 |
| | Starling | 51 | 276,000 |
| | Cardinal | 50 | 275,000 |
| | Bobwhite | 49 | 275,000 |
| Pasture | Horned Lark | 20 | 508,000 |
| | Redwinged Blackbird | 18 | 458,000 |
| | Junco | 14 | 356,000 |
| | Robin | 14 | 356,000 |
| Hay | Horned Lark | 33 | 508,000 |
| | Lapland Longspur | 23 | 322,000 |
| | Meadowlark (sp.) | 16 | 223,000 |
| Long-term grass and legume | Junco (sp.) | 39 | 155,000 |
| | Bobwhite | 30 | 119,000 |
| | Tree Sparrow | 24 | 95,000 |
| Orchard | Starling | 53 | 10,000 |
| | Robin | 47 | 9,000 |
| | Junco (sp.) | 32 | 6,000 |
| Corn | Horned Lark | 29 | 1,479,000 |
| | Lapland Longspur | 28 | 1,428,000 |
| | Junco (sp.) | 20 | 1,020,000 |
| | Redwinged Blackbird | 9 | 459,000 |
| | Meadowlark (sp.) | 6 | 306,000 |
| Wheat | Horned Lark | 17 | 203,000 |
| | Tree Sparrow | 5 | 60,000 |
| | Lapland Longspur | 4 | 48,000 |
| Other small grains | Starling | 53 | 523,000 |
| | Meadowlark (sp.) | 17 | 168,000 |
| | Horned Lark | 13 | 128,000 |
| | Lapland Longspur | 12 | 118,000 |
| Soybeans | Redwinged Blackbird | 59 | 1,389,000 |
| | Horned Lark | 47 | 1,067,000 |
| | Meadowlark (sp.) | 20 | 454,000 |
| | Lapland Longspur | 17 | 386,000 |
| Other Crops | Horned Lark | 61 | 369,000 |
| | Lapland Longspur | 3 | 18,000 |

not only sing and defend their territories against encroachment by other members of their own species, but also "stay put" on the same territories for several weeks or more. Careful mapping of singing males on each of 8 or more days spread through April, May, and June results in a reasonably accurate census of a 15 to 40 acre area.

In an analysis presented in Table 17, state figures were calculated by extrapolation. The total figure of almost 97 million birds for Indiana is surprisingly large. I suspect that it is a little too high, for these reasons: (1) The forest density figure is based on forest areas of richer types; no censuses have been made in poorer forests, such as oak-hickory or heavily-grazed woods. (2) The pasture density figure is based on only

TABLE 17. Indiana Breeding Bird Populations

| Area | Acres in State (8,21) | Density (Birds/ 10 acres) | Authority | Total Birds in State |
|---|---|---|---|---|
| Forest | 4,140,000 | 948 | Webster, 1964 | 39,300,000 |
| Brushland (=shrubland) | 540,000 (estimated) | 402 | Graber, 1963 | 2,170,000 |
| Pasture, hay, long-term grasses and legumes | 4,340,000 | 912 | Baker, 1965 | 39,600,000 |
| Orchard | 19,000 | 368 | Gregory, 1955 | 70,000 |
| Corn | 5,103,000 | 66 | Graber, 1963 | 3,370,000 |
| Wheat | 1,197,000 | 100 | Graber, 1963 | 1,197,000 |
| Oats | 867,000 | 153 | Graber, 1963 | 1,327,000 |
| Soybeans | 2,269,000 | 53 | Graber, 1963 | 1,204,000 |
| Other crops | 723,000 | 93 | None— Average of 4 preceding | 672,000 |
| Other land (Waste, roads, houses, marsh, grassland, probably more brush. Much of it urban and suburban.) | 3,960,000 (No areal breakdown figures available.) | 200 | None— estimate. (Marsh and residential suburb densities have been measured in Indiana.) | 7,920,000 |
| Total | 23,158,000 | | | 96,830,000 |

by Mrs. H. A. Baker.[1] Mrs. Baker's pasture is probably more
bird-rich than most. Nonetheless, I feel confident that Indiana

TABLE 18. Breeding Bird Populations by Species.

| Area | 1st species in abundance | Density (total birds/100 acres) | Total in state in this habitat |
|---|---|---|---|
| Forest | Red-eyed Vireo | 46 | 1,905,000 |
| | Cerulean Warbler | 29 | 1,201,000 |
| | Tufted Titmouse | 25 | 1,036,000 |
| | Acadian Flycatcher | 25 | 1,036,000 |
| | Cardinal | 24 | 944,000 |
| | Wood Pewee | 18 | 746,000 |
| | Wood Thrush | 17 | 705,000 |
| | Chickadee (sp.) | 16 | 663,000 |
| | Crested Flycatcher | 16 | 663,000 |
| Brushland | Field Sparrow | 69 | 373,000 |
| | Redwinged Blackbird | 40 | 216,000 |
| | American Goldfinch | 30 | 162,000 |
| | Indigo Bunting | 22 | 119,000 |
| | Brown-headed Cowbird | 21 | 113,000 |
| Pasture, Hay | Field Sparrow | 38 | 1,650,000 |
| | Song Sparrow | 37 | 1,608,000 |
| | Redwinged Blackbird | 34 | 1,476,000 |
| | Meadowlark (sp.) | 29 | 1,259,000 |
| | Brown Thrasher | 27 | 1,172,000 |
| | Grasshopper Sparrow | 22 | 955,000 |
| | Common Grackle | 22 | 955,000 |
| Orchard | Field Sparrow | 40 | 8,000 |
| | Mourning Dove | 28 | 5,000 |
| Corn | Horned Lark | 23 | 1,173,000 |
| | Common Grackle | 6 | 306,000 |
| | Redwinged Blackbird | 5 | 255,000 |
| Wheat | Redwinged Blackbird | 33 | 395,000 |
| | Dickcissel | 15 | 180,000 |
| | Indigo Bunting | 9 | 108,000 |
| Oats | Redwinged Blackbird | 53 | 459,000 |
| | Bobolink | 26 | 225,000 |
| | House Sparrow | 26 | 225,000 |
| Soybeans | Horned Lark | 23 | 523,000 |
| | Common Grackle | 66 | 306,000 |
| | Redwinged Blackbird | 5 | 114,000 |
| Other land | (Mostly Starling, Song Sparrow, House Sparrow, and Redwinged Blackbird) | | |

has more birds in June that the 60 million estimated for Illinois by the Grabers.[6] One of the reasons for the larger number of birds in a smaller state is that Indiana has larger areas of forest and brush—the habitats where birds are most dense.

As to the species populations listed in Table 18, the most abundant listed ones are:

| | |
|---|---|
| Redwinged Blackbird | 2.9 million in Indiana |
| Field Sparrow | 2.6 million in Indiana |
| Red-eyed Vireo | 1.9 million in Indiana |
| Horned Lark | 1.7 million in Indiana |

In each case, the total would be higher if the figures from "other land" could be calculated, and if minor species components of included habitats were calculated in. In fact, the total number of Redwinged Blackbirds, under these circumstances, would doubtless be considerably higher.

Characteristics of bird populations other than total numbers have been gathered for a few species. For instance, annual vital statistics for the Black Duck from 1945 to 1953 were as given in Table 19.

TABLE 19. Average Annual Data on Black Duck

| Date | Item | Gain | Loss | Current Population |
|---|---|---|---|---|
| Oct. 1 | Original Population | | | 100 |
| | Hunting loss (including crippling loss | | 43 | |
| March 1 | Winter loss | | 17 | 40 |
| April 18 | Eggs laid | 108 | | 148 |
| | Eggs lost | | 12 | |
| May 30 | Hatching | | | 136 |
| | Juvenile mortality | | 20 | |
| | Adult mortality in spring and summer | | 16 | |
| Oct. 1 | Final Population | | | 100 |

This population appeared to be stable, and statistics were reasonably accurate for all phases of the life cycle of this water bird, which breeds in Eastern Canada and winters all over the Eastern half of the United States.[25] Some of the varied factors involved in bird mortality are pointed up in the table above. For the Black Duck, the largest mortality factor is hunting by man.

## Changes in Indiana Bird Life

Changes in the avifauna—the kinds and numbers of birds which inhabit an area—result from several factors of change. Most important in Indiana have been changes in the major plant associations on which birds depend and with which they are intimately bound. Second in importance has been a tremendous increase in human population, together with greatly increased hunting pressure and more efficient weapons.[2, 3] Third has been the effect of increased use of ever-increasingly toxic chemical pesticides.

Changes in plant associations in Indiana have been radical, and yet not always appreciated in their relationship to birds. The clearing of vast areas of forest and replacement by croplands, pastures, and brushlands in the nineteenth century drastically reduced the numbers of forest birds, but increased the numbers of such open field birds as the Horned Lark and brushland birds as the Cardinal. Abandonment of poor, eroded farmlands (mainly in the southern part of the state) in the last three decades has greatly increased the numbers of brushland birds and those of early tree stages of succession. Plowing of the prairies, in many places followed by abandonment and growth of brush and timber, resulted in reduction of the less adaptable prairie birds, and finally the extirpation, only two years ago, of the Prairie Chicken. Drainage of marshes and sloughs, with replacement by croplands, eliminated most of our breeding ducks, rails, and marsh wrens. Adoption of chemical weed-killers in agriculture resulted, by eliminating certain weeds, in reduction of some bird species, although this has not been carefully measured. Removal of hedgerows in modern "clean" farming, has reduced radically the numbers of Bluebird, Kingbird, Bobwhite, and other hedgerow birds.

Actual killing by the human predator has tended radically to reduce the number of large birds. Swans, geese, turkeys, ibises, hawks and eagles have been especially affected. On the other hand, hunting pressure on middle-sized species that reproduce rapidly, such as Bobwhite and Prairie Chicken, has been less important than habitat changes. Elimination of the Passenger Pigeon[19] was accomplished primarily by slaughter on the breeding grounds, mainly in Minnesota, Wisconsin, Michigan, and Ontario, but also in Northern Indiana. Notice that no small-sized bird had been extirpated from Indiana.

Chemicals used in agriculture to control arthropod pests have reduced the numbers of birds both by reducing insect food, and by direct poisoning. Although I am unaware of any Indiana studies, careful work in Michigan, Illinois, and other areas has measured these changes. Especially distressing have been the reductions in Robins, Bluebirds, and hawks. Apparently "top carnivores" such as eagles, large owls, Osprey, and Cooper's Hawk which feed largely on carnivores have been especially poisoned because D.D.T. and similar stable insecticides tend to pile up in this terminus of the one-way food-chain.[4] We may hope that agriculture research in Indiana will become ecologically oriented enough to study the effects of pesticides upon the agricultural landscape.

### Migrations of Indiana Birds

Why do birds migrate? To where do they fly? When do they arrive and leave? How do they find their way without map, compass, or road signs? Only partial answers can be given.

*Why?* In a long term sense, a bird migrates because he is built that way. Through many generations of natural selection, the species has been adapted in its anatomy, physiology, and behavior for migration in spring and fall. He is "programmed" for a flight, let us say, from Indiana to Colombia in September and for the 2000-mile return flight in May. The Scarlet Tanager can no more avoid the journey than he can turn himself blue! It may seem very intelligent of the warmth-loving, fruit-eating tanager to avoid the cold, fruitless forests of our midwestern winter. But does this not misuse the word "intelligent?"

In a short-term sense we know something of the physiology of migration—particularly of spring migration in members of the sparrow family wintering in the United States.[16]

As this diagram indicates, increasing day length is the environmental trigger that sets off a series of physiological changes, culminating in the northward flight, although other environmental stimuli may be involved in a secondary fashion. Obviously, this is not a complete physiological explanation for spring migration, for many of our birds winter on the equator,

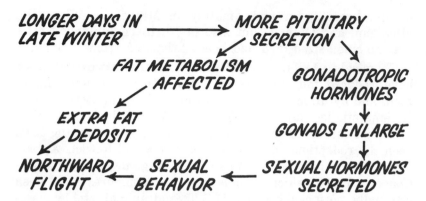

where there is virtually no change in day length, or even in the Southern Hemisphere, where the day length changes in the wrong direction. Presumably, different environmental triggers or internal mechanisms time the spring physiology of those species.

*Where to?* Our Indiana bird fauna includes 239 reasonably common species of which all but 20 are at least partially migratory. Summer resident describes 71 of them; they breed here in the summer, but fly south beyond the Ohio River in the fall. Winter visitant applies to 23 of them; they breed to the north, but winter in our temperate latitude. Migrant, or bird-of-passage, is the term for 80 species, which travel through Indiana in spring or fall, or both, *en route* to and from out-of-state points. Some 33 species are permanent residents, being either non-migratory or such short-distance migrants that they stay in the state at all seasons. Still another category is that of the 28 combination species, each of which includes large populations that belong in each of two or more of the above categories. As I went through the Indiana list and made this division, it was surprising how many species were difficult to classify. For instance, is the Myrtle Warbler mainly a winter visitant or a migrant, considering that the species is easy to see in May, but obscure in January? (I decided that it is much more numerous as a migrant).

The above categories are more meaningful with examples. A summer resident is the Red-eyed Vireo, which spends May to September in Indiana forests, but November to April in the tropical forests of the upper Amazon Valley. A winter visitant is the Purple Finch which summers in the coniferous forests of Canada and northern edge of the United States, but spends its winters here. A migrant is the Golden Plover, which winters on the *playas* and *pampas* of Argentine, but starts north about April 1, and flies through South America, Central America, the Mississippi Valley (many stop to rest on the plowed fields of Indiana), and on to the Arctic. In fall, the southward route is along the Atlantic Coast and over the open ocean. A permanent resident is the Cardinal, which seldom moves over a half-mile in a lifetime. A "combination" is the Song Sparrow. Some Song Sparrows are permanent residents, especially in Southern Indiana; but in February and March more arrive from Kentucky and Tennessee to breed here, and others, wintering here or to the south, move on north to breed in Michigan and Canada; and in October the southward switch occurs. In other words, many Song Sparrows seen in Indiana are spring and summer residents, many are permanent residents, many are winter visitants, and many are purely migrants.

Migratory flightlines are not very well marked in such a flat state as Indiana; most migrating birds seem to fly in straight lines. However, the north-trending Wabash River serves to channel many migrants, and the Whitewater River serves as a similar route in the east.[3] Near Hanover, in spring and fall, I have seen many hawks, Blue Jays, and swallows following the bluffs along the Indiana side of the Ohio River in northbound and southbound paths. Ducks and shorebirds usually follow the river more closely. Night-flying migrants, such as small song birds, probably follow these north-south valleys, too, by starlight or moonlight, but this remains to be proved.

*When?* Migratory birds go more by the calendar year than anything else in their timing. However, they usually do wait for a favoring wind and rising temperature in spring or falling temperature in autumn before taking off. This means that most northward flights in spring in the central United States are behind an advancing warm front which is bringing spring-like air (and showers) to Indiana. And in the fall this means that most southward flights are behind an advancing cold front, which is bringing Canadian air southeast.

Migration dates have been kept by Indiana bird-watchers for 75 years, now. For instance, the Least Sandpiper is a fairly common migrant in Indiana both in spring and fall. Near Indianapolis, the earliest spring date when it was seen was April 28, in 1935, and the latest on May 30, in 1954, with the largest number (flock of 211) May 29, 1955. The earliest fall date was July 13, 1956, the latest November 13, 1950, and the largest number (flock of 50) September 2, 1945. The Spotted Sandpiper is a common summer resident and still commoner migrant. In the state the earliest spring date of record is March 18, 1897, and the latest fall date November 7, 1954. Migration peaks of largest numbers near Indianapolis are in the first two weeks of May and the first week of September.[13]

*How do they find their way?* Obviously, birds do find their way, with an accuracy almost as good as that of a skilled human airplane navigator. Yet the birds have neither sextant, magnetic compass, sun compass, radio-detection finder, nor chart! However, birds apparently have excellent sensory instruments—their eyes—and excellent memories for landmarks.

Careful experimentation in the last 20 years (none of it in Indiana) has shown that migrant birds orient by the sun during the day and on into the evening. During the night they orient by the moon and the stars with great facility. And always memory for visual landmarks aids them in finding their way along previously followed paths with sure skill.[14] Other means of navigation, as for instance by wind orientation, are probable, but have not been demonstrated.

## LITERATURE

1. Baker, H. A. 1965. Breeding bird census; grazed brushy fields. Audubon Field Notes **19**:624-625. Also 10 previous years.
2. Butler, 1896. A century of changes in the aspects of nature. Proc. Indiana Acad. Sci. for 1895:31-42.
3. ——— 1897. Birds of Indiana. Ind. Dept. Geol. Nat. Res., Ann. Rept. **22**:687-745 and 1172-1173.
4. Clement, R. C., Dykstra, W. W., and Poole, D. A. 1964. Report of the conservation committee. Wilson Bull. **76**:306-312.
5. Cope, J. B. 1966. Personal communication: Status of Indiana breeding birds.
6. Graber, R. R. and Graber, J. W. 1963. A comparative study of bird populations in Illinois, 1906-1909 and 1956-1958. Ill. Nat. Hist. Survey Bull. **28**:377-528.
7. Gregory, R. I. 1955. Breeding bird census; apple orchard. Aud. Field Notes **9**:426-427. Also preceding year.
8. ——— 1956. Winter bird population study; commercial apple orchard. Audubon Field Notes **10**:296. Also 2 previous years.
9. Hutchinson, O. K. 1956. Indiana's forest resources and industries. U. S. Dept. Agric., Forest Service. Forest Res. Rept. **10**:1-44.
10. Indiana Audubon Society. 1951. Daily field check list; birds of Indiana.
11. ——— 1961-1965. Christmas count. Indiana Audubon Quarterly **39-43**, (1) annually.
12. ——— 1963-1965. Annual May count, Indiana Audubon Quarterly **41-43**, (3) annually.

13. KELLER, C. E. 1958. The shorebird families of Indiana, Part 4. Indiana Audubon Quarterly **36**:2-39.
14. KRAMER, G. 1961. Long distance orientation. In Marshall, A. J. (editor), Biology and comparative physiology of birds, **2**:341-371. Academic Press, New York.
15. LINDSEY, A. A., CRANKSHAW, W. B. and QADIR, S. A. 1965. Soil relations and distribution map of the vegetation of presettlement Indiana. Bot. Gazette, **126**:155-163.
16. MARSHALL, A. J. 1961. Breeding seasons and migration. In Biology and comparative physiology of birds, **2**:307-339. Academic Press, New York.
17. MUMFORD, R. E. 1966. Personal communication: manuscript of additions to the Indiana bird list.
18. NATIONAL AUDUBON SOCIETY. 1961-1965. Christmas bird count. Audubon Field Notes **15-19**. (2) annually.
19. SCHORGER, A. W. 1955. The Passenger Pigeon. Univ. Wisconsin Press, Madison.
20. SINTZ, J. K. 1963. Winter bird population study; abandoned fields dominated by broomsedge. Audubon Field Notes **17**, 368-369.
21. TRANSEAU, E. N. 1935. The prairie peninsula. Ecology **16**:423-437.
22. U. S. BUREAU OF THE CENSUS. 1961. U. S. Census of Agriculture: 1959. 1, Counties, Part 11, Indiana.
23. WEBSTER, J. D. 1964. Breeding bird census; tornado-disturbed beech maple forest. Audubon Field Notes, **18**:548-549. Also 5 previous years.
24. ———— 1965. Winter bird population study; beech-maple forest. Audubon Field Notes **19**:423-424. (Also 3 previous years).
25. WRIGHT, B. S. 1954. High tide and an east wind. The Stackpole Co., Harrisburg.

# 26
# *Mammals*

RUSSELL E. MUMFORD
Purdue University

As a group, mammals are rather poorly known and many persons living in Indiana cannot name more than 20 native species. The more conspicuous or diurnal forms, such as the woodchuck (groundhog), fox squirrel, and raccoon, are familiar to most people. The same is true of most fur and game species. Many mammals are nocturnal, small, and secretive; the average person sees them mostly by chance. Mice, bats, and shrews are not only difficult to observe, but many look alike. An expert has trouble distinguishing between certain ones, even in the hand. For positive identification of some shrews and mice, the skulls must be extracted, cleaned, and studied under a microscope. Mammals belong to the Class Mammalia, a group of animals characterized by the presence of hair on the body, mammary glands for suckling the young, and warm-bloodedness (the ability to maintain a constant body temperature). Other features separate the mammals from the warm-blooded birds and from the cold-blooded fishes, amphibians, and reptiles. Of the 3,500 species of mammals in the world, 54 probably occur in Indiana; the status of the bobcat and woodland jumping mouse is uncertain. One or two others may eventually be found in the state.

## Mammal Distributions in Indiana

In any given area, certain mammals are present and others absent. Many factors determine whether a particular habitat is suitable or unsuitable for a species. Vegetation plays an important role. Some mammals dwell in the forest; others are found only in open fields. The amount and type of water present in the habitat is important to aquatic forms. Species that burrow underground may be sensitive to soil texture, composition, and moisture. Man and his activities also have a tremendous effect on distribution.

Many of the mammals that occur in Indiana are species found elsewhere in the eastern United States. Before settlement, Indiana was mostly covered by deciduous forest and throughout most of the state the native animals were woodland forms. Some of northwestern Indiana was prairie; here were found mammals characteristic of prairie regions farther west. The third major habitat was an aquatic one that included marshes, swamps, rivers, and lakes. As woodlands were cut, swamps and marshes drained, and more land was cultivated, much of Indiana lost its three distinctive habitats and became more uniform. The unglaciated south-central part of the state was mostly too rugged to farm and has remained more like its pre-settlement condition. Even here, logging altered the woodlands greatly and considerable farming took place on ridge tops and along flat stream valleys.

As man caused much of Indiana to tend toward a single type of habitat, several mammals that were formerly restricted to the prairies moved into new regions. However, many species that depended upon the forest could not survive in the prairie-like farmlands; some became extinct and others decreased greatly both in range and numbers. Habitat changes and the resulting range alterations are still taking place today and will continue as long as the environment is alterd by man or natural agents. From available information, I judge that as of 1816 there were 66 species of mammals living within the boundaries of Indiana. Those that have since been exterminated are the porcupine, gray (timber) wolf, red wolf, black bear, fisher, wolverine, eastern spotted skunk, river otter, mountain lion, lynx, wapiti (elk), and bison. The woodland jumping mouse may also be gone (it is known from a single specimen collected in 1930). There is some question as to whether the bobcat still occurs in Indiana; for the present, it is assumed that it does. There are no state specimens of the bobcat in any museum collection.

The following mammals are found in all, or most, Indiana counties: opossum, short-tailed shrew, least shrew, eastern mole, little brown bat, Keen's bat, Indiana bat, silver-haired bat, big brown bat, red bat, hoary bat, evening bat, eastern cottontail, eastern chipmunk, woodchuck, gray squirrel, fox squirrel, southern flying squirrel, beaver, deer mouse, white-footed mouse, meadow vole, pine vole, muskrat, southern bog lemming, Norway rat, house mouse, meadow jumping mouse, coyote, red fox, gray fox, raccoon, long-tailed weasel, mink, striped skunk, white-tailed deer. Of these, the beaver and white-tailed deer were once extirpated and reintroduced. The fact that the above mammals now occur throughout Indiana points up the uniformity of the present habitat. The masked shrew and prairie vole may occupy all of the state; inadequate collecting has been done in many areas. At present, the masked shrew appears to be absent from most of southeastern Indiana and the prairie vole has not been collected in extreme northeastern Indiana.

Species with restricted Indiana ranges include the masked shrew, southeastern shrew, star-nosed mole, southeastern bat, gray bat, eastern pipistrelle, Rafinesque's big-eared bat, swamp rabbit, thirteen-lined ground squirrel, Franklin's ground squirrel, red squirrel, plains pocket gopher, eastern wood rat, prairie vole, woodland jumping mouse, least weasel, badger, and bobcat. Of these, the star-nosed mole, masked shrew, red squirrel, and least weasel are essentially northern animals; that is, most of their total range lies north of Indiana. Western species are the thirteen-lined and Franklin's ground squirrels, plains pocket gopher, prairie vole, and badger. Franklin's ground squirrel and the pocket gopher are restricted to a small part of northwestern Indiana. Southern species include the eastern pipistrelle, swamp rabbit, southeastern shrew, southeastern bat, gray bat, Rafinesque's big-eared bat, and eastern wood rat. The swamp rabbit is definitely known from only Posey, Spencer, and Warrick Counties; it evidently prefers floodplain forests. The southeastern bat is known from Crawford, Greene, Lawrence, and Washington Counties. Gray bats have been taken in Crawford and Lawrence Counties. Big-eared bat records are from Lawrence, Putnam, Tippecanoe, and Washington Counties. The presence of caves appears to play an important role in determining the distribution of the above bats, all of which are rare in the state. The eastern wood rat occurs, to our present knowledge, only in Harrison County. Formerly, this rat was found in other south-central Indiana localities as far north as Lawrence County. Today it is found in caves and along limestone escarpments near the Ohio River.

A good example of a mammal that has taken advantage of changing habitat conditions and moved into new areas is the thirteen-lined ground squirrel. This squirrel was formerly confined to the prairie. It has made an extensive shift in distribution to the southeast, now being found to Franklin and Johnson Counties, and may still be increasing its range. No doubt other animals originally restricted to non-wooded regions have followed somewhat the same pattern as the ground squirrel. At any rate, the prairie vole, deer mouse, and eastern cottontail (to name some) have successfully invaded those regions that were at one time forested.

## Accounts of Species

For ease of discussion, the native mammals have been grouped below into Orders, as currently assigned in their classification. Significant or interesting facts are presented for each group, making use mainly of information gathered through studies in Indiana. There is much to be learned, so gaps will appear in the data. Further information about mammals is available in many state mammal books, field guides, and museum publications.

Order MARSUPIALIA. This group includes the opossums, kangaroos, and many others, most of which have a pouch (marsupium) for carrying the young. The opossum is a well known Indiana mammal that frequents many habitats, such as wooded areas, fence rows, ditches, roadsides, streams, and buildings. It lives in hollow trees, brushpiles, woodchuck dens, and other sites. The opossum is more abundant in southern than in northern Indiana, where it was formerly quite rare, especially for periods following severe winters. Individual animals sometimes lose the tips of their ears or end of the tail to frostbite. The largest recorded specimen from the state weighted 12 pounds. Color varies from nearly white to almost black, but generally is grayish.

Opossums feed on many vegetable and animal foods, thus are omnivorous. They are known to eat corn, apples, persimmons, grasshoppers, poultry, carrion, and other foods. At birth opossums are less than an inch long and incompletely developed. They crawl into the female's pouch, where they are carried and suckled for about three months. The number of young per litter, as observed in Indiana, varies from 3 to 10, but litters of from 15 to 17 (actually counted in the pouch) have been reported from other states. Small young have been collected from April to October, indicating that the breeding season is quite long; probably two litters are produced each year. The habit of feigning death ("playing 'possum") when startled is evidently a nervous reaction.

Order INSECTIVORA. Six species of insect-eaters (moles and shrews) are found in Indiana. They have glands that emit a strong, musky odor. For this reason, foxes and other predators sometimes kill shrews and moles, then leave them uneaten. Most of the insectivores are small and some of our native shrews are among the smallest of mammals. All are rather secretive (moles spend much time underground) and difficult to observe. The masked shrew and the southeastern shrew are tiny, relatively rare, long-tailed animals measuring about 3 inches from the tip of the snout to the end of their inch-long tails. They are found in various habitats where the ground cover is at least moderately dense. Masked shrews are most abundant in northern Indiana; the southeastern shrew occurs mainly in southwestern and western Indiana. Both have an average weight of about 3 grams, the masked shrew being a bit heavier; they range in color from grayish to brownish. The two species can be identified with certainty only by tooth characteristics. The least shrew is a tiny, short-tailed animal found mostly in old fields; it weighs about 5 grams and varies (seasonally) from gray to reddish brown. Short-tailed shrews are larger, usually slate-gray, weigh about 17 grams, and measure 4 to 5 inches in total length. The short-tailed shrew and the white-footed mouse are the two most abundant and widespread mammals in the state.

All shrews eat insects, other small animals, seeds, nuts, and other foods. Least shrews are known to enter bee hives to feed on bee broods. The short-tailed shrew feeds to some extent on mice and has a poison in its saliva that is introduced into its victims when they are bitten. The poison may aid in paralyzing prey, such as earthworms or mice. Shrews are active throughout the year and because of their high rate of metabolism and the necessity for maintaining their body temperature must eat almost constantly to keep alive. There is practically nothing known about the reproduction of shrews in Indiana. A short-tailed shrew female was captured in a nest with 4 young and another female contained 6 embryos.

The eastern mole is the species most often encountered by Hoosiers, for it it is found in most habitats, including gardens and lawns, and is common. The star-nosed mole is known from marshy sites in Allen, Kosciusko, LaGrange, Steuben, and St. Joseph Counties, but the animal probably occurs in other areas. Both moles construct tunnels near the ground suface and mounds ("molehills") ; the latter are sometimes pushed up through the snow. Many persons confuse short-tailed shrews with baby moles. Moles are dark gray to blackish, 6 to 7 inches long, and have broad front feet for digging. Eastern moles often have whitish spots or, more rarely, are completely cream-colored. Star-nosed moles have a circular series of 22 fleshy growths (the "star") on the nose. This species is more aquatic than the eastern mole and is frequently caught in traps set under the water for muskrats. Moles feed mainly on earthworms and insects. The tunnels constructed by moles are often used by mice, shrews, and other animals. Little is known about the number of young produced or when they are born. One eastern mole contained 3 large young on May 7 ; in southern Indiana, most mating takes place in February.

Order CHIROPTERA. Most of the twelve species of bats in Indiana are widely distributed. Bats are found in trees, buildings, caves, rocky outcrops, and under bridges. Most spend the winter in caves, where thousands may be found, but some survive in heated buildings. There is a possibility that a few winter in tree holes. The solitary red bat, hoary bat, and silver-haired bat spend the summer mainly in trees and presumably migrate long distances in spring and fall. Other species make shorter flights. Bats seem to be decreasing in number in Indiana. Rabid red bats and silver-haired bats have been recorded and other Indiana species may carry rabies. Live bats should be handled with gloves or left alone. Native bats range in length from 3 inches (pipistrelle) to 6 inches (hoary bat). Most are some shade of brown, but red bats are reddish, hoary bats grayish-white, and silver-haired bats blackish with whitish tips on the fur. The identification of the several similar species is a job for an expert. Many thousand bats have been banded in Indiana over the past twenty years in an attempt to learn more about their migrations, movements from wintering and summering sites, and longevity. Some of these animals have been recaptured after ten years.

All Indiana bats feed solely on insects, most of which are caught in flight with the aid of the bat's echo-location system.

Some bats may occasionally alight on foliage to pick off insects. More information on specific foods is desired. One sample of red bat stomachs was composed mainly of the adult of the spittle bug. A big brown bat, shot at dusk, had a chafer beetle in its mouth. Water is scooped up in flight with the lower jaw as the bat skims over the water's surface. Since bats are not ordinarily active in the daytime, we know relatively little about their habits or life history. One young at birth is the usual number, but two to 4 young per litter are produced, depending upon the species. Red bats normally have 3 (sometimes 4) young. One litter is born each year. The young are able to fly when about four weeks old.

Order LAGOMORPHA. The eastern cottontail is common throughout the state, but the swamp rabbit occurs only in extreme southwestern Indiana. The latter is larger, has proportionately shorter and broader ears, browner tail, and darker hind feet. Cottontails weigh about 3 pounds and swamp rabbits about 5 pounds. Swamp rabbits live in wetter habitats, swim well, and often deposit fecal pellets on top of logs and stumps. Rabbits are herbivorous (plant-eaters) and take a wide variety of foods. Cottontails eat earth, perhaps for its mineral content. Young cottontails are born from January to at least September in shallow nests dug into the ground and lined with grasses and hair from the female rabbit. The number of young per cottontail litter (for 30 litters) ranged from 3 to 7 and averaged 5. One nest containing 12 young has been found. There is no information on swamp rabbit breeding in Indiana. Indiana hunters harvest over 2,500,000 cottontails per year in years of normal abundance.

Order RODENTIA. Indiana rodents include the following species: eastern chipmunk, woodchuck, thirteen-lined ground squirrel, Franklin's ground squirrel, gray squirrel, fox squirrel, red squirrel, southern flying squirrel, plains pocket gopher, beaver, deer mouse, white-footed mouse, eastern wood rat, meadow vole, prairie vole, pine vole, muskrat, southern bog lemming, Norway rat, house mouse, meadow jumping mouse, woodland jumping mouse. Rodents are gnawing animals with large incisor teeth and are mostly herbivorous. Some eat animal matter and a few are even cannibalistic. The incisors grow continuously throughout the life of the rodent, so the animal must gnaw enough to keep these teeth from becoming too long. In abnormal cases, the incisors grow in such a way as to close the animal's mouth, thus making it impossible for it to eat.

Some rodents burrow underground (pocket gopher, muskrat, Norway rat, woodchuck, chipmunk, ground squirrels), some glide from tree to tree (flying squirrel), some are mostly aquatic (muskrat, beaver), and others spend much of their lives in trees (tree squirrels). The group is represented in most habitats, including buildings and caves. Hibernating species are the woodchuck, both ground squirrels, and the jumping mice. The chipmunk may hibernate, but is also seen above ground on warm winter days. The chipmunk, woodchuck, ground squirrels, and tree squirrels (except flying squirrels) are primarily diurnal. Fox squirrels are sometimes active at night. Pocket gophers are active day and night and beavers, muskrats, voles, and jumping mice are somewhat diurnal. The remainder are essentially nocturnal, thus not observed so often by the average person. Pocket gophers are the least known, for they seldom leave their burrows. Their numerous mounds, which resemble the smaller mounds made by moles, are evidence of their presence. Beavers were probably eliminated from practically all of Indiana by 1840. In the 1930's beavers were detected in northern Indiana, then many were brought from Wisconsin and Michigan and released. Beavers are now found in all sections of the state. Rodents that live primarily in open, non-wooded areas are the ground squirrels, pocket gopher, deer mouse, meadow vole, prairie vole, and bog lemming. Others depend more or less on woodlands and are therefore in danger of losing more and more habitat in future years.

By weight, the deer mouse, house mouse, and jumping mice are the smallest Indiana rodents; beavers are by far the largest, reaching a weight of nearly 70 pounds.

The chipmunk, tree squirrels, and wood rat feed mainly on nuts, grain, seeds, and fruits; chipmunks and squirrels also eat animal matter, including birds and their eggs. Snails, slugs, and earthworms have been found in the cheek pouches of trapped chipmunks. The wood rat collects such foods as wild grape and pokeberry and stores them in cavities around the walls of its cave. Non-food items are gathered by this animal and stored in huge piles along rocky cliffs or in caves. Such things as bones, bits of glass, paper, metal, sticks, bark, and any other conceivable small item the rats can transport may be found in these piles of debris. The deer mouse, white-footed mouse, and jumping mouse consume seeds and nuts, but add insects and other small animals to their diet. Species that feed mainly on grasses and other herbs are the wood-chuck, ground squirrels, pocket gopher, voles, and bog lem-ming. For many of these, bluegrass appears to be important; voles also eat bark, sometimes causing considerable damage to young orchards or pine plantations. The beaver subsists mainly on bark and cambium, seemingly utilizing, when avail-able, such trees as aspen, cottonwood, and willow to a great extent; beavers will cut almost any species of tree, however. The cattail is a favorite food of the muskrat, but it also eats corn and other foods. Both the Norway rat and house mouse are omnivorous and able to subsist on a wide variety of plant or animal foods; rats will take baby chickens and other such animals.

There is much to be learned about the breeding seasons, number of young per litter, and number of litters produced by many Indiana rodents. Most of what is known has been summarized in Table 20.

Rodents are of considerable importance to Hoosiers. Some provide furs (the beaver was originally most important in this respect); others are much sought by hunters for sport and food. Indiana hunters shoot more than 1,500,000 squirrels each year. Norway rats and house mice do much damage to stored grains and other foods; rats transmit diseases to man. The smaller rodents (mostly voles) are in conflict with man under certain, local conditions, especially when rodent popu-lations reach a peak of abundance. These animals sometimes reach extremely high densities in clover fields. Visitors to state parks, state forests, and other recreational areas enjoy the sight of squirrels, chipmunks, woodchucks, beaver, and other species. Perhaps more thought should be given to the esthetic value of such mammals. Burrows constructed by the woodchuck are used by many other animals, such as cotton-tails, raccoons, opossums, skunks, weasels, some birds, frogs, snakes, toads, and lizards. On the other hand, woodchucks damage railroad grades and at times must be kept in check. Muskrat houses furnish turtles with sunning and egg-laying

TABLE 20. Summary of breeding data for Indiana Rodentia.

| Species | Date young born | Average No. Per Litter |
|---|---|---|
| Eastern Chipmunk | May to August | 3 to 4 |
| Woodchuck | no data | no data |
| Thirteen-lined Ground Squirrel | May and June | 8 to 9 |
| Franklin's Ground Squirrel | no data | no data |
| Gray Squirrel | February to October | 3 |
| Fox Squirrel | February to October | 3 |
| Red Squirrel | no data | nest with 5 young |
| Pocket Gopher | May | 4 to 5 |
| Beaver | no data | 9 fetuses in 1 female |
| Deer Mouse | throughout year | 4 |
| White-footed Mouse | throughout year | 4 to 5 |
| Wood Rat | no data | 2 fetuses in 1 female |
| Meadow Vole | throughout year | 4 to 5 |
| Prairie Vole | throughout year | 3 to 4 |
| Pine Vole | April to November | 2 |
| Muskrat | April to December | 6 |
| Bog Lemming | throughout year | 3 |
| Norway Rat | no data | 11 fetuses in 1 female |
| House Mouse | probably all year | 7 (12 fetuses in 1 female) |
| Meadow Jumping Mouse | July | 5 |

sites. The masked shrew occasionally nests in a muskrat house and some marsh birds nest on them. Mice and voles comprise a major portion of the food of hawks and owls and predatory mammals. These small rodents are quite prolific and their populations undergo drastic fluctuations from time to time. Especially during the high peak of the population cycle, mice and voles are so abundant that foxes, hawks, and owls find it easy to catch them; these predators turn to eating more mice and thus ease the pressure on rabbits, songbirds, and other more desirable species. Even gray squirrels may be locally abundant; more than 25 were trapped on one lawn in West Lafayette during a single spring.

The "signs" (tracks, nests, food refuse, runways, burrows, etc.) left by rodents are all about us. To appreciate these animals more in their natural surroundings, one must learn to read such signs. Look for the meadow jumping mouse in low, damp, grassy or weedy areas in fields or woods. Sometimes they can be found in dense weeds on the floodplains of small creeks. When startled, they try to escape by a series of leaps (much like those of a frog) until they reach their burrows. Flying squirrels often take over bird nesting-boxes, but also live in fence posts, hollow trees, and buildings; in winter, more than a dozen may be found in a single tree cavity. Fox squirrels, gray squirrels, and red squirrels all construct rather globular nests of leaves and twigs among the branches of trees; such nests are used mostly in warmer weather and the winter season is spent inside hollow trees. Red squirrel nests contain less leaves, are smaller, and usually composed of more soft plant materials, shredded bark, etc., than the leaf nests of the gray squirrel and fox squirrel. Red squirrels also store food by placing it on horizontal tree limbs, usually in a fork. White-footed mice often take over abandoned bird nests in trees, bushes, briars, vines, or bird nesting-boxes and add a covering of soft plant fibers, feathers, hair, or grasses, thus making the nest suitable for a winter home for the mice. One house mouse has been heard to give a high-pitched, whining sound; this may have been a "singing" mouse, as reported from other parts of the world. Voles make a network of runways on the surface of the ground in grassy areas; such runs are an inch or more wide and are sometimes used so much the ground is worn bare. Under more persistent usage, the runs become depressed into the soil. Along the runs one can find inch-long pieces of green grass that the voles cut and drop.

Order CARNIVORA. The carnivores (meat-eaters) in Indiana include the coyote, red fox, gray fox, raccoon, least weasel, long-tailed weasel, mink, badger, and striped skunk. All have large canine teeth, which are usually curved. Foxes, dogs, wolves, and the coyote make up the family Canidae. The raccoon is related to the ringtail, coati, and other species of raccoons. Remaining Indiana carnivores are all in the weasel family, Mustelidae, characterized by the presence of anal scent glands. The secretion from these glands has a strong, musky odor and is ejected as a protective mechanism.

The coyote was formerly restricted to the prairie regions of the state, but now occurs in all sections. It is commonly referred to as a wolf or brush wolf; there are no wolves in Indiana. Recent coyote specimens ranged in weight from 25 to 40 pounds; timber wolves are much heavier, reaching weights of 175 pounds. There are numerous records of dog-coyote hybrids; some of these are quite large and difficult to identify. Coyotes are seldom heard howling in Indiana. The gray fox is more numerous in southern Indiana and more prone to live in wooded or brushy areas then the red fox. Thus, the red fox has prospered more from logging and the gray fox has decreased. Both may occur in the same area, depending upon the right conditions of habitat. Red foxes and gray foxes weigh from 9 to 10 pounds; one male red fox weighed over 13 pounds. In general, the gray fox is lighter.

Foxes and coyotes eat many foods, composed mainly of birds and mammals. Mice, other rodents, rabbits, gound-inhabiting birds, snakes, salamanders, fishes, and insects (mostly grass-hoppers) have been identified in fox stomachs. When rabbits are available, they constitute a large proportion of the food. Other foods include corn, wheat, clover, grasses, beechnuts, pokeweed, wild grape, wild rose, hickory nuts, apples, pears, persimmons, wild cherry, and raspberries. There is no specific information on the food habits of Indiana coyotes.

The number of young contained by 30 gravid female red foxes averaged 7 and varied from 4 to 13. Excavated dens have contained from 3 to 6 young. Gray foxes evidently pro-duce litters of about the same size; at five dens there were 3 to 5 young. Data on Indiana coyotes are largely lacking, but one observer reported litters of from 5 to 12. Fox dens are usually in the ground and may be in rocky areas, about caves, under buildings, or under stumps and other debris piled on the ground. An adult gray fox with 3 young was found in the base of a hollow beech snag in Jackson County.

The raccoon is now common throughout Indiana, but its num-bers have fluctuated from time to time — perhaps due to disease or unknown factors. Canine distemper occurs in rac-coons. Adult raccoons range from 12 to 20 pounds, but larger animals are sometimes captured. Some are nearly black and color is quite variable. The raccoon is omnivorous and lives on fruits, grain, nuts, berries, birds, mammals, crayfish, mus-sels, fishes, eggs, honey, and many other foods. Usually 4 or 5 young make up a litter.

The weasel family is represented in Indiana by the long-tailed weasel, least weasel, mink, badger, and striped skunk. Least weasels are known to occur only north of a line connecting Vigo and Wayne Counties. Badgers are seen most frequently in northeastern Indiana, but are recorded south to Daviess (possibly Gibson) and Franklin Counties. The badger may still be extending its range southward. It is not common and has been placed on the protected list by the Indiana Division of Fish and Game. The least weasel is the smallest carnivore in the world. It is about 7 inches long (including the short tail) and weighs about 43 grams. Long-tailed weasels are 12 to 16 inches in total length and weigh from 100 to 220 grams; females are considerably smaller than males in the weasel family. The mink is about 25 inches long and averages about 1,100 grams (2½ pounds). The relatively few Indiana badgers examined ranged in weight from 16 to 27 pounds and averaged 21 pounds. Adult striped skunks weigh about 4 pounds. Less than five per cent of the long-tailed weasels in Indiana turn white (with a black-tipped tail) in winter; white animals are most frequently reported from northern Indiana, but there are records from Jackson, Knox, and Monroe Counties. Some least weasels also turn white in winter; these lack the solid black tail tip. Striped skunks vary a great deal in the amount of black or white on the body; some are almost completely black. Minks also show much color variation, ranging from quite pale to very dark.

Most of the mustelids seem to prefer living prey. Except for the striped skunk, much of the food is made up of birds and mammals. In summer, skunks take great numbers of insect larvae, which they dig out of the ground. They also feed on vegetable matter and carrion. Weasels prey heavily on mice and other small rodents; the long-tailed weasel is capable of killing an adult cottontail. The mink adds crayfish, frogs, mussels, and fishes to its diet and also feeds on muskrats and poultry. Badgers take rodents such as the thirteen-lined ground squirrel and Norway rats. One Indiana badger had fed on a woodchuck. Much food is obtained by digging the prey from its burrow. There is little information regarding reproduction of weasels and minks in Indiana. A least weasel contained 6 small embryos. An adult female long-tailed weasel was found with 6 young in a nest. One female mink was accompanied by 3 young. Badger females with 3 and 5 young have been observed. Striped skunk litters usually contain 4 to 6 young.

Order ARTIODACTYLA. The white-tailed deer is the sole survivor of this group found now in Indiana. Deer had become rare in many parts of the state by 1850 and it seems likely that all had been extirpated by 1900. In the 1930's, deer were brought from Michigan, North Carolina, Pennsylvania, and Wisconsin and released in Indiana. The reintroduction was quite successful and by 1951 an estimated 5,000 animals were present. Deer probably occur in each Indiana county, but the number per county varies.

Male deer average about 150 pounds and females about 110 pounds. Females may reach a weight of 200 and males a weight of 325 pounds. Deer have a reddish color in summer and a grayer color in winter. They are herbivorous animals and eat many types of plant food. Recorded foods are corn, other grains, alfalfa, soybeans, sassafras, poison ivy, mint, honeysuckle, sumac, acorns, tobacco, tomatoes, and watermelons. Fawns are evidently born in many months of the year in Indiana, but most are born in May and June. Does giving birth for the first time usually have a single fawn; in the second and succeeding years twins are the rule.

## Albinism and Melanism

Albino animals always create much interest and stimulate much discussion. Albinos may occur in any species, including man, and are probably far more common than most persons realize. Pure or complete albinos are totally white and have pink eyes. Partial or incomplete albinos may be white spotted, mostly white, all white with dark eyes, or an overall tan or otherwise pale (dilute) color. Complete albinos are much less commonly observed than incomplete albinos, possibly because something associated with complete albinism makes it more difficult for these animals to survive long after birth. Totally white mammals reported from Indiana include the short-tailed shrew, eastern mole, eastern chipmunk, woodchuck, thirteen-lined ground squirrel, gray squirrel, fox squirrel, red squirrel, flying squirrel, deer mouse, white-footed mouse, prairie vole, muskrat, Norway rat, raccoon, and white-tailed deer. White spotted individuals of the following additional species are known: little brown bat, Indiana bat, pipistrelle, house mouse. Tan or "blond" specimens of the meadow vole, prairie vole, muskrat, and raccoon have been collected. Fox squirrels and gray squirrels with completely white tails (but otherwise normally colored pelage) have been infrequently reported.

Melanism, or excessive blackness, appears much less frequently than albinism. In extreme cases, the animal is totally black, but (as in albinism) considerable variation occurs. Black gray squirrels, prairie voles, woodchucks, badgers, and raccoons are known from Indiana. A recent specimen of the gray fox was quite dark, but still retained some of the grayness of a normal pelt. Fox squirrels with the entire underparts black have been collected in several counties.

## LITERATURE

1. EVERMANN, B. W. and A. W. Butler. 1894. Preliminary list of Indiana mammals. Proc. Ind. Acad. Sci. 3: 124-139.
2. HAHN, W. L. 1909. The mammals of Indiana. 33rd. Ann. Rept, Ind, Dept, Geol. Nat. Resources pp. 419-654.
3. LYON, M. W., Jr., 1936. Mammals of Indiana. Amer. Midl. Nat. 17:1-384
4. MUMFORD, R. E. 1961. The mammals of Indiana—history and current PhD. thesis, Purdue University, 286 pp.

# 27
# Cultural History of the Indians

J. H. KELLAR

Indiana University

## Introduction

Writing systems, except for incipient developments in Middle America, were never produced by the American Indian; consequently, written reports based upon the direct observation of the Indian way-of-life are obtainable only after the European intrusion into the New World. These reports, important as they are, document only the last few centuries of an occupation that persisted for more than 10,000 years. Therefore, a knowledge of the beginnings and development of the cultures that preceded our own is dependent upon other kinds of evidence. This evidence consists of all those things that may survive to record human actions: Man-made objects (artifacts), remains of plants and animals used by man, human burials and associated materials, and the contexts in which these occur (archaeological sites). The interpretation of this evidence is the primary task of the archaeologist.

Every area in Indiana has produced at least some evidence of the kind mentioned above. Tools chipped from native flint, chert, and chalcedony are of fairly common occurrence and may be found along almost every stream terrace. A closer inspection of the ground where these are found will sometimes reveal fire-cracked stone, animal bone, shell, and, perhaps, fragments of pottery. Such debris marks past camps and villages, and though these are the most common kinds of sites of concern to the archaeologist, there are many others. Included are large garbage heaps composed of mussel shell, burial mounds made of earth and/or stone, circles, squares, and more complex geometric patterns delimited by low earth walls, cemetery areas, "workshops" where raw materials were exploited, and earth mounds upon which were constructed important town buildings.

The frequency and kinds of archaeological sites are not equally distributed throughout the state. To the contrary, the aboriginal inhabitants were tied more closely to the natural environment than we are, and site distributions in Indiana reflect the greater potential and differential resources of the several areas. For example, the broken uplands in the south-central sector and the Tipton Till Plain in the north-central generally contain fewer and less intensively occupied sites than the northern lake and moraine region or the Wabash Lowlands in the southwest. Similarly, some areas appear to have been utilized at one time more than at others. The south-central upland was more attractive to the earlier populations dependent upon hunting and gathering than to the later horti-culturally oriented groups, who found the broad river valleys more to their liking. Also, the presence of a sought-after ma-terial influences site distribution, and the large number of quarry-workshops in the Harrison County area is a product of the accessibility to a good quality flint. As a rule, the major river valleys—Ohio, Whitewater, Wabash, both forks of the White, and the Kankakee—are the most productive and site frequency and the intensity of occupation diminishes the farther one gets from these valleys and from the river junc-tures.

### A Frame of Reference

The cultural history of the Indian in Indiana[6] is only a seg-ment of that perceived for the eastern United States.[11] Some 120 years of archaeological work in this region has produced a generally understood frame of reference that attempts to comprehend the facts of changing ways of life through time. This broad frame of reference, beginning with the earliest and continuing to the most recent, is as follows:

*Paleo-Indian* (ca. 13,000 B. C. to 8000 B. C.) refers to the earliest population, presumably small groups of migrant hunters, occupying North America during the closing phases of the Pleistocene.

*Archaic* (8000 B.C. to 1000 B.C.) populations lived during a time when environment was beginning to approximate that of the present following the Pleistocene. Subsistence was de-pendant upon hunting, gathering and collecting, but regional differences can be perceived.

*Early Woodland* (1000 B.C. to A.D. 200) is characterized by the introduction of pottery, the initial evidence for plant do-mestication, and in some areas, the presence of burial mounds.

Hunting, collecting, and gathering activities continued to be the major supplier of food.

*Middle Woodland* (200 B.C. to A.D. 600) represents a continuation of trends observed during the preceding Early Woodland. Burial mound construction and associated burial ritualism attained a kind of peak of development, geometric-shaped earthworks were constructed, trade relationships extended over much of the eastern U.S., maize was present and horticulture undoubtedly contributed increased food supplies, though hunting and gathering were still of basic importance.

*Late Woodland* (A.D. 600 into Historic Period), though somewhat ill-defined and not well understood over much of the area, represents the decline of burial ceremonialism observed during the preceding Middle Woodland. Groups appear to have been somewhat more isolated one from another, and horticulture played an increasingly important role in subsistence activities. In certain instances, Late Woodland persisted into the historic period; in others it is markedly influenced or is replaced by the following:

*Mississippian* (A.D. 900 into Historic Period) peoples were dependent upon cultivated maize, beans, squash, pumpkins and lived in relatively stable villages, the largest of which might more properly be classed as a town. The major settlements were often protected by a stockade; flat-topped earth mounds served as foundations for elevating major buildings above the general level of the village, and the regularity of house placement within the villages clearly indicates some degree of planning. Mississippian continued into the historic period, as represented in southeastern United States by such groups as the Natchez, Chickasaw, etc.

The dates for the preceding are based upon Carbon 14 determinations and, though they may be interpreted as reflecting the general order of magnitude, they should not be read as absolutes. First, the $C^{14}$ method provides dates in terms of statistical probabilities and not chronological certainty; second, the periods so dated represent continuities through time and efforts to define "beginnings" and "endings" must always be somewhat arbitrary; third, it should be recognized that developments were not identical or occurring at the same time in all the subareas of the eastern United States, or, for that matter, within the geographically artificial boundaries of a single state.

### Paleo-Indian

There is good inferential evidence that man originally entered the New World from Asia across what is now Bering Straits. That the immediate point of departure is Asia is attested by the fact that the American Indian shares some physical traits with some eastern Asiatic groups. The condition for the migration occurred during the Late Pleistocene, at which time the storage of available moisture in the ice sheet lowered the ocean levels sufficiently to expose a broad plain several hundred miles in width in the Bering Straits area. That this plain was open to passage during at least portions of its existence is verified by geomorphological studies and by the presence of similar "ice age" animals in both Asia and North America at the same approximate time. The movement of these latter forms between the two continents also provided the impetus for the migratory hunters to move into the previously uninhabited area.

The earliest time of human occupation in the New World is still an open question. There are incontrovertible associations of tools, generally projectile points, and extinct animals in the high plains, portions of the Southwest and into Mexico, and these consistently date in a range of 15,000 to 9000 years ago. There are a few dates that more than double the oldest of these, but most American archaeologists are unwilling to accept these, because they are exceptional as to time and the associations of tools with materials dated, or the evidence of human intervention presently is unconvincing.

Indiana, in common with most of the eastern states, produces a kind of distinctive projectile point that was used to kill some of the now-extinct large ice-age animals in more western areas. The points are characterized by their "leaf-shape," concave base, and lower edges which have been ground smooth, probably to protect the materials used to bind it to the spear shaft. Additionally, a narrow flake was removed from one or both faces of the blade. The groove that results is referred to as a "flute," hence the name, fluted point. Though widely distributed in the eastern United States, fluted points have never been found associated with animal remains in this area, and most are surface finds. However, their near identity to dated examples farther to the west suggests the contemporaniety of both. The only fluted point site dated by $C^{14}$ at this time is in Massachusetts; dates of approximately 9500 years ago were obtained.

One approach to dating fluted points has been to assemble evidence for their distribution and then attempt to correlate this information with known geological features. For instance, if such points were being used by man when the glacial ice mass yet covered some areas, as is suggested by the available dates, one would anticipate finding fluted points near, but not in the areas so covered. Knowing the date of the glacier would then provide an inferential date for the artifacts.

A recent distributional study of fluted points in Indiana reveals such a pattern. Though they are found in most parts of the state, it is suggested that there is a gap in their distribution in the Allen, Huntington, Wells, and Adams county area. An explanation of this is that a lobe of the retreating ice mass was present, or its melting had produced swampy conditions, making human habitation impossible. It is concluded that the maximum date for these conditions is about 14,000 years ago. This conclusion tends to support similar studies undertaken in Michigan and Ohio, and generally fits a developing picture derived from several areas in North America.

### Archaic

The time of the Archaic is one during which the climate underwent gradual modification from the relatively cooler and damper conditions of the immediate post-Pleistocene with its associated flora and fauna to a natural environment such as we experience today. Though this modification was probably not a simple unilineal change—there are indications of a relatively warmer and drier interval at about 4000 B.C.— the overall trend is as suggested. Correlated with this trend are changes in the life-ways of the New World occupants, reflecting increased skill in the utilization of the natural resources. Whereas the Paleo-Indian occupation was relatively uniform, at least insofar as one can determine from the few artifact categories available, the Archaic develops through time until there are many classes of specialized tools and distinctive regional "cultures" can be identified. Though the Archaic is generally prior to the invention of the bow and pottery and the discovery of plant domestication, groups were able to obtain relatively abundant supplies of food in some of the regions.

The earliest phases of the Archaic in the eastern United States are represented by large projectile points and a few other classes of stone tools. Some of the former appear to be modifications of and developments from the earlier fluted points, and undoubtedly represent the continuation of a basic migratory hunting subsistence pattern. Dated sequences of such points, along with others that are stemmed and notched, have been obtained from deeply stratified rock shelters and alluvial deposits in Missouri, Illinois, West Virginia, North Carolina, and Alabama.

About 6000 years ago, groups living in the southeast began to utilize as a major source of food the meat of the mussel, an oyster-like bivalve formerly present in large quantities in the rivers of the area. Camps were established on the river bank near this source, the discarded shells accumulated, and the well-drained eminences that resulted were used as living sites. Their continued occupation over many centuries produced refuse heaps, some of which were more than 25 feet in depth.

Shell middens are relatively common in the extreme southern portion of the state, and are found along the Ohio River from Clark County in the east to the Wabash, up the Wabash to Knox and Sullivan counties, and along the East Fork of the White River to Lawrence and Orange counties. Those in the flood plain of the Ohio River are often buried beneath an accumulation of alluvium, and their discovery is possible only along a caving bank or where erosion or construction removes the top soil. Similar midden deposits may be found on the edge of high bluffs in the other areas.[8]

A few characteristics recorded from these sites are as follows: Clay deposits probably representing habitation floors, pits used as fireplaces, flexed human burials, the domesticated dog, stemmed and side notched projectile points, grooved stone axes, the use of the spear thrower, bone and deer antler from which were made a variety of perforating tools and handles, bone and shell beads. Large quantities of fire-broken stone are encountered and it seems likely that, lacking pottery for cooking, liquids in skin containers were heated by immersing heated stones. The presence of some marine shells and copper indicates trade with groups in the Florida and upper Great Lakes areas.

Shell middens are the most conspicuous remains left by these early inhabitants but it should not be assumed that mussel was the only source of food or that occupation was confined to these sites. To the contrary, the quantities of deer and other animal remains point up the importance of hunting and charred seeds and nut shells, as well as stone pestles used for seed grinding, attest to the use of a variety of natural food products. Artifacts and burials typical of the shell mound context are also found in other situations. The many rock shelters formed in the sandstone outcroppings of the Crawford Upland in south central Indiana served as camp sites and it appears likely that seasonal occupation was common. Also, there are sites on the uplands away from the major rivers and a few where the natural environment was not conducive to long-term settlement (Brown and Monroe counties.) All of these represent the migratory patterns of the more southern groups.

The later Archaic in the northern portion of the state, like that of the Great Lakes area generally, is less well understood. Actual habitation sites are few, small in size, and not intensively occupied, and it is probable that migratory hunting and collecting groups are represented.

Sometime prior to 3000 B.C., perhaps as early as 5000 B.C., populations in the upper Great Lakes began to utilize the readily available sources of native copper as a raw material for the manufacture of tools. Smelting as such was unknown, but a variety of tanged and socketed spear points, adzes, axes, and perforating tools, many which they placed with the dead, were made by hammering the material into shape. Named the Old Copper Culture, it represents one of the first uses of metal anywhere in the world. Though no Old Copper sites are known in Indiana, a few tanged and socketed points have been found on the surface, one of the latter having been found as far south as Jay County.

Most of our knowledge of the northern Archaic derives from accidentally discovered cemeteries, and the artifacts and other materials associated with the human remains have led to the conclusion that an incipient burial ceremonialism is present. These cemeteries, unmarked by any surface evidence, are generally found in low sand or gravel ridges formed by glacial outwash. Following the geological nomenclature for such features, the culture is referred to as Glacial Kame. Round pits were excavated into these natural features and one or more flexed human burials were placed therein. Materials sometimes associated include copper and shell beads, bone awls, circular and "sandal sole-shaped" gorgets cut from large marine shells, and objects made from slate that resemble stylized birds in profile, hence the name "birdstone." Red ochre (iron oxide) was powdered and substantial quantities are often encountered in the graves. Glacial Kamelike artifacts, some associated with burials, have been recovered over much of northeastern Indiana and southward into Shelby County.

It is possible that yet another Archaic complex, Red Ocher, is present in northwestern Indiana. It, too, is best known in its burial manifestations. Included among the artifacts in the complex are bi-pointed flint blades that are side-notched near one of the ends. These are commonly named "turkey-tail" points and have been found individually and in caches in the state.

Old Copper, Glacial Kame, and Red Ocher are all part of a so-called "northern" or "boreal" Archaic, which extended over much of northeastern United States-southeastern Canada, and it appears probable that the burial ceremonialism of the Early and Middle Woodland periods is partially derived from this source.

### Early Woodland

The introduction of pottery generally marks the beginning of Early Woodland in northeastern United States, but the source of this culture element is as yet undetermined. It first appears in the archaeological record about 2000 B.C. in the Georgia-Florida area in the form of crudely made vessels, the clay of which has had vegetable fibres intermixed. However, it is not certain that this is the source of the later ceramic development. Because some of the earliest pottery in the northeast has surface cord impressions and similar patterns occur in eastern Asia at an earlier date, the latter has been proposed as the source. Similarly, the earlier date for ceramics in Meso-America has led to the proposition that the idea diffused from there. Yet others have argued for a local development. Be that as it may, the earliest pottery in our area is thick, heavy, and coarse: cord and fabric impressions are sometimes found on both inner and outer surfaces; and "flower-pot" shaped vessels are common. Local varieties of early ceramics include Fayette Thick in the southeast, Baumer in the southwest, and Marion Thick in the west and central portion of the State.

No significant changes in the subsistence activities of the people are readily apparent, though there is much less dependence placed on the riverine mussel. Habitation sites continue to be small, but a relatively intensive occupation is indicated in some instances, particularly in southwestern Indiana. Though the direct evidence is somewhat tenuous, there is support for the conclusion that domesticated plants in the form of sunflowers, squash, and chenopodium are present.

It is during Early Woodland that burial mounds begin to be constructed in numbers and the earliest of these, at least in terms of present evidence, occur in the middle to upper portion of the Ohio River Valley. Named Adena after the Ohio estate where the type site was excavated, these mounds exhibit some features reminiscent of the northern archaic burial complex, and it is hypothesized that Adena represents a partial development from these horizons.[4] This is a sharp contrast with an earlier and now unsupportable view that Adena resulted from a migration of peoples from Mexico into the Ohio Valley.

Adena mounds were constructed over the remains of individuals who occupied important positions in the society. This interpretation is supported by the fact that relatively few burials may be encountered in a large mound, that individual burial areas were prepared with great care, artifacts associated with burials are frequently of a non-utilitarian nature and/or involve the use of raw materials obtained by trade from other areas, and, of course, the rather imposing nature of the mound itself.

Most mounds are small in size, but two Adena tumuli, Grave Creek, West Virginia, and Miamisburg, Ohio, approximate

70 feet in height. Many rise to heights in excess of 15 feet. These are not simple structures in the sense that work, once begun, continued unbroken until the final form was obtained. Rather, the mounds accreted through time as major burials were added, and a single large mound usually contains several major building phases. The recognition of these in excavation is important because the sequence of mound growth and the associated cultural material provides some insight into how the culture changed through time.

Log tombs are the major feature encountered within Adena mounds. Trees were felled and sections of the trunk were cut into lengths of approximately four to ten feet; the logs were then laid on the surface of the ground to define an open rectangular area. Much variability of this basic pattern was possible and later tombs appear to have been more complex than the earlier ones. Sometimes logs were placed parallel until a sizable area was covered; at other times they were piled one on top of another to form a raised margin; cryptlike structures were made by roofing over the burial area using support posts, logs, and tree bark; limestone slabs define graves in a few instances; and pits excavated below ground level or into existing mounds are found upon occasion. The purpose was to prepare an area for the reception of the important dead, and there are suggestions that some tombs were left open for a time before beginning the task of carrying in baskets of earth to construct the mound.

Materials associated with burials include such things as red ochre, beads made of copper, shell, or bone, cut animal jaws, human crania, human cremations, copper bracelets, tubular pipes, a variety of slate artifacts, bone awls, etc.

Very few Adena villages have been recorded, because their mounds were often constructed at the dwelling sites and the debris that accumulated was scooped up and redeposited in the mound itself. However, segments of their villages have been preserved under the tumuli. These are generally shallow and indicate short-term occupancy, though large multi-nuclear family houses are suggested. These houses are circular in ground plan with walls sloping outward from the base. Framed with logs, bark appears to have been utilized for wall and roof covering.

It is probable that most of the earth burial mounds and

some of those in which limestone slabs are a major inclusion in southeastern Indiana are Adena. These occur from Dearborn and Ohio counties northward up the Whitewater River valley to Randolph County and west to Johnson County.

There were many mounds in the Whitewater drainage at one time, but most of the smaller ones have been destroyed by cultivation, and the remaining larger ones almost without exception have been gutted by clandestine excavators. However, systematic work in the region has demonstrated their late Adena character.[2, 6]

Near Winchester, Newcastle, at Anderson Mounds State Park, and in Wayne County are earthworks of a somewhat different character. These remains, circular, rectangular, and panduriform in ground-plan, were shaped by excavating a trench and throwing the earth to the outside of the trench. Recent excavations suggest these, too, are late Adena.

### Middle Woodland

Middle Woodland has as one of its major complexes the elaboration of the burial ceremonialism observed in incipient form in the northern Archaic and further developed in Adena. There is indeed much evidence that considerable energy, talent, and many resources were consumed with the dead. Many burial mounds were constructed, aesthetically sophisticated artifacts made from raw materials obtained as far distant as the Rocky Mountains were placed in the graves, and some individuals were apparently intentionally killed in order to be entombed. A few writers have referred to this activity as evidence of a "burial cult," suggesting that the death and the attendant ritualism was the central focus of interest. On the other hand, the expended energy, talent, and resources are also an indication of the relatively higher status of the individual when alive, and too much emphasis may be placed on the end product.

There is much regional variability during Middle Woodland times. In the Ohio Valley the period is synonymous with Hopewell, the name of the property owner of the Ohio type site, and it is from this area that influences spread southward to the Gulf coast and northward to the upper Great Lakes. These influences are primarily seen in the form of burial practices and, particularly, in some rather specific artifact forms.

These latter include such items as clay figurines, copper pan pipes, copper ear spools, "monitor" type pipes, and some styles of pottery decoration. All of these tend to occur with burials in mounds over a wide area of eastern United States.

A Middle Woodland climax is reached in southern Ohio shortly after the beginning of the Christian Era. This development includes the construction of sizeable "ceremonial" centers circumscribed by low earth walls, geometric earthworks which were sometimes joined one to another by passageways delimited by parallel earth walls, and large burial mounds. Charnel houses were built for the dead and both inhumation and cremation were practiced. Some of the artifacts exhibit considerable skill in stone carving and working cold copper, and in a few instances, the quantity of material recovered was imposing. Further, raw materials were obtained from many sources: Obsidian and grizzly bear teeth from the Rocky Mountains, copper from the upper Great Lakes, mica from the southern Appalachians, marine shells from the Gulf area. Most of the large Ohio Hopewell sites were excavated during the nineteenth and early twentieth centuries and in the absence of an abundance of comparative material, their seeming uniqueness was emphasized. However, it has since been determined that a longer Hopewellian sequence occurs in portions of the Illinois River valley, and at least some of the Ohio development may result from these more western influences on the resident Adena populations. There is much cultural interplay in the Ohio Valley and over a much wider area during Middle Woodland, though there was not a single uniform culture as is suggested by the common label, "mound-builder culture."

The determination of the food-producing activities utilized to support the trade, craft, and earthwork construction, and the inferred status differences, has been a particularly vexing problem, which has not been finally resolved. The earlier emphasis on burial mound excavation was not designed to provide much data on daily life. Later, when archaeological emphasis had shifted, few habitation sites of the period could be found in Ohio, though substantial villages were found in other regions. Recent excavations in such contexts, including Ohio, indicate that a great variety of natural and plant foods were exploited and cultivated maize is present.

In Indiana, most of the recognized Middle Woodland sites are in the western portion of the state. One of the largest of these is located in Posey County. This village, more properly a series of small villages, covers several hundred acres and in addition to burial mounds, aerial photographs reveal a small circular and two large rectangular enclosures. The burial mounds were excavated in the 1870's, and apparently produced a variety of burial artifacts characteristic for the period.[1] The village proper has been of interest, because of the presence of decorated pottery similar to that resident in Georgia-Florida, indicating some measure of direct contact between the regions.

Recently a circular enclosure has been identified near Vincennes, and a site with possible earthen walls is located in Spencer County.

Many mounds were present along the Wabash at least as far north as Tippecanoe County, and others occurred along the White into Greene County. Near Vincennes there are three rather notable tumuli, which have traditionally served as local landmarks because of their relatively large size. Named the Sugarloaf, Pyramid, the Terrace mounds, it is quite possible that all of them may be natural loess deposits, rather than artificially constructed mounds. One of these has produced many instrusive burials from the upper levels, but these seem to be much later than Middle Woodland.

Another clustering of Middle Woodland mounds occurred in the Kankakee drainage. However, this occupation, though related, differs to some extent from that farther south, and is related to Hopewellian in the Illinois River drainage.[9]

### Late Woodland—Mississippian

Late Woodland is a time of considerable cultural change. First, the ceremonialism of the preceding period is much attenuated. Second, the cultures of our area came under the influence of groups in the central Mississippi valley, some of which undoubtedly moved into the southwest corner of Indiana at a late date.

The extensive trade patterns, many of the non-utilitarian artifact forms, earthwork construction, and the inferred individual status differences are absent from the archaeological record beginning about A.D. 600. This should not be interpreted to mean that any great cataclysmic event occurred to bring about a sudden elimination of the responsible populations. To the contrary, the subsistence activities and the day-to-day life of the people probably remained much as it had, and the villages representing the earlier portion of the period, though often relatively small, were occupied with some intensity. At the same time, there are many regional differences suggesting that populations were somewhat more isolated one from another than had been the case earlier.

In Indiana, there is a distinction between the pottery in the north and south. Surface cord-marking, common in the Woodland cultures during all of the earlier periods, continues, but there is greater emphasis in the north on the use of heavy cordage to impress regular designs on the clay vessels. Also, the upper rim portions are thickened and expanded to form a kind of collar around the opening. These generally do not occur to the south.

Some Late Woodland burial mounds occur, but these tend to be repositories for greater numbers of individuals than previously. Many of the stone mounds in southeastern Indiana are such examples. In the Wabash valley natural elevations were utilized as cemetery areas and the so-called Albee Mound in Sullivan County is actually misnamed, if by the term we mean a man-made tumulus.[7]

About A.D. 900 in the central Mississippi valley, a new development becomes apparent. Referred to as Mississippian Culture, it represents a product of long-time cultural trends in the area combined with at least some ideas diffused from the high culture centers of Meso-America. Quantitatively and qualitatively, Mississippian represents the highest development of aboriginal culture in the eastern United States and it had an influence on most of the late populations in our area.

Angel Mounds State Memorial near Evansville is an outstanding example of such a Mississippian village or town in Indiana.[3] Inhabited by perhaps a thousand people at its peak period during the fifteenth century, the occupation extended over slightly more than 100 acres. The residents were protected by more than a mile of high stockade constructed of logs plastered with clay. In the approximate center of the town was a large earth mound measuring 600 by 300 feet. A large structure, probably reserved for the "chief," was built on the flat upper surface. Other smaller flat-top mounds are present and these were utilized for other specialized structures. An open village plaza was present just west of the central mound, and it was undoubtedly the scene of significant community and regional functions. Substantial houses following consistent orientations were present throughout the remainder of the site. They were square or rectangular in ground plan, though a few were round, and, like the stockade, were built of logs set vertically and covered with "wattle and daub." Roofs were grass thatched.

The Mississippian peoples were skilled craftsmen and produced a variety of distinctive pottery, some of which was painted, and a wide range of stone, bone, and shell artifacts used as tools and for personal adornment. They also relied upon domesticated maize, beans, and other plants for food, but hunting, fishing, and gathering continued to make substantial contributions to the diet.

Though no other known Mississippian village in Indiana duplicates the complexity of Angel Mounds, there are many closely related sites; but the distribution appears to be limited to the southwestern sector. The special ecological conditions of the Wabash Lowlands undoubtedly are a factor. Some transient encampments were made in the rockshelters of the Crawford Upland, but these certainly represent the activities of small hunting parties.

This southwestern occupation is referred to as Middle Mississippi to distinguish it from the somewhat different but related cultures to the north and the south in the Mississippi valley. Middle Mississippi represents an enclave in Indiana and undoubtedly results from a movement of people into the area from the lower Ohio River valley.

Mississippian culture had a profound influence on the long-resident Woodland populations. From north of Indianapolis into southeastern Indiana, the Mississippian influenced culture is Fort Ancient. Many distinctive Mississippian characteristics, such as the mixing of crushed shell with the pottery clay and handles on pottery vessels, combine with the Woodland practice of cord-impressing to produce a distinctive ceramic complex. In the Upper Wabash recent excavations revealed two small flat-top mounds; in the same area small triangular Mississippian arrow points occur in contexts that are

Late Woodland in most other respects. Comparable combinations are present in northwestern Indiana. The inference, and it is supported by excavational data, is that the impact is considerable and carries with it a major reliance upon domesticated plant cultivation.

## Historic Period

What is the relationship of this long development to Indiana's historic Indians? Unfortunately, this seemingly simple question does not have a similarly simple answer. The reason is that such Indiana Indians as the Miami, Potowatomi, and Delaware were all relatively late (17th and 18th centuries) migrants into the area, and, lacking specific data as to their movements prior to historic records, one cannot identify them through the kinds of materials they left behind. Material culture reflects technology most directly, and technology cuts across group identities, and ethnic differences are often lost in the archaeological record. There is some evidence suggesting that Fort Ancient, at least in part, is Shawnee. The overall Woodland development probably represents the historic Algonquian, the Miami, Potawatami, and Delaware being representative of this widespread linquistic family. On the other hand, inferences from Middle Mississippian are complicated by the fact that no major population concentrations were present in the Ohio Valley at the beginning of the historic period.

## LITERATURE

1. ADAMS, W. R. 1949. Archaeological notes on Posey County, Indiana. Indiana Hist. Bur. 48-52.
2. BLACK, G. A. 1936. Excavation of the Nowlin Mound. Indiana Hist. Bulletin 14:2.
3. _____ 1944. Angel site, Vanderburgh County, Indiana: An Introduction. Prehistory Research Series. Indiana Hist. Soc. 2:5.
4. DRAGOO, D. W. 1963. Mounds for the dead. Annals of the Carnegie Museum 37. Pittsburgh.
5. KELLAR, J. H. 1960. The C. L. Lewis Stone Mound. Prehistory Research Series. Indiana Hist. Soc. 3:4.
6. LILLY, E. 1937. Prehistoric antiquities of Indiana. Indianapolis.
7. MACLEAN, J. A. 1931. Excavation of the Albee Mound. Indiana Hist. Bulletin. Ind. Hist. Bur. 8:4.
8. MILLER, R. K. 1941. McCain site, Dubois County, Indiana. Prehistory Research Series. Indiana Hist. Soc. 2:2.
9. QUIMBY, G. I. 1941. The Goodall focus. Prehistory Research Series. Indiana Hist. Soc. 2:2.
10. QUIMBY, G. I. 1960. Indian life in the Upper Great Lakes. Chicago.
11. WILLEY, G. 1966. An introduction to American archaeology. New York.

# 28

# Racial History of the Indians

GEORG K. NEUMANN
Indiana University

The exploration of the relationship of man to an ecological area and the delimitation of a series of prehistoric populations that inhabited it since post-glacial times is fraught with a number of difficulties. It presupposes (a) that problems of human ecology have been worked out in the broader areas that surround the state, since the ecological areas are obviously not coterminous with state boundaries, (b) that statistical samples of reliably dated skeletal material are available for the different time periods so that stabilized breeding populations can be delimited and described, and (c) that we should know something of the racial history on a continental scale in order to distinguish between the advent of new groups into an area and local differentiation of older populations. Only then can we investigate particular adaptations to local conditions.

Other factors that have to be taken into consideration are that the region south of the Great Lakes has been transitional in regards to the northward shift of ecological zones with the retreat of the glaciers, and at present represents a transitional area between the plains to the west and open woodlands to east, glacial moraine country in the north and an unglaciated area with karst topography in the south. Needless to say, the listed prerequisites for a complete study are just now beginning to be worked out. Earlier summaries which are herewith revised are to be found in four papers by the writer and his sons.[9, 11, 12, 13]

Earlier attempts to elucidate ecological relationships, (such as that by Wissler in 1926[18], who properly pointed out the permissive nature of the environment rather than determinative nature, as far as man is concerned) were seriously hampered by the lack of a chronological framework for the cultures as well as the lack of information on continuities and possible replacements of populations.

Man is unique among animals in that, by virtue of his culture, he is the least dependent on his environment and with the passage of time he has been able to modify or control it to an increasing extent. This fact makes it exceedingly difficult to point out specific causal relationships and to examine relationships which, ecologically speaking, cover rather limited spans of time. It is therefore at this time only possible to sketch these relationships in the broadest outline in the hope that it will provide a framework the details of which can be filled in with the accumulation of specific data.

The physiographic province under consideration covers most of the central part of the United States, and, if we follow Fenneman,[4] especially the Great Lakes section and the Central Lowlands east of the Mississippi. The latter comprises local lowlands and uplands and constitutes an area that is being dissected in the true plateau fashion. The elevation of the province ranges from 1500 feet on the western edge to 300 feet on the shores of Lake Ontario. To the west it is bordered by the Great Plains which cover 532,000 square miles in ten states, an area that is characterized by its flat-lying rocks. Glaciation dominates most of the landscape.

The province boundary is marked by a visible contrast of topography along its borders. The topographic distinctions in this area depend not so much on underlying rocks as they do on the glaciations. The ice is known to have advanced at least a half dozen times followed by a retreat. Each successive glaciation covered some territory not reached by its successors.

The major glaciations are generally classified as the: Nebraskan (bottom), Kansan, Illinoian, Iowan, and the Wisconsin. The present drift cover falls into three main divisions: Kansan, Illinoian, and the more recent sheets.

The northeastern part of the Central Lowlands is characterized by lakes which are very abundant although they are not evenly distributed. Swamps represented intermediate stages between lakes and dry land, and flat plains bordered the Great Lakes. Much of the area is covered with marginal moraines, outwash plains, and rolling ground moraines — all evidences of recent glaciation. The lowlands, south of the Great Lakes section with its drift areas, reflects the features due to underlying rocks to a much greater extent. The dominant structural features here are the northern part of the

Cincinnati anticline which brings Ordovician rocks to the surface, and the southern Illinois syncline, which bed the Carboniferous coal measures. Deeply dissected areas and minor
uplands have repeatedly served as refuge areas for Archaic
populations.

It soon becomes obvious to anyone who carries on archaeological excavations in a number of cultural horizons of a
particular area, and studies them in their ecological setting,
that the prehistoric remains exhibit considerable differences
in settlement patterns as one goes back into time. It can be
equally well demonstrated that there was an increase in dependence on the natural resources of the immediate localities inhabited as one proceeds into the past. The dependence
is, of course, greatest in the most ancient hunting and gathering groups or those that retained such an economy until
historic times mainly because of local abundance of game and
fish. With food production, an increase in population, and
the expansion of trade, dependence on immediate surroundings becomes less direct, and the nature of population pressure changes.

With the retreat of the last glaciers in the Middle West
eleven to thirteen thousand years ago, we note the first shift
in economy. The Paleo-Indian hunters gradually shifted from
dependence on Pleistocene big game, especially various species of now extinct bison, to hunting smaller game such as
deer that spread into the area accompanying a change from
prairic to woodland conditions. Concomitant with this change
from a Paleo-Indian to an Archaic level we also find a greater
dependence, at least seasonally, on the molluscs found in the
larger streams.

The Archaic Pattern was followed by a Woodland Pattern
with increasing forestation and the development of regional
cultural traditions. The Middle Woodland period was characterized by considerable interaction of traditions and the
rise of secondary culture centers. Toward its end, corn is introduced to supplement the mixed diet of the hunting and
gathering economy, and the emergence of the Mississippi
Pattern.

The Mississippi Pattern which developed in the middle Mississippi area represented a marked change in the way of life
— a food-producing tradition supporting town dwellers. The

proto-historic period, finally, saw a reemergence of the Woodland Pattern and the fusion of Mississippi and Woodland traditions in several localities, a process that was only stopped by the advent of Whites and subsequent displacement of the Indians.

The varieties referred to in this paper constitute stabilized biological populations of an intermediate order of differentiation, characterized by a combination of a selected number of inherited morphological characteristics that reflect the history of the group. The prehistoric populations are delimited in time and space by cultural assemblages with which the skeletal material is associated. It should be emphasized that the delimitation of the biological population precedes the description and listing of the characteristics that distinguish it from other varieties.

## The Paleo Indian

Given an immediate post-glacial period of 12,000 to 15,000 years, we can thus observe considerable climatic changes accompanying drastic shifts in ecology. With the ecological changes we can trace evolutionary cultural changes that allow certain groups to occupy particular ecological niches.

As Mason has recently demonstrated[8] on the basis of the distribution of Folsom spear-points and other lithic remains attributed to the Paleo-Indian, the earliest hunters occupied the Great Lakes region soon after the retreat of the last glacier. Radiocarbon dates from Wisconsin indicate that this took place around 13,000 B.C. An earlier occupation of the continent by the Paleo-Indian is well substantiated by many radiocarbon dates, which indicate that man was contemporary with a Pleistocene mammalian fauna which includes the horse, camelops, the ground sloth, the mastodon, and a number of species of now extinct bison.

Areas vacated by retreating glaciers pass through a regular sequence of climatic and ecological zones during the course of several thousand years as the temperature rises. At first tundra conditions prevail. Gradually grasses begin to cover the flat, barren, lake-studded land. Arctic forms of mammals prevail. During the Sangamon Inter-glacial Period even musk oxen roamed as far south as central Illinois.[10] As northern Indiana became swampy around 10,000 years ago, herds of mastodons seasonally wandered north for forage. Their remains are frequently encountered in ancient peat bogs, one of which has recently yielded a human skull of an early mastodon hunter. These mastodons were hunted in the West from Wyoming to the Valley of Mexico. One find in particular from Wyoming has been described as a hunting camp where one of these animals had been killed. Undoubtedly the Paleo-Indian followed the mastodons into the Great Lakes area. Mason recently suggested that the early hunters, who made the fluted points which are part of the Paleoeastern culture, entered the Lower Peninsula of Michigan about 11,500 years ago from Indiana and Illinois, following closely on the retreating margins of the Cary ice. From the scattered remains a slowly changing hunting culture is indicated. Mason emphasizes the fact that the fluted points are definitely not a trait of the eastern Archaic cultures, but part of the Paleoeastern complex that ceased to exist by the time that recognizable Archaic manifestations had developed. His distribution maps of fluted spear points clearly demonstrate that they are limited to the southern half of the Lower Peninsula, the northernmost finds having been made in a tier of counties west from Saginaw Bay across the state. This strongly suggests that the Paleo-Indian occupation of the lower part of the state was contemporaneous with the glacial cover of the northern half of the peninsula.

Since the original peopling of the New World was a process lasting thousands of years during which small bands gradually spread over both continents, considerable physical diversity is to be expected even though all the groups are derived from a common gene pool. Validated radiocarbon dates indicate that these Proto-Mongoloids which we class as Paleo-Indians had arrived in Venezuela about 13,000 B.C., and reached Tierra del Fuego about 9,800 B.C. As differentiation is at a maximum in small populations in which genetic drift is operative and an adaptation to local ecological conditions is likely, considerable population variability is to be expected, and is indeed observable when Andean, Amazonian, and Patagonian groups are compared. Thus, the scattered finds of greatest antiquity that we do have, dating from the Upper Cave finds at Choukoutien to the American Archaic, vary greatly and obviously cannot be described in terms of a single variety. At best they can be grouped into a Paleamerind series of populations. Judging from their descendants in the Great Lakes area these early hunters probably resembled the Lenid variety population of the Northern Archaic cultures quite closely.[12]

## The Archaic Period

Sometime around 8000 B.C. with changing ecological conditions and forestation of formerly glaciated areas an Eastern Archaic culture began to differentiate. During the Terminal Glacial retreat between 6000 and 3000 B.C. the climate changed from a damp cool to a warm dry climate.[15] Pines achieved dominance during the first part of the period, and were followed by an expansion of great grasslands, which spread eastward across the area as far as New York state. After 2000 B.C. the climate became cooler again and conditions had become much as they are today. The mastodons had left the region and deer and elk replaced the barren-ground caribou. The period of seven thousand years duration reflects various adjustments to a mixed hunting and gathering economy within a woodland ecological setting.

In many parts of the world populations, now living in larger aggregations, seasonally supplemented their diet of small game and wild seeds with shellfish. Large shellheaps found along the shallows of the majority of larger streams throughout the Middle West and the South attest to the extensive use of clams for food. The fact that the people of this period often seem to have been malnourished and undersized and their cultures of low vigor has led Jensen[7] to suggest that grave thiamin deficiencies from the destruction of thiamin by thiaminase of shellfish may be the reason. The enzyme in these foods is destroyed by cooking, which is known to have been practiced at that time because of the presence of hearths with fire-cracked rocks used in "stone-boiling."

By studying the remains found on Archaic sites it can be inferred that the people certainly lived in family groups or bands up to about fifty individuals leading a migratory way of life in pursuit of game.

Winter[2] described this seasonal shift from one riparine camp site to another as follows:

As the seasons changed they moved from camp to camp, taking advantage of various natural resources, both plant and animal, or seeking shelter in inclement weather. Thus, were we able to follow a typical band throughout the year, we might find them during the fall in a camp near a grove of nut trees. After their departure from this camp, the ground would be left littered with the pebble grinding stones, pestles, grinding slabs, and nutting stones which had been used in preparing the harvest of nuts and other ripe seeds for consumption and storage. The winter would perhaps be spent in a rock shelter, where campfires placed towards the front of the shelter would warm the interior both directly and by heat reflected from the rock above. There would be innumerable fragments of burned sandstone or other rock scattered around the hearths, since throughout the year stone boiling was a standard procedure for cooking food. That is, stones were heated in the hearths and dropped in the skin or bark food containers. Part of their food would be supplied from the fall harvest which had been stored in pits in the floor of the shelter. Deer and other game would have formed another part of their diet, since hunting was very likely a year-round activity. As always, there was need for chipping dart and spear points and making other stone tools. Perhaps time was also spent in making the beautiful tools of ground stone which have been found on so many Archaic sites in Illinois. With the coming of spring, open campsites would again be reoccupied for the gathering of edible plants and roots. In the following months, the camp would move from time to time as game was depleted in the area and as new food sources become available in other areas. With the fall, we should again find our band at its site near the nut groves, completing its seasonal round. (pp. 9-10)

It was towards the end of the early Archaic period, perhaps around 6000 B.C., that inhabitants of the area learned to utilize their woodland environment. This corresponds to Caldwell's[3] first economic level. In a recent paper he demonstrates that there have been three dominant trends in the prehistory of Eastern United States which lead to three stages or economic levels: (a) the establishment of primary forest efficiency, (b) the dominance of regional differentiation and stylistic change in artifacts, and (c) increasing connections with Nuclear Middle American civilization. The first two transformations, which had been completed at the time of European contact, depend to a greater or lesser degree on ecological conditions prevalent at the times the particular cultures existed. All evidence points to a very slow cultural development during the Archaic period, and emphasizes the fact that a culture must have advanced to a certain level before proper utilization of particular ecological resources can take place. Despite a greater concentration of population and living in villages, the Archaic people had to await the advent of pottery, food production (corn, beans, and squash) and a more complex socio-religious organization that served as a cohesive factor, before undergoing a radical change in the way of life typical of the more advanced Neolithic agricultural town dwellers. In northeastern North America the innovations were adopted in the Terminal Archaic after 1000 B.C., which allowed the Archaic groups to become gradually identified with the Woodland culture.

With the advent of the Archaic Period we deal for the first time with larger population aggregates and well-documented skeletal series found in their radio-carbon dated archaeological contexts. According to the best evidence available, differentiation from a common Paleo-Indian ancestor into a southern Archaic Iswanid variety and a northern Archaic Lenid variety was well on its way by about 6000 B.C. The Paleo-amerind, Early Archaic ancestor of botn groups can in all probability be linked with a Gulf-Algonquian linguistic forbear, who under conditions of relative isolation gave rise to the Muskogean and the Algonquian linguistic groups in the Middle Mississippi and the Great Lakes areas. Adequate Middle Archaic level skeletal series in both areas are clearly differentiated into Iswanid and Lenid varieties, respectively, by about 4000 B.C. The Archaic Indian Knoll series from Kentucky, and the Old Copper series from Wisconsin furnish classic examples. These two varieties, which meet in the central part of our state undoubtedly made a number of adaptations to local ecological conditions.[12]

## The Early and Middle Woodland Period

As mentioned in the preceding section, the onset of the Woodland period was gradual, varied with the locality, and lasted as the Early Woodland period over a span of two thousand years, that is, from 2500 to 500 B.C. Archaeologically the Woodland sites can be recognized by the presence of pottery, generally sherds of conoidal vessels with cordmarked or stamp-decorated surfaces. Evidently at least two ceramic traditions developed, the northern remaining relatively unchanged, whereas the southern or Mississippi tradition became quite distinct. The ultimate origin of the Early Woodland pottery has not been ascertained, for some hold that it is a local development, while others have attempted to trace it to northeastern Siberia.

The Middle Woodland Period is distinguished by an elaborate assemblage of traits of the Indians of the widespread Hopewell culture, which flourished in two centers between 300 B.C. and 500 A.D. The center in the Illinois River Valley yields radiocarbon dates that are somewhat earlier than those from the center that was located in southern Ohio (2, p. 21).

Struever[17] especially has been greatly interested in the ecological relationships of the Middle Woodland peoples. Whereas the Early Woodland (Black Sand Focus) people of the Illinois Valley, who are directly ancestral to the Hopewell group in that area, invariably occupy river bottom sites which were located right on the river bank, often on sand bars, the Middle Woodland peoples generally occupied higher ground, which has been characterized as bluff-base occupation. This suggests canoe nomadism for the former, and a sedentary occupation for the latter. The Middle Woodland Hopewellian groups are well-known for their erection of earthworks and burial mounds. So far no evidence for the cultivation of maize has been discovered in Hopewellian sites in Illinois, though the fact that one finds a concentration of population in large villages around the ceremonial earthworks and burial mounds strongly suggests food production. Struever believes that even the Classic Hopewellians still maintained a hunting and seed-gathering economy. As proof he discovered remains of large quantities of pigweed *(Chenopodium)* seeds in cache pits. Nuts, berries, roots also made up an appreciable percentage of the diet. Chief dependence was still on the Virginia deer and a number of smaller mammalian species. Rabbit bones are noteworthy because of their absence — a fact that may have some connection with a mythological role the rabbit plays in trickster tales of the Algonquin tribes. We thus have a hunting-oriented culture which nevertheless congregated in fairly large population asemblages for socio-religious reasons, which was only possible in favorable, rather restricted environments. Streuver points out that it was in the riverine alluvium, along the mud-flats bordering sloughs and river banks that presented just such density and diversity of natural food products, and Caldwell[3] holds that it must have been under just such conditions that the earliest cultivation was practiced. Subsistence thus restricted the concentration of people to the broad river valleys along which we indeed find the greatest population expansion of the Hopewellian period. There is little doubt that horticulture, that is food production, and the actual introduction of the maize plant was from the south.

An elaborate mound burial complex in which the ruling families were buried in specially prepared mound tombs while ordinary people were individually buried or cremated (Ohio), indicating a socio-religious cohesive factor; artifacts and materials demonstrating extensive trade and far-ranging contacts; and the increase in cultural complexity and elaborateness of ceremonialism and settlement pattern in a series of ecological zones — all raise interesting questions regarding the relationship between subsistence patterns and particular ecological niches.

According to McGregor[2] (p. 24) the Classic or Late Middle Woodland people had maize and practiced limited agriculture. Be that as it may, in general the Middle Woodland peoples represent a cultural peak in the prehistory of the area, and a way of life that led to the development of extensive permanent settlements.

Physically, in general, the Early Woodland groups continue as Algonquian-speaking tribes of the Lenid variety through the Hopewellian or Middle Woodland period.[6] They comprise the dominant population extending from the Mississippi to West Virginia north of the Ohio River. It is only toward the end of the Middle Woodland period in the Illinois Valley that we note a gradual change in physical type involving mainly brachycephalization. This change can be recognized as far as upper New York state in the East. This Meta-amerind or derived group has been delimited and described as the Illinid variety.[12]

### The Middle Mississippi Tradition

It is now the consensus of archaeologists that the Middle Mississippi cultural tradition is an outgrowth of the Woodland Pattern with its regional traditions. The interactions of a number of these regional developments, near the mouth of the Missouri and in the Tennessee-Cumberland area, led to the emergence of a culture that was primarily agricultural but centered around towns. These towns, which served as religious centers, furnished the necessary cohesion. The

earliest developments probably date back as far as A.D. 500
with good-sized villages by 900, and the climax of well developed religious centers between 1200 and 1450. An analagous
development of politico-religious centers and daughter colonies occurred in the South.

Practically all of the towns with their temple mounds,
chief's mounds, and town squares were established in areas
with similar climatic conditions, such as found in northern
Mississippi and western Tennessee. They were in areas with
a warm humid climate and a long growing season, with winter temperatures that rarely fall much below freezing. The
palisaded towns were found along the main river courses
where cane, pecans, and cypress grew. Intense cultivation
of the soil was carried on by the farmers in the river bottoms
surrounding the towns. Although there were no definite
streets, the square wattle-and-daub houses with their grass-
thatched gabled roofs were oriented with their corners to the
four cardinal points. Grass-lined storage pits for corn dotted
the whole site within the stockade.

Subsistence was based on growing maize, beans, and squash,
supplemented by game (deer), fowl, and fish. Camp refuse
from such sites yield reliable information about food habits
and species of animals utilized for food, as well as approximate proportions of plant food to game and fish.[1, 10, 14] It has
been estimated that the larger centers may have had between
1000 and 2000 inhabitants and a population that may have increased in times of festivities or times of danger when the
farmers of the surrounding countryside would flock to the
towns. Such a concentration of a sedentary population probably led to an exhaustion of local resources, for we find that
most of the towns seem to have a rather brief occupational
history. Most of the settlements were contemporaneous, for
there was wide trade, and such uniformity in settlement pattern that Indians from a thousand miles away would know
what to expect in the settlements.

It has been evident for some time that the Walcolid variety
of Indians is the result of a long continued process of differentiation from southern Archaic populations over a wide area.
On the basis of evidence from the Modoc Rock Shelter in southwestern Illinois, which provides a continuous record of occupation from 8000 B.C. to 1000 A.D., there occurs a gradual

change from roughly 3000 B.C. onward. This marks the origin of a derived or Meta-amerind population and the origin of the Walcolid variety that largely became associated with the development of Middle Mississippi and related cultural manifestations and languages which have been placed into the Muskogean linguistic family.[12] By A.D. 900 the Middle Mississippi Phase people are well differentiated,[13] and subsequently become predominantly Walcolid in all southern Illinois and Tennessee-Cumberland Aspect sites. In southwestern Indiana, where this culture is centered in our state, the Angel Site near Evansville represents the best known settlement.

### The Historic Period

The mode of life and ecological relationships of the historic tribes corresponded roughly to three ecological and culture areas. In the northeastern Woodlands and eastern Canada the tribes belonged mainly to the great Algonquian linguistic family. Tribes such as the Menomini, Potawatomi, Ottawa, Chippewa, Miami, Illinois, Shawnee, and Delaware were the descendants of the Archaic (Northern) and Early Woodland peoples, native to the area for at least five thousand years. They were adapted to a hunting economy in a northern forest environment. Food production was secondary and the growing of maize directly dependent on the length of the growing season. The densest populations were found in the river valleys and lake regions, in locations where forage was most plentiful for deer. Transportation was by birch-bark canoes, and settlements, consisting of an aggregation of bark or mat-covered wigwams, were invariably located immediately on the banks of streams.

Similarly, in the South, the tribes had been indigenous to the area for seven thousand or more years, again derived from an Archaic (Southern) population. The linguistic homogeneity — most of the tribes spoke langugages of the Muskogean linguistic family — is attested by the continuous block of related languages, revealing very little of the shatter pattern characteristic of marginal populations. Tribes such as the Chickasaw, Choctaw, Creek, Seminole, and the Iroquoian-speaking Cherokee are typical. Their culture was largely of the Mississippi Pattern, largely food producing, and, as previously described, centered in towns. Since the Indians never had draught ani-

mals and the plow to cut the hard soil, settlement was largely
limited to the fertile river bottoms where the soil was tilled
with digging sticks and flint hoes. It has been estimated that
maize, beans, and squash formed about seventy per cent of
the diet. It was supplemented by game (mainly Virginia deer),
fowl, and fish. Transportation in contrast to that of the northeastern Woodlands was by dug-out canoes. The towns, as
described for the Middle Mississippi period above, were palisaded and located along the main river courses.

The third major culture area that impinges on the Middle
Western region is the Plains area, where subsistence was
based chiefly on the hunting of the bison. Linguistically, the
Indians of the area were largely Siouan-speaking. The expansion of the Southern Village Indians, who grew maize,
occurred mainly between A.D. 1100 and 1300. The movement
from the St. Louis area was largely directed up the Missouri,
Mississippi, and Illinois rivers. Tribes like the Wichita, Caddo,
Pawnee, and Arikara were Caddoan-speaking and still formed
linguistic islands along the Missouri in historic times, after
being engulfed by the Siouan tribes that spread from southwestern Minnesota and the eastern Dakotas to the southwest
across the Plains. The Teton, Brule, Ogalala, Yankton, Kansa,
Osage, Iowa, Missouri and Winnebago are the best known.
Subsistence, in the contact period, was almost entirely based
on hunting of the bison. But there is good evidence[5] that the
large herds of "buffalo" (Bison bison) are a rather recent
development, perhaps since 3000 B.C. The Siouan expansion
into the Plains dates largely after 1300, and is closely related
to the advent of the horse (1540-1740), which gave these
tribes greater mobility. Some bison ranged over northern Illinois and northern Indiana and were hunted by the Sauk and
Fox and the Winnebago Indians, who introduced Plains area
customs into this section of the region under consideration.
Archaeologists have been able to trace this historic eastward
movement by the presence of Oneota (Iowa) pottery and
skeletal remains which definitely points to Siouan influences.
It must, however, be kept in mind that this only represents
a historic movement, rather than a long range adaptation to
ecological conditions.

In proto-historic and historic times the tier of three states:
Illinois, Indiana and Ohio constituted a marginal region of the

three ecological and cultural areas mentioned above. Contacts and mixtures — cultural, linguistic, and physical—characterize this period. The Ohio Valley formed the ancient contact zone between Late Woodland and Middle Mississippi cultural traditions resulting in the Upper Mississippian Fort Ancient culture. But the three hundred years of contact, roughly between 1400 and 1700 were not sufficient to produce a secondary variety of Indian. Similarly to the west, contacts during the four hundred year time span merely resulted in various degrees of cultural and physical mixture.[16] Oneota (Upper Mississippi) cultural influences from the Plains are only discernible in northern Illinois and northwestern Indiana, and physical admixture from the Ceno-amerind Dakotid variety are just barely indicated in the same area.

## LITERATURE

1. ADAMS, W. R. 1949. Faunal remains for the Angel Site. M. A. Thesis, Indiana University, (unpublished).
2. BLUHM, E. A. (ed) 1959. Illinois archaeology. Bull. No. 1, Ill. Archaeological Survey.
3. CALDWELL, J. R. 1958. Trend and tradition in the prehistory of the Eastern United States. Scientific Papers, Vol. X. Illinois State Museum.
4. FENNEMAN, N. M. 1938. Physiography of Eastern United States.
5. HORNADAY, W. T. 1889. The extermination of the American Bison. Smithsonian Institution. Report of the National Museum for 1886-1887, pp. 369-548.
6. HUNTER, K. B. 1965. Preliminary report on the Hopewellian skeletons from the Klunk Site, Calhoun County, Illinois. Proc. Indiana Acad. Sci. **74**,81-83.
7. JENSEN, L. B. 1953. Man's foods. p. 35.
8. MASON, R. J. 1958. Late Pleistocene geochronology and the Paleo-Indian penetration into the Lower Michigan Peninsula. Anthropological Papers, No. **11**, University of Michigan.
9. NEUMANN, E. A. 1964. Post glacial ecology and prehistoric settlement patterns in the Central States Area. Proc. Indiana Acad. Sci. **72**:47-55.
10. NEUMANN, G. K. 1937. Faunal remains from Fulton County Sites. In: F. C. Cole and T. Deuel, Rediscovering Illinois. pp. 265-268.
11. NEUMANN, G. K. 1952. Archaeology and Race in the American Indian. In: J. B. Griffin, ed. Archeology of Eastern United States, 13-34.
12. NEUMANN, G. K. 1960. Origins of the Indians of the Middle Mississippi Area. Proc. Indiana Acad. Sci. **69**: 66-68.
13. NEUMANN, H. W. 1960. Diagnostic Morphological Traits for the Walcolid Variety of American Indians. Proc. Indiana Acad. Sci. **69**: 69-72.
14. NEUMANN, H. W. 1961. The Identification of a Sample of Unmodified Faunal Remains from the Angel Site. Proc. Indiana Acad. Sci. **71**: 53-56.
15. QUIMBY, G. I. 1958. Fluted Points and Geochronology of the Lake Michigan Basin. American Antiquity **23**:3. 247-254.
16. SMAIL, J. K. 1965. The use of female crania in demonstrating racial relationships as exemplified in two Upper Mississippi Amerind Groups. Proc. Indiana Acad. Sci. **74**, 72-79.
17. STRUEVER, S. 1961. Local diversity and the problem of Hopewellian development in the Valley Riverine-Western Great Lake Area. Paper, 1961 AAA meeting.
18. WISSLER, C. 1926, The relation of nature to man in aboriginal America.

# 29

# Changing Patterns of Agriculture

HELMUT KOHNKE AND L. S. ROBERTSON
Purdue University

Indiana is blessed with good soils and a climate that is favorable for agriculture. There is enough rain and sunshine for good crops and the summer is warm enough and long enough for corn to ripen.

Most of Indiana was in forest when the white man first came. With the trees removed, the surface soil was rich in humus and nutrients and when it was put under the plow, it produced rich harvests. But the layer of the black soil was thin and in time its nutrients diminished as the crops were removed year after year and as erosion took its toll. Farmers used manure to make up for part of the losses.

Toward the middle of the 1800's they started cautiously to fertilize, especially with potassium and phosphate, but the yields did not increase substantially until around 1940, when progressive agronomists, led by Dr. George Scarseth, pointed to the necessity of applying massive doses of nitrogen to the crops, especially to corn. At the same time plant breeders improved the crops, developing resistances to pests and diseases and making them more efficient in converting sun, rain and the generously supplied plant nutrients into bumper crops. The use of "hybrid vigor" in corn in the 1930's and later on in other crops also helped substantially to boost yields.

At the same time farmers and animal scientists were busy breeding livestock for higher performance and more efficient use of the constantly increasing feed supply.

Directly or indirectly many branches of industry helped to increase farm production. The most obvious case is the development of the many implements and machines, that have made it possible for a single worker on a commercial farm in Indiana to supply enough food for 40 people.

The graphs in Fig. 84 give statistical evidence of some of the changes that have taken place in the agriculture of Indiana during the first 150 years of the state.

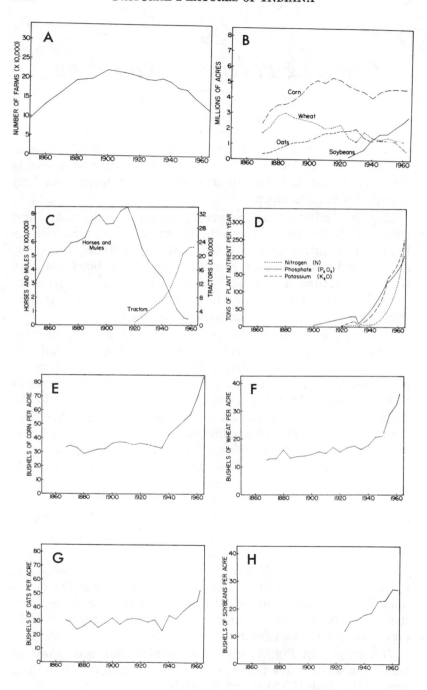

In order to obtain a clearer picture of the changing patterns of agriculture in Indiana, let us drop in on a typical farm in each of the three main periods:

1816—1865 The pioneer period

1866—1915 The horse and buggy period

1916—1966 Industrialized agriculture

## An Indiana Farm of 1840

In imagination, let us pay a visit to a typical Indiana farm of the first half century of Indiana statehood, say about 1840.

Fig. 84. A—*Number of Farms*. The number of farm enterprises has increased until a maximum of 222,000 farms was reached at the turn of the century. Increasing farm size and use of land for roads and for urban and industrial purposes has steadily decreased farm numbers. B—*Crop Acreages*. Along with the increase of farms there was an increase of the acreage used for the main grain crops. The wheat acreage began to decrease before the end of the century, because at this time the North Central States began to produce good bread wheat. The soft winter wheat grown in Indiana is best for pastries. The increase and decrease of oat acreage reflects the increase and decrease of the number of horses. The corn acreage reached its peak in 1917, about the time when the soybean made its appearance in Indiana. C—*Horses, Mules and Tractors*. The increase in the number of horses went along with the increased land in cultivation. The introduction of tractors in the teens of this century caused the rapid decrease in the number of horses. D—*Fertilizer Use*. Small quantities of fertilizer were used in the 19th century in Indiana. Acid phosphate and bone meal were the more important of the early fertilizers. Gradually more potassium was used, while farmers still depended largely on legumes and the native power of the soil for the nitrogen supply. The depression years of the thirties caused a great reduction in fertilizer use. After this the use of phosphate and potassium increased steadily. It was not until after the ingenious experiments at Purdue University in the late thirties and the early forties that nitrogen was used in generous amounts. E—*Corn Yields*. Up to the middle thirties corn yields changed very little — except for annual fluctuation resulting from the weather of the different seasons. Introduction of hybrid corn in the thirties was responsible for about a ten bushel increase. Continued improvement of corn hybrids, efficient chemicals to combat weeds, insects and fungi and improved soil treatment, especially the general use of large amounts of nitrogen fertilizer has sky-rocketed corn yields. F—*Wheat Yields*. Continuous improvement of the wheat varieties and of the cultural practices have gradually raised the yields from 1870 to 1940. Further improvement of varieties and heavy fertilization have tripled wheat yields from 1870 to 1964. G—*Oat Yields*. In spite of improved varieties, oat yields have not increased as much as have corn and wheat. With the lessening use for oats it is probable that they have been shifted to poorer soils. Besides, the climate of southern Indiana is somewhat too warm for oats. H—*Soybean Yields*. The low yields of soybeans in the 1920's reflect the lack of experience of the farmers with this new crop. Constantly improved varieties and cultural practices together with a general increase of the plant nutrient level in the soils of Indiana have been responsible for a tremendous increase in yields.

It was most likely located in the hills of the south part of the state, as that was the portion first occupied.

Dan Carson (fictitious name), operator of the farm, had come down the Ohio River from an eastern state a few years before with his wife, three small children, a span of oxen, a few household goods, hand farm tools, and a long-barrelled rifle. From the government he had purchased his 120-acre farm of wooded land at $1.25 an acre.

By 1840 Dan, an excellent axman from long experience, had cut the timber from 50 acres of his farm, plowed this land with a wooden-mold-board plow and put it into crops, some still between the stumps. But the stumps didn't bother him much, as the crop work was done mostly by hand, except for oxen pulling a few small implements.

Dan was destined to continue his clearing operations for many years. The first logs he cut were used for the construction of his house, and later ones for other buildings, for rail fences to protect his crops, for fuel burned in the fireplace, and for other purposes such as making lye for soap.

For many years the crops Dan raised were mostly for home consumption, as market opportunities were meager. The only outlet from his farm, except cross country through the woods, was a crooked ungraded road, sometimes made impassable by mud, particularly in the spring when the ground was thawing, and in places crossed by a fence with gate to be opened. Even communication with other people was very limited. Telephones, radios, television and regular newspapers were developments of a much later period. Mail, when there was any, was received or delivered only when someone visited the little post office a dozen miles away.

Even in these early years, corn was Dan's principal crop. He used it to feed his two oxen, his saddle horse, his two family cows with their offspring, a little for his chickens, and a lot for grinding into corn meal for family food. The corn was planted by hand. No commercial fertilizer was used. Little barnyard manure was produced, as livestock ran in the woods most of the year. Dan was just beginning to spread what manure he had on the corn land instead of dumping it on the ice in the stream to get rid of it. Cultivation was done with a hoe or ox-pulled wide-shovel cultivator. Little was known about controlling the ravages of army worms or other pests. When the corn was ripe in the fall, Dan and his family cut the stalks by hand and tied them into shocks that could be hauled in for hand husking during the winter, sometimes in the "husking bees" that were popular neighborhood gatherings in these early days, with the stover used for feeding the cattle and oxen. Sometimes, just before the corn was fully ripe, he "topped" the corn (cut the stalks just above the ears) to get just the most palatable portion of the stalks.

A few acres of oats and wheat were also grown. They were sowed by hand, covered by pulling a brush drag (tree limb) over the ground, harvested with a cradle and threshed with a flail or by tramping with oxen or horses, and then throwing the grain and chaff into the air for the wind to blow away the chaff. The wheat was hauled in sacks, mostly on the back of the horse, to a near-by grist mill for grinding for home use. Flax occupied a larger acreage than oats and wheat together, as the flax fiber, sometimes mixed with wool to make "linsey-woolsey," was needed for home spinning to make clothes for the family. Along the creek bottom Dan grew a little rice for family food. The farm had a good home garden, including potatoes and sweet potatoes, as vegetables were almost impossible to purchase. The hay that supplemented the corn stover as roughage was cut with a scythe from the wild meadow in the creek valley and raked by hand with a homemade wooden rake. Dan had planted a few apple trees which promised fruit for later years, as codling moths and other fruit pests had not yet become numerous. Dan had two or three low-producing cows which supplied him with milk for home consumption and cream for churning butter for family use. From these cows he occasionally had a young animal to butcher. He raised a few pigs of the razor-back type which ran wild most of the time and subsisted largely on beech mast and succulent roots supplemented, particularly in the winter, with kitchen "slop" and a small amount of corn. Most of his dozen hens hatched a brood of chicks sometime during the spring or summer. The entire group of chickens scratched for most of the feed, as did the few other types of poultry raised. The eggs and the poultry that survived the attacks of the numeorus hawks, foxes, wolves and other enemies went into the family diet. Wild game such as deer, bears and wild turkeys also contributed to the food supply. The forest furnished other food for Dan and his family. Occasionally he was fortunate enough to find a bee tree for honey and early each spring he cooperated with a neighbor in tapping a group of sugar maples to catch the sweet water which boiled down to make maple syrup and maple sugar.

The log house that Dan had built was a clap-board shingled structure of two rooms separated by a threshing or general utility floor which was open at the sides but roofed above. Each room was heated by a large stone fireplace. In one of these the cooking was done, much of it in a "dutch oven" (a cast iron covered skillet). Candles furnished the light, except that which came through the oiled-paper which substituted for glass in the windows. Water for house use was carried in from a near-by spring. The pieces of furniture, such as benches, rockers, tables and bunks were hand made but substantial. The doors hung on heavy home-made leather hinges. A dash churn (a jar-like container with a round wooden disc from which rose a wooden rod to be moved up and down by hand) and lard-rendering equipment were in evidence.

Measured in terms of the standards of conveniences, improvements and techniques of modern times, Dan and his family must have had a difficult time. We would not want to go back to the conditions under which the family and other farm families lived. Yet who can say that those hardy pioneers, despite their difficulties and struggles, were any less happy than their descendants of later generations.

### An Indiana Farm of 1890

John Loomis, a hypothetical Indiana farmer of 1890, operated and lived in a vastly different way from his grandfather of 1840.

John's 160-acre farm in central Indiana was all cleared except for trees along the stream and a thinned-out 15-acre woodlot, used for pasture, fuel and the timbers occasionally needed on the farm. This woodlot was in the back corner of the farm, as the clearing of land had been started near the house in early years and gradually spread farther away. His fields were fenced, partly with old rails but mostly with barbed and woven wire. Tile strings opening into surface ditches drained most of the depressions in his crop land, although inadvertently. A large square frame house roofed with purchased cedar shingles replaced the earlier log cabin. A barn, constructed from boards nailed on a log frame work, already had a lean-to built on one side. Other major frame buildings consisited of a machine shed, a combined corn crib and a granary, and a poultry house.

Corn was the major crop on John's farm, as on the farms of his Indiana ancestors, with wheat and oats next in importance. For hay and pasture for his increased amount of livestock, John raised a mixture of clover and timothy. Occasionally he sowed a little barley or rye and sometimes, when he could not get his corn planted in time, he produced some buckwheat. Flax and rice were no longer produced.

In crop production John's methods differed widely from those of his grandfather. Machine work had replaced most of the hand work of earlier days. Instead of oxen, horses furnished the power for pulling these machines. Wooden moldboard plows had given way to metal plows and "brush" drags had been replaced by metal-tooth harrows. Hand planting of corn had given way to check-row planting, two rows at a time. Two-horse riding corn cultivators with smaller shovels did an improved job in corn cultivating. His corn was husked by hand from the standing stalk. He still burned his corn stalks to get rid of them for the next crop but was beginning to have a guilty conscience about it. However he saved as much of his barnyard manure as he could conveniently and spread it on his fields, usually for corn, using a mechanical horse-pulled manure spreader. He was beginning to use commercial fertilizer on his corn, despite the contention of many of his neighbors that it was hurting his land, but in quantities very small in terms of later-year standards. He was still not conscious of the need for soil conservation.

On John's farm a grain drill had replaced hand sowing of oats and wheat. The greatest machinery developments were in harvesting and threshing small grain. The cradle had given way to the reaper and this to the self-binder. The small grain bundles were now run through a grain separator, operated at first by horse tread power or sweep but now, in John's time, by a steam engine.

John had a horse-pulled mowing machine for cutting his hay and instead of using wooden hand rakes he had a horse-drawn dump rake, owned in partnership with a neighbor, which proved to be a great saver of labor. A few of John's neighbors had horse-drawn hay loaders but John still pitched his hay onto the wagon by hand. However, he put it into the barn loft from the hay rack with a horse-pulled hay fork.

Livestock production in John's time also had undergone considerable change from the earlier days. The natural advantages of Indiana as a corn-growing state were encouraging the production of corn-consuming animals, particularly hogs. Cattle production had become more specialized. On John's farm he fattened each year a car load of purchased western-grown "feeders" (calves or yearlings that have been raised on pasture and are too thin for slaughter). Some of his neighbors, particularly those with considerable land better suited to pasture than to crops, had herds of beef cows from which they raised their own calves for fattening. Some farmers had herds of dairy cows. The larger dairy herds were mostly near the large cities, as milk for fresh consumption was still handled in milk cans and these could not be moved far without having the milk deteriorate. But many farms farther from cities had a few milk cows and sold sour cream for making butter.

In all classes of livestock John and his neighbors were beginning to take increased pride in quality. Leading farmers over the state had, for some time, been introducing pure-bred stock and improving it by selection. But neither John nor other livestock producers had much knowledge regarding nutrition, disease control, or other phases of livestock production considered essential. Hog cholera, tuberculosis, undulant fever and other livestock diseases were much less under control than in recent yeears. Agricultural colleges and experiment stations had not been in operation long enough to have built up the wealth of scientific and technical knowledge now available, and no public Agricultural Extension Service was yet in existence to bring to farmers even the small amount of discoveries already made. But John and his neighbors were beginning to supplement their own experiences with the facts reported in farm journals.

John, like other Indiana farmers in 1890, was beginning to be less of a "self sufficient" and more of a "commercial" farmer than his ancestors, although he still produced much more for home consumption and purchased fewer articles than his descendants of later years. While he had no truck nor automobile, he lived on a fairly good gravel road that was passable most of the time. Many small towns in his own and surrounding counties and a number of larger cities at greater distance offered potential markets for his farm products, many of them consumed in processed form. Railroads had spread their lines from centers of population in the east and had largely replaced waterways as movers of farm products. These developments had begun to encourage the commercial type of agriculture which was to be developed even further in subsequent years.

In living conveniences John's home was much better equipped than the homes of his progenitors, but far less than the farm homes of recent years. Candles had given way to kerosene lamps and fire places to wood-burning and even coal-burning stoves. Water from a nearby well still had to be carried into the house, but a hand operated lift pump brought soft water from the cistern to the kitchen sink. Glass was in the windows but the windows and doors were still unscreened, with flies and mosquitoes numerous. A cellar under John's house provided a convenient place for storage of food products, without refrigeration. Many staple food products, formerly produced on the farm, were now purchased. John and his family, like other farm people in his day, did not have the frequent urban contacts of later years but were much less isolated than were farm people in the early days, of Indiana statehood.

While John Loomis' representative Indiana farm of 1890 was vastly different from a typical Indiana farm of 1840, the changes that had taken place were, nonetheless, much smaller than the changes that were destined to take place from the second to the third half century of Indiana statehood.

### An Indiana Farm of 1966

With farming highly commercialized and therefore highly specialized by the end of the third half century of Indiana statehood, it is impossible to picture a typical Indiana farm in 1966. But let us assume one of the most common types of farming in central Indiana to illustrate some of the very significant changes that have taken place. Let's look at Joe Brown's farm.

Joe Brown is farming 400 acres in 1966. He owns 200 acres of this and rents the other 200 for a share of the crop. Most of the land is cleared and in crops although 15 acres is classified as "woods pasture" but has only scattered trees remaining.

The land is fenced with woven wire in large fields, some of which are broken up into more than one use because of government programs which limit acreages of corn or other so-called soil depleting crops or require at least minimum acreages of soil-improving crops in return for price benefits given through government loans or subsidies.

Joe's farm is mechanically operated, with his son and himself constituting the labor force except for a small amount of exchange labor with neighbors and some special services hired. He has three tractors, two of them large enough to pull 4-bottom plows or other land-preparation equipment of comparable power requirement. A one-ton truck and a smaller pick-up truck take care of the necessary hauling except for the larger loads of products or farm supplies that may be hauled commercially, particularly in rush periods of farm work, or for the grain wagons that may be pulled by tractors. There are no horses on Joe's farm.

Joe's crop of greatest acreage and value is corn, with soybeans second. On many fields he grows these crops continuously. Only enough oats and wheat are raised to serve as companion (nurse) crop to start a small acreage of alfalfa-grass mixture.

In corn production, Joe pays attention to research discoveries, of which there have been many in recent years. He is able to do this because the Cooperative Extension Service, farm journals and commercial agencies are making increased effort to provide him with the information. While planting corn he applies pre-emergence spray to the land to control weeds and insects. He uses hybrid corn seed of several promising varieties to test them under his conditions. With ample tractor power he usually is successful in getting his corn planted by May 10, knowing that later-planted corn is likely to have lower yields because it takes less advantage of the sun's rays. He drills his corn thick enough to have a population of at least 20,000 plants per acre and is studying possibilities of narrower row spacing for even greater population and yield. But Joe knows that high yields require large amounts of plant food and he applies commercial fertilizer, particularly nitrogen at rates 10 to 50 times the rates used by farmers back in his grandfather's time. With all these precautions, Joe is disappointed if he gets a yield of only 100 bushels per acre. His goal is to average much higher than this. He doesn't mind having to harvest the larger crop, as he does it with a picker-sheller that delivers the shelled corn into trucks or tractor-pulled grain wagons which haul it to the farmstead for artificial drying which removes enough moisture so that it will keep in storage. Much of his corn is stored in large metal bins.

Joe's soybean crop, except that needed for seed, constitutes his principal cash receipt from crops, although he sells wheat when he produces it. He seldom sells any of his corn, but feeds it to hogs and cattle. Sometimes he buys additional corn for feeding.

Hogs are the main source of income on Joe's farm. He breeds enough sows so that around 100 farrow twice a year, in batches spaced so that he keeps his farrowing houses, pig nurseries and fattening quarters occupied a fairly large percentage of the time. Immediately after one batch is removed he cleans and disinfects the quarters. With his corn he feeds purchased protein, antibiotics and other supplements. He vaccinates for cholera and checks carefully with his veterinarian on the control of other hog diseases. When the hog cycle indicates the probability of higher prices with a smaller prospective pig crop in the country he makes sure that he will be feeding out at least his average number of hogs even if some feeder pigs need to be purchased. But when the prospect is for an unusually large pig crop he tries to keep his hog production business stable or to adjust it in the opposite direction from the average.

Joe's other livestock enterprise is feeding cattle. Each fall he purchases about 40 feeders, usually roughs them through the winter (keeps them growing with forages but no grain) and then fattens them out to be marketed in the early fall or other time depending on the size and type of cattle he has purchased. He makes abundant use of silage in connection with these cattle and is giving serious thought to substituting "haylage" (forage ensiled in air-tight storage).

No poultry or sheep are kept on Joe's farm. But he has some neighbors who specialize in either one of these enterprises or in the dairy business. His good dairy neighbors have cows with average milk production of 10,000 pounds a year, nearly twice as high as the production from his grandfather's cows. And the milk from these cows does not go into cans but through tubes of farm tanks from which it is pumped directly into refrigerated tank trucks for shipment to dairy plants.

The apple orchard which at one time provided a source of income on Joe's farm has been grubbed out and the ground put into other crops, leaving apple production to the large specialized fruit producers who have the equipment and the know-how necessary to compete successfully in this field. Joe has a good small garden but places less emphasis than his grandfather did on a home-grown food supply, as it is easier for him to purchase produce, some of it shipped in from other areas in seasons when it is not grown locally.

Inside the house Joe's family enjoys most of the conveniences available to his city friends. Kerosene lights have been replaced by electric lights. He has a kitchen refrigerator, a large freezer, an automatic clothes washer and dryer, vacuum cleaner, an electric range, an oil furnace for central heat, running hot and cold water, indoor flush toilets, shower and bath tub facilities, a septic tank for sewage disposal, and has even just bought an air conditioner.

Joe needs to have much more capital than did his predecessors of earlier generations. This is because of the increased size of farm, the increased value of land per acre, the more expensive improvements, the necessary cash outlay for purchased supplies, and particularly the large amount of costly equipment required. His tractors, trucks and machines alone, at new prices, would cost him $50,000 or more. If he owned all the capital he uses, free from mortgage, he would need to have around $250,000 to $300,000. He avoids a lot of this by·renting part of his land, thus utilizing the landlord's capital. He is not reluctant to borrow money. For example, he carries a mortgage on the land he owns. And each purchase of feeder cattle is financed by borrowing on a chattel mortgage, with the note paid off when the cattle are sold.

Joe is much less distinctly a farmer in appearance and thinking than were his forebears. He lives on a blacktop road and has two automobiles in addition to his trucks. He hires people to do many services that farmers formerly performed for themselves, such as fencing, butchering, spreading lime, or spraying. He makes frequent urban contacts in selling farm products, purchasing supplies and equipment or hiring services. Many services come regularly to his farm such as daily mail delivery, daily newspaper delivery, and food delivery (including bread, bakery products, milk, butter, margarine, and general staple groceries). He and members of his family belong to many organizations. He has numerous rural neighbors who are non-farmers or only part-time farmers. Members of his own family do considerable non-farm work away from home for pay. By reason of these non-farm contacts Joe and his city cousins have become hard to tell apart in appearance and action. Joe has broadened out to become a citizen of the world, with a realization of the interdependence of people of all classes and in all places.

*     *     *

Great as these changes in Indiana agriculture have been, they are small compared to what can be expected for the future.

# 30
# Changing Patterns of Population

BENJAMIN MOULTON

Indiana State University

## Introduction

A trek across the Hoosier landscape soon reveals familiar sights now indicative of changing patterns in population in Indiana. The abandoned farm, the decaying village, the squat spread of new bungalows and the upward thrusting apartment house offer evidence of change in the last 150 years. The geographer might think this young landscape with the relics of its beginning simple to work with as compared to older landscapes. Certainly man could not have confused the record too badly to eradicate the story; the changing pattern should be traceable. A short time of research soon reveals that not all is perfect and what is hoped for in detail is lacking. Only broad generalities exist for much of this short time.

Contributions to the literature in the study of the population of Indiana have been produced for a considerable span of time. Notable remarks by Carmony[1] and Van Bolt[2] are found in their writings of the history of the state. Appearing in the Indiana Academy of Science Proceedings are papers by Visher[3], Gentilcore[4], Barton[5], and, more recently, Hart[6] on general population features. Beginning with the 1850 U. S. Census reports[7], population details are given which enrich the record. The format of census figures has not been uniform, however, and much interpolation is necessary to draw essential continuity. The Indiana State Board of Health in recent years has provided inter-census estimates and migration statistics.[8] Records and reports have encouraged many writers to attempt to forecast future population patterns. Nearly every community planning project will generally attempt such predictions. Some years ago, Bartholomew Associates wrote a report on Indianapolis for the Indianapolis Railways. This report predicted future numbers for Indianapolis and where they might live if permitted or where they might settle if restricted by zoning laws.[9] The U. S. Corps of Engineers recently published preliminary population projections for the Wabash Valley up to the year 2020.[10]

In order to get the best use of capital expenditures for regional improvements for public work projects, water and flood control projects, it is necessary to have some idea of the future population of the state and where they might live. One cannot deny the need to gather every line of evidence to achieve accurate future planning.

The contemporary observer interested in Hoosier population problems finds many generalities which are not completely substantiated. They include such things as:

1. Many counties in Indiana have lost population for successive decades.

2. Our largest counties have continued to expand in population in the past few decades and are exceeded in rate of growth by only a few counties adjacent to them.

3. Our metropolitan center counties are centers of in-migration and our small communities and their counties are centers of out-migration.

These beliefs appear to be well established. If the patterns of change are predictable as interpreted by researchers, the reasons behind such changes must also be recognizable. It also remains true that the causes for shifts in populations have changed from time to time. This is the hardest factor for the researcher to interpret since few wish to predict social change patterns.

## Population Patterns

In 1810 the population of the state was 24,520. These people occupied a "U" shaped pattern from the upper Whitewater Valley down to the Ohio, west along the Ohio and up the Wabash to Vincennes. This involved those 17 counties that now form the boundary of Indiana from Knox County, down the Wabash, up the Ohio River and up the eastern boundary to Union County. Tongues of occupation, reaching up from the Ohio into smaller valleys, perforated the southern Indiana landscape. Most were farmers and few lived in settlements; 80% of them lived within 75 miles of the Ohio. Nearly all, 90-95%, had lived in Indiana for ten years or less. In the next decade they would be the minority, overwhelmed by the 125,000 immigrants who joined them, filled in the empty spaces, pushed northward, but still lived predominantly in the southern half of the state.

A series of maps clearly shows where the major proportion of the people lived in Indiana in the years 1860, 1910
and 1960.

The first map shows the population pattern of 1860 (Fig.
85). Indiana had increased to a little more than a million and
a third; 54 times the number of 1810. Major concentrations
were found in Marion, Jefferson, Allen, Tippecanoe, Dearborn, LaPorte, Vigo and Wayne Counties. Yet these concentrations represented only 10 per cent of the population of
the state. If any stage in Indiana's history could be considered a period in which a high level of uniform occupance prevailed, this was it. Ten additional counties had around 20,000
each and 33 had from 15,000 to 20,000 each. The fifty-one
counties shown on the map had 71% of the population of
the state. Of the dominant counties today (1960), only Allen
and Marion appear on this map. The counties of Clark and
Floyd were as important as Allen and Marion.

By 1910 the population had doubled since 1860 and the rate
of growth was only about a third of the national average
(Fig. 86). From 1870 on, the population growth had not kept
up with national levels. Concentrations of population appeared
in large urban centers. Indianapolis, Marion County, was
nearly three times as populous as any other center. The secondary counties of Allen, Lake, Vigo, and Vanderburgh had
over 75,000 each. These five counties had one sixth of the
population of the state. Five other counties, Elkhart, La-
Porte, Grant, Delaware, Madison and the dual counties of
Clark and Floyd had 50,000 or more each. These eleven or
twelve counties had nearly 35% of the population of the
state. Forty-one additional counties, ranging from 20,000 to
50,000, showed the dispersal of the rest of the population.
The fifty years from 1860 to 1910 showed concentration
toward the Lake Michigan shore, the area northeast of Indianapolis and Indianapolis itself.

The near contemporary pattern is given in the map of 1960
which shows two counties, Lake and Marion, with over a
quarter of the population of the state. Elkhart, St. Joseph,
LaPorte, Madison, Delaware, Vigo, Allen, Vanderburgh, and

Fig. 85. Principal counties of population, 1860: 47 counties shaded
represent 71% of the population. 1. population 25,000 or more; 2. population 20,000-24,999; 3. population 15,000-19,999.

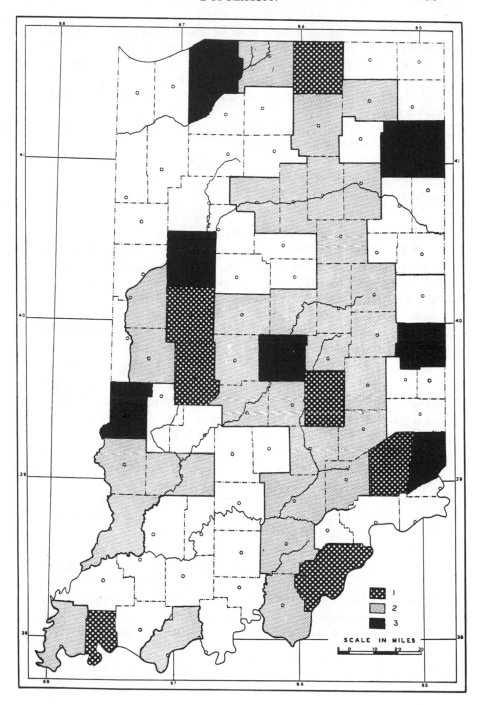

SCALE IN MILES

the dual counties of Floyd and Clark account for 2,750,000 people (Fig. 87). In 1960, 53% of the people lived in 12 of the 92 counties. Six centers are continuing the development begun 100 years ago. These concentration are:

1. Lake Michigan shore counties from Elkhart county westward.

2. Marion County and contiguous counties, extending to Madison, Grant, and Delaware.

3. Vanderburgh County area.

4. Floyd-Clark counties area.

5. Allen County.

6. Vigo County.

### Rate of Growth in Indiana

In the decade of 1950-1960, Indiana grew at the approximate rate of the national growth, 18.4% compared to 18.5% for the nation. The 1870 census revealed that for the first time in Indiana's history its growth was not in excess of national rates. For the next 90 years, growth would be slower than the national rate except for the 1940-1950 decade when state growth exceeded national growth by .3 per cent.

Table 21 summarizes growth rates for the state and nation.

County rate of growth reveals remarkable deviations from the state growth. Many see declining population growth rates as a plague on our landscape while others view them as an adjustment to the changing demands for survival in our society. Since 1930, two counties have lost population in all three successive decades (Fig. 88). Ten counties have lost population steadily since the 1940 census. The total loss is not great in numbers and certainly not large compared to gains for the state as a whole. Most of the static or declining counties are in Southwestern Indiana.

Growth above the national average was experienced by 29 counties between 1950 and 1960 (Fig. 89). Most of these were in large urbanized counties and non-farm rural counties. Fifteen of the 29 had grown for the past two or more decades above the national rate; two college counties are represented. Their pattern is contemporary, not only because of growth

Fig. 86. Principal counties of population, 1910; Five darkest counties had 10% of population of state; twelve darkest counties had 33% of population of state. 1. population 75,000 or more; 2. population 50,000 to 74,999; 3. population 20,000 to 49,999.

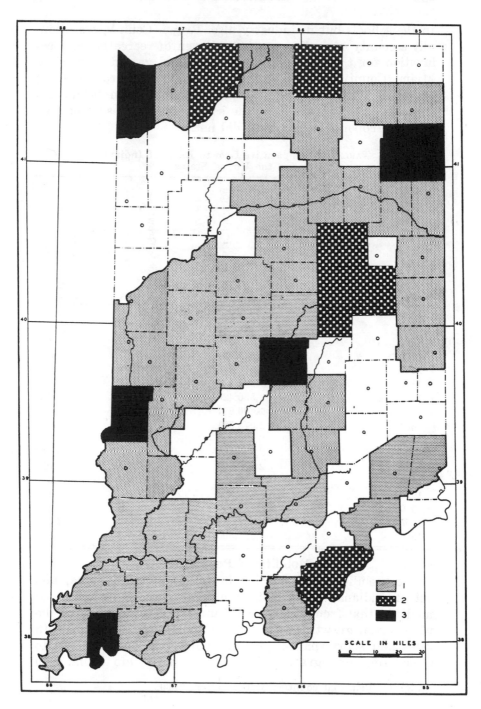

in the schools but in industry also. Brown County, traditionally a county of decline, proved a haven of recreation and relaxation for the capitol city residents and gained therefrom.
Miami County benefited from the defense program and an
air base. Where several counties benefited from peripheral
contacts of out-state cities, the southeast counties associated
with Metropolitan Cincinnati did not.

Table 21. Comparative Growth Rates of Indiana
and the United States

| Decade | Indiana's Population | Indiana's Growth Rate | U.S. Growth Rate |
|---|---|---|---|
| 1800 | 5,041 | | |
| 1810 | 24,520 | 334.7 | 36.4 |
| 1820 | 147,178 | 500.2 | 33.1 |
| 1830 | 343,031 | 133.1 | 33.5 |
| 1840 | 685,866 | 99.9 | 32.7 |
| 1850 | 988,416 | 44.1 | 35.9 |
| 1860 | 1,350,428 | 36.6 | 35.6 |
| 1870 | 1,680,637 | 24.5 | 27.6 |
| 1880 | 1,978,301 | 17.7 | 30.1 |
| 1890 | 2,192,404 | 10.8 | 25.5 |
| 1900 | 2,516,462 | 14.8 | 20.71 |
| 1910 | 2,700,514 | 7.3 | 21.0 |
| 1920 | 2,930,390 | 8.5 | 14.9 |
| 1930 | 3,238,503 | 10.5 | 16.1 |
| 1940 | 3,427,796 | 5.8 | 7.2 |
| 1950 | 3,934,224 | 14.8 | 14.5 |
| 1960 | 4,662,500 | 18.4 | 18.5 |

## Mobility of Population

The mobility of population in Indiana, into Indiana, and
out of Indiana, is difficult to measure. There seems to be
no doubt that from 1800 to 1870 migration accounted for the
phenomenal growth of the state. Considering the high death
rates and short span of life in earlier days, growth had to
come from immigration. People did move into Indiana in

Fig. 87. Principal counties of population, 1960.

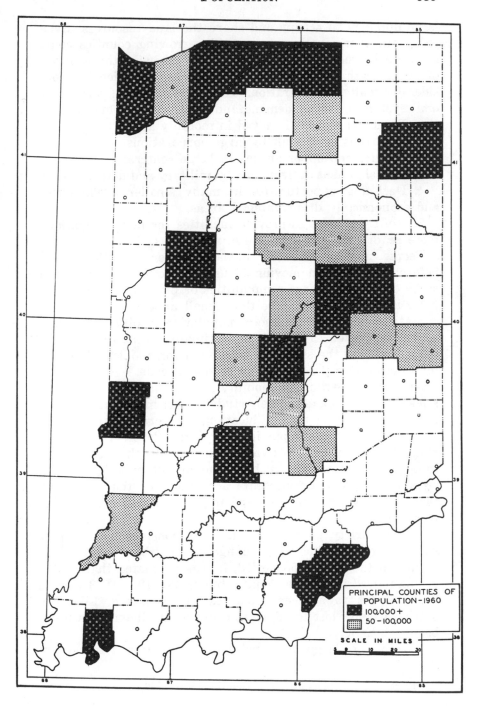

PRINCIPAL COUNTIES OF
POPULATION - 1960
100,000 +
50 - 100,000

SCALE IN MILES
5  0  10  20  30

large numbers to occupy and share the land resources. Even today our gains in the more rapidly growing counties could not be achieved without in-migration. Likewise the counties of low growth or losses in population are experiencing considerable outward migration. The transportation and economic systems of today demand and facilitate a mobile population. Principal reasons involved in mobility are:

1. The transfer of staff by large corporations.
2. Greater job opportunities in large centers.
3. Reassignment of personnel by military and defense units.
4. Declining opportunities in many smaller communities and economically disadvantaged areas.
5. Ability of man to provide facilities for new occupations more readily than ever before in new areas.

People moving generally demand better conditions than before. The goal in moving is usually better economic and social conditions. Large communities or peripheral areas offer these in greater abundance than small areas.

Statistics on the influence of population mobility are limited. In the decade 1940-1950, the estimate is that 100,000 people moved into the state and accounted for about 20% of the total increase in the population of that decade.

Another indication of mobility of population is found in school registrations; the new student is easily identified. The Indiana Department of Education,[11] records that, on the average, 12% of the pupils in each of the classrooms are new students. In large schools and urban schools, this can run up to 50% in a year. The mobile student not only indicates a sizeable change but represents a segment of the population that is young and vigorous and might add still more to the population.

For a variety of reasons, there is considerable mobility within a county, including change from urban to suburban living. In the 1950-1958 period, it was estimated that 56,000 people moved into Lake County, but in the 1960-1963 period, 21,000 went to adjacent counties or elsewhere. Likewise, Marion County lost to adjacent counties as shown by a number of statistics.

Within the large metropolitan urban areas, frequently

Fig. 88. Loss in population, by counties, 1930-1960.

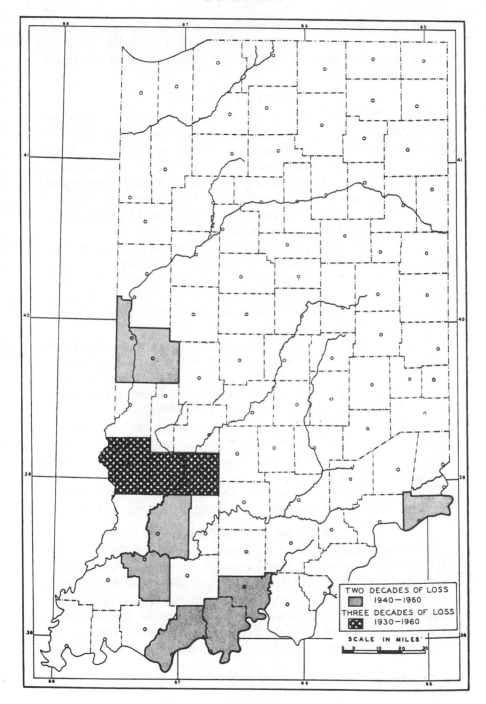

there appears to be great mobility. This is frequently associated with public housing, urban renewal projects, expressways, shopping centers and other projects that bring about mobile populations.

## Urban-Rural Patterns

The state has fifteen counties in which 60% or more of the population is classified as urban. Although there may be some disagreement with census interpretation of the term "urban", counties containing our large cities are represented. There are three along the southern border of the state and three in the north; the remaining nine are clustered in the center. Five of the nine are contiguous but Marion, Tippecanoe, Vigo, and Allen are isolated units (Fig. 90).

Counties in which more than 60% of the population is classified as rural number fifty-one. These counties form the well-known areas of Dearborn Upland, Norman Upland, Crawford Upland, and Lake and Moraine Region. In addition, some of our outstanding corn-belt counties are largely rural and becoming increasingly so.

A few counties not now classified as urban have increased in urban population at above average rates. These are mostly adjacent to Marion County and Lake County; Fountain County is the exception. A few counties, such as Greene, lost urban population as did Posey, Pike and Vermillion.

Several counties gained rural population at phenomenal rates. These reflect the spread of people from urban to rural sites. A greater number of highways as well as improved roads provide easy access to and from rural areas. In addition to the counties adjacent to Marion County, Bartholomew, Elkhart and Miami counties have gained in rural population.

## Age Distribution Patterns

Indiana's age patterns of populations are difficult to define except in terms of broad general averages. There is support for the belief that the rapidly growing counties have a higher percentage of young people while in the slowly growing or declining counties, older people are in the majority. Nearly every county during the decade 1950-1960 statistically lost one to two per cent of the population in the 25-34 age

Fig. 89. Counties growing above national rate: 1. 1940-1960; 2. 1950-1960; 3. 1940-1950.

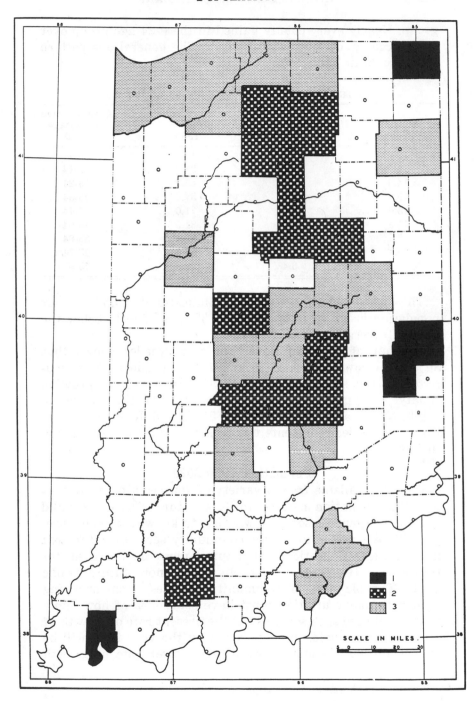

group. Nearly every county gained in the 0-24 age group over the preceding decade (1940-1950)). The general age pattern is as shown in Table 22.

TABLE 22. Age Distribution Patterns of Indiana

| Age Group | Percentage of Population 1950 | 1960 | Accumulative Percentage 1960 |
|---|---|---|---|
| 10.7 | 11.6 | 11.6 | 0-4 |
| 16.0 | 20.1 | 31.7 | 5-14 |
| 14.5 | 13.5 | 45.2 | 15-24 |
| 15.6 | 12.7 | 57.9 | 25-34 |
| 13.6 | 13.7 | 71.0 | 35-44 |
| 11.3 | 10.9 | 81.9 | 45-54 |
| 9.1 | 8.5 | 90.4 | 55-64 |
| 6.1 | 6.1 | 96.5 | 65-74 |
| 3.1 | 3.4 | 99.9 | 75 + |

The age distribution study also indicates that 45% of our population is 24 years or younger. This is slightly below the national average of nearly 50%.

A count of recorded losses for two decades shows that 30% are below the age of 25 and 73% are under 55 as compared to the states record of 81.9%. In a rapidly growing county, as typified by Hendricks, 47.9% of the population are below 25 and 85% are under 55. The difference between the two counties represents the greatest extremes to be found in Indiana.

### Population, 1970-2020

Reports available from a variety of sources attempt to predict the population pattern for the future. There are valid and even urgent reasons for wanting to know how many people will be expected to use the community services in the next five decades. Educational structures must be designed for future use. Highway builders have to know future traffic needs. The planners of community services, from shopping centers to public utilities, must have some idea of how many people will need such services. At the present rate of growth of the state as a whole, the population by the year 2000 will be over 8,000,000. Estimates based on a lower rate of growth

Fig. 90. Urban versus rural population.

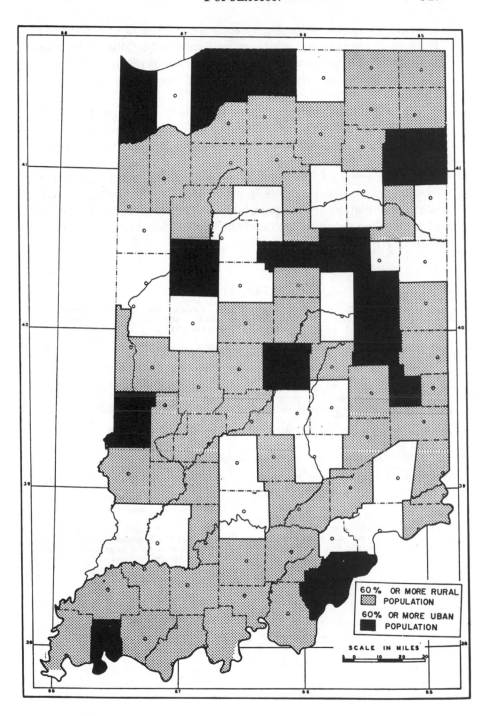

60% OR MORE RURAL POPULATION

60% OR MORE UBAN POPULATION

SCALE IN MILES
5 0 10 20 30

comparable to the 1930-1940 decade set the figure at 5,200,000. Even if there was an arbitrary midpoint of 6,600,000 by the year 2000, it represents almost 2,000,000 more people in about 40 years for whom resources and services must be provided.

The population pattern would probably increase its trend to urbanization in the present urban or near urban sites. By the year 2000, Indianapolis would have a population of about two million.

The geographer has to deal with a great many variables in attempting such predictions which could bring about changes for more or less population, depending upon the point of view. One thing is certain, the writer for the second centennial will know.

## LITERATURE

1.  BARNHART, J. D. and CARMONY, D. F. 1954. Indiana from frontier to industrial commonwealth. New York: Lewis Historical Publishing Co., Inc., Vol. 2.
2.  VAN BOLT, R. H. "The Indiana scene in the 1840's." Indiana Magazine of History. Vol. 47. p. 336-354.
3.  VISHER, S. S. "Population changes in Indiana 1840-1940." Indiana Acad. Sci. Proceedings. Vol. 51. p. 179-193.
4.  GENTILCORE, R. L. "Curves of population change in Indiana 1850-1940." Indiana Acad. of Sci. Proceedings. Vol. 62: 272-276.
5.  BARTON, T. F. "Notes on size, distribution, and growth of Indiana cities." Indiana Acad. of Sci. Proceedings. Vol. 58 p. 222-224.
6.  HART, J. F. "Migration and population change in Indiana." Indiana Acad. of Sci. Proceedings. Vol. 66. p. 195-203.
    HART, J. F. "Rural population density in Indiana." Indiana Acad. of Sci. Proceedings. Vol. 68: 218-224.
7.  U. S. BUREAU OF THE CENSUS. Washington 25, D. C.; Government Printing Office. For purpose of this paper, the complete listing is eliminated of each census report.
8.  INDIANA STATE BOARD OF HEALTH 1962. County population reports 1950-1960. Mimeographed. Indianapolis Railways, Inc.
9.  BARTHOLOMEW, HARLAND, et. al. 1945. A preliminary report upon the growth and distribution of population for Indianapolis, Indiana, and environs. Mimeographed. Indianapolis Railways, Inc.
10. CORPS OF ENGINEERS. Economic base projections by County 1970-2020, Population, labor force, and employment. Louisville: U. S. Army Engineers, January 1966.
11. EATON, MERRILL, ANN BEEMAN, and N. PHILIP. Patterns of pupil migration. Indiana Department of Public Instruction. Vol. 3, #3. March 1956.

# 31

## *Forestry*

W. C. BRAMBLE and F. T. MILLER
Purdue University

As seen by early French explorers, the great forests sprawling from the lower tip of Lake Michigan, far southward to the Ohio River, were a magnificent yet forbidding wilderness of giant hardwoods. True, White Pine and an unusual variety of other plant life flourished in the sand dunes area of the north. Tamarack, hemlock, red cedar, Virginia pine, and bald cypress were found in other locations from north to south. However, with the exception of these areas, plus the more extensive prairies and sloughs of the north, scattered meadows and Indian clearings along the Wabash, the great hardwoods dominated and overwhelmed as far as the eye could reach. It was later estimated these forests covered nearly 20 million acres of what is now Indiana.

Following the fall of British-controlled Vincennes (Fort Sackville) to the American General George Rogers Clark in 1779, the American pioneer treked farther into the territory. Now this was his land. He was hungry for a new life and rich soil to till. As isolated settlements sprang up, the great trees began to fall. After simple construction needs were met the remaining forest giants remained a barrier, comparable to the hostile Indians. Hundreds were felled, rolled into the closest ravine and burned, to make way for the plow. Nature's abundance did not yield easily. The dates of birth and death seen today on tottering gravestones attest to the harsh life of our ancestors. Entire families were wiped out within the span of one or two short years, stricken with fevers and other ills, for which there was little or no medical aid. In many cases the pioneer cleared the ridges and high ground first to remove the family from the mosquitoes and fevers of the swamps and lowlands. Many of our first soil erosion problems occurred on these steep uplands.

The Shawnee massacre of the Pigeon Roost Settlement in 1812, just 25 miles north of the Ohio is further evidence of common hardships faced. A monument to these pioneers of

Pigeon Roost may be seen just a few miles north of the present Clark State Forest.

Despite such hardships the pioneers persisted, and as the Indian slowly retreated, the great trees continued to fall and Indiana became a state of the Union in 1816. Located first at Corydon, near the Ohio, the new capital was to be moved in 1825 to a small, centrally located, Fall Creek settlement and named Indianapolis.

The difficulty of clearing land is evidenced by early geologic survey reports. These surveys gave documented reports of tree measurements carefully made. Trees of from five, up to twelve feet and more in diameter at three feet above the ground were not uncommon. One tulip tree in the Wabash Valley measured one hundred and ninety feet tall, twenty-five feet in circumference at three feet above the ground, and ninety-one feet to the first limb. Forty-two species of hardwoods in the Wabash Valley were reported to have reached a height of one hundred and fifty feet or more. A few remnants of this once mighty forest are now to be seen only in small areas protected by law and in a few isolated private ownerships, held by one family for several generations.

### The Early Timber Industry

Although lumber production in Indiana was not reported in the U. S. Census of 1820, we know that crude water-powered mills slowy and laboriously produced rough lumber to some extent. For example, the historical records of Jennings County reveal that the Blankenship mill sawed 250 feet of lumber per day by means of a water-powered sash saw.

During this period and later, large log rafts were a common sight on Indiana's major rivers during the spring of the year. Loading produce such as lard and salted pork on these rafts, pioneers made the long float to New Orleans. There they traded or sold their produce, and the log rafts were broken up and sold for European timber export. It is reported that many pioneers paid for their new land with the proceeds from these log sales. Some of these pioneers walked all the way back to Indiana if boats or horses were not available.

By 1837 wild land speculation had plunged the new state into bankruptcy with a debt of 14 million dollars. As Indiana regained its balance, new roads and canals were to contribute to increased trade and expansion of industry. The use of choice native timber supported expansion and was an early source of wealth.

The U. S. Census of 1840 reported 1,248 sawmills operating in Indiana. The lumber produced was valued at $420,791. Thirty-seven lumber yards were listed with a capital value of $90,000. Furniture and carriage production was valued at $374,000. This was no doubt a period of great expansion in the uses and trade of timber. However, demand for new farm land continued to speed the clearing of timber which could not be used. Much of it was still burned to make way for the plow. The areas where lumber production flourished were largely near rivers, canals and new roads. By 1849 the value of lumber produced in Indiana was $2,195,551.

With the advent of steam-powered sawmills and the expansion of railroads, the lumber industry expanded tremendously. With only 29 more mills reported in 1860 than in 1840, the Census reveals lumber production was valued at $4,271,600. The cost of raw materials was reported at $1,688,386. and capital investment in the industry was $2,482,900. A work force of 3,430 men was employed. Fifteen planing mills, two hundred furniture establishments, 134 wagon firms and two veneer firms were employing 1,391 persons and manufacturing products valued at $1,322,420. By 1869 total annual lumber production in Indiana was reported at 656 million board feet. The Civil War had increased timber use and domestic demand increased continually.

In the year 1870 the acreage of virgin timber remaining in Indiana was estimated to have dropped to 7,189,000 acres. Good trees reportedly sold for $100. each in Rush County, and timbered land in the county had a higher sale value than cleared land. This was then, and remains today, some of the richest farmland in Indiana.

### Early Concern over Forest Conservation

In 1879 the census reported 918 million board feet of lumber produced in Indiana. Of this, 52 million board feet was reported to be white and yellow pine. It is assumed the white pine was in the extreme north portion of the state and the Virginia pine was in the southern knobs region. In some early reports Virginia pine was erroneously identified as the more southern shortleaf pine.

The period 1880 to 1900 saw 2,604,000 acres cleared but

only 1,174,000 acres entered into cultivation. Timber acreage was estimated to have dropped from 4,335,000 acres to 1,500,-000 acres, again apparently referring to virgin stands. Second growth timber was often thought of as brush and, unfortunately, this same idea prevails yet in certain areas. Mass clearing had visibly affected stream flow. Wildlife was disappearing to an alarming degree. The white tail deer was gone. The passenger pigeon was gone from Indiana.

In the year 1899, Indiana led the nation with a lumber production of 1,036,999,000 board feet. Of this, only slightly over 5,000,000 board feet was pine. In a period of slightly over 50 years the great forests has been reduced to sad remnants and some of the finest hardwoods in the world were gone.

### Beginning of Forestry

It is ironic that forestry legislation, when it came, was faulty and unworkable. House Bill No. 436 was passed by the Indiana General Assembly on March 8, 1899. Becoming law without the Governor's signature, the Act provided for tax relief for certain specified woodland acreages and conditions. Up to one-eighth of any one individual's woodland could qualify if it met certain specifications of density. Protection from livestock was required until the trees were four inches in diameter. Not more than one-fifth of the trees could be harvested in any one year, and a tree must be planted for each one cut. County officials were responsible for recording and checking compliance.

During the same year, Sam Burkholder of Crawfordsville initiated a program to organize an Indiana Hardwood Lumberman's Association. This was later to develop into a strong progressive group, effective today in improving the industry and in encouraging forestry education and legislation.

House Bill No. 192 of the Indiana General Assembly passed on March 4, 1901, provided that a five-man, State Board of Forestry be appointed immediately by the Governor. The first board was composed of Dean Stanley Coulter of Purdue University, Arthur Lieber, W. H. Freeman, F. C. Carson and John Cochran.

State legislation of March, 1903, provided for the purchase and establishment of the first State Forest Reservation. A section of 2,000 acres in the rugged Clark County knobs area near Henryville, Indiana, was purchased that year. Portions of the reserve were from the original grant of land made to General George Rogers Clark, his officers and men, for their services in the War of Independence. The reservation became the early scene of field investigations in the reforestation of hardwood species. The State Board published results of early plantings and information on botany, woodland management and marketing.

State legislation in 1905 provided a penalty for setting fire to the woodland of another, or for placing fire on one's own land and carelessly permitting it to spread to the woodland of another. This law with a rather inadequate penalty has remained unchanged despite many efforts to strengthen it.

During the same year the State Board of Forestry reported repeal of the Act of 1899, this piece of legislation having proved unworkable.

Long to be remembered was the appointment of Charles C. Deam as first State Forester of Indiana and Secretary of the State Board of Forestry in 1909. An untiring and talented botanist, Deam initiated the first extensive field investigations in reforestation on the Clark State Forest Reservation at Henryville, Indiana. His continuous trials of native hardwood species, along with meticulous record-keeping convinced him within a few years that the native hardwoods were not successful in reclaiming wornout land or in producing a quality product on such soil. His experiments in the use of conifers starting in 1912 soon convinced him of their value, and extensive plantings of conifers have continued since that time.

### Development of Forestry Instruction

With a budding state forestry program in Indiana, evidence was increasing that forestry research and instruction was needed at a professional level. Stanley Coulter, Dean of the Purdue University School of Science, was instrumental in fulfilling this need. Beginning in 1905 courses in forestry were taught by him as biology courses with forestry titles. By 1913, ten forestry courses were listed in the University Catalogue under biology by which "the student may fit himself for practical work."

A letter from Coulter arrived by stage at a remote outpost in Montana one day in the summer of 1914. Since there was no box for the deposit of mail, it was tucked in a crevice of a tree stump, with the hope that it would be found. Fortunately, Burr N. Prentice, in charge of a U. S. Forest Service party working in the area found the letter which was addressed to him. As a result, Prentice came to Purdue in the fall with a background in Forest Service work and an advanced degree from the New York College of Forestry. He was first assigned to the staff of the School of Science, and gave the first professional instruction in forestry in Indiana.

Forestry instruction remained in the School of Science from 1914 to 1926 when it was transferred to the School of Agriculture as a Department and made a part of the Agricultural Experiment Station. Wildlife Conservation was added in 1934 upon transfer from Biology, and Conservation Education added in 1945, to form the Department of Forestry and Conservation which exists today.

In 1942, the Department was accredited by the Society of American Foresters and remains as one of the 28 accredited "schools" in the United States. This meant that it has been recognized by that professional body as being fully capable of offering complete training in forestry at an acceptable level with strong supporting sciences. The Department was reaccredited in 1961 by the Society Committee for Advancement of Forestry Education after a periodic reexamination.

## Development of Forestry Research

Basic to development of forestry in Indiana has been the research program which began in the early years and continued to develop as forestry progressed. Stanley Coulter, a pioneer in Indiana forestry, published a series of 15 papers on forestry from 1891 through 1926 in the Proceedings of the Indiana Academy. Major interest at this time lay in the need for reforestation and tree growth rates.

When in 1926, the Department at Purdue was transferred to Agriculture, research in forestry came under the Experiment Station at the University where it remains today. In the 1930's, research concentrated upon nursery management and the effects of cattle grazing on woodlands. Daniel DenUyl and others detailed the destructive effects of woodland grazing and the low quality of pasture afforded by farm woods. Indiana became a leader in this area of research in the country.

Also in those first years, research was begun on timber management of small woodlands. This has been continued through to today when the results of a long-term study of costs and return from 50 small woodlands has been summarized to show that between 4-5 per cent returns have been realized on the investments involved. In recent years, research in this area has led to development of programming forest management using the digital computer. As forest management deals with complex biological and economic systems, such a tool is proving invaluable to the forest manager.

One of the outstanding contributions of Indiana in forest measurements was development of the Purdue hardwood log grades from 1946 to 1958. These were the first useable hardwood tree grading systems to be developed in the United States and permitted evaluation of standing timber for sale and management. In the early 1960's, outstanding mensuration research was done on the use of cruising prisms in point sampling for measuring volumes of standing timber. In this work, a special Purdue Point Sampling Block was developed.

In the area of reforestation, Indiana has been instrumental in developing successful reclamation of strip-mined lands. Research has indicated that the way to reintroduce hardwoods on old fields is to plant pines; hardwoods have proven most successful and tend to replace planted conifers by invasion on spoil banks.

Indiana has long been a leader in research on wood beginning in 1902. Following outstanding studies on wood anatomy and properties, in the late 1950's, a structural research program produced outstanding results. These include contributions to development of a nail-glued roof truss which were quickly put into use by industry. Also of special value was the development of critically needed mathematical solutions for calculating stresses in wood trusses for use in light construction.

In the area of forest products marketing and economics, Indiana has long been a leader in selected areas. Marketing of hardwood products has been studied since 1928 and analyses have been made of wood-using industries of the state. Timber price reports have been issued continuously since 1938. Other economic aspects of Indiana forestry have been studied in the area of forest management which have produced insight into small woodland management including the cost-returns study mentioned earlier. In recent years, the economics of outdoor recreation have been studied to learn more of the needs and problems of private enterprise.

## Early Development of The Department of Conservation

By Act of the 71st General Assembly, the Indiana Department of Conservation was created in 1919, with Col. Richard Lieber as its first director. The Divisions of Entomology, Geology, Fish and Game, Forestry and Lands and Waters became parts of a unified program of conservation.

By this time Indiana had dropped to 13th place nationally in hardwood lumber production. However, capital investment in Hoosier wood-using industries was about one sixth of the total capital investment of all industries of the state, with 70,000 persons employed. Lumber production in 1919 was reported as 282,487,000 board feet in Indiana. Great amounts of Indiana walnut had gone into World War I gun stocks, along with much other hardwood lumber for ship timbers, aircraft propellers, and other war uses.

With increased awareness of forestry problems, the Indiana General Assembly of 1921 passed the Forest Tax Classification Act. The Act offered a very low tax for woodland owners who would, under written agreement with the State Forester, enter a basic program of forest protection. No limit was set on the amount of land entered as was stipulated in the Act of 1899. Recognizing that forests would perpetuate themselves under livestock and fire protection and normal harvesting operations, no harvesting regulations were attached to the Act. State Foresters were required to inspect and approve lands entered, and to periodically check compliance and advise on timber management. The assessed valuation of land approved was $1.00 per acre. Provision was also made for entry of open land, with a requirement that it be reforested within three years. This Act has remained unchanged, except for an amendment simplifying surveying and mapping methods. A unique program among all the states, it has passed the test of time very well.

In 1925, State Senator Oliver LaFuse of Liberty, Indiana, a champion of the Forest Classification Act, sponsored new legislation which was to bear his name. The LaFuse Act, passed during the year, provided a forestry tax of one half mill on each one hundred dollars of taxable valuation. Forestry was no longer a stepchild, supported only by periodic allotments from the General Fund.

By 1932, Indiana under State Forester Ralph H. Wilcox had

five state forests in operation comprising some 25,000 acres
and had expanded all other state forestry programs. Under the
Federal Clarke-McNary Act, the U. S. Forest Service was aiding in the development of a more effective fire protection
program. Still plagued by a lack of funds, State Forester
Wilcox and George W. Freeman of the Indiana General Assembly flew over sections of southern Indiana in 1929 search-
ing for more evidence to support their claims. Five large forest
fires were sighted and eroded waste lands were seldom out of
sight. During the following session of the General Assembly
the 2-mill, forestry tax was amended to allow funds for protection of private as well as state lands.

### Forestry Extension

As management of public forests developed, a need was
seen for also improving the management of small private
woodlands which by far exceeded the acreage in other ownerships. The first move in this direction was made in 1930
when, with the aid of funds from the federal Clark-McNary
Act, Thomas E. Shaw was employed as Indiana's first extension forester. Among other activities, Shaw produced a popular weekly radio program on which he appeared as "Uncle
Ted." He also revised Dean's, "Trees of Indiana" which remains as the official book on the state's trees. Later, Shaw
published a bulletin, "Fifty Trees of Indiana," which is the
only elementary field manual available on Indiana tree identification.

In 1945-6, the work of forestry extension was divided into
four districts with a forester headquartered in each. This
highly successful system is continued today with five districts
covering the state and furnishing local sources of assistance
to landowners. It also has enabled a youth program in 4-H
forestry and wildlife to grow from 1,763 projects in 1945 to
over 15,000 in 1965.

Outstanding activities in forestry extension beginning in
those early years included the demonstration woods program
begun in 1947. Not only do these woods provide show pieces of
forest management but also furnish valuable information on
the annual costs and returns to be expected from private
woodlands.

Another successful activity has been the annual Farm Boys
Forestry Camp, sponsored by the Indiana Hardwood Lumber-

man's Association since 1950. And a similar program in 4-H Conservation Camps handles about 200 campers annually.

Increased activity in meetings and short courses involving wood-using industries led to the addition of an extension specialist in wood utilization in 1960. Headquartered in the Wood Research Laboratory, extension work in this area has been concentrated upon architectural uses of wood and problems of secondary industries that use wood in manufacture.

While not yet completely covering the areas in conservation needing educational assistance, the forestry extension program has become one of the finest in the country. It has set an organizational pattern which has been unusual and highly successful. New uses of land for Christmas tree growing have been stimulated and guided and older uses of forest, such as maple syrup production have been given new life. The indirect effect of extension upon public forestry agencies has been considerable and it has been a stable force for better forest conservation in Indiana.

### Coal Land Reclamation

During the massive conservation movements of the thirties, it was to be expected that open cut coal mining with its attendant upturning of thousands of acres of land, would draw added attention. The Indiana Coal Producers Association was well into reforestation by 1926, but the over-all problem not under direct jurisdiction of this group increased each year.

Legislation of 1941 produced an Act for Regulation of Strip Coal Mining. The Indiana Farm Bureau and the Indiana Coal Producers Association worked closely with the Indiana Department of Conservation in advising the General Assembly concerning this legislation. The new law, in brief, required all open cut mine companies to reforest or revegetate denuded areas, to plant annually an area equal to the amount stripped each year, plus a percentage for area of land stripped in the past. A forester was employed in the Indiana Department of Conservation to advise recommended practices and to check compliance. In 1951 and 1963 the Act was amended slightly to require a limited amount of leveling. Today the Act also involves open cut Clay Mines and Shale Mines.

Progress in surface mine reclamation in Indiana has been considerable with the coal producers and the Department of Conservation acting in cooperation under the state law. By

1964, 62,171 acres had been reforested and 6,921 acres seeded. Of these reclaimed acres, 20,568 acres had been put to special uses such as state forests, recreation areas and private home-sites. One of the more important effects of mining has been the creation of 9,476 acres in small lakes which offer a valuable potential resource for recreational use and for local water supply.

## Further Progress in State Forestry

Thomas E. Shaw, State Extension Forester of Indiana, answered the request of the Indiana Department of Conservation and became Acting State Forester for the duration of World War II. With strong support from Governor Henry Schricker and Conservation Director Hugh Barnhart, Shaw did a remarkable job of what he termed "holding the line."

Timber sales on state forests increased sharply. Christmas tree sales added to income and state forest acreage increased by some 6,300 acres. For the first time in many years, all Classified Forests were re-inspected and 6,100 acres of additional privately owned woodlands were entered in this program. Improved nursery operations and grading practices were instituted in cooperation with the Purdue University Forestry Department and the Soil Conservation Service.

In cooperation with the U. S. Forest Service, special fire wardens were trained, equipped and made responsible for forest fire protection in areas surrounding large defense installations. This aided in later establishment of full-time county fire wardens in critical fire areas.

A long range forestry plan for Indiana was prepared by Division Foresters and Purdue Forestry Department staff members. Shaw listed this as one of the major accomplishments of fiscal year 1944.

With the end of World War II, Acting State Forester "Ted" Shaw was soon to return to Purdue University. He worked diligently for an orderly change in leadership. Shaw encouraged the re-employment of Ralph F. Wilcox as State Forester, to assure experienced professional leadership. Wilcox accepted the position as he returned from service in the Army Air Corps.

Aided by the passage of additional revenue legislation in 1945, raising the forestry tax to five mills, Wilcox initiated a greatly expanded state program, backed by Governor Ralph

Gates and Conservation Director Milton Matter. Matter favored professionally trained men in conservation and attempted to move more of them into key positions.

With this backing, Wilcox established ten forestry districts throughout the state. Two of the new districts were soon designated as Farm Forestry Districts, with the aid of Norris-Doxey funds, administered by the U. S. Forest Service. The first Farm Forestry District in the United States had been established at Madison, Indiana in 1939, under U. S. Soil Conservation Service direction. With much smaller work areas than in the past, district foresters for the first time, were able to give quick attention to requests for woodland assistance on privately owned lands.

### Postwar Forest Service Activities

After World War II, land acquisition increased greatly in Indiana's Purchase Units of the U. S. Forest Service which had been approved in 1935. Under the able administration of Supervisor Rudolph Grabow, well-developed forest management plans were beginning to yield profit in numerous timber sales, beneficial to both local communities and the state. Reforestation of Forest Service open lands expanded greatly, aided by increased production from the Forest Service Tree Nursery at Vallonia, Indiana. Fire protection organization and equipment was improved to a great extent. Near the end of the war, public-spirited citizens and organizations were working to preserve an unique tract of virgin timber near Paoli, Indiana. Rudolph Grabow was very active in this movement and responsible for creating much public interest in the project. Fifty percent of the purchase price of this area was contributed by the citizens and groups interested.

Approved by the Acting Chief of the U. S. Forest Service, L. F. Kneipp, on January 21, 1944, the 88 acre Cox woods was acquired and designated as the Pioneer Mother's Memorial. Thus was preserved one of the last vestiges of the virgin Indiana forest. Its scientific and esthetic values are great, and it serves to associate the presettlement-type forest with the courageous women who first helped to establish homes and families in the wilderness.

By order of the Secretary of Agriculture, October 1, 1951 the four purchase units of the U. S. Forest Service in Indiana, were declared the Hoosier National Forest.

The Forest has expanded sales of mature timber, to the financial advantage of many local communities. In 1959 about 65 sales were made totalling 3.2 million board feet. Many of the sales were made to local farmers who are part-time loggers. In 1964 timber harvested amounted to 4.6 million board feet. The direct return to the state and county governments in lieu of taxes in the areas harvested amounted to $9,690.00 in fiscal year 1964. The over-all returns involved in logging, milling and processing amount to many times this amount every year to the benefit of local communities. These forest lands will produce increasing timber volume and financial returns under present management plans.

Reforestation of eroded lands now involves the planting of about 1,000 acres per year. Thinnings from earlier pine plantings provide stumpage sales of posts and poles. This adds to the growth of remaining trees and adds to volume growth to provide more profitable future harvests.

Under the recent Accelerated Public Works Program, work already planned was given a great boost in programs for which no regular funds were available. Aside from increasing the extent of regular activities such as reforestation and timber stand improvement of some 7,741 acres, recreation was benefited by the establishment of 81 camping and picnicking units. Many fishing ponds and wildlife areas, combined with other recreation areas, have contributed substantially to the great need of Hoosiers for more room to enjoy the out-of-doors. In 1964 some 196,000 visits were made to the Hoosier National Forest by the public.

### Recent Developments in State Forestry

With the employment of Robert D. Raisch as State Forester in 1962, the Indiana Division was soon to recover from previous reverses, and expand even beyond the program of 1946 to 1953. A new era of professionalism developed as well-qualified forestry graduates were recruited to expand both the district and state forest management program.

Under Executive order of Governor Matthew Welsh a merit system was placed in effect in 1962 requiring competitive examinations for all division foresters. This move has helped attract many fine young professional foresters both from Indiana and elsewhere in the United States. The morale and level of performance have been raised considerably to provide better management of Indiana's forest resources.

State Forests of Indiana now include 126,288 acres in thirteen state properties. Under sound management plans they yield increasing profits in timber sales, soil and water conservation and the rapidly expanding field of recreation.

Recreation development has been expanded by the development of new camp grounds, picnic areas, and swimming and boating activities on Indiana State Forests.

State Tree nurseries distributed 5,545,175 seedlings during the spring of 1964.

Division foresters are also engaged in cooperative work with the U. S. Soil Conservation Service and Purdue University in The Rural Conservation and Development program of the U. S. Department of Agriculture. Present plans include employment of foresters to aid in the forestry development of the U. S. Soil Conservation Service Small Watershed Programs.

The privately owned classified Forests of Indiana, adminstered by the State Division of Forestry, now constitutes 243,000 acres of woodland divided among 4,059 owners. This program continues to expand and encourage woodland owners in improved long range management. Considerable thought has been given to possible legislation which might raise the required standards of management on these areas, beyond the protection required, since the law's inception in 1921.

Effective July 1st, 1965, under the leadership of Director John Mitchell the Department of National Resources was created by House Bill 1666, re-organizing the Department of Conservation. The new department consists of a 12-man, bipartisan commission, served by two major bureaus, The Bureau of Land, Forest and Wildlife Resources and the Bureau of Water and Mineral Resources. Each Bureau is served by a twelve-member, bi-partisan advisory council, and the chairman of each sits upon the State Resources Commission. The future for Indiana forestry looks bright indeed.

# 32

# *State Parks*

HOWARD H. MICHAUD

Purdue University

## History of the Indiana State Parks

In this sesquicentennial year for Indiana, 1966, it is significant that the state park system is celebrating its fiftieth anniversary. In 1915, Honorable Samuel M. Ralston, Governor of Indiana, appointed a State Park Commission and in 1916 they took over two tracts of land on behalf of the state of Indiana, "the Canyon of McCormick's Creek" and "Turkey Run".

This marked the beginning of state parks for Indiana. McCormick's Creek Canyon State Park was purchased jointly by the people of Owen County and the State from the estate of Dr. Frederick Denkewalter. However, the acquisition of Turkey Run represented a rather bitter first engagement and was won only because of the plodding of a group of men and women whose heroic efforts served to inaugurate a new epoch toward the conservation of the unique scenic areas of the state.

In 1915, a small but determined group, composed of Colonel Richard Lieber, Juliette Strauss, Dr. Frank B. Wynn, Sol S. Kiser and Leo Rappaport, conceived the idea of raising funds to be used for the purchase of Turkey Run and to present the property to the state of Indiana the following year as a centennial gift. The estate, it was known, was in the process of settlement and would be offered at public auction the following spring. After considerable effort, the committee was successful in raising $20,000.

The auction was conducted in April, 1916. Lumber dealers had been requested to withhold bidding. The committee felt that they had a clear course and that they should have sufficient funds to pay for the property. However, such was not the case, and after spirited bidding, the property was sold for $30,200 to an individual representing a lumber company whose interests were solely in the commercial value of the timber.

Undaunted, the committee began immediate negotiations

with the purchaser, who offered to surrender it if the valuable virgin timber could first be removed. The offer was naturally rejected. Later, the company offered to sell the property intact, at an advance of $10,000.

The committee set to work immediately to raise more funds. In October, 1916, it succeeded in interesting Mr. Carl Fischer to spend a day visiting the area. Mr. Fischer was tremendously impressed and made a very generous offer to donate $5,000. Furthermore, he was successful later as a member of the Board of Directors of the Indianapolis Motor Speedway, to persuade them to contribute ten percent of the proceeds of the next Memorial Day Race. Also, Mr. Arthur Newby, another member of the Board of Directors, made a personal contribution of $5,000.

With these funds and an appropriation of the General Assembly of 1917, the committee was able to complete negotiations for the purchase of the area and on November 11, 1916, signed the papers for 288 acres, which constituted the original tract at Turkey Run State Park.

The original agitation for setting aside state parks was part of a national movement. Stephen T. Mather, Director of the National Park Service, 1915 - 1928, was under pressure from many quarters to endorse areas for national parks. But he favored areas only that were large, primitive, and unique enough to be of national significance. It was largely due to the agitation for national parks that Mather promoted the development of state parks. It was through the organization of the National Parks Conference that he became acquainted with many state leaders who were prominent in the state park movement.

Indiana was fortunate in having farsighted leaders among its citizens who willingly devoted time and energy toward setting aside some of the relatively untouched scenic areas of the state for the future enjoyment of its people. Edward Barrett, State Geologist, in the annual report of the Indiana Department of Geology in 1916, reported that he had been advocating the preservation of natural areas for state parks for more than six years. Dean Stanley Coulter, eminent scientist and Dean of the School of Science at Purdue University, was a member of the first Conservation Commission appointed in 1919. In an address to the Ohio Valley Regional

Conference on State Parks at Clifty Falls in 1925, he said:

> Whether it was wrought out by abstract reasoning, or was a feat by intuition, or sounded deep in some primal instinct, the park system, State and National, was inaugurated; and soon, startlingly soon indeed, we began to realize that scenery—our rivers and lakes, our hills and mountains, our fertile plains and forests, our peaks of privilege, whence we could see great vistas and glowing sunsets and myriad stars—is our greatest natural resource.

Colonel Richard Lieber, first director of the Indiana Department of Conservation, in an address delivered to the Ohio Valley Conference, Wheeling, West Virginia in 1928, defined a state park as "a typical portion of the state's original domain; a tract of adequate size, preserved in primeval, unspoilt, 'unimproved', or 'beautified' condition. It is a physical expression of life, liberty and the pursuit of happiness".

"A state park must have either scenic or historic value or both, — and is dedicated to the public for the intelligent use of its leisure time".

These statements by prominent persons associated with the early development of Indiana State Parks were largely responsible for the policies that have governed their administration through the years.

The second phase of park expansion was instituted under a long-range program outlined by Charles A. DeTurk, Director of State Parks in 1944. The plan suggested that it was highly probable that the state parks of the future would follow the pattern set by the previous 28 years of experience in managing the parks. It further emphasized and re-affirmed the standards applicable to the establishment and development of new areas. These were:

1. To preserve and protect for present and future generations areas of the finest remaining, natural, unspoiled scenery of the state.

2. To provide outdoor recreation—opportunity for the public to enjoy, use and live for a while upon the land that is, in the truest sense, their own.

3. To preserve or commemorate some of the state's historical background, or some of its people whose lives have affected the history or culture of the state. It was intended in this way to create respect and pride in the state, as well as, to provide encouragement and inspiration to future generations.

In order to follow the standards set forth in the plan, it was necessary to recognize first, that the prominent scenic or historic sites had to be acquired where they existed, regardless of geographic location. Secondly, true recreation areas had to be planned with geographic and population factors as paramount considerations. Consequently, if the plan was to be based on these premises, it was important to give careful consideration to the natural features of the state which could meet the necessary requirements. The following is a brief resume of that portion of the plan which suggested special areas that should receive attention:

1. To determine the prominent scenic areas available that would include representative Hoosier geographical and physical types of landscape that should be preserved. It was suggested that all areas to be considered should be at least 1,000 acres in extent and should be surrounded by buffer strips for protection in which good forestry and wildlife practices could be maintained. Suggested areas included:

    a. An unspoiled natural lake area in north central Indiana.

    b. Fifty to one hundred miles of outstanding Indiana waterways, including both banks and sufficient acreage to constitute an administrative unit. Rivers mentioned were the Tippecanoe, Mississinewa, Wabash, Whitewater and Sugar Creek.

    c. An area in the upland, glaciated, gently rolling land between Fort Wayne and Richmond east of Indianapolis.

    d. An area on the bluffs of the lower Wabash River, preferably in connection with the New Harmony Memorial.

    e. The superb hill and timberland and caves in the Wyandotte Cave area.

    f. One typical and natural prairie area in northwest Indiana in Lake, Newton, or Benton Counties.

2. To determine by geographical and population maps the need for recreational areas to better serve the Indiana public in its heavily populated centers. The plan visualized a state park located within easy driving range of every

community of the state. Population concentration centers mentioned included: the Calumet area, the South Bend area, the Logansport-Peru-Rochester area, the Fort Wayne area, the Lafayette area, the Marion-Muncie-Anderson area, the Indianapolis area, the Richmond area, the Evansville area, the Vincennes-Washington area, and the Louisville-New Albany-Jeffersonville area.

3. To determine the historical areas, buildings or communities that have a definite, significant and important effect in the progress and development of Indiana and its people which are in present or ultimate danger of destruction. Examples of state-wide significance were: the New Harmony Community; old canal systems such as the Whitewater and Wabash-Erie; residences of historical importance included the Gene Stratton Porter, James Whitcomb Riley, and William Henry Harrison homes; structures in Vincennes of the Indiana territory era; an original tavern, the Halfway House, on old pioneer road 40; the Bright Angel Mounds near Evansville, representing an area of outstanding Mound Builder culture; the Frances Slocum area as an example of Indian culture; and the development of a "Trading Post" center.

The remainder of the plan was devoted to a general development scheme that would provide facilities for access and use-areas to accommodate public enjoyment compatible with the objectives for properly preserving the natural, cultural, esthetic and historical values inherent in the properties.

Many of the proposals advocated in 1944 have been completed. Parks added since 1944 include Chain O'Lakes State Park (1960), Lieber State Park (1956), Raccoon Lake State Recreation Area (1961), Scales Lake State Beach (1951), Shades State Park (1947), Whitewater State Park (1947), Oubache State Recreation Area (1962), three recreation areas on the Monroe Reservoir (1965), and eight state memorials.

The third and current phase of state park development is a new ten year plan formulated for the Indiana Department of Natural Resources by the Vollmer Associates, Engineers and Landscape Architects. A master plan for acquisition and development has been proposed to meet the expanding needs for conservation and recreation for the years 1965 to 1975.

The state has been divided into seven arbitrarily selected

geographical regions as follows: northwest, northeast, west central, central, east central, southwest and southeast. Proposals for development in each region will include not only state parks, but state forests, game preserves and recreational lands that will become available, adjacent to the new flood control reservoirs that have been constructed by the Army Corps of Engineers.

The impact of the current ten year plan on parks and their development promises to be significant. Especially noteworthy are the proposals for increasing the acreage of each park and the reallocation of many existing facilities to relieve the ecological impact of recreation use on the quality of the park's valuable natural resources. The pressures of recreational use have expanded so that the orginal minimum of 1,000 acres to establish a park is no longer adequate. A new standard of a minimum of 3,000 acres has been set for the establishment of any new park or recreation area.

## The Unique Aspects of Indiana State Parks

Space does not permit a detailed account of the unique natural qualities of each state park. Many parks have special features of geology, history, topography, flora and fauna in common depending upon their relative locations. In order to organize the significant features of the parks geographically, they will be described under three headings, namely: (1) southern, (2) central, and (3) northern Indiana.

### Southern Indiana

Although the state park sites have been selected primarily for their scenic qualities and to distribute recreational opportunities to the people of all parts of the state, they furnish an interesting sequence of the geological outcroppings in the state. The oldest exposed rocks in geologic time are of the Ordovician period. The upper Ordovician, the Silurian and the base of the Devonian are strata included in the exposed rocks at Clifty Falls State Park. Versailles and Whitewater State Parks are underlain by the shales of the upper Ordovician group, although the strata are not so well exposed and part of the outcrops are covered by glacial deposits. Next in geological sequence is Muscatatuk State Park, which is located in strata of the Devonian age. It is in the Ordovician and Devonian rocks of Clifty Falls, Versailles and Muscatatuk

State Parks where the fossil remains of myriads of sea in-habiting creatures may be found. Large colonial forms of corals, horn corals, many species of brachiopods, bryozoa, cephalopods, and occasionally trilobites are present in the ex-posed rocks.

The sandstones and shales of the lower Mississippian age are of the Borden formation, extending from Floyd County north and west to Brown and eastern Monroe counties. This area was originally designated by the more descriptive term Knobstone. Brown County State Park includes exposed rocks of the Borden formation only.

The Harrodsburg, Salem, St. Louis and St. Genevieve are the four Mississippian limestone formations that lie above the Borden. It is among these limestones in south-central Indiana that solution from ground water has produced many caves, sinkholes and other forms of karst topography. Both Donald-son's Cave and Twin Caves at Spring Mill State Park are examples of large water-coursed caverns. The underground river flowing through the caves at Spring Mill offer park visitors the opportunity for a boat ride and the rare chance of seeing the unusual inhabitants of the stream—the blind fish (Amblyopsis) and crayfish, each of which are white and blind.

The numerous sinkholes, springs and small sinkhole caverns at *McCormick's Creek State Park* are evidence of the work of ground water. The St. Louis and St. Genevieve are the strata in both these parks that are especially subject to the formation of caves. The Salem, which lies below the St. Genevieve, is fairly soft and quite porous and permits water to percolate through easily so that it is not as readily dissolved. It is the source of the Indiana building limestone and an old quarry is located near the White River in McCormick's Creek State Park. The quarry is historically significant since it provided some of the stone used in the construction of the state capitol.

Geologists believe that most of the canyon at McCormick's Creek (Fig. 91) was formed in post-glacial time. The contin-ental glacier crossed the White River and invaded a portion of the Mitchell Plain a few miles east of Spencer. Drainage into the White River was dammed and a temporary lake was formed in the Flatwoods area. It is thought that post-glacial drainage of the Flatwoods lake began with underground drainage through the present canyon at McCormick's Creek. The combined action of solution, stream erosion and probably collapse of the cave roof was responsible for the canyon.

McCormick's Creek State Park encompasses a topographical variety of limestone canyons, wooded valleys and hillsides, beech and maple woods, about one hundred fifty acres of pine plantings, sinkholes and grassy meadows, which provide an interesting ecological environment. Over twenty species of ferns, seventy-five varieties of native trees and several hundred wildflowers may be found in the park. McCormick's Creek is especially well known for its profusion of early spring flowers.

Fig. 91. The Falls in the upper canyon at McCormick's Creek State Park. Photo, Indiana Department of Natural Resources.

*Shakamak State Park* lies on bedrock strata of the later Pennsylvanian period. This was the geologic period when an abundance of prehistoric plants grew along the shores of temperate inland seas and their remains contributed the important coal seams of southwestern Indiana. Shakamak is located in a rather flat area with not more than 85 feet of variation in elevation. Exposures of bedrock are not common, but some of the largest coal mines in the state are found within the vicinity of the park. At one place in the park there is an exhibit of an exposed coal mine.

Although the deciduous forest is common to all of Indiana, there is the usual distinction of forest types due to local factors of climate and topography. The higher, drier, well drained sites culminate in the oak-hickory forest type. In many southern Indiana counties there is an intermingling of species that are distinctly more typical of the south. A small grove of chestnut oak, the southern red oak, and yellow buckeye are unusual trees to be observed at Clifty Falls. In the upper poorly drained "crawfish flats" at Versailles State Park, the secondary successional forest of red maple—sweet gum is common. Left to flourish to climatic maturity, these forests will assume a more typical beech—maple climax.

The visitor to *Spring Mill State Park* is privileged to witness one of the few primeval forests of Indiana. That unique portion of approximately 200 acres of virgin forest called Donaldson's Woods, is one of the reasons Spring Mill became a park. Some of the splendid old monarchs of the forest, the tuliptree and white oak may be seen along Trail 3. Also, the full beauty of the American beech trees may be viewed along Trail 2.

The story of Spring Mill would be incomplete without a brief account of the fascinating history of the pioneer village in the park. In 1814, two years before Indiana was admitted to the Union, Ensign Samuel Jackson, retired from the Navy, turned toward the west in search of fortune and health from wounds he had received while serving with Perry in the battle of Lake Erie.

His voyage westward led him to the hill-sheltered cove known today as Spring Mill. With his family, Jackson erected a small cabin in the protected valley, set up a small log grist mill near the mouth of Hamer's Cave, carved a limestone quarry out of the rocky slopes and began commercial relations with the few families of the vicinity.

Jackson found the life of the wilderness difficult and somewhat frightening. Perhaps because of his love of the sea, or reasons not clear, in 1817 he sold his property to Cuthbert and Thomas Bullitt of Louisville, and returned to Pennsylvania.

The Bullitt brothers, known as the "merchants of Louisville", were the real developers of Spring Mill. They immediately employed stone masons, mechanics and carpenters to work on a larger mill with stone walls and an overshot waterwheel. The new mill was an immediate success and after seven years, it became a property of considerable value.

Following this period, the Spring Mill properties were sold to Joseph and William Montgomery of Philadelphia. Business continued to flourish and a tavern, distillery and several new homes were built.

On June 11, 1832, the village and mill were sold again to two brothers, millers by trade, named Hugh and Thomas Hamer. Much of the pioneer renown of the village was established during the proprietorship of the Hamers. Spring Mill became the center of the social life of the community, as well as maintaining its repute as a business center. The village grew into clusters of buildings protected by low walls of stone with wide lawns. The area between houses was transformed into gardens. Other pioneer industries were added on either side of the mill, including a loom house, a pottery shop, a cobbler's establishment, a hattery, a cabinet shop, an apothecary, a tannery and blacksmith shop, a lime kiln and a postoffice. A church and school were built, along with various residences. A boat yard was constructed on White River about a mile north of the village. Here flatboats were built to transport Spring Mill products to New Orleans.

The hey-dey of Spring Mill during the 1850's found stage coaches and carriages stopping for food and lodging at the tavern. Many prominent people visited the thriving village and there was no real let-up to the business activity until the advent of the Ohio and Mississippi railroad, now the Baltimore and Ohio, which established Mitchell's crossing in 1859 in what is now known as Mitchell.

Hugh Hamer tried to keep things going but the decline of the village was inevitable. Upon his death in 1872, the village was sold again to Jonathan Turley, who successfully operated the mill and distillery until sometime in the 80's. One by one the villagers abandoned the town, leaving its buildings and shops to the wind and the weather. The Lehigh-Portland Cement Company was the last private owner and they utilized the water from Hamer's Cave for the Mitchell Plant of the company. Through the generosity of this company, the site of Spring Mill Village and approximately 400 acres of the surrounding area was given to the state in 1927.

The village was restored by the state and today its shops and mills are open to visitors who may experience, for a short time, the atmosphere of pioneer life of more than 100 years ago in Indiana (Fig. 92).

Fig. 92. The mill, overshot waterwheel, and flume in the restored village at Spring Mill State Park. Photo, Indiana Department of Natural Resources.

*Brown County State Park* is the largest Indiana state park, covering more than 15,000 acres. It is famous as the home of "Abe Martin" and a pioneer atmosphere that has been an inspiration for artists since the turn of the century. The beauty of its fall coloration and the flowering attraction of early spring lures thousands of visitors during these seasons, but the scenic appeal of its quiet hills is always there. A wide variety of plant life thrives within the park and the roadways lined with oak, tuliptree, maple and sassafras are especially attractive in fall colors among its rolling, wooded hills.

*Lincoln State Park* which adjoins the Lincoln Boyhood National Memorial is located in Spencer County. The historical national memorial is significant for all Americans because it was here that Abraham Lincoln spent fourteen formative years. Most of the nature and outdoor recreation activities are centered about the 85 acre artificial lake and Camp Lincoln—the most modern group camp in the state park system.

### Central Indiana

The story of Turkey Run and the nearby Shades State Parks begins with the sedimentary sandstone formations of the Pennsylvanian system. Both parks contain deep cut gorges carved from the Mansfield formation at the base of the Pennsylvanian.

The canyons at *Turkey Run* reveal mostly coarse and often crossbedded sandstones of the Mansfield. There are some beds of shale and generally a thin bed of coal toward the base. Cross-bedding and ripple marks are considered evidence of the deposition of the Mansfield near or above sea level where waves and shifting currents operated. Following the deposition of the Mansfield sandstone, the great inland sea became shallow and was replaced gradually by numerous marshes. In these marshes, under a tropical climate, there developed a profusion of vegetation. Fossil remains of a rank carboniferous vegetation such as ferns, giant club mosses (Lepidodendron), Calamites and Sigillaria, with leaf scars of longitudinal rows help to reconstruct the life in these prehistoric marshes.

The Mansfield sandstone is massive and resists decomposition. Where post-glacial streams have cut valleys into the bedrock (Figs. 93-94), deep cliffs of sandstone rise almost vertically for 50 feet or more. In some places Turkey Run Hollow, along Trail 6, is not half as wide as it is deep. Many pot-holes, waterfalls, boulders and fallen rock are geological objects of interest in addition to the wooded, overhanging cliffs.

Due to the rare vision of those few who pioneered the park system in Indiana there are a few remnants of the forest primeval preserved at Turkey Run State Park. The largest tuliptree on Trail 6 measures more than 14 feet in circumference at four and one-half feet from the ground. Many other trees of large size, some measuring more than seven feet in circumference may be found along Trail 1, including the sycamore, black walnut and black cherry.

Fig. 93. A scenic trail along a sandstone canyon at the Shades State Park. Photo, Indiana Department of Natural Resources.

Most of the trees in the park are hardwoods, or "broad-leaved" trees, but the eastern helmock grows along the higher canyon rims along with the Canada yew, an evergreen shrub usually found growing beneath the hemlock.

There are many unique features that add particular distinction to the park such as the Lusk Homestead, the narrows of Sugar Creek, the covered bridge and the old mill site. These features are a part of the pioneer history associated with the names of Salmon Lusk, Polly Beard Lusk and John Lusk. The State Cabin, used as a small nature museum, was built by Daniel Gay about 1841 and moved to its present site in 1917. The old log church is located on the ridge above Turkey Run Hollow. It is a sample of a pioneer church used by Hoosiers in 1875. It was moved to the park in 1923.

The nearby *Shades State Park* of 2,640 acres includes one of the most picturesque regions of forests and canyons in the state. Large white oaks, gray-trunked beeches and evergreen hemlocks and white pines are prominent in its forests. In fall, the pageantry of color along Sugar Creek is enhanced by the brilliant reds of the black gum, red maple, dogwood and sumac.

Originally the area was called the "Shades of Death" in reference to the deep shadows beneath the heavy canopy of its forests and because of the pioneer's ingrained fear of the Indians lurking in the perpetual twilight. Shortly before the turn of the century, when the land was opened as a recreation spot, the name was shortened and made more attractive.

Among the many interesting features of the park are the "Devil's Punchbowl", a large circular grotto cut from solid sandstone by two small streams; "Silver Cascade" (Bridal Veil Falls), a nearly vertical cliff over which the waters of "Little Ranty Run" pour in glistening cataract; and "Inspiration Point" from which the panorama of the scenic valley of Sugar Creek unfolds 210 feet below.

On October 16, 1961, the *Pine Hills Natural Area* was added to the Shades State Park. The area was presented to the state by the Nature Conservancy to be preserved without artificial developments. The outstanding scenic attractions of the tract of approximately 600 acres are the four "backbones" — narrow ridges carved from solid rock, the persistent work of two meandering streams, Clifty Creek and Indian Creek. There are no comparable natural formations in the state. The backbones range from 70 to 125 feet in height and from 400 to 1,000 feet in length. The "Devil's Backbone" is over 100 feet high and at one point narrows to less than six feet in width. It is the most spectacular of the ridges and is often mistaken for a man-made structure. Five miles of clear streams flow a mean-

Fig. 94. A familiar trail among the sandstone outcroppings and overhanging trees along Sugar Creek at Turkey Run State Park. Photo, Indiana Department of Natural Resources.

dering course through the tract and pass by long stretches of overhanging cliffs and treacherous rock slides. (Plate 1.)

The area is of special botanical significance due to the groves of white pine and hemlock that clothe the backbones and terraces. These forests are considered to be the remnants of a far northern type of vegetation that covered Indiana several thousand years ago following the last advance of the late Wisconsin glaciation. The rare Canada yew and wintergreen occur in a few places beneath the groves of conifers.

The flatlands above the canyons include magnificent forests of sugar maple, beech, tuliptree, red and white oaks and many other hardwood trees. Redbud and dogwood form an attractive understory and a variety of ferns and wildflowers grow beneath them. Floodplain forests along the streams include sycamore, black walnut, Kentucky coffeetree, cottonwood and many other species.

### Northern Indiana

The geological features of the state parks of northern Indiana are of the Pleistocene, or Recent age. Each area is deeply covered by glacial drift. Pokagon, Indiana Dunes and Chain O'Lakes state parks are the most spectacular areas, but Tippecanoe, Bass Lake and Ouabache are also attractive park areas.

*Pokagon State Park* on Lake James is a good example of a region well covered by drift as much as 500 feet thick in some places, where lakes of glacial origin are abundant. Evidences of glaciation are abundantly present in moraines, kames, kettleholes, outwash deposits and erratic boulders. The three basins of Lake James, Bass Lake and the Chain O'Lakes are good examples of glacial lakes.

The rolling hills, forests and swamps are the characteristic features of the landscape at Pokagon. Beautiful Lake James, the third largest natural lake in the state, consists of three basins and opens beyond the Narrows to the north into Snow Lake. The irregular lobes and arms of Lake James winding among the hills account for miles of scenic shoreline. Cattail marshes along portions of the low lying shorelines and along the channels to Snow and Otter lakes to the north account for excellent habitat for marsh nesting birds such as the Redwinged blackbird, least bittern, and marsh wrens. A wealth of common spring flowers grace the forest floor each spring and rarities such as the showy orchid and Golden seal are well protected in their inaccessible habitats.

Potawatomi Inn is named after one of the Indian tribes that held the soil of Indiana before the advent of the white man. The Potawatomi were probably the most numerous counting those that occupied part of lower Michigan. It was estimated that they numbered 3,400 in 1820. The tribe occupied most of what is now Indiana north of the Wabash River. Their spread southward was checked by the Miamis along the Wabash and the Delaware in the White River valley.

Less than 150 years ago, the several Indian tribes still owned and occupied many lands of the state. The story of the Potawatomi from the time that white migration began to encroach upon their domain to the final enforced removal is a tragic one. By six separate treaties within a short period of eleven years, and virtually against their wills, the tribe signed away all their lands in the state with the exception of a few small tracts that were reserved to a few chiefs and their followers. Within a few years the United States acquired possession of these reserves and the Indians were left without a home and many were forced to move westward.

For some reason the Pokagon band of Potawatomi Indians were never removed west although the elder Leopold surrendered the southern half of Steuben County in the treaty of 1828. Leopold and his wife Elizabeth lived in southern Michigan and were given their Christian names when they were converted to the Catholic faith. While Leopold was head chief of all of the tribes he unwillingly signed away a million acres of land including the land where Chicago now stands. The price the treaty called for amounted to three cents per acre, and even at that figure it was sixty years before the land was paid for. Leopold died in Cass County, Michigan about 1841.

Simon, son of Leopold, was the last of the Pokagon family. He was reared in the Catholic faith and was educated at Notre Dame College, Oberlin College and a school at Twinsburg, Ohio. He was regarded as the best educated Indian of the time and it was intended that he should enter the priesthood. Instead, he returned to the Indian life and as his father before him became chief of the Potawatomi tribe. He was credited with ably and faithfully administering the affairs of some 300 tribesmen that acknowledged his leadership.

A semi-biographical book entitled "O-gi-maw-kwe Mit-i-gwa-ki" (Queen of the Woods) was published after his death through the kindness of a sympathetic friend. It provides an interesting insight into the mind and nature of the Indian. The story also relates a beautiful romance in Simon's love and marriage to Lonidaw, the Indian girl, whom he named "Queen of the Woods." They had two children, a boy Olondo, and a girl, whom they called "Hazel Eye." Both children's lives ended in tragedy, the boy as a result of a fatal appetite for liquor, and the girl was run down by two drunken boatmen while she was alone on the lake in her canoe. Lonidaw, in an attempt to rescue the child, was nearly drowned. The incident resulted in the mother's loss of sanity. Simon Pokagon lived for many years thereafter, always conciliatory, never with bitterness since he was a true Christian and a gentleman by nature.

The names of Potawatomi and Pokagon are deeply inscribed in the atmosphere of Pokagon State Park. The spirit of the Indian is but a legend in our lives today but the forests, lakes and the wildlife were a part of the everyday existence of the real Indian little more than a century ago.

The picturesque features of the *Indiana Dunes State Park* include approximately three miles of beach along the south shore of Lake Michigan and a succession of forested sand ridges and valleys inland. The process of dune making has proceeded relentlessly through the ages and is all the more fascinating because it continues to reveal its slow but certain influence upon the landscape today.

In each wave that bathes the shoreline there is left a seemingly minute ridge-line of sand. Winds dry the wet sand which can be carried inland to varying distances according to the force of the prevailing wind. Some of the sand is deposited but a short distance from the shore to form the fore-dune. Stronger winds carry sand still farther to the next ridge to become part of the secondary, or high-dune. The older, more distant inland ridges are the old dune regions, marking ancient beach lines formed when the waters of the big lake reached many miles farther south.

There is a constant competition between the vegetation of the dunes and the shifting sands. For a short distance, rarely more than 50 to 100 yards, up the sloping shore the mechanical forces of nature seem to dominate; then life in the form of sand plants such as beach grasses, sand cherry, sand beach willow, beach pea and an occasional cottonwood of disreputable form appear on the shifting waste and flourish where it would seem that no life could be sustained. To the east, the shore dune encroaches more upon the shore and this zone becomes increasingly narrow.

The secondary, or high dunes have attained the most striking elevations of the dune region. This is most likely due to their more recent origin and continuing growth. The older ridges, fairly well covered with forest, have been considerably diminished in height by wind and rain erosion. At the eastern limit is Mt. Tom, the highest of all the dunes, which is 193 feet above the lake waters at its northern base. Many of the high dunes are covered more or less with trees to the tops, as is the case with Mt. Tom. Some of the dunes have broken areas due to wind erosion while still others reveal large unprotected masses of constantly moving sands that are deposited on the low-lying interior lands.

Another interesting phenomenon of the dunes is shown in several spectacular bowl-shaped, scooped out areas called "blowouts" resulting from wind erosion. "Blowouts" generally occur as a result of trenches cut through the fore-dune by strong winds after the stabilizing vegetation of the fore dune has been destroyed. The "Beach House Blowout" on Trail 2 and the "Big Blowout" toward the eastern boundary of the park are examples of such activity. The shifting loads of sand are carried farther inland and dump their burden upon established stands of mature forests. Thus, long established, successional forest stages are frequently covered by the slowly encroaching sands as the large sand hills gradually flow forward toward the leeward side.

Likewise, forests that were buried ages ago may be uncovered once more to display the stark and skeletal trunks of an ancient forest. The result provides a very pronounced feature commonly referred to as a "dunes graveyard." Many of the tree trunks are quite large indicating that the forest once had reached a fairly stable condition. The dead trees are white pine and white cedar, intermixed with various hard-

TABLE 23. Acquisition of Land for the Indiana State Parks and
Indiana State Memorials by Decades and Population of Indiana

| Decade & Population (last year of decade) | Name of Property | Year Acquired | Acreage As Of 3/23/66 |
|---|---|---|---|
| 1911-1920 | McCormick's Creek State Park | 1916 | 1,671.65 |
| | Turkey Run State Park | 1916 | 1,814.62 |
| 2,930,390 | Corydon Capitol State Memorial | 1917 | .60 |
| | Clifty Falls State Park | 1920 | 1,357.00 |
| | | | 4,843.87 |
| 1921-1930 | Muscatatuck S.P. & Game Farm | 1921 | 260.60 |
| | Indiana Dunes State Park | 1925 | 2,182.43 |
| 3,238,503 | Pokagon State Park | 1925 | 1,173.49 |
| | Tippecanoe Battlefield S.M. | 1925 | 16.69 |
| | J.F.D. Lanier State Memorial | 1926 | 4.15 |
| | Spring Mill State Park | 1927 | 1,319.18 |
| | Shakamak State Park | 1929 | 1,016.24 |
| | Brown County State Park | 1929 | 15,332.00 |
| | Pigeon Roost State Memorial | 1929 | 4.82 |
| | Mounds State Park | 1930 | 254.46 |
| | | | 21,564.06 |
| 1931-1940 | Bass Lake State Beach | 1931 | 21.21 |
| | Lincoln State Park | 1932 | 1,749.16 |
| 3,427,796 | G. R. Clark State Memorial | 1940 | 16.22 |
| | | | 1,786.59 |
| 1941-1950 | Wilbur Wright State Memorial | 1941 | 5.00 |
| | Tippecanoe River State Park | 1943 | 2,743.54 |
| 3,934,165 | Versailles State Park | 1943 | 5,873.70 |
| | T. C. Steele State Memorial | 1945 | 211.00 |
| | Whitewater Canal State Memorial | 1945 | |
| | Angel Mounds State Memorial | 1946 | 421.40 |
| | G. S. Porter State Memorial | 1946 | 13.61 |
| | Shades State Park | 1947 | 2,639.92 |
| | Limberlost State Memorial | 1947 | 1.20 |
| | Indiana Territory State Memorial | 1948 | 1.86 |
| | Whitewater State Park | 1949 | 1,515.23 |
| | | | 13,426.46 |
| 1951-1960 | Scales Lake State Beach | 1951 | 477.00 |
| | New Harmony State Memorial | 1955 | 7.11 |
| 4,662,498 | Lieber State Park | 1956 | 8,248.00 |
| | Chain O' Lakes State Park | 1960 | 2,660.22 |
| | | | 11,392.33 |
| 1961-1970 | Raccoon Lake State Rec. Area | 1961 | 4,068.00 |
| | Ouabache State Rec. Area | 1962 | 1,089.00 |
| | Old State Bank State Memorial | 1963 | .18 |
| | Monroe Reservoir (land only, in 4 areas) | 1965 | 1,151.00 |
| | Southwest State Rec. Area (New Harmony) | 1966 | 697.04 |
| | | | 7,005.22 |
| | TOTAL | | 60,018.53 |

wood, to show the remnants of a forest community of past ages (Frontispiece).

The dunes cannot be appreciated without an understanding of the evolving changes that bind their past to the ever-changing moods of the present. Also, the dunes are the cross roads of vegetation of north and south, prairie and forest, swamp and upland, pond and lake, where the vicissitudes of wind and weather are expressed in an abundance of unusual plants.

* * *

The foregoing account of some of the special features of Indiana State Parks is presented with the hope that the citizens of our state shall become more genuinely sensitive to the values of our natural outdoor heritage and will become increasingly dedicated to preserving them. There have been those among each generation who have had the foresight to stand against economic encroachment upon such areas as are significantly worthy of being maintained intact for the inspiration and enrichment of our people. We owe our thanks to those leaders of the past and need to pause for a few refreshing moments to renew vigorously our desires to hold fast to the few remaining natural areas.

Although a few state park areas have not been mentioned, there is a complete listing of the state parks and memorials under the administration of the Division of State Parks of the Indiana Department of Natural Resources in Table 23.

## LITERATURE

1. DOWNING, ELLIOTT R. 1922. A naturalist in the Great Lakes Region. University of Chicago Press, Chicago, Illinois.
2. FREEMAN, OTIS W. 1946. Geologic contrasts in Indiana State Parks. Proc. Indiana Acad. Sci. 55: 83-88.
3. McCORMICK, JACK. 1962. Vascular flora of Shades State Park and Pine Hills Natural Area, Indiana. Bull. Amer. Museum Nat. Hist. 123: (7) 357-421. New York.
4. MICHAUD, HOWARD H. 1957. Conservation of recreational and scenic resources. Proc. Indiana Acad. Sci. 66: 268-274.
5. PEPOON, H. S. 1927. Flora of the Chicago Region. Chicago Academy of Science. The Lakeside Press, R. R. Donnelley and Sons, Chicago, Illinois.

# 33

## *Perspective*

### *"Without Vision A Land Will Die"—Lieber*

THOMAS E. DUSTIN
President, Indiana Division
Izaak Walton League of America

Is the preservationist era of conservation out of style? Is it a dead theology no longer relevant to the natural resource base of 20th Century Indiana? At a time when the watchword of resource handling is "total development," have we completely given up the fundamental concept that nature itself provides the greatest of all spiritual, educational and esthetic rejuvenation?

I think not. For these terms, and others—"improvement", "enhancement", "access"—must be interpreted in their broadest senses. There is only an apparent surrender of the ethical principle that man has a right and even a duty to find some of his fulfillment through the knowledge, understanding and love of unimpaired natural things. The sense of opinion that man has a right to the kind of environment which will enable him to understand, or at least to sense that there is a relationship with these things, is probably greater today than it has ever been.

Still, preservation is the least officially acknowledged or realized of all the great components of "multiple use," the most often forgotten of the principles of conservation when the alternatives of "development" or "preservation" are the choices presented. That there is unquestionably a broad base of support for the principles of preservation, however, is found in many statutes either already enacted or now pending: The Wilderness Act, The Wild Rivers bills, the Ecological Research and Surveys bill, the Multiple Use Act, and the many national park bills designed to preserve remnants of the natural heritage.

A growing number of states, beginning I believe with New Jersey in the 1930's, and now including others, such as Illinois, Wisconsin and Iowa, have enacted statutes providing official bases for state systems of nature preserves.

This principle stands at the very apex of our most sensitive environmental attitudes; for it is in this principle that we find man making his greatest effort to associate his own destiny with that of the nature which surrounds him.

The absence of this ethic is an immediate part of the same social pattern which permits the continued pollution and degradation of the total environment. Only when we achieve a state of mind which can relate to the natural community will our senses be attuned to the misuses of that community. A purely economic base will always permit environmental downgrading. For example, it is only when pollution of water reaches such intolerable levels that it interferes with other economic bases that we really try to do something about it. The moral and ethical considerations still do not govern very heavily. We act on pollution when we find the cost of not acting is higher.

But this is not a paper on water or air pollution. It is intended to point to the positive phases of environmental preservation as the seed and root of social morality and responsibility toward the natural resource base which sustains our bodies and our spirits.

Let me make a few distinctions:

Swings and slides in conventional parks release energy and help maintain physical tone, but of themselves provide little creative or spiritual regeneration. Powerboating, driving for pleasure and swimming are superb types of recreation, but provide very few insights which develop a special sense of contact with nature's machinery.

Fishing and hunting are satisfying and pleasurable experiences, but of themselves teach few lessons we must have in order to perpetuate the environmental qualities in which those pursuits remain possible.

No one disagrees that we must have highways, reservoirs, productive agricultural lands, and continuously yielding forests, but the techniques involved, of themselves, are too often applied outside the framework of highest environmental understanding.

In selecting the highway's course within the singular framework of economic technique, did this single use forever terminate uses of values of even greater importance? Did the reclamation, tilling and diversion of an undisturbed flood plain cost more in terms of other uses and purposes than its pre-emption for a single use contributed? Did the reservoir inundate outstanding geological history and reduce a scene of excellence and diversity to a conventional and rigid set of uses commonly provided at many other points in the same region?

Did the woodland contain outstanding individuals and an excellent remnant of post-glacial communities which would have served a broader base of need than the single use of furniture veneer? Did the draining of a swamp or bog seriously narrow the values it previously contained, and substitute a vertical and commonplace return for a whole system of opportunities which should have been preserved?

"What would it profit," Thoreau asked, "if men gained a whole continent, but in the process lost contact with the wellspring of human renewal?"

The point here is not that we stop logging or building roads or stop farming. The point is that in spite of our use of the word "comprehensive", a great deal of our thinking is becoming narrower rather than broader. We lose the opportunity for personal renewal because we do not sufficiently associate that renewal with the truth of nature itself.

Multiple use is the greatest statement of principle we have, and the language of the implementing statute clearly identifies preservation as part of the concept. The problem lies in our narrow interpretations of this venerable idea, and in the reduction of this principle to "catch-phrase" status. The term has suffered a certain amount of inversion, with many of the practical applications reducing rather than expanding the multiplicity of uses of the resource base.

"We need wilderness sanctuaries for a full life," Justice William O. Douglas said; "we want some of the original America left in its primitive condition so that 100 years from now a lad can walk the hills and see what God has wrought."

There is a tendency to give credibility to such statements, but in our area, we think that the principles are applicable only to the vast public lands of the west. The ethic is all right at a distance, but we do not relate to it sufficiently in terms of immediate opportunity and need here, at arms length. But it is equally applicable, and even more urgently needed here, because the resource base for its practice here is so much smaller. Additionally, the realization of the principle will largely rest in our own hands here in Indiana, with relatively small exceptions. So it is especially important that we relate directly and personally to it.

Consider a supporting fact: All state parks in the nation total only one-fifth of the area set aside in our national parks; but three times as many people visit state facilities because most of these are nearer to the metropolitan centers. The fact that our region of the country has only 4% of the national parks only multiplies this factor. Our own north central region creates greater man-day pressure on public parks than any other region of the nation, including New England and the Middle Atlantic region; and even the average state park use in the U. S. has risen 250% in the past quarter century.

The pressure on the state lands of Indiana will be perhaps the heaviest of any state in the nation; this is at least a certainty in the east north central states as a region.

Since we will not often be able to rely upon outside units of government to respond to areas in which we are deficient, it becomes even more critically important that we think and plan with maximum breadth and sensitivity. Such an objective can only be realized if enough of our people relate themselves sufficiently and provide the political base for needed accomplishment.

And this will not be possible unless emphatic leadership is taken in educating to the ethics of the resource base. This alone can create the agreement needed that preservation and ecological restoration are among the greatest elements of multiple use.

The world has always been in a state of change; but it occurs so rapidly today that we can see it happening on practically a 24-hour basis. A man worked 38 hours a week in 1960; in 10 years, he will work 36; and in just 34 years he is expected to work only 30 hours a week. In 1960, he had just over two weeks of vacation; he'll have four weeks by the year 2000, and 12 paid holidays instead of the seven he had in 1960. Even now, one-fifth of his leisure time is spent in outdoor recreation, and the proportion is rising.

These are dull gray but realistic facts, and we are the ones who have to cope with them today. Still, we continue to give the heaviest weight to such factors as admission fees, board feet, and yield per acre as the governing criteria in our natural resource attitudes. No one is arguing that these things are not important, but many would agree that it is very difficult to derive ethical standards from a wholly materialistic orientation. In the absence of more stress on environmental ethics in our schools, it would seem likely that resource uses will continue to become more limited and stereotyped; and multiple use will be defeated rather than realized.

The most relevant question in our state's 150th year is whether we are really preparing to meet this avalanche with truly spectral choices which can satisfy quality desires and disperse high intensity loads, or whether through limited thinking we are actually moving to mediocre commonality and dreary sameness.

This is a restless age we live in, an age of jaded and cynical tastes in which personal fulfillment and creative purpose are difficult to come by. We will not be able to handle the problems by strict recreational formulae—by the number of boat landings we provide, by the number of lakes we create, or by the number of campsites, or by the size of our parking lots or hotel accommodations. These are fine things, and we need them; but of themselves they may actually conceal rather than disclose the greater meaning of life's communities.

"In the woods we return to faith and reason," Ralph Waldo Emerson said. And a hundred years later, President Kennedy added: "On the one hand, science has opened up great new sources of energy and great new means of control. On the other hand, new technical processes and devices litter the countryside with waste and refuse, contaminate water and air, imperil wildlife and man and endanger the balance of nature itself. Our economic standard of living rises," the President said, "but our environmental standard of living — our access to nature and respect for it — deteriorates."

But, as Stewart Udall said in Quiet Crisis, "Ideas must precede action, and sometimes the seeds of thought have a long period of germination. Reform must begin in the minds of men," he said; "and a significant segment of society would have to accept the Walden values before effective action could commence."

Some of our ethical ideas have truly been a long time in germinating. In 1847, George Perkins Marsh, lawyer, land philosopher and Congressman, said: "Men now begin to realize what as wandering shepherds they had before dimly suspected, that man has a right to the use, not the abuse, of the products of nature; that consumption should everywhere compensate by increased production; and that it is false economy to encroach upon a capital, the interest of which is sufficient for our lawful uses."

There is serious doubt whether we have even accepted the Walden values mentioned by Udall. I have personally seen Walden Pond in the past three years, and can concur with Justice Douglas when he describes it as "no peaceful pool, but a bathing beach. Across the road are hot-dog stands and trailer camps." And it was only by action of the Massachusetts Supreme Court that the pond was saved from concrete beach ramps, bank excavation to fill in part of the pond, concrete bath-houses and parking lots.

But this is not an indictment of hot-dog stands or parking lots; it is only a criticism of the lack of understanding and sensitivity which we continue to display. It is just another demonstration that we still have not developed ethical standards which permit us to live harmoniously with environmental values, or to discriminate among the several values.

Indiana's own Richard Lieber put it in other words in 1939: "Today, there is an ill-starred tendency to scramble all recreational eggs and call the result a state park."

Lieber said "State parks are meant to be the show windows of a state but more than that state parks are a dedication to the soul of the land. . . It is the land on which we all depend in the last essence. It is the land and the very soil, the trees and waters, the dales and glens which we love. Without vision a land will die. Without inspiration we remain disconnected from the immortal order of all things."

Aldo Leopold provides additional support for this datum when he called for a new land ethic: "Do we not already sing our love for and obligation to the land of the free and the home of the brave?" he asked. "Yes, but just what and whom do we love? Certainly not the soil, which we are sending helter-skelter downriver. Certainly not the waters, which we assume have no function except to turn turbines, float barges, and carry off sewage. Certainly not the plants, of which we exterminate whole communities without batting an eye. Certainly not the animals, of which we have already extirpated many of the largest and most beautiful species . . . a land ethic changes the role of *Homo sapiens* from conqueror of the land community to plain member and citizen of it. It implies respect for his fellow-members, and also respect for the community as such."

It is certainly a major question today whether our society has moved to a point in its development which can permit the survival or rebirth of the ethics of Lieber, Leopold, or Douglas. The commitment to artificality is all but overpowering; yet, almost all of the discussion of this conference relies directly upon this survival and rebirth. But it is really not necessary to challenge the artificial in order to elevate ethical land standards. Let us give proper credit to artificiality. It has provided us with the time in which to contemplate the ethic itself. The major fault in artificiality is that we do not fully utilize the benefits it provides. We accept the term "progress" without asking the larger question: "Progress toward what?" We envision artificiality as an end in itself rather than mitigating that point of view with the better idea that artificiality is a means to an end. It is an avenue to purpose and understanding, and not the purpose itself.

It is truly a mark of genius that we can re-create at will an immediate environment under any and all circumstances which will sustain our lives. We make that environment, package it around ourselves, and take it wherever we choose to go — even to the moon in a few years. But we have also permitted artificiality to insulate us and to limit, not broaden, our understanding of nature. In this process, we become the slaves, and artificiality the dictatorial master.

Now, in Indiana's 150th year, we are arriving at irreducible minimums. The opportunity to perpetuate the cathedrals of nature and its truths and idealisms is almost gone. "Today," Justice Douglas said, "we look backward to a time when there was more wilderness than the people of America needed. Today we look forward (and only a matter of a few years) to a time when all the wilderness now existing will not be enough. It would, I think, be wise right now to stop all new road-building into wild lands, all damming of wild rivers, all logging of virgin forests. The Americans of 2000 A.D. will thank us if we take that course . . ."

To imagine that this injunction applies only in distant places merely turns away from reality. It applies right here — actually within a dozen or so miles from this meeting hall — as well as to dozens of other locations in our own state. To dismiss this counsel as an extreme point of view would be an equal error, for it is addressed to only the tiniest fragment of our resource base in terms of total area — probably not more than one-third of one per cent of Indiana's 23,000,000 acres. To say that we should practice wilderness or natural concepts on so small an area, and with such enormous benefits coming from it, should not be considered an unreasonable suggestion.

Wilderness and natural areas do return a solidly based good for all of the people, even for those who do not use them directly for inspirational or recreational purposes. As places for education and as sources for scientific information, they simply have no equal or substitute. As areas for perpetuation of indigenous wildlife species, they can be equalled by no zoo. As stabilized portions of our watersheds, they provide probably the best regulation and most reliable outflows.

But we will not have these values; the people will forever be denied the diversified choice which they represent; they will see natural streams and valleys and unspoiled woodlands only in diorama displays and photographs, and in the writings of John Muir, Sigurd Olson and Olaus Murie. The civilizations of today and tomorrow are entitled to have these values perpetuated; but that will only be possible if we visualize multiple use as a mosaic of different types of chips and pieces of the total environment.

It will take strength and understanding and sensitivity to agree and pursue the idea that multiple use of a land system implies simplicity and even singularity on designated parts of that system. I am not saying we do not have some grasp of this idea now; but it is not strongly enough entrenched and not widely enough supported. A highway or an irrigation ditch are single uses, and we have to agree that they are necessary; but we must see the natural area and the wilderness on at least a par with these other things; in fact, we would be wise to give these latter values an even higher position on the value scale because the opportunities are so much smaller and so much more rare.

Why should we elect to recognize and perpetuate natural areas as a matter of public policy? Can't society get along without them? Couldn't we substitute one kind of fulfillment for another? Must the human spirit have direct access to nature's cycle in order to achieve meaning?

This whole area of discussion is full of such questions, but I think you might agree that the threads of thought go beyond, while including, matters of natural science. At hand are deep social questions, even theological questions. We have investigative man, and we have contemplative man; often they are found in the same persons, but not always.

Contemplative man requires havens or citadels in which he can explore his own deepest questions, places where he can develop his own original thoughts, and where he can come to terms of peace with life and even with religious principles which resolve truth for him as he chooses to see it.

Investigative man must have unprostituted environment to serve as bases of comparison and as anchors of uncompromised information. And a third, esthetic man, must have his places of inspiration. All men, whether they represent numerical majorities or minorities, are entitled to a genuine choice of environments, including the best representative undisturbed natural areas. If we do not agree to that principle, then we shall shortly see most of our surroundings reduced to commonality with no choices except those in present vogue. And vogues change capriciously; and when they do, there can be no returns to the most exquisite unmanaged communities required by investigative, contemplative or esthetic man. The opportunities to share in the knowledge of Krutch's chains of life, and to observe directly the continuing cycles of germination, growth, fruiting, decline, death, decay and renewal would be gone as a meaningful display of natural forces. And we would have lost the chance to see the webs of interdependencies found so obviously in nature.

Man must adjust to artificiality, but much of it is psychically alien no matter how much needed or enjoyed. In man's ages of icons and icon smashing, and in our periods which lay open and vulnerable our deepest psychic caverns, we would be very wise, I think, to guard and perpetuate the integrity of nature, so that the balance and stability and assurance it represents will always be there when we most need it; and that time is here now, not distant, and not elsewhere. The integrity of nature can not be protected by heavy hands, nor by the distortions of anthropomorphic manipulating. It can't be made over or improved and still retain any inherent value. The genius of nature requires that we accept it for what it is, and derive from it our own rewards non-destructively.

In comparison to civilization of only 150 years ago, our technical and mechanical power have become almost unlimited, but I think our pushbuttons, which can literally move mountains or halt a river, may often confuse us and distort our judgment. We derive an anxious kind of comfort and assurance in the constant proof that we are better and stronger than nature, but haunting questions which we can't quite ignore are left in the rubble. While we need these capacities, and will go right on improving them, I do not think they actually define the value of our civilization. What will define our civilization, and what may even establish whether we are civilized at all, will be how carefully and sensitively we restrain the powers which have been developed.

The most needed wealth will be produced within the spirit and conscience of a people who finally achieve the realization that we are part of, rather than apart from, nature.

Lieber's counsel, given 25 years ago, is even more valid today than it was in 1941:

"Converse with nature," he wrote, "restores happiness; communion with its mysterious forces, Antaeus-like, fills us with renewed strength and rids us of fear. It is the land and all it contains which performs the miracle."

# INDEX